SONGS OF
PRAISE

ENLARGED EDITION

WITH MUSIC

LONDON
OXFORD UNIVERSITY PRESS

Oxford University Press, Ely House, London W. 1

GLASGOW   NEW YORK   TORONTO   MELBOURNE   WELLINGTON
CAPE TOWN   SALISBURY   IBADAN   NAIROBI   LUSAKA   ADDIS ABABA
BOMBAY   CALCUTTA   MADRAS   KARACHI   LAHORE   DACCA
KUALA LUMPUR   HONG KONG   TOKYO

Words Editor
PERCY DEARMER

Music Editors
RALPH VAUGHAN WILLIAMS
MARTIN SHAW

Full Music Edition
REVISED AND ENLARGED EDITION 1931
TWENTIETH IMPRESSION 1968

PRINTED IN GREAT BRITAIN

PREFACE TO THE ENLARGED EDITION

WHEN *Songs of Praise* was first published in 1925, the object was to make, so far as was then possible, a collection of hymns that should be national in character; and a hope was expressed in the Preface that the book might be of use to those who bear the responsibility of our national education. The response which followed exceeded all expectations. A County Education Authority immediately issued, through the Oxford University Press, *Prayers and Hymns for Use in Schools*, with *Songs of Praise* as its basis; and many of the greatest Education Authorities have since taken the same course, till it has become evident that the national character of *Songs of Praise* is already established.

Meanwhile, *Songs of Praise* has been adopted by many churches; and its very success has shown the necessity of producing an enlarged edition. This question of enlargement was discussed during a conference in 1929 at which over twelve hundred people were present, and it was decided to assist the work by the formation of a special committee. A series of meetings was also held in the north of England at which eighty-nine parsons discussed the various hymns in common use, votes being registered and tabulated. Two other bodies of representative men and women were also consulted on the subject of both additions and omissions. Moreover, ever since the first appearance of *Songs of Praise*, invaluable help has been received in continuous conference and co-operation with County Education Authorities and with the masters and mistresses of both Primary and Secondary Schools in different parts of the country.

Very great assistance has been given in these ways to the difficult task of deciding between the respective merits of hymns that have association values. Such hymns, with their tunes, should be included whenever they reach an adequate standard. At the same time our advisers and we ourselves have borne well in mind the fact that our churches, both Anglican and Free Church, have alienated during the last half-century much of the strongest character and intelligence of the Nation by the use of weak verse and music, and that the process of attraction or repulsion takes place every time a service is held. The position to-day is not easy. On the one hand it must be admitted that occasionally, to use the words of hymn 309, 'Time makes ancient good uncouth,' and the very success, for instance, of oversea work may cause a missionary hymn to be no longer in accordance with facts; yet it is none the less plain that new poems, expressing truth as we can grasp it to-day, have to be introduced gradually, since use and wont must be strong factors among those who have not given up church-going. New tunes also, however splendid, have to be sung a few times before ordinary people come to love them. But it must also be remembered that these tunes are now being taught in the schools and are already becoming familiar in many cities and counties: there is indeed already evidence that young people who have learnt better things at school will not be content to revert to a poorer standard in church.

PREFACE

Much attention has been given to the supply of an ample selection of stirring hymns for such long seasons as the four weeks of Advent, those after Christmas and Epiphany, and the six weeks after Easter. Special occasions have also been fully provided for; and the General section (now printed at the end of the book, to allow of possible additions, in years to come, without alteration of the numbers) has been greatly enlarged. All this has been accomplished, not only by the inclusion of well-known and deservedly loved hymns, but also by the discovery or rediscovery of many fine poems and magnificent tunes. We have, indeed, attempted in *Songs of Praise* to meet the new spiritual and intellectual needs which are so widely felt to-day; and we have endeavoured at the same time to preserve in their best form all those older lyrics, melodies, and settings which have made our British and American hymnody the greatest in the world.

We cannot conclude without grateful mention of the late Poet Laureate, Robert Bridges, whose genius as a poet and lover of good music began the present revival of hymnody. His *Yattendon Hymnal* (the initials of which are printed at the head of his hymns, in accordance with his wish) was published in 1899 by the Oxford University Press, and was the first challenge to the debased hymnody of that era: his noble hymns were first brought into common use and popularized throughout the world by the *English Hymnal* in 1906; and his example and help have been with us in all our subsequent work. It was due to his initiative that hymnody first recovered from the contempt into which it had fallen. In the future, intelligent men will be able to take up a hymn-book and read it with as much interest and appreciation as any other collection of poetry or music. Dr. Bridges died while our proofs were in the press. The number of his contributions to *Songs of Praise* had then already been increased, and more hymns had also been added from the pen of his successor in the Laureateship, Dr. Masefield.

Among others who have helped and encouraged us out of their knowledge and experience we would also mention with especial gratitude the following names: F. R. Barry, D.S.O.; Canon G. W. Briggs*; E. Noel Burghes*; P. B. Clayton, M.C.; A. T. Woodman Dowding; Herbert Dunnico, M.P.; F. W. Dwelly*, Dean of Liverpool; Dr. R. C. Gillie*; Mervyn Haigh, Bishop of Coventry; R. T. Howard; Professor W. F. Lofthouse; Pat McCormick, D.S.O.; Joyce Maxtone Graham*; W. Charter Piggott*; Canon Guy Rogers, M.C.; Canon C. T. Rust; Joan Shaw*; Dr. H. R. L. Sheppard, C.H.; and Archdeacon V. F. Storr. Those whose names are marked with an asterisk carried out much of the work in conjunction with the Editors.

FROM THE PREFACE TO THE ORIGINAL EDITION

IN this book we have endeavoured to make a national collection of hymns for use in public worship, and also of such 'spiritual songs' as are akin to hymns and suitable for certain kinds of services in church, as well as for schools, lecture meetings, and other public gatherings. *Songs of Praise* is intended to be national, in the sense of including a full expression of that faith which is common to the English-speaking peoples to-day, both in the British Commonwealth and in the United States, to which latter country we owe so many of the best nineteenth-century hymns.

All the hymn-books of the present century, notably the *English Hymnal* in its great and increasing success, have shown that the present generation desires to enter into the heritage of noble religious verse which is ours. That heritage is ours by right of the great poetry in which the English tongue is supreme, by right also of the magnificent prose which since Coverdale and Cranmer has formed the substance of our Christian worship, though it was never adequately matched by the hymns in common use. Our English hymns, indeed, few of which are earlier than Dr. Watts and most of which were the product of the Victorian era, were not in that era worthy of the English Bible and the English Prayer Book; and the bulk of the tunes to which they were sung illustrated a period of British music which the musicians of to-day are anxious to forget, and which, fortunately for our reputation, has been superseded by a national revival that has now given our music a foremost place in Europe again. It is therefore a hopeful sign that all our newer hymnals have shown courage in replacing many weak and poor hymns by words and music more worthy of our great traditions and more suitable to be used in the worship of God. Some courage in omission will indeed be a necessary part of the religious recovery for which the Churches look: we have all become accustomed to unworthy things which came into use because the older books provided nothing better, and each of us has to make a sacrifice of old habits now and again for the common good. A collection of standard hymns cannot be of enormous bulk; and the bad must go in order that the good may be added. Most people will miss one or two familiar hymns from this, as indeed from any other modern collection; but if they will read such hymns over carefully and dispassionately they will understand the omission. At the same time it must be remembered that a hymn-book can never be the same as an anthology: practical considerations cause the retention of some hymns which editors would otherwise omit; musical considerations affect the position of others.

There had been 400,000 hymns in common use by the end of the nineteenth century (of which over 600 were written by Isaac Watts, and at least 6,500 by Charles Wesley): yet in seven important and representative hymnals published during the last nineteen years there are only sixteen hymns common to them all, and fifty which are common to the six largest of them—only sixteen which they all agree to treat as indispensable. Such is the enormous disparity between the mass of hymns which has been offered by various compilers and the minute collection which has been universally accepted. Since, however, there must be more than fifty fine hymns in our language, it is manifest that the canons of acceptance need improving as well as the canons of rejection. There have been in fact something like two hundred really good hymns in common use (besides many unused); and there are others which are convenient, and in varying degrees sufficient in quality, to be selected from the thousands of hymns that exist. Besides these, every good collection of hymns, like every collection of songs, must contain a certain number of 'carriers'—of pieces, that is, which have been written to carry a particularly fine tune in some unusual metre, and which must at least be free from obvious faults in technique and sense. Some of these, from the days of Shakespeare onwards, have been very happy. In the present collection we have in some cases endeavoured to find such means for recovering old tunes of exceptional vigour and beauty; we have also endeavoured to provide new tunes which may bring into use some famous lyrics or excerpts from lyrics by poets whose names will be found in the index; and we have discovered some fine hymns which have not hitherto been available for common use. Among these are a few congregational songs, to which the name of 'cansons' has been applied: some of these are suitable, as we have said, for special services in church, others for use in schools, at lectures, and at the best kind of public meeting, which will, we hope, be increasingly graced by corporate singing. Perhaps of especial use in this way, as well as at the conclusion of services, will be the Doxologies, which we have gathered in a section by themselves, and have treated, not as mere endings of hymns, but as independent acts of praise, strong in their music and easily remembered.

In the Music Edition is printed a *Table of Hymns Arranged for Sundays throughout the Year*, as a help to those who have the difficult and responsible task of choosing the hymns to be sung in church. Some hymns have indeed been greatly overworked, and among these we may mention the so easily chosen evening hymns, of which thousands exist, many being marked by a rather somnolent sentimentality which must have tended to depress rather than to raise the spiritual vigour of those who sang them. If the Churches are to recover during the present century the ground which was lost during the last, much will depend upon the hymn-books used, but much also upon the way the hymns are chosen for each week.

It is hoped that this book will be found specially suitable for young people, and may prove not unacceptable to those who bear the responsibility of our national education. With this end in view, the hymns most suitable for young people are marked ° in the Index, and in the Small Edition the hymns themselves are distinguished by this sign. Even young children (for whom a section is provided in Part VI) should be brought up on the standard hymns, and it is supremely important that they should know and love the best simple hymns and tunes that are sung by adults.

EXPLANATORY NOTES

The sign † after an author's name means that an alteration has been made in one line only; the sign ‡ denotes alterations in two or three lines; when more than one writer has materially altered the original (as in the case, for instance, of 'Hark! the herald angels sing'), the words *and others* may be added; the letter *V* (version) denotes that a hymn has been recast. Where there is no sign, the verses are as the author wrote them, unless the word *cento* is added to show that a selection of lines has been made in order to make a poem possible for congregational singing. The letters *Tr.* are prefixed to the names of all translators; but when the rendering is so free as to amount to a paraphrase the letters *Pr.* are used.

Choruses and refrains are printed once for all in italic. 'Amen' is omitted, except in Part VIII, since its use is not generally to be recommended, and even after a doxology is not essential. When a hymn is divided into Parts, roman numerals are used, for the convenience of places where lists of the numbers of hymns are written, printed, or set up on boards.[1] The sign *

means that, in a hymn of about twenty-four lines or more, the verse so marked may be omitted without doing violence to the sense: many more short hymns are thus made available. The verses are numbered, and a full point is printed after the number of the last verse, in order to show where the final verse of a hymn is reached at the bottom of a page. For convenience the hymns are normally printed in alphabetical order; but this order is not used as a principle from which no departure is possible.

ACKNOWLEDGEMENTS
(WORDS OF HYMNS)

Our first thanks are due to the proprietors of the *English Hymnal*, whose hymns we have been freely allowed to use, including those by the late Rev. Dr. Charles Bigg, the Rev. Gabriel Gillett, the late Rev. Canon Scott Holland, Mr. Laurence Housman, the Rev. Canon T. A. Lacey, and Mr. R. Ellis Roberts.

We also acknowledge the copyright hymns under the initials A. F., A. G., B. R., C. W. H., E. H., N. B. L., O. B. C., O. B. C. V., S. P., S. P. B. G., S. P. V., S. T., T. S. N.; also the centos, and versions marked † or ‡, including the following, which are also copyright: Nos. 149, 152, 211, 213, 304, 477, 505, 515, 571.

Very warm thanks are also due to the following authors and copyright owners for permission to include their hymns, many of which were specially written for *Songs of Praise*, viz.:

The Hon. and Rev. J. G. Adderley (269); Rev. Dr. C. A. Alington (154, 164); Messrs. George Allen & Unwin (316, from *Chants of Labour*); Mr. J. S. Arkwright (293); Association for Promoting Christian Knowledge, Dublin (412, 528); Mr. Clifford Bax (329); Miss Maud Bell (330); Rt. Rev. G. K. A. Bell,

---

[1] If the Parts are counted as separate numbers, there are over 750 hymns in the enlarged *Songs of Praise*.

PREFACE

Bishop of Chichester (242); Mrs. Beeching and John Lane The Bodley Head Limited (504); Mr. Laurence Binyon (493); Messrs. Boosey & Co. and Mr. Norman Gale (518); Rev. Dr. W. Russell Bowie (562); Mr. G. F. Bradby (296); Mr. H. N. Brailsford (445); Rev. Canon G. W. Briggs (60, 109, 266, 275, 337, 357, 360, 361, 400, 403, 566, 572, 638, 660); Miss Honor Brooke (539, 558); Professor F. C. Burkitt and S.P.C.K. (183); Messrs. Burns, Oates & Washbourne (411); The Rt. Rev. E. A. Burroughs, Bishop of Ripon (343); Mrs. A. F. Butler (560); Mrs. Canton (375, 379, 519); Mr. G. E. Chatfield (106); Mr. G. K. Chesterton for the copyright of 308 given to Dr. Dearmer; Rev. P. B. Clayton (456, 470); Rev. Canon J. M. C. Crum (220, 376); Messrs. J. Curwen & Sons (362); 439 from Curwen Edition No. 6,333, Copyright, U.S.A. 1926; Mr. R. F. Davis and Messrs. J. M. Dent & Sons (387); The Venble. J. R. Darbyshire (142, 218, 241, 286); Mr. Geoffrey Dearmer (193, 222, 224, 407, 663, 669); Messrs. P. J. and A. E. Dobell (651); Madame Mary Duclaux (616); Rev. Dr. Henry van Dyke and Messrs. Charles Scribner's Sons, New York, Copyright, 1904 and 1920 (18); English Hymnal Committee (44, 66, 139, 148, 221, 227, 228, 231, 246, 552); Miss Eleanor Farjeon (11, 30, 569, 579); Mr. Frank Fletcher (611); Miss Rose Fyleman (3); Mr. William Galbraith (535); Mr. Norman Gale and Messrs. Boosey & Co. (518); Mrs. Gannett (655); Dr. Philip Gosse (590); Mr. Edward Grubb (621); Mrs. Gurney (283); Lt.-Col. Sir Maurice P. A. Hankey (568); Miss Beatrice Hatch (458); Messrs. William Heinemann, Ltd. (81); Mrs. Hinkson (196); Messrs. Hodder & Stoughton (450, 469); Mr. R. Holland (378); Hon. Mrs. Silvester Horne (495); Mr. W. H. Hortin (252); Messrs. Houghton Mifflin Company (331, 531, 620, 697); Mr. Laurence Housman (326, 409); Mr. F. D. How (7, 15); Industrial Christian Fellowship (698); The Rev. the Warden, Keble College, Oxford (237, 261); Mr. Rudyard Kipling (317 from *The Five Nations* published by Messrs. Methuen & Co., and 488 from *Puck of Pook's Hill* published by Messrs. Macmillan & Co.); John Lane The Bodley Head Limited and Mrs. Beeching (504); Mrs. Lanning (192, 322, 347, 575, 589, 614, 680); Mrs. E. Rutter Leatham (404); the Principal of Loughborough College (243); the Head Master of Loughborough Grammar School and the Head Mistress of Loughborough High School (194); Rev. S. C. Lowry (339); Dr. Greville MacDonald (668); Messrs. Macmillan & Co. (5, 75, 122, 305, 328, 386 III, 649, 684); Ven. F. B. Macnutt (156); Dr. John Masefield, Poet Laureate (86, 165, 593); Miss Christabel Massey (313); Rev. Walter J. Mathams (363); Trustees of the late Miss Jane G. Matheson's Estate (576); Mr. Basil Mathews (299); Miss Mary Maude (258); Mr. G. K. Menzies (325); Rev. Dr. W. P. Merrill and *The Continent*, Chicago (635); Mr. Wilfrid Meynell (617); Estate of the late Mr. Thomas B. Mosher (499); Mrs. Muirhead (248); Mr. John Murray (312, 319, 452, 681); Mrs. Myers (591); The National Sunday School Union (359); Mrs. E. J. Newell (225); Sir Henry Newbolt (323); Mr. H. H. Oakley (482); Mr. John Oxenham (537); Oxford University Press (39, 56, 141, 338, 400, 403, 497, and those by P. Dearmer); Professor E. Allison Peers (600, written for the 25th Anniversary of the University of Liverpool); Rev. W. Charter Piggott (289, 342, 346, 516, 538); Rev. R. Martin Pope (37); Miss M. F. Pott (147); Messrs. A. W. Ridley & Co. (49, 397, 583, 678); Mrs. K. E. Roberts (251); Mr. R. Ellis Roberts (231); Mr. W. H. C. Romanis (52, 234); Sir Ronald Ross and Mr. John Murray (452); Messrs. Charles Scribner's Sons (18, 126, 290); Miss Verena Shuttleworth (338); Messrs. Skeffington & Son, Ltd. (293); Society for Promoting Christian Knowledge (92, 183, 240, 300); Jan Struther (63, 162, 163, 219, 223, 233, 236, 282, 354, 377, 565, 692); Mr. L. G. P. Thring (388); Mr. R. C. Trevelyan (352); Mr. A. Cyprian Bourne Webb (274); Mr. Steuart Wilson (344, 627); Miss Edith Williams (546); and we are greatly indebted to the late Dr. Robert Bridges for hymns 33, 50, 57, 99, 128, 179, 208, 245, 291, 324, 442, 483, 484, 498, 509, 574, 584, 631 and 661, from the *Yattendon Hymnal* and elsewhere.

PERCY DEARMER.

NOTES ON THE MUSIC

(a) *Pitch.*—The pitch of each tune has been fixed as low as possible for the sake of mixed congregations. Except in the case of tunes with a very wide compass, the upper limit is E. In those churches where the hymns are sung by the choir alone, the organist will presumably be competent to transpose the tune to a higher key if desirable.

(b) *Unison Singing.*—Every tune is so arranged that it can be sung in unison, accompanied by the organ. In any case, the congregation must always sing the *melody*, and the melody *only*. Settings of many better-known tunes are given in Fa-burden and Descant; in these cases both choir and people have their definite part to perform.

(c) *Pace.*—It is the custom in English churches to sing Chorales and the older tunes much too fast. The pace at which, in the Editors' opinion, a tune should be sung is indicated above the tune. But the size of the building and the powers of the singers must be the deciding factor in the matter of pace. Commas (') and pauses (⌒) have been added to most of the tunes. A metronomically rigid rendering of a hymn-tune is both artistically wrong and congregationally impossible.

(d) *Plainsong.*—In singing these unison melodies, it is important to observe the following points:
(1) The rhythm is free, i.e. it is essentially a speech-rhythm, though not always wholly so, since single syllables are sometimes allied to groups of notes (neums). The melodies must therefore flow easily: they are not strings of rigidly equal quavers.
(2) The first note of every neum is slightly accented.
(3) A slight rallentando is made at the end of each line, especially the last.
(4) It is best to sing alternate verses in contrast—of volume, or pitch—but the first and last verses full. It is customary for the first line of the first verse to be chanted, i.e. to be sung by one or two voices, unaccompanied.
A heavy use of the organ clouds the light flow of the melody.

MUSIC ACKNOWLEDGEMENTS

The thanks of the Editors are due to the following, who have composed or arranged tunes especially for this book:

(*The numbers marked with an asterisk* (*) *denote a Fa-burden or Descant Version.*)

Dr. Thomas Armstrong, 469; Sir Ivor Atkins, 323, 370; Dr. E. C. Bairstow, 114*; Mr. Arnold Bax, 107; Miss Ina Boyle, 240; Rev. Canon G. W. Briggs, 572; Dr. Ernest Bullock, 46*, 216*, 590; Mr. E. T. Cook, 570*; Mr. H. Goss Custard, 507*; Dr. Harold E. Darke, 41, 200*, 547(2)*; Mr. Ronald Dussek, App. 2; Mr. Harry Farjeon, 569; Mr. Hubert J. Foss, 170(2); Dr. Nicholas Gatty, 152; Mr. Armstrong Gibbs, 81; Dr. Harvey Grace, 349(2)*, 610*; Mr. Patrick Hadley, 311; Dr. William H. Harris, 84*, 554(1); Mr. Patrick Harvey, 131*; Mr. Gustav Holst, 293(1), 348, 397, 534; Mr. Herbert Howells, 582; Mr. T. H. Ingham, 63; Mr. John Ireland, 164; the late Miss J. M. Joseph, 651; Dr. A. Leech-Wilkinson, 491(2); Dr. Henry G. Ley, 96*, 230, 611; Dr. Stanley Marchant, 682*; Mr. S. Mason, 206; Mr. R. H. Milford, 504, 517*; Mr. R. O. Morris, 92, 501(1); Dr. Sydney H. Nicholson, 458*, 566*; Dr. C. Charlton Palmer, 12*; Rev. Herbert Popple, 331; Rev. Canon R. E. Roberts, 251; Mr. Edgar C. Robinson, 440*, 527(2)*; Mr. J. B. Rooper, 568; Dr. Cyril B. Rootham, 301*; Mr. S. L. Russell, 115(1), 340, 697; Miss Evelyn Sharpe, 367; Mr. Geoffrey Shaw, 18, 499, 558*, 588, 634, 657*; Dr. Gordon Slater, 361, 579; Sir Arthur Somervell, 394, 399; Mr. Heathcote Statham, 328(2); Mr. C. Hylton Stewart, 105*; Mr. Herbert W. Sumsion, 210(1)*; Mr. R. S. Thatcher, 465; Mr. Guy Warrack, 29*, 219; Mr. Arthur S. Warrell, 689; Mr. Percy Whitlock, 460*; the late Dr. Charles Wood, 288; Dr. Thomas Wood, 344, 511.

Also to the following, who have allowed the use of their compositions or arrangements in the book:

Rev. Canon G. W. Briggs, 194(2), 360, 401, 439, 501(2); Dr. P. C. Buck, 148(2), 247, 593; Mr. K. G. Finlay, 354; Mr. Armstrong Gibbs, 646(1), 661(2); Mr. W. Greatorex, 299; Dr. Basil Harwood, 255(3), 607(2); Mr. Gustav Holst, 75, 86, 496, 498, 502; Mr. T. H. Ingham, 500*; Mr. John Ireland, 127(1); Dr. H. G. Ley, 154, 391; Mr. Michael Mullinar, 497; Dr. E. W. Naylor, 641(1); the Executors of the late Mr. F. G. Russell, 698; Mr. J. S. Scott, 471; Miss Evelyn Sharpe, 358; Mr. Geoffrey Shaw, 11, 85(2), 169, 326, 385, 386(3), 402, 467; Dr. Gordon Slater, 527(1); Sir Arthur Somervell, 332.

The Editors also wish to thank Mr. J. H. Arnold for his contribution of section (d) to the Notes on the Music and for his harmonization of the following Plainsong melodies:

33 Part I (1), 33 Part II (1), 44(1), 51(1), 130(1), 148(1), 180(1), 186(1), 190(1), 389, 548, 549(1).

Also the following, who have allowed tunes or arrangements which are their copyright to be included:

Mr. G. E. P. Arkwright, 395 (iii); Messrs. H. Aschehoug & Co., 59 (melody),

232 (melody); Association for Promoting Christian Knowledge, Dublin, 294, 310; Miss N. M. Bicknell, 136; Messrs. Boosey & Co., 647; Cambridge University Press, 97*, 189(1), 197(2)*, 199*, 211*, 303*, 477*, 491(1)*, 542*, 683*; the Caniedydd Committee of the Union of Welsh Independents, 312, 479; the Head Master, Charterhouse School, 212, 646(1), 661(2); Messrs. J. B. Cramer & Co., Ltd., 345; Messrs. J. Curwen & Sons, Ltd., 73*, 78*, 81, 319(1), 444, 446, 502, 578, 594, 649; also for the following: 5 from Curwen Edition No. 71795, 86 from Curwen Edition No. 61239, 165 from Curwen Edition No. 3686, 335 from Curwen Edition No. 80667; 386(i), 386(ii), 386(iii, first tune), 386(iv), 386(v), and 386(vi) from Curwen Edition No. 8606; 432 from Curwen Edition No. 71619, 434 from Curwen Edition No. 80644, 498 from Curwen Edition No. 80656, 646(1) from Curwen Edition No. 80675 (printed by arrangement with Charterhouse School), 661(2) from Curwen Edition No. 80673 (printed by arrangement with Charterhouse School); 64, 93(2), 106*, 187(2), 356, 472, 543, 556, 586(1), 597*, 598*, 624, 644, 678, from *Additional Tunes and Settings* by Martin Shaw in Curwen Edition No. 6300; Mr. L. L. Dix, 268; the Rev. the Abbot of Downside, 91, 190(2), 217(1); The Educational Company of Ireland, Limited, 565 (melod); English Hymnal Co., 48(2), 157, 177, 202, 260, 289, 314, 334, 390, 583; Dr. David Evans, 47, 54, 69, 89, 193(1), 233, 242, 270, 283, 339, 464(2), 505(1), 592, 609, 643(2), 665; Messrs. W. Gwenlyn Evans & Son, 309; The Faith Press, Ltd., 100*, 116*, 132*, 133*, 160*, 175*, 250*, 449*, 468*, 503*, 545*, 618*, 653*, 664*, 699*, 701*, from the *Tenor Tune Book*; Hope Publishing Company, Chicago, 353 (melody); Miss M. Morley Horder, 79(2); Messrs. Hughes & Son, 441, 542; Proprietors of *Hymns Ancient and Modern*, 56(2), 307; Dr. Ernest Jones, 25 (Part II); Miss V. Little, 280(1); Mrs. G. T. Lewis, 222; the Principal of Loughborough College, 243; Mr. W. Percy Merrick, 336; Mr. E. J. Moeran, 393(1) melody; National Sunday School Union, 359; Messrs. Novello & Co., Ltd., 25 (Part I)*, 74, 76, 95, 117, 137*, 350*, 481(1), 631*, 677*; Mr. J. T. Rees, 241; Messrs. A. W. Ridley & Co., 49, 493; Professor Julius Röntgen, 173(1), 352; Messrs. Schott & Co., Ltd., 271; Exor. of the late Cecil J. Sharp, 15, 201, 377, 378 (melody), 484 (melody); Mr. Geoffrey Shaw, 55, 438, 463, 494, 614, 620, 688; Miss A. H. Small, 17; Mr. J. F. R. Stainer, 373; Messrs. Stainer & Bell, Ltd., 315(2), 322(1), 325, 528 (Part II); Miss Geraldine M. Stanford, 528(1), 654(1); the Editor of *A Students' Hymnal*, 668; Rev. Canon H. Van de Wattyne, 7; Dr. J. Lloyd Williams, 158, 462 (melody); Rev. Canon David F. R. Wilson, 541, 601, from *Church Hymnal*, A.P.C.K., Dublin; also from the *Yattendon Hymnal*, 245.

The following tunes and arrangements are the copyright of the Musical Editors:

3, 4, 6, 16, 21, 23, 28(1), 30, 31*, 33 Part II(2), 34, 35, 39, 53, 56(1), 58, 59, 65*, 71, 77, 79(1), 80(2), 87*, 88, 94, 98, 102, 104, 115(2), 118, 120(1), 126, 129(1), 143(1), 150(2), 151*, 158, 161, 162, 163, 166, 167, 182, 183, 186(2), 196, 205, 213, 221, 224, 225, 226, 232, 239, 259, 269, 272, 275*, 282, 285, 286, 293(2), 300, 302, 304, 308, 313, 316, 319(2), 321, 322(2), 327, 329, 341, 343, 355, 365, 369, 376, 378, 381, 382, 383, 384, 392, 393(1), 393(2), 400, 433, 437*, 447, 448, 451, 461, 464(1), 478, 484, 489, 495, 508(1), 510, 513, 515, 516(2), 518, 523, 525, 530, 538, 546, 550, 562, 565, 567, 573(2), 576, 577, 580, 587, 599, 600, 602, 616, 617, 627, 636(1), 637(2), 639, 642, 647, 655, 660, 662, 685, 692, 700, 702*, App. 1.

PREFACE

The following tunes and arrangements are the copyright of the Oxford University Press:

12*, 18, 33 Part I (1), 33 Part II (1), 36, 41, 44(1), 46*, 51(1), 63, 84*, 96*, 105*, 107, 114*, 115(1), 130(1), 131*, 148(1), 154, 170(2), 180(1), 186(1), 190(1), 194(2), 200*, 206, 210(1)*, 216*, 229, 230, 240, 248, 251, 258, 288, 301*, 311, 323, 328(1), 328(2), 331, 340, 344, 349(2)*, 358, 360, 361, 363, 364, 367, 370, 371, 372, 379, 380, 389, 393(3), 394, 396(1), 396(2), 396(3), 399, 401, 440*, 458*, 459(1), 460*, 465, 467, 469, 486, 491(2), 497, 499, 500*, 501(2), 504, 507*, 511, 517*, 527(1), 527(2)*, 529, 547(2)*, 548, 549(1), 554(1), 558*, 566*, 568, 569, 570*, 572, 579, 582, 588, 590, 610*, 611, 634, 657*, 682*, 689, 697.

The Editors wish to thank Mr. W. Gandy for help in research work; also Professor F. C. Burkitt for communicating the melody of No. 183, Mr. John Goss for communicating the melody of No. 282, and the Rev. C. H. Shawe for information and advice on the hymn-tunes of the Bohemian Brethren.

R. VAUGHAN WILLIAMS.
MARTIN SHAW.

1931.

CONTENTS

BOOK I

PART I

PART II

PART III

CONTENTS

CONTENTS

PART IX

BOOK I
PART I
TIMES AND SEASONS
NEW YEAR

1

CULBACH. (7 7. 7 7.)
Moderately slow.

From a Chorale in SCHEFFLER'S
Heilige Seelenlust, 1657.

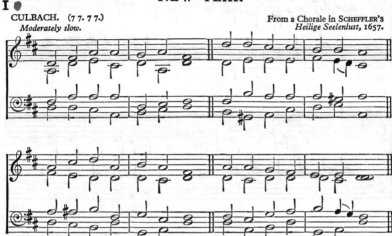

H. Downton,† 1818–85.

FOR thy mercy and thy grace,
   Faithful through another year,
Hear our song of thankfulness,
   Father and Redeemer, hear.

2 Lo, our sins on thee we cast,
   Lo, to thee we now arise
And, forgetting all the past,
   Press towards our glorious prize.

3 Dark the future: let thy light
   Guide us, bright and morning Star;
Fierce our foes, and hard the fight:
   Arm us, Saviour, for the war.

4 In our weakness and distress,
   Rock of strength, be thou our stay;
In the pathless wilderness
   Be our true and living way.

5. Keep us faithful, keep us pure,
   Keep us evermore thine own;
Help, O help us to endure;
   Fit us for the promised crown.

See also

(1)

B

SPRING

DA CHRISTUS GEBOREN WAR. (7 7. 7 7.)
In moderate time.

Melody arranged by J. F. DOLES, 1715–97.

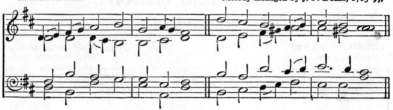

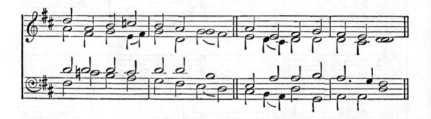

J. Newton,† 1725–1807.

KINDLY spring again is here,
Trees and fields in bloom appear;
Hark! the birds with artless lays
Warble their creator's praise.

2 Where in winter all was snow,
Now the flowers in clusters grow;
And the corn, in green array,
Promises a harvest-day.

3 Lord, afford a spring to me,
Let me feel like what I see;
Speak, and by thy gracious voice,
Make my drooping soul rejoice.

4. On thy garden deign to smile,
Raise the plants, enrich the soil;
Soon thy presence will restore
Life to what seemed dead before.

3

GRACE SOIT.   (6 5. 6 5. D. and refrain.)

Moderately quick.

French Carol Melody.

Al - le - lu - ya, Al - le - lu - - ya! Praise the Lord with thanks - giv - ing: Prais - es sing to God.

Spring Festival.

Rose Fyleman, 1877-1957.

LIFT your hidden faces,
  Ye who wept and prayed;
Leave your covert places,
  Ye who were afraid.
Here 's a golden story,
  Here is silver news,
Here be gifts of glory
  For all men to choose:

  Alleluya, alleluya!
  Praise the Lord with thanksgiving:
  Praises sing to God.

2 Now from mead and spinney,
    Now from flood and foam,
  Feathered, furred, and finny,
    All ye creatures come.
  Here ye shall discover
    That for which ye wait;
  Winter days are over,
    Sing and celebrate:

3. Fathers, leave your labours;
    Sons, be glad and gay;
  Tell your friends and neighbours
    Of our holy-day.
  Joyfully forgather;
    Sorrow now is done:
  We have found a Father,
    We have found a Son:

(3)

SPRING

TEMPUS ADEST FLORIDUM. (7 6. 7 6. D.)

In moderate time.

Melody from *Piae Cantiones*, 1582.

A Fa-burden will be found in The Oxford Book of Carols, 99.

Flower Carol.

Piae Cantiones (1582), Tr. O. B. C.

SPRING has now unwrapped the
Day is fast reviving, [flowers,
Life in all her growing powers
Towards the light is striving:
Gone the iron touch of cold,
Winter time and frost time,
Seedlings, working through the mould,
Now make up for lost time.

2 Herb and plant that, winter long,
Slumbered at their leisure,
Now bestirring, green and strong,
Find in growth their pleasure:
All the world with beauty fills,
Gold the green enhancing;
Flowers make merry on the hills,
Set the meadows dancing.

3 Through each wonder of fair days
God himself expresses;
Beauty follows all his ways,
As the world he blesses:

So, as he renews the earth,
Artist without rival,
In his grace of glad new birth
We must seek revival.

4*Earth is garbed in revelry,
Flowers and grasses hide her;
We go forth in charity—
Brothers all beside her;
For, as man this glory sees
In the awakening season,
Reason learns the heart's decrees,
Hearts are led by reason.

5. Praise the Maker, all ye saints;
He with glory girt you,
He who skies and meadows paints
Fashioned all your virtue;
Praise him, seers, heroes, kings,
Heralds of perfection;
Brothers, praise him, for he brings
All to resurrection!

5

SPRING. (4. 10.)

Easter Song.

Christina Rossetti, 1830–94.

Martin Shaw, 1876–1958.

Moderately quick. Voices in unison.

1 Spring bursts to-day, For Christ is ris'n and all the earth's at play.

2 Flash forth, thou sun, The rain is o-ver and gone, its work is done.

3 Win-ter is past, Sweet spring is come at last, is come at last.

4 Bud, fig and vine, Bud, o-live, fat with fruit and oil, and wine.

5 (*continued*)

Slightly slower.

5 Break forth this morn In ros - es, thou but yes - ter-day a thorn.

6 Up-lift thy head, O pure white li - ly through the win - ter dead.

Tempo 1mo.

7 Be - side your dams Leap and re-joice, you mer - ry-mak-ing lambs.

8 All herds and flocks Re - joice, all beasts of thick - ets and of rocks. 9. Sing, crea - tures, sing, An - gels and men and birds, and ev - 'ry - thing. . . .

6

BAMBERG. (5 5. 4 5. D.)

Moderately quick.   Unison.

17th century Melody (slightly adapted).

Robert Browning, 1812–89.

THE year's at the spring,
　And day's at the morn;
Morning's at seven;
　The hill-side's dew-pearled;

The lark's on the wing;
　The snail's on the thorn;
God's in his heaven—
　All's right with the world!

See also

19 Hark, my soul, how everything
360 Hark a hundred notes
30 Morning has broken

650 Sweet day, so cool
229 *May Carol.* The winter's sleep
21 When spring unlocks

SUMMER

7

GHENT (ADORO TE, No. 2). (6 5. 6 5. D.)

In moderate time.

Melody of 'Adoro Te' as given by Canon VAN DAMME of Ghent.

[This hymn may also be sung to GLENFINLAS, 354.]

Bishop Walsham How, 1823–97.

SUMMER suns are glowing
　Over land and sea,
Happy light is flowing
　Bountiful and free.
Everything rejoices
　In the mellow rays,
All earth's thousand voices
　Swell the psalm of praise.

2 God's free mercy streameth
　Over all the world,
And his banner gleameth
　Everywhere unfurled.
Broad and deep and glorious
　As the heaven above,
Shines in might victorious
　His eternal love.

3 Lord, upon our blindness
    Thy pure radiance pour;
For thy loving-kindness
    Make us love thee more.
And when clouds are drifting
    Dark across our sky,
Then, the veil uplifting,
    Father, be thou nigh.

4. We will never doubt thee,
    Though thou veil thy light;
Life is dark without thee;
    Death with thee is bright.
Light of light! shine o'er us
    On our pilgrim way,
Go thou still before us
    To the endless day.

8

SOLL'S SEIN. (D.C.M.)
Slow.

Melody from CORNER'S *Geistliche Nachtigall*, 1658.

S. Longfellow,‡ 1819–92.

THE summer days are come again;
    Once more the glad earth yields
Her golden wealth of ripening grain,
    And breath of clover fields,
And deepening shade of summer woods,
    And glow of summer air,
And winging thoughts, and happy moods
    Of love and joy and prayer.

2. The summer days are come again;
    The birds are on the wing;
God's praises, in their loving strain,
    Unconsciously they sing.
We know who giveth all the good
    That doth our cup o'erbrim;
For summer joy in field and wood
    We lift our song to him.

See also

439 All creatures
444 *All things bright*
  19 Hark, my soul, how everything

518 Here in the country's heart
  21 When spring unlocks

HARVEST

ST. GEORGE. (77. 77. D.)

Brightly.

G. J. ELVEY, 1816–93.

H. Alford,‡ 1810–71.

COME, ye thankful people, come,
Raise the song of harvest-home!
All be safely gathered in,
Ere the winter storms begin;
God, our Maker, doth provide
For our wants to be supplied;
Come to God's own temple, come;
Raise the song of harvest-home!

2 All this world is God's own field,
Fruit unto his praise to yield;
Wheat and tares together sown,
Unto joy or sorrow grown;
First the blade and then the ear,
Then the full corn shall appear;
Lord of harvest, grant that we
Wholesome grain and pure may be.

3 For the Lord our God shall come,
And shall take his harvest home;
From his field shall purge away
All that doth offend to-day;
Give his angels charge at last
In the fire the tares to cast,
But the fruitful wheat to store
In his barn for evermore.

HARVEST

4.* Then, thou Church triumphant, come,
Raise the song of harvest-home;
All be safely gathered in,
Free from sorrow, free from sin,
There for ever purified
In God's garner to abide:
Come, ten thousand angels, come,
Raise the glorious harvest-home!

SELMA. (S.M.)
In moderate time.

Adapted by R. A. SMITH (1780–1829)
from a traditional Melody of the Isle of Arran.

[This hymn may also be sung to FALCON STREET, 635.]

J. Hampden Gurney, 1802–62.

FAIR waved the golden corn
In Canaan's pleasant land,
When full of joy, some shining morn,
Went forth the reaper-band.

2   To God so good and great
Their cheerful thanks they pour;
Then carry to his temple-gate
The choicest of their store.

3   Like Israel, Lord, we give
Our earliest fruits to thee,
And pray that, long as we shall live,
We may thy children be.

4   Thine is our youthful prime,
And life and all its powers;
Be with us in our morning time,
And bless our evening hours.

5.   In wisdom let us grow,
As years and strength are given,
That we may serve thy Church below,
And join thy saints in heaven.

11

CORNFIELDS. (7 6. 7 6. 7 7 6. 7 7 6.)

Moderately fast.

Melody from Bohemian Brethren's *Gesangbuch,* 1539.

Eleanor Farjeon.

FIELDS of corn, give up your ears,
Now your ears are heavy,
Wheat and oats and barley-spears,
All your harvest-levy.
Where your sheaves of plenty lean,
Men once more the grain shall glean
Of the Ever-Living;
God the Lord will bless the field,
Bringing in its autumn yield
Gladly to Thanksgiving.

2 Vines, send in your bunch of grapes,
Now the bunch is clustered,
Be your gold and purple shapes
Round the altar mustered.
Where the hanging bunches shine

Men once more shall taste the wine
Of the Ever-Living;
God the Lord will bless the root,
Bringing in its autumn fruit
Gladly to Thanksgiving.

3. Garden, give your gayest flowers,
Hedge, your wildest bring in,
Turn the churches into bowers
Little birds shall sing in.
Where the children sing their glee
Men once more the flower shall see
Of the Ever-Living;
God the Lord will bless the throng,
Lifting up its autumn song
Gladly in Thanksgiving.

12

MONKLAND. (7 7. 7 7.)

In moderate time.

Melody from *Hymn Tunes of the United Brethren,* 1824.
Arranged by J. WILKES (1861).

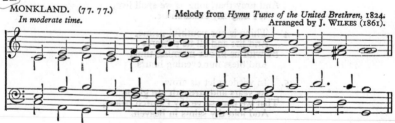

HARVEST

ALTERNATIVE VERSION

Trebles.

Descant by C. CHARLTON PALMER.

CHOIR OR ORGAN.

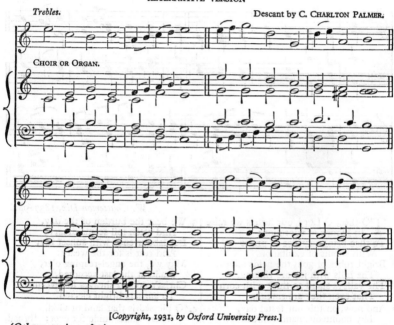

(*Other occasions also.*)
Ps. 136.

J. Milton,‡ 1608–74.

L ET us, with a gladsome mind,
   Praise the Lord, for he is kind:
     For his mercies ay endure,
     Ever faithful, ever sure.

2 Let us blaze his name abroad,
  For of gods he is the God:

3*He with all-commanding might
  Filled the new-made world with light:

4 He the golden-tressèd sun
  Caused all day his course to run:

5 The hornèd moon to shine by night,
  'Mid her spangled sisters bright:

6 All things living he doth feed,
  His full hand supplies their need:

7.*Let us, with a gladsome mind,
  Praise the Lord, for he is kind:

(13)

13

ST. GALL. (87. 87. D.)
Moderately fast.

St. Gall Gesangbuch, 1863.

W. Chatterton Dix, 1837–98.

TO thee, O Lord, our hearts we raise
    In hymns of adoration;
To thee bring sacrifice of praise
    With shouts of exultation.
Bright robes of gold the fields adorn,
    The hills with joy are ringing,
The valleys stand so thick with corn
    That even they are singing.

2 And now, on this our festal day,
    Thy bounteous hand confessing,
Upon thine altar, Lord, we lay
    The first-fruits of thy blessing;
By thee the souls of men are fed
    With gifts of grace supernal;
Thou who dost give us daily bread,
    Give us the Bread eternal.

3 We bear the burden of the day,
    And often toil seems dreary;
But labour ends with sunset ray,
    And rest is for the weary;
May we, the angel-reaping o'er,
    Stand at the last accepted,
Christ's golden sheaves for evermore
    To garners bright elected.

4.*O blessèd is that land of God,
    Where saints abide for ever; [broad,
Where golden fields spread fair and
    Where flows the crystal river:
The strains of all its holy throng
    With ours to-day are blending;
Thrice blessèd is that harvest-song
    Which never hath an ending.

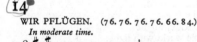

WIR PFLÜGEN. (76. 76. 76. 76. 66. 84.)
In moderate time.

Bible Class Magazine, 1854, said to be
arranged from J. A. P. Schulz, 1747–1800.

HARVEST

A little slower.

M. Claudius, 1740–1815. Tr. J. M. Campbell.

Wir pflügen und wir streuen.

WE plough the fields, and scatter
　　The good seed on the land,
But it is fed and watered
　　By God's almighty hand:
He sends the snow in winter,
　　The warmth to swell the grain,
The breezes and the sunshine,
　　And soft refreshing rain:

All good gifts around us
*　　Are sent from heaven above;*
Then thank the Lord, O thank the Lord,
*　　For all his love.*

2 He only is the maker
　　Of all things near and far,
He paints the wayside flower,
　　He lights the evening star.
The winds and waves obey him,
　　By him the birds are fed;
Much more to us, his children,
　　He gives our daily bread:

3. We thank thee then, O Father,
　　For all things bright and good;
The seed-time and the harvest,
　　Our life, our health, our food.
No gifts have we to offer
　　For all thy love imparts,
But that which thou desirest,
　　Our humble, thankful hearts:

See also

(15)

AUTUMN

15

HAMBRIDGE. (7 6. 7 6.)
In moderate time.

English Traditional Melody.

[This hymn may also be sung to DEVONSHIRE, 459.]

Bishop W. W. How, 1823-97.

THE year is swiftly waning,
  The summer days are past;
And life, brief life, is speeding;
  The end is nearing fast.

2 The ever-changing seasons
  In silence come and go;
But thou, eternal Father,
  No time or change canst know.

3 O pour thy grace upon us,
  That we may worthier be,
Each year that passes o'er us,
  To dwell in heaven with thee.

4 Behold the bending orchards
  With bounteous fruits are crowned;
Lord, in our hearts more richly
  Let heavenly fruits abound.

5*O by each mercy sent us,
  And by each grief and pain,
By blessings like the sunshine,
  And sorrows like the rain,

6.*Our barren hearts make fruitful
  With every goodly grace,
That we thy name may hallow,
  And see at last thy face.

See also

521 Hosannal Music is divine | 12 Let us, with a gladsome

16

WINTER

DANBY. (L.M.)
In moderate time. Voices in unison.

English Traditional Melody.

[*Copyright*, 1925, by R. *Vaughan Williams.*]

(16)

S. Longfellow, 1819–92.

'TIS winter now; the fallen snow
  Has left the heavens all coldly clear;
Through leafless boughs the sharp winds blow,
  And all the earth lies dead and drear.

2 And yet God's love is not withdrawn;
    His life within the keen air breathes;
  His beauty paints the crimson dawn,
    And clothes the boughs with glittering wreaths.

3 And though abroad the sharp winds blow,
    And skies are chill, and frosts are keen,
  Home closer draws her circle now,
    And warmer glows her light within.

4. O God! who giv'st the winter's cold,
    As well as summer's joyous rays,
  Us warmly in thy love enfold,
    And keep us through life's wintry days.

See also
21 When spring unlocks

SEASONS: GENERAL

17

SHANGHAI. (8 7. 8 7.)
In moderate time.

Adapted from a Chinese Melody.

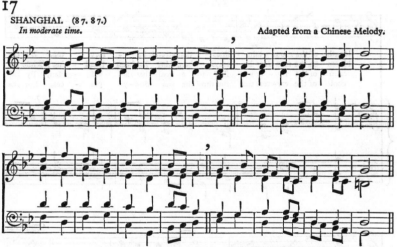

[This hymn may also be sung to SHIPSTON, 364.]

Christopher Smart, 1722–71.

ALL the scenes of nature quicken,
  By the genial spirit fanned;
And the painted beauties thicken,
  Coloured by the Master's hand;

2 Earth her vigour repossessing,
    As the blasts are held in ward,
  Blessing heaped and pressed on blessing,
    Yield the measure of the Lord.

3 Cowslips seize upon the fallow,
    And the cardamine in white,
  Where the cornflowers join the mallow,
    Joy and health and thrift unite.

4 Hark! aloud the blackbird whistles,
    With surrounding fragrance blest,
  And the goldfinch in the thistles
    Makes provision for her nest.

5. Prayer and praise be mine employment
    Without grudging or regret:
  Lasting life and long enjoyment
    Are not here, and are not yet.

(Cardamines are lady-smocks.)

(17)

HICKLING BROAD. (Irregular.)

Broadly and not too fast. Voices in unison.

GEOFFREY SHAW, 1879–1943.

1 By the breadth of the blue that shines in si - lence o'er me, By the
2 While the trem - u-lous leaf - y haze on the wood-land is spread - ing, And the
3 By the faith that the flow'rs show when they bloom un - bid - den, By the
4. For the com-fort-ing warmth of the sun that my bo - dy em - bra - ces, For the

length of the moun - tain - lines that stretch be - fore me, By the
bloom on the mea-dow be - trays where May has been tread - ing ; While the
calm of the riv - er's flow to a goal that is hid - den, By the
cool of the wa - ters that run thro' the sha - dow-y pla - ces, For the

Omit v. 1.

height of the cloud that sails, with rest in mo - tion,
birds on the branch-es a - bove, and the brooks flowing un - der, Are
trust of the tree that clings to its deep foun - da - tion, By the
balm of the breez - es that brush my face with their fin - gers, For the

Omit v. 1.

Ov - er the plains and the vales to the mea - sure-less o - cean,
sing - ing to - geth - er of love in a world full of won - der,
cou - rage of wild . . birds' wings on the long . . . mi - gra - tion,
ves - per - hymn of the thrush when the twi - - light lin - gers,

(O, how the sight of the things that are great en - lar - ges the eyes!)
(Lo, in the mar - vel of spring - time, dreams are changed in - to truth!)
(Won - der - ful se - cret of peace that a - bid - eth in Na - ture's breast!)
Now with a breath that is deep - drawn, breath of a heart with - out care,

Draw me a - way from my - self to the peace of the hills and the skies.
Quick-en my heart, and re - store the beau - ti - ful hopes of youth.
Teach me how to con - fide, and live my life, and rest.
I will give thanks and a - dore thee, God of the o - pen air

[Copyright, 1931, by Oxford University Press.]   Henry van Dyke,
                                                    1852–1933.

19

LYNE. (7 7. 7 7.)
In moderate time.

Magdalen Hymns (c. 1760).

J. Austin, 1613–69.

HARK, my soul, how everything
Strives to serve our bounteous King;
Each a double tribute pays,
Sings its part, and then obeys.

2 Nature's chief and sweetest choir
Him with cheerful notes admire;
Chanting every day their lauds,
While the grove their song applauds.

3 Though their voices lower be,
Streams have too their melody;
Night and day they warbling run,
Never pause, but still sing on.

4 All the flowers that gild the spring
Hither their still music bring;
If heaven bless them, thankful, they
Smell more sweet, and look more gay.

5*Wake! for shame, my sluggish heart,
Wake! and gladly sing thy part;
Learn of birds, and springs, and flowers,
How to use thy nobler powers.

6. Call whole nature to thy aid,
Since 'twas he whole nature made;
Join in one eternal song,
Who to one God all belong.

NEW 113TH. (8 8. 8 8. 8 8.)
Moderately slow.

W. HAYES, 1706–77.

Thomas Moore, 1779–1852.

THOU art, O God, the life and light
　Of all this wondrous world we see;
Its glow by day, its smile by night,
　Are but reflections caught from thee:
Where'er we turn, thy glories shine,
And all things fair and bright are thine.

2 When day with farewell beam delays
　　Among the opening clouds of even,
And we can almost think we gaze
　　Through golden vistas into heaven,—
Those hues that make the sun's decline
So soft, so radiant, Lord, are thine.

3 When night with wings of starry gloom
　　O'ershadows all the earth and skies,
Like some dark beauteous bird whose plume
　　Is sparkling with unnumbered eyes,—
That sacred gloom, those fires divine,
So grand, so countless, Lord, are thine.

4.* When youthful spring around us breathes,
　　Thy Spirit warms her fragrant sigh,
And every flower the summer wreathes
　　Is born beneath that kindling eye,—
Where'er we turn, thy glories shine,
And all things fair and bright are thine.

GOSTERWOOD. (13 13. 14 14.)
In moderate time. English Traditional Melody.

Bishop R. Heber, 1783–1826.

WHEN spring unlocks the flowers, to paint the laughing soil;
When summer's balmy showers refresh the mower's toil;
When winter binds in frosty chains the fallow and the flood;
In God the earth rejoiceth still, and owns his maker good.

2 The birds that wake the morning, and those that love the shade;
The winds that sweep the mountain, or lull the drowsy glade;
The sun that from his amber bower rejoiceth on his way,
The moon and stars—their master's name in silent pomp display.

3 Shall man, the lord of nature, expectant of the sky,
Shall man alone, unthankful, his little praise deny?
No; let the year forsake his course, the seasons cease to be,
Thee, Master, must we always love, and, Saviour, honour thee.

4.*The flowers of spring may wither, the hope of summer fade,
The autumn droop in winter, the birds forsake the shade;
The winds be lulled, the sun and moon forget their old decree:
But we, in nature's latest hour, O Lord, will cling to thee!

See also

439 All creatures	494 For the beauty	664 There is a book
444 *All things bright*	521 Hosanna! Music is divine	690 We sing of God
445 All things which live	434 *Song of the Creatures.* O	691 We thank thee
448 Angels holy	most high	692 We thank you
421 *Benedicite*	659 The spacious firmament	

22 SUNDAY

FARLEY CASTLE. (10 10. 10 10.)
In moderate time. H. LAWES, 1596–1662.

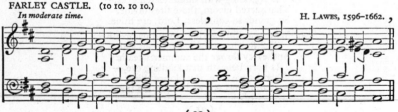

Verse 4 begins here.

Sunday Morning.   *Edmund Spenser, c.* 1552–99.

M OST glorious Lord of life, that on this day
    Didst make thy triumph over death and sin,
And having harrowed hell, didst bring away
    Captivity thence captive, us to win:

2 This joyous day, dear Lord, with joy begin,
    And grant that we for whom thou diddest die,
Being with thy dear blood clean washed from sin,
    May live for ever in felicity:

3 And that thy love we weighing worthily,
    May likewise love thee for the same again;
And for thy sake, that all like dear didst buy,
    With love may one another entertain;

4. So let us love, dear Love, like as we ought;
    Love is the lesson which the Lord us taught.

23

BROMSGROVE. (C.M.)

In moderate time.   Later form of melody from *Psalmodia Evangelica,* 1789.

Isaac Watts, 1674–1748.

T HIS is the day the Lord hath made;
    He calls the hours his own;
Let heaven rejoice, let earth be glad,
And praise surround the throne.

2 To-day he rose and left the dead,
    And Satan's empire fell;
To-day the saints his triumphs spread,
    And all his wonders tell.

3 Hosanna to the anointed King,
    To David's holy Son!

Make haste to help us, Lord, and bring
    Salvation from thy throne.

4 Blest be the Lord, who comes to men
    With messages of grace;
Who comes, in God his Father's name,
    To save our sinful race.

5. Hosanna in the highest strains
    The Church on earth can raise;
The highest heavens in which he reigns
    Shall give him nobler praise.

See also
390 Welcome, Day of the Lord

24

RATISBON (JESU, MEINE ZUVERSICHT). (7 7. 7 7. 7 7.)

Slow.   Later form of Melody attributed to J. CRÜGER, 1598–1662.

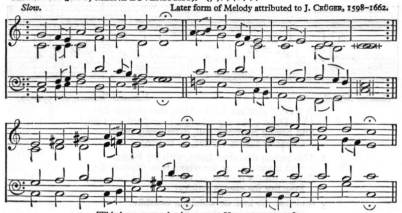

[This hymn may also be sung to HEATHLANDS, 170.]

W. Bright, 1824–1901.

AT thy feet, O Christ, we lay
Thine own gift of this new day;
Doubt of what it holds in store
Makes us crave thine aid the more;
Lest it prove a time of loss,
Mark it, Saviour, with thy cross.

2 If it flow on calm and bright,
Be thyself our chief delight;
If it bring unknown distress,
Good is all that thou canst bless;
Only, while its hours begin,
Pray we, keep them clear of sin.

3*Fain would we thy word embrace,
Live each moment on thy grace,
All our selves to thee consign,
Fold up all our wills in thine,
Think, and speak, and do, and be
Simply that which pleases thee.

4. Hear us, Lord, and that right soon;
Hear, and grant the choicest boon
That thy love can e'er impart,
Loyal singleness of heart;
So shall this and all our days,
Christ our God, show forth thy praise.

25

MORNING HYMN. (L.M.)   PART I

In moderate time.   F. H. BARTHÉLÉMON, 1741–1808.

A - men.

Bishop T. Ken, 1637–1711.

AWAKE, my soul, and with the sun
Thy daily stage of duty run;
Shake off dull sloth, and joyful rise
To pay thy morning sacrifice.

MORNING

2 Redeem thy mis-spent time that 's past;
Live this day as if 'twere thy last;
Improve thy talent with due care;
For the great day thyself prepare.

3 Let all thy converse be sincere,
Thy conscience as the noon-day clear;
Think how all-seeing God thy ways
And all thy secret thoughts surveys.

4 By influence of the Light divine
Let thy own light in good works shine;
Reflect all heaven's propitious ways
In ardent love and cheerful praise.

Praise God, from whom all blessings flow;
Praise him, all creatures here below;
Praise him above, ye heavenly host;
Praise Father, Son, and Holy Ghost.

ALTERNATIVE VERSION

DESCANT (Trebles).   Descant by GEOFFREY SHAW.

MELODY   (All other Voices.)

ORGAN.

[By permission of Novello & Co., Ltd.]

25 (*continued*)

PART II

RICHARD. (L.M.)
Moderately slow.

MORFYDD OWEN, 1892–1918.

A-men.

5 Wake, and lift up thyself, my heart,
And with the angels bear thy part,
Who all night long unwearied sing
High praise to the eternal King.

6 Awake, awake, ye heavenly choir,
May your devotion me inspire,
That I like you my age may spend,
Like you may on my God attend.

PART III

WARRINGTON. (L.M.)
In moderate time.

R. HARRISON, 1748–1810.

A - men.

[The third part of this hymn may also be sung to TALLIS' CANON, 45.]

7 Glory to thee, who safe hast kept
And hast refreshed me whilst I slept;
Grant, Lord, when I from death shall
wake
I may of endless light partake.

8 Heaven is, dear Lord, where'er thou
art,
O never then from me depart;
For to my soul 'tis hell to be
But for one moment void of thee.

9 Lord, I my vows to thee renew;
Scatter my sins as morning dew;
Guard my first springs of thought and
will,
And with thyself my spirit fill.

10 Direct, control, suggest, this day
All I design, or do, or say;
That all my powers, with all their
might,
In thy sole glory may unite.

Doxology after any Part

11. Praise God, from whom all blessings flow;
Praise him, all creatures here below;
Praise him above, ye heavenly host;
Praise Father, Son, and Holy Ghost.

MINISTRES DE L'ÉTERNEL. (7 7. 7 7. 7 7.)
In moderate time.

Psalm 135 in the *Genevan Psalter*, 1562
(rhythm of line 2 slightly simplified).

[This hymn may also be sung to HEATHLANDS, 170.]

C. Wesley, 1707–88.

CHRIST, whose glory fills the skies,
Christ, the true, the only Light,
Sun of Righteousness, arise,
Triumph o'er the shades of night;
Dayspring from on high, be near;
Daystar, in my heart appear.

2 Dark and cheerless is the morn
Unaccompanied by thee;
Joyless is the day's return,

Till thy mercy's beams I see;
Till they inward light impart,
Glad my eyes, and warm my heart.

3. Visit then this soul of mine,
Pierce the gloom of sin and grief;
Fill me, radiancy divine,
Scatter all my unbelief;
More and more thyself display,
Shining to the perfect day.

27

MORGENGLANZ DER EWIGKEIT. (7 8. 7 8. 7 3.)

In moderate time.

Melody from FREYLINGHAUSEN'S
Geistreiches Gesangbuch, 1704.

C. Knorr, Baron von Rosenroth, 1636–89. *Tr. R. Massie‡* (1857).

Morgenglanz der Ewigkeit.

COME, thou bright and morning star,
Light of light, without beginning,
Shine upon us from afar,
Like the morn when mists are thinning;
Drive away by thy clear light
Our dark night.

2 Let thy grace, like morning dew
Falling on the barren places,
Comfort, quicken, and renew
All dry souls and dying graces;
Bless thy flock from thy rich store
Evermore.

3 May thy fervent love destroy
All cold works, in us awaking
Ardent courage, zeal, and joy,
At the purple morn's first breaking;
Let us truly rise, ere yet
Life has set.

4.*Light us to the heavenly spheres,
Sun of grace, in glory shrouded;
Lead us through this vale of tears,
To the land where days unclouded,
Purest joy, and perfect peace,
Never cease.

28

FIRST TUNE

PLAINSONG. (11 11. 11 5.) *In free rhythm.*

Mode vi.

SECOND TUNE

UT QUEANT LAXIS. (11 11. 11 5.)
In moderate time. Unison.

Paris Antiphoner, 1681.

Ascr. to St. Gregory. 6th cent. Tr. E. H.

Nocte surgentes.

FATHER, we praise thee, now the night is over,
　Active and watchful, stand we all before thee;
Singing we offer prayer and meditation:
　　　Thus we adore thee.

2 Monarch of all things, fit us for thy mansions;
　Banish our weakness, health and wholeness sending;
Bring us to heaven, where thy saints united
　　　Joy without ending.

3. All-holy Father, Son, and equal Spirit,
　Trinity blessèd, send us thy salvation;
Thine is the glory, gleaming and resounding
　　　Through all creation.

(29)

ANGEL'S SONG (SONG 34). (L.M.)

Original version of melody by
O. GIBBONS, 1583-1625.

ALTERNATIVE VERSION

Trebles (other voices sing the melody ANGEL'S SONG).

Descant by GUY WARRACK.

(Noon also.)

C. Wesley, 1707–88.

FORTH in thy name, O Lord, I go,
My daily labour to pursue;
Thee, only thee, resolved to know,
In all I think, or speak, or do.

2 Preserve me from my calling's snare,
And hide my simple heart above,
Above the thorns of choking care,
The gilded baits of worldly love.

MORNING

3 Thee may I set at my right hand,
   Whose eyes my inmost substance see,
And labour on at thy command,
   And offer all my works to thee.

4 Give me to bear thy easy yoke,
   And every moment watch and pray,
And still to things eternal look,
   And hasten to thy glorious day;

5. For thee delightfully employ
   Whate'er thy bounteous grace hath given,
And run my course with even joy,
   And closely walk with thee to heaven.

30 *sub-Christian euphoria*

BUNESSAN. (5 5. 5 4. D.)

In moderate time.   Old Gaelic Melody.

Thanks for a Day.   *Eleanor Farjeon.*

MORNING has broken
   Like the first morning,
Blackbird has spoken
   Like the first bird.
     Praise for the singing!
     Praise for the morning!
     Praise for them, springing
     Fresh from the Word!

2 Sweet the rain's new fall
   Sunlit from heaven,
Like the first dewfall
   On the first grass.
     Praise for the sweetness
     Of the wet garden,
     Sprung in completeness
     Where his feet pass.

3. Mine is the sunlight!
   Mine is the morning
Born of the one light
   Eden saw play!
     Praise with elation,
     Praise every morning,
     God's re-creation
     Of the new day!

31

MELCOMBE. (L.M.)
Moderately slow.

S. WEBBE (the elder), 1740-1816.

ALTERNATIVE VERSION

Melody in the Tenor.

Fa-burden by MARTIN SHAW.

J. Keble, 1792-1866.

NEW every morning is the love
  Our wakening and uprising prove;
Through sleep and darkness safely
    brought,
Restored to life, and power, and thought.

2 New mercies, each returning day,
  Hover around us while we pray;
New perils past, new sins forgiven,
New thoughts of God, new hopes of
    heaven.

3*If on our daily course our mind
  Be set to hallow all we find,
New treasures still, of countless price,
God will provide for sacrifice.

4 Old friends, old scenes, will lovelier be,
  As more of heaven in each we see;

Some softening gleam of love and
    prayer
Shall dawn on every cross and care.

5 We need not bid, for cloistered cell,
  Our neighbour and our work farewell,
Nor strive to wind ourselves too high
For sinful man beneath the sky:

6 The trivial round, the common task,
  Would furnish all we ought to ask,—
Room to deny ourselves, a road
To bring us daily nearer God.

7.*Only, O Lord, in thy dear love
  Fit us for perfect rest above;
And help us this and every day
To live more nearly as we pray.

FIRST TUNE

GOTT DES HIMMELS. (8 7. 8 7. 7 7.)

In moderate time.

H. ALBERT, 1604–51.

SECOND TUNE

ST. LEONARD. (8 7. 8 7. 7 7.)

In moderate time.

Melody by J. C. BACH, 1642–1703.

H. *Albert*, 1604–51. *Tr. H. J. Buckoll‡* (1842).

Gott des Himmels und der Erden.

NOW the morn new light is pouring:
　Lord, may we our spirits raise,
Through thy grace our souls restoring;
　So, on thy great day of days,
We with joy its dawn may meet
Fearless at the mercy-seat.

2 Jesus, who our steps art guiding
　By thy word's celestial light,
Now and evermore abiding,
　Our defence, our rock of might:
Nowhere, save alone in thee,
Can we rest from danger free.

3. Lo! we yield to thy direction
　Soul and body, heart and mind;
Keep thou all by thy protection,
　To thy mighty hand resigned.
Thee our glorious God we own;
Let us, Lord, be thine alone.

33 PART I

PLAINSONG. (L.M.) *In free rhythm.*

Melody from the *Sarum Antiphonal.*

A - men.

[Copyright, 1925, by Oxford University Press.]
For alternative Plainsong melody see next page.

SECOND TUNE

SOLEMNIS HAEC FESTIVITAS. (L.M.)

With vigour. Unison.

Paris Gradual, 1685.

A - - men.

St. Ambrose, 340–97. Tr. R. Bridges.

Splendor paternae gloriae.

PART I

1. O SPLENDOUR of God's glory bright,
O thou that bringest light from light,
O Light of light, light's living spring,
O Day, all days illumining,

2. O thou true Sun, on us thy glance
Let fall in royal radiance,
The Spirit's sanctifying beam
Upon our earthly senses stream.

3. The Father, too, our prayers implore,
Father of glory evermore;
The Father of all grace and might,
To banish sin from our delight:

4. To guide whate'er we nobly do,
With love all envy to subdue,
To make ill-fortune turn to fair,
And give us grace our wrongs to bear.

MORNING

FIRST TUNE

PLAINSONG. (L.M.) *In free rhythm.*

Melody from the *Sarum Antiphonal.*

A - men.

[*Copyright, 1925, by Oxford University Press.*]

SECOND TUNE

SPLENDOUR (PUER NOBIS NASCITUR). (L.M.)

Moderately fast.

Composed or adapted by M. PRAETORIUS, 1571–1621.

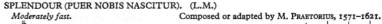

A - men.

PART II

5 Our mind be in his keeping placed,
Our body true to him and chaste,
Where only faith her fire shall feed,
To burn the tares of Satan's seed.

6 And Christ to us for food shall be,
From him our drink that welleth free,
The Spirit's wine, that maketh whole,
And, mocking not, exalts the soul.

7 Rejoicing may this day go hence,
Like virgin dawn our innocence,
Like fiery noon our faith appear,
Nor know the gloom of twilight drear.

8 Morn in her rosy car is borne;
Let him come forth, our perfect Morn,
The Word in God the Father one,
The Father perfect in the Son.

Doxology after either Part

9. All laud to God the Father be,
All praise, eternal Son, to thee;
All glory, as is ever meet,
To God the holy Paraclete.

(*For a short morning hymn, verses 1, 2, 3, or 1, 2, 8, or 7, 8, are suitable.*)

(35)

MORNING

34

HARDWICK. (6 5. 6 5. D. Irregular.)

In moderate time. Unison.

English Traditional Melody.

[Copyright, 1925, by R. Vaughan Williams.]

Thomas Carlyle, 1795–1881.

SO here hath been dawning
   Another blue day.
Think, wilt thou let it
   Slip useless away?

2 Out of eternity
   This new day is born;
Into eternity,
   At night, will return.

3 Behold it aforetime
   No eye ever did:
So soon it for ever
   From all eyes is hid.

4. Here hath been dawning
   Another blue day.
Think, wilt thou let it
   Slip useless away?

35

CREDITON. (C.M.)

In moderate time.

THOMAS CLARK, 1775–1859.

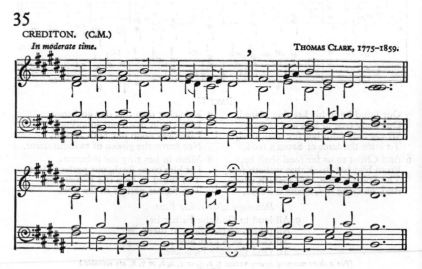

C. Coffin (1736). *Tr. Abp. Benson* (1860).
O Luce qui mortalibus.

THE splendours of thy glory, Lord,
 Hath no man seen nor known,
And highest angels veil their eyes
 Before thy shining throne.

2 So bright a day for us prepared,
 For us thou hast in store,
That this all-glorious sun shall fade
 Its sevenfold light before.

3 When mortal bonds are rent, my God,
 My soul to thee shall soar,
And see thy face, and praise thee well,
 And love thee evermore.

4. Grant us, O Lord, thy splendid peace,
 Fair love and saintly might;
And on our dim and fleeting day
 Shed thine immortal light.

36

GARDEN. (10. 10.)

In moderate time.   Adapted from an English Traditional Melody.

Based on Robert Herrick, 1591–1674.

WHEN virgin morn doth call thee to arise,
 Come thus in sober joy to sacrifice:

2 First wash thy heart in innocence, then bring
 Pure hands, pure habits; make pure everything.

3 Next humbly kneel before God's throne, and thence
 Give up thy soul in clouds of frankincense.

4. Censers of gold, thus filled with odours sweet,
 Shall make thy actions with their ends to meet.

(37)

37

AETERNA CHRISTI MUNERA. (L.M.)

In free rhythm. Unison.

Melody from GUIDETTI, *Directorium Chori*, 1582.

[This hymn may also be sung to DEUS TUORUM MILITUM, 633.]

LUCIS CREATOR. (L.M.)

In moderate time. Unison.

Lyons Antiphoner, 1738.

Prudentius, b. 348. Tr. R. M. Pope.

Nox et tenebrae et nubila.

YE clouds and darkness, hosts of night,
  That breed confusion and affright,
Begone! o'erhead the dawn shines clear,
The light breaks in and Christ is here.

2 Earth's gloom flees broken and dispersed,
  By the sun's piercing shafts coerced:
The day-star's eyes rain influence bright,
And colours glimmer back to sight.

3 Thee, Christ, alone we know; to thee
  We bend in pure simplicity;
Our songs with tears to thee arise;
Prove thou our hearts with thy clear eyes.

4. Though we be stained with blots within,
  Thy quickening rays shall purge our sin;
Light of the Morning Star, thy grace
Shed on us from thy cloudless face.

38

GRÄFENBERG (NUN DANKET ALL). (C.M.)

Moderately slow.

Praxis Pietatis Melica, 1653.

George Gascoigne, c. 1525–77.

YOU that have spent the silent night
  In sleep and quiet rest,
And joy to see the cheerful light
  That riseth in the east,

2 Now clear your voice, now cheer your
    heart,
  Come help me now to sing;
Each willing wight come bear a part,
  To praise the heavenly King.

3 The little birds which sing so sweet
  Are like the angels' voice,
Which render God his praises meet,
  And teach us to rejoice.

4 And as they more esteem that mirth
  Than dread the night's annoy,
So must we deem our days on earth
  But hell to heavenly joy.

5 Unto which joys for to attain
  God grant us all his grace,
And send us after worldly pain
  In heaven to have a place;

6. Where we may still enjoy that light,
  Which never shall decay:
Lord, for thy mercy lend us might
  To see that joyful day.

NOON

39

FERRY. (C.M.)

In moderate time.

(*Or other hours.*)

J. Ellerton, 1826–93.

BEHOLD us, Lord, a little space
From daily tasks set free,
And met within thy holy place
To rest awhile with thee.

2 Around us rolls the ceaseless tide
Of business, toil, and care;
And scarcely can we turn aside
For one brief hour of prayer.

3 Yet these are not the only walls
Wherein thou may'st be sought;
On homeliest work thy blessing falls,
In truth and patience wrought.

4 Thine is the loom, the forge, the mart,
The wealth of land and sea;
The worlds of science and of art,
Revealed and ruled by thee.

5 Then let us prove our heavenly birth
In all we do and know;
And claim the kingdom of the earth
For thee, and not thy foe.

6.*Work shall be prayer, if all be wrought
As thou would'st have it done;
And prayer, by thee inspired and taught,
Itself with work be one.

40

HERR JESU CHRIST. (L.M.)

Very slow and dignified.

Later form of melody from *Pensum Sacrum* (Görlitz, 1648).

[This hymn may also be sung to BRESLAU, 132.]

(40)

William Wordsworth, 1770–1850.

BLEST are the moments, doubly
blest,
That, drawn from this one hour of rest,
Are with a ready heart bestowed
Upon the service of our God!

2 Each field is then a hallowed spot,
An altar is in each man's cot,
A church in every grove that spreads
Its living roof above our heads.

3 Look up to heaven! the industrious sun
Already half his race hath run;

He cannot halt or go astray,
But our immortal spirits may.

4 Lord, since his rising in the east,
If we have faltered or transgressed,
Guide, from thy love's abundant source,
What yet remains of this day's course;

5. Help with thy grace, through life's short
day,
Our upward and our downward way;
And glorify for us the west,
When we shall sink to final rest.

See also
29 Forth in thy name

EVENING

41

CORNHILL. (C.M.)
In moderate time.

HAROLD E. DARKE.

[*Copyright, 1931, by Oxford University Press.*]
[This hymn may also be sung to DUNSTAN, 393.]

End of Service.

W. Bright, 1824–1901.

AND now the wants are told that
Thy children to thy knee; [brought
Here lingering still, we ask for nought,
But simply worship thee.

2*The hope of heaven's eternal days
Absorbs not all the heart
That gives thee glory, love, and praise,
For being what thou art.

3 For thou art God, the One, the same,
O'er all things high and bright;
And round us, when we speak thy name,
There spreads a heaven of light.

4 O wondrous peace, in thought to dwell
On excellence divine;
To know that nought in man can tell
How fair thy beauties shine!

5*O thou, above all blessing blest,
O'er thanks exalted far,
Thy very greatness is a rest
To weaklings as we are;

6.*For when we feel the praise of thee
A task beyond our powers,
We say, 'A perfect God is he,
And he is fully ours.'

(41)

42

FIRST TUNE

CALVISIUS (ACH BLEIB BEI UNS). (L.M.)

Founded on a melody by S. CALVISIUS (1594).
Harmonized by J. S. BACH, 1685–1750.

Slow.

SECOND TUNE

ANGELUS (DU MEINER SEELEN). (L.M.)

Cantica Spiritualia, 1847 (founded on a melody by G. JOSEPH, 1657).

Slow.

[This hymn may also be sung to CAMERONIAN MIDNIGHT HYMN, 514.]

H. *Twells*,‡ 1823–1900.

AT even when the sun was set
The sick, O Lord, around thee lay;
O in what divers pains they met!
O with what joy they went away!

2 Once more 'tis eventide, and we
Oppressed with various ills draw near;
What if thy form we cannot see?
We know and feel that thou art here.

3 O Saviour Christ, our woes dispel;
For some are sick, and some are sad,
And some have never loved thee well,
And some have lost the love they had;

4 O Saviour Christ, thou too art man;
Thou hast been troubled, tempted, tried;
Thy kind but searching glance can scan
The very wounds that shame would hide;

5. Thy touch has still its ancient power,
No word from thee can fruitless fall;
Hear in this solemn evening hour,
And in thy mercy heal us all.

43

OLD 18TH. (D.C.M.)

Day's Psalter, 1564.
Version of Melody and Harmony from W. COBBOLD in *Este's Psalter,* 1592.

Slow.

[This hymn may also be sung to OLD 22ND, 176.]

George Wither, 1588–1667.

BEHOLD the sun, that seemed but now
Enthronèd overhead,
Beginning to decline below
This globe whereon we tread;
And he, whom yet we look upon
With comfort and delight,
Will quite depart from hence anon,
And leave us to the night.

2 Thus time, unheeded, steals away
The life which nature gave;
Thus are our bodies every day
Declining to the grave;

Thus from us all those pleasures fly
Whereon we set our heart;
And when the night of death draws nigh,
Thus will they all depart.

3. Lord! though the sun forsake our sight,
And mortal hopes are vain,
Let still thine everlasting light
Within our souls remain;
And in the nights of our distress
Vouchsafe those rays divine,
Which from the Sun of Righteousness
For ever brightly shine!

44

FIRST TUNE

PLAINSONG. (L.M.)

In free rhythm.

Melody from the *Sarum Antiphonal.*

[*Copyright, 1925, by Oxford University Press.*]

[This hymn may also be sung to LUCIS CREATOR, 37.]

SECOND TUNE

BEATA NOBIS GAUDIA. (L.M.)

In free rhythm. Unison.

Melody from *Psalterium Chorale*, Constance, 1510;

St. Ambrose, 340–97. Tr. Charles Bigg.

Deus creator omnium.

PART I

CREATOR of the earth and sky,
Ruling the firmament on high,
Clothing the day with robes of light,
Blessing with gracious sleep the night,

2 That rest may comfort weary men,
And brace to useful toil again,
And soothe awhile the harassed mind,
And sorrow's heavy load unbind:

3 Day sinks; we thank thee for thy gift;
Night comes; and once again we lift
Our prayer and vows and hymns that we
Against all ills may shielded be.

PART II

4 Thee let the secret heart acclaim,
Thee let our tuneful voices name,
Round thee our chaste affections cling,
Thee sober reason own as King.

5 That when black darkness closes day,
And shadows thicken round our way,
Faith may no darkness know, and night
From faith's clear beam may borrow light.

6 Rest not, my heaven-born mind and will;
Rest, all ye thoughts and deeds of ill;
My faith its watch unwearied keep,
And cool the dreaming warmth of sleep.

7. From cheats of sense, Lord, keep me free,
And let my heart's depth dream of thee;
Let not my envious foe draw near,
To break my rest with any fear.

45

TALLIS' CANON. (L.M.)

Slow and dignified.

T. TALLIS, c. 1510–85.

Bishop T. Ken, 1637–1711.

GLORY to thee, my God, this night
For all the blessings of the light;
Keep me, O keep me, King of Kings,
Beneath thy own almighty wings.

2 Forgive me, Lord, for thy dear Son,
The ill that I this day have done,
That with the world, myself, and thee,
I, ere I sleep, at peace may be.

3 Teach me to live, that I may dread
The grave as little as my bed;
Teach me to die, that so I may
Rise glorious at the aweful day.

4 O may my soul on thee repose,
And with sweet sleep mine eyelids close,
Sleep that may me more vigorous make
To serve my God when I awake.

5. Praise God, from whom all blessings flow;
Praise him, all creatures here below;
Praise him above, ye heavenly host;
Praise Father, Son, and Holy Ghost.

A-men.

EVENING

ALTERNATIVE VERSION

PEOPLE'S PART.

Fa-burden from *Ravenscroft's Psalter*, 1621.

CHOIR OR ORGAN.

This version may be used in connexion with the other for one or more verses, the people singing the melody as usual or the CHOIR SINGING ALONE. *Prominence should be given to the tenor part, which in this version leads the canon.*

EVENING

AR HYD Y NOS. (8 4. 8 4. 8 8. 8 4.)

In moderate time.

Welsh Traditional Melody.

ALTERNATIVE VERSION

Melody in the Tenor.

Fa-burden by ERNEST BULLOCK.

1. *Bishop Heber* (1827).
2. *Archbishop Whately*‡ (1855).

GOD, that madest earth and heaven,
  Darkness and light;
Who the day for toil hast given,
  For rest the night;
May thine angel-guards defend us,
Slumber sweet thy mercy send us,
Holy dreams and hopes attend us,
  This livelong night.

2. Guard us waking, guard us sleeping;
  And, when we die,
May we in thy mighty keeping
  All peaceful lie:
So when death to life shall wake us,
Thou may'st like the angels make us, —
And to reign in glory take us
  With thee on high.

BBC Do not than O lord forsake us. — But —

47

TON-MÂN. (7 7 7. 5.)

In moderate time. DAVID EVANS, 1874–1948 (adapted by permission).

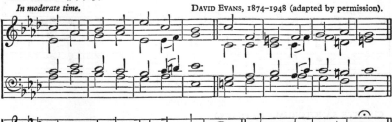

[This hymn may also be sung to CAPE TOWN, 507.]

R. H. Robinson, 1842–92.

HOLY Father, cheer our way
  With thy love's perpetual ray;
Grant us every closing day
  Light at evening time.

2 Holy Saviour, calm our fears
  When earth's brightness disappears;
Grant us in our latter years
  Light at evening time.

3 Holy Spirit, be thou nigh
  When in mortal pains we lie;
Grant us, as we come to die,
  Light at evening time.

4. Holy, blessèd Trinity,
  Darkness is not dark with thee;
Those thou keepest always see
  Light at evening time.

48

FIRST TUNE

DIE NACHT IST KOMMEN. (11 11. 11 5.)

Slow. Melody by P. NIGIDIUS, 1550 (adapted by H. SCHEIN, 1627).

SECOND TUNE

CHRISTE SANCTORUM. (11 11. 11 5.)

In moderate time. Unison. *Paris Antiphoner, 1681.*

Petrus Herbert (1566). *Tr. A. G.*

Die Nacht ist kommen.

NOW God be with us, for the night is falling,
 Soon sleep will take us, restfully enthralling;
Then may the Father, while our dreams possess us,
 Shelter and bless us.

2 May evil fancies flee away before us,
   Great-hearted spirits keep their watches o'er us:
   In soul and body, Lord, amend and tend us,
   Subtly defend us.

3 When we are sleeping, rest we in thy favour;
   Gaily awaking, never from thee waver;
   Ever observant, truth and right pursuing
   In all our doing.

4 Lover of all men, laughter give for sighing;
   Cheer those in sorrow, those in sickness lying,
   All the bereavèd, all the poor, distressèd,
   All the oppressèd.

5.*Hallowed, O Father, be thy Name; thy Kingdom
   Come now among us; be thy Will effected;
   Feed us, forgive us, keep us clear of trial,
   Freed and protected.

(Verses 4 and 5 may be sung as a separate hymn.)

49

EUDOXIA. (6 5. 6 5.)

Moderately slow.

S. BARING-GOULD, 1834–1924.

A-men.

[By permission of A. W. Ridley & Co.]
[This hymn may also be sung to BELSIZE, 543.]

S. Baring-Gould, 1834–1924.

NOW the day is over,
   Night is drawing nigh,
Shadows of the evening
   Steal across the sky.

2 Now the darkness gathers,
   Stars begin to peep,
Birds and beasts and flowers
   Soon will be asleep.

3 Jesus, give the weary
   Calm and sweet repose;
With thy tenderest blessing
   May our eyelids close.

4 Grant to little children
   Visions bright of thee;
Guard the sailors tossing
   On the deep blue sea.

5 Comfort every sufferer
   Watching late in pain;
Those who plan some evil
   From their sin restrain.

6*Through the long night watches
   May thine angels spread
Their white wings above me,
   Watching round my bed

7*When the morning wakens,
   Then may I arise
Pure, and fresh, and sinless
   In thy holy eyes.

8. Glory to the Father,
   Glory to the Son,
And to thee, blest Spirit,
   Whilst all ages run.

(51)

50

NUNC DIMITTIS. (6 6 7. 6 6 7.)   Composed or adapted by L. BOURGEOIS, in 1549, for the
Moderately slow, dignified.   Genevan *Psalter.* Harmony chiefly from C. Goudimel (d. 1572).

R. Bridges, 1844–1930,
based on 7th century hymn.

Φῶς ἱλαρόν.

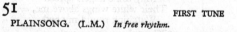

O GLADSOME light, O grace
    Of God the Father's face,
The eternal splendour wearing;
    Celestial, holy, blest,
    Our Saviour Jesus Christ,
Joyful in thine appearing.

2   Now, ere day fadeth quite,
    We see the evening light,
Our wonted hymn outpouring;
    Father of might unknown,
    Thee, his incarnate Son,
And Holy Spirit adoring.

3,   To thee of right belongs
    All praise of holy songs,
O Son of God, lifegiver;
    Thee, therefore, O most high,
    The world doth glorify,
And shalt exalt for ever.

51

FIRST TUNE

PLAINSONG. (L.M.) *In free rhythm.*   Melody from the *Sarum Antiphonal.*

EVENING

SECOND TUNE

ADESTO SANCTA TRINITAS. (L.M.)

In moderate time. Unison.

Chartres Antiphoner, 1784.

St. Ambrose, 340–97. Tr. J. M. Neale.

O lux beata Trinitas.

O TRINITY of blessèd light,
O Unity of princely might,
The fiery sun now goes his way;
Shed thou within our hearts thy ray.

2 To thee our morning song of praise,
To thee our evening prayer we raise;
Thy glory suppliant we adore
For ever and for evermore.

3. All laud to God the Father be;
All praise, eternal Son, to thee;
All glory, as is ever meet,
To God the holy Paraclete.

FIRST TUNE

A - men.

SECOND TUNE

A - men.

52

ARNSTADT (SEELENBRÄUTIGAM). (5 5. 8 8. 5 5.)

Slow.

A. DRESE, 1620–1701.

W. Romanis, 1824–99.

ROUND me falls the night;
  Saviour, be my light:
Through the hours in darkness shrouded
Let me see thy face unclouded;
  Let thy glory shine
  In this heart of mine.

2 Earthly work is done,
   Earthly sounds are none;
 Rest in sleep and silence seeking,
 Let me hear thee softly speaking;
   In my spirit's ear
   Whisper, 'I am near.'

3. Blessèd, heavenly Light,
   Shining through earth's night;
 Voice, that oft of love hast told me;
 Arms, so strong to clasp and hold me;
   Thou thy watch wilt keep,
   Saviour, o'er my sleep.

EVENING

53

MAGDA. (10 10. 10 10.)

In moderate time, not too slow.

R. Vaughan Williams, 1872–1958.

[*Copyright, 1925, by R. Vaughan Williams.*]

J. Ellerton, 1826–93.

SAVIOUR, again to thy dear name we raise
With one accord our parting hymn of praise.
Guard thou the lips from sin, the hearts from shame,
That in this house have called upon thy name.

2 Grant us thy peace, Lord, through the coming night;
Turn thou for us its darkness into light;
From harm and danger keep thy children free,
For dark and light are both alike to thee.

3 Grant us thy peace throughout our earthly life;
Peace to thy Church from error and from strife;
Peace to our land, the fruit of truth and love;
Peace in each heart, thy Spirit from above:

4. Thy peace in life, the balm of every pain;
Thy peace in death, the hope to rise again;
Then, when thy voice shall bid our conflict cease,
Call us, O Lord, to thine eternal peace.

54

GWALIA. (8 7. 8 7. D.)

In moderate time.

Welsh Hymn Melody.
Harmonized by DAVID EVANS, 1874–1948.

[This hymn may be sung to PLEADING SAVIOUR, 516.]

J. Edmeston,‡ 1791–1867.

SAVIOUR, shed an evening blessing,
  Ere repose our spirits seal;
Sin and want we come confessing;
  Thou canst save, and thou canst heal.
Though destruction walk around us,
  Though the arrow past us fly,
Angel-guards from thee surround us;
  We are safe if thou art nigh.

2. Though the night seem dark and endless,
  Darkness nothing hides from thee;
Though the day be lone and friendless,
  Still our comrade thou shalt be.
Should swift death this night o'ertake us
  Ere to-morrow's sun doth rise,
May the morn in heaven awake us,
  Clad in robes of Paradise.

55

BIRLING. (L.M.)

Not too slow.

From an early 19th cent. MS.

J. Keble, 1792–1866.

SUN of my soul, thou Saviour dear,
It is not night if thou be near:
O may no earth-born cloud arise
To hide thee from thy servant's eyes.

2*When the soft dews of kindly sleep
My wearied eyelids gently steep,
Be my last thought, how sweet to rest
For ever on my Saviour's breast.

3 Abide with me from morn till eve,
For without thee I cannot live;
Abide with me when night is nigh,
For without thee I dare not die.

4 If some poor wandering child of thine
Have spurned to-day the voice divine,
Now, Lord, the gracious work begin;
Let him no more lie down in sin.

5 Watch by the sick; enrich the poor
With blessings from thy boundless store;
Be every mourner's sleep to-night
Like infant's slumbers, pure and light.

6. Come near and bless us when we wake,
Ere through the world our way we take;
Till in the ocean of thy love
We lose ourselves in heaven above.

EVENING

56

FIRST TUNE

LES COMMANDEMENS DE DIEU. (9 8. 9 8.)

Moderately slow.

Original form of melody composed or adapted by L. BOURGEOIS for the *Genevan Psalter*, 1543.

SECOND TUNE

JOLDWYNDS. (9 8. 9 8.)

In moderate time.

C. V. STANFORD, 1852–1924.

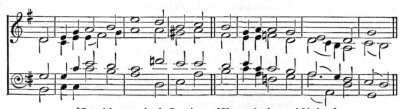

[*Copyright*, 1904, *by the Proprietors of* Hymns Ancient and Modern.]

J. *Ellerton*, 1826–93.

THE day thou gavest, Lord, is ended,
The darkness falls at thy behest;
To thee our morning hymns ascended,
Thy praise shall sanctify our rest.

2 We thank thee that thy Church unsleeping,
While earth rolls onward into light,
Through all the world her watch is keeping,
And rests not now by day or night.

3 As o'er each continent and island
The dawn leads on another day,

The voice of prayer is never silent,
Nor dies the strain of praise away.

4 The sun that bids us rest is waking
Our brethren 'neath the western sky,
And hour by hour fresh lips are making
Thy wondrous doings heard on high.

5. So be it, Lord; thy throne shall never,
Like earth's proud empires, pass away;
Thy kingdom stands, and grows for ever,
Till all thy creatures own thy sway.

(58)

EVENING

57

INNSBRUCK. (7 7 6. 7 7 8.)   Traditional German Melody, possibly by H. ISAAK (c. 1490).
Very slow and solemn.   Adapted and harmonized by J. S. BACH, 1685–1750.

R. Bridges, 1844–1930, based on Nun ruhen alle Wälder. *P. Gerhardt, 1607–76.*

THE duteous day now closeth,
  Each flower and tree reposeth,
    Shade creeps o'er wild and wood:
Let us, as night is falling,
On God our maker calling,
    Give thanks to him, the giver good.

2 Now all the heavenly splendour
  Breaks forth in starlight tender
    From myriad worlds unknown;
And man, the marvel seeing,
Forgets his selfish being,
    For joy of beauty not his own.

3 His care he drowneth yonder,
  Lost in the abyss of wonder;
    To heaven his soul doth steal:
This life he disesteemeth,
The day it is that dreameth,
    That doth from truth his vision seal.

4. Awhile his mortal blindness
  May miss God's loving-kindness,
    And grope in faithless strife:
But when life's day is over
Shall death's fair night discover
    The fields of everlasting life.

(59)

58

OAKLEY. (8 8. 8 8. 7 7. 7 7.)

In moderate time.

R. Vaughan Williams, 1872–1958.

[*Copyright,* 1925, *by R. Vaughan Williams.*]

Sir Thomas Browne (cento),† 1605–82.

THE night is come like to the day:
 Depart not thou, great God, away;
Let not my sins, black as the night,
Eclipse the lustre of thy light.
  Thou, whose nature cannot sleep,
  On my temples sentry keep;
  Make my sleep a holy trance;
  While I rest, my soul advance.

2. So may I then, my rest being wrought,
 Awake into some holy thought,
And with as active vigour run
My course as doth the nimble sun.
  Sleep's a death: O make me try
  Sleeping, what it is to die!
  Come the hour when I shall never
  Sleep again, but wake for ever!

THE CHURCH'S YEAR

ADVENT

59

ST. OLAF'S SEQUENCE. (8 8 7. D.)

Norwegian Ecclesiastical Melody
(as given in *Koralbok for den Norske Kirke*, 1926).

Slow.

[This hymn may also be sung to AUCTOR OMNIUM BONORUM, 212.]

The Kingdom.

P. Dearmer, 1867–1936.

AH! think not, 'The Lord delayeth':
'I am with you,' still he sayeth,
'Do you yet not understand?'
Look not back, the past regretting:
On the Dawn your hearts be setting:
Rise, and join the Lord's command.

2 For e'en now the Reign of Heaven
Spreads throughout the world like leaven,
Unobserved, and very near:
Like the seed when no man knoweth,
Like the sheltering tree that groweth,
Comes the Life Eternal here.

3. Not for us to find the reasons,
Or to know the times and seasons,
Comes the Lord when strikes the hour:
Ours to bear the faithful witness
Which can shape the world to fitness;
Thine, O God, to give the power.

(61)

60

RINKART (KOMMT SEELEN). (6 7. 6 7. 6 6. 6 6.)

In moderate time. Unison.

Melody and Bass by
J. S. BACH, 1685–1750.

[This hymn may also be sung to DARMSTADT (O GOTT, DU FROMMER GOTT), 621.]

(Also Epiphany, and Missions Oversea.)

G. W. Briggs, 1875–1959.

CHRIST is the world's true Light,
  Its Captain of salvation,
The Daystar clear and bright
  Of every man and nation;
New life, new hope awakes,
  Where'er men own his sway:
Freedom her bondage breaks,
  And night is turned to day.

2 In Christ all races meet,
    Their ancient feuds forgetting,
  The whole round world complete,
    From sunrise to its setting:
  When Christ is throned as Lord,
    Men shall forsake their fear,
  To ploughshare beat the sword,
    To pruning-hook the spear.

3. One Lord, in one great name
    Unite us all who own thee;
  Cast out our pride and shame
    That hinder to enthrone thee;
  The world has waited long,
    Has travailed long in pain;
  To heal its ancient wrong,
    Come, Prince of Peace, and reign.

(62)

61

MERTON.   (8 7. 8 7.)
Moderately slow.
W. H. MONK, 1823–89.

[This hymn may also be sung to STUTTGART, 84.]

6th cent.   S. P. V.

Vox clara ecce intonat.

HARK! a herald voice is calling:
  'Christ is nigh,' it seems to say;
'Cast away the dreams of darkness,
  O ye children of the day!'

2 Wakened by the solemn warning,
  Let the earth-bound soul arise;
Christ, her Sun, all sloth dispelling,
  Shines upon the morning skies.

3 Lo! the Power, so long expected,
  Comes with pardon down from heaven;
Let us haste, with tears of sorrow,
  One and all to be forgiven;

4 So when love comes forth in judgment,
  Debts and doubts and wrongs to clear,
Faithful may he find his servants,
  Watching till the dawn appear.

5. Honour, glory, might, and blessing
  To the Father and the Son
And the eternal Spirit give we,
  While unending ages run.

A - men.

(63)

62

BRISTOL. (C.M.)

Moderately slow.

Melody from *Ravenscroft's Psalter*, 1621.

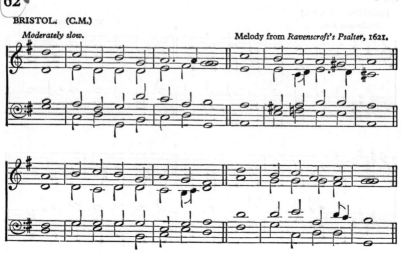

ALTERNATIVE VERSION

PEOPLE'S PART. Melody in the Tenor.   Fa-burden by T. RAVENSCROFT, in his Psalter.

CHOIR OR ORGAN.

ADVENT

To en - rich ; ; the hum - ble poor.

This version may be used for verse 3, the people singing the melody as usual.

(Other occasions also.)   *P. Doddridge, 1702–51.*

HARK the glad sound! the Saviour comes,
  The Saviour promised long!
Let every heart prepare a throne,
  And every voice a song.

2 He comes the prisoners to release
    In Satan's bondage held;
  The gates of brass before him burst,
    The iron fetters yield.

3 He comes the broken heart to bind,
    The bleeding soul to cure,
  And with the treasures of his grace   (mind?)
    To enrich the humble poor.

4. Our glad hosannas, Prince of peace,
    Thy welcome shall proclaim;
  And heaven's eternal arches ring
    With thy belovèd name.

63

WATCHMAN. (6 4. 6 4. 6 6 6. 4.)

In moderate time.

T. H. INGHAM, 1878–1948.

[*Copyright, 1931, by Oxford University Press.*]

I am with you, like the dawn upon the mountains.   Jan Struther, 1901–53.

HIGH o'er the lonely hills
  Black turns to grey,
Birdsong the valley fills,
  Mists fold away;
Grey wakes to green again,
Beauty is seen again—
Gold and serene again
  Dawneth the day.

2 So, o'er the hills of life,
  Stormy, forlorn,
Out of the cloud and strife
  Sunrise is born;
Swift grows the light for us;
Ended is night for us;
Soundless and bright for us
  Breaketh God's morn.

3 Hear we no beat of drums,
  Fanfare nor cry,
When Christ the herald comes
  Quietly nigh;
Splendour he makes on earth;
Colour awakes on earth;
Suddenly breaks on earth
  Light from the sky.

4.*Bid then farewell to sleep:
  Rise up and run!
What though the hill be steep?
  Strength 's in the sun.
Now shall you find at last
Night 's left behind at last,
And for mankind at last
  Day has begun!

64

LITTLE CORNARD. (6 6. 6 6. 8 8.)

With vigour.

MARTIN SHAW, 1875–1958.

Org.

(Also Epiphany, and Missions Oversea.)
Charles E. Oakley, 1832–65.

HILLS of the North, rejoice;
  River and mountain-spring,
Hark to the advent voice;
  Valley and lowland, sing;
Though absent long, your Lord is nigh;
He judgment brings and victory.

2 Isles of the southern seas,
  Deep in your coral caves
Pent be each warring breeze,
  Lulled be your restless waves:
He comes to reign with boundless sway,
And makes your wastes his great highway.

3 Lands of the East, awake,
  Soon shall your sons be free;
The sleep of ages break,
  And rise to liberty.
On your far hills, long cold and grey,
Has dawned the everlasting day.

4 Shores of the utmost West,
  Ye that have waited long,
Unvisited, unblest,
  Break forth to swelling song;
High raise the note, that Jesus died,
Yet lives and reigns, the Crucified.

5.* Shout, while ye journey home;
  Songs be in every mouth;
Lo, from the North we come,
  From East, and West, and South.
City of God, the bond are free,
We come to live and reign in thee!

HELMSLEY. (8 7. 8 7. 4 7.) English melody of the 18th century.

Moderately slow, very dignified. May be sung in unison throughout.

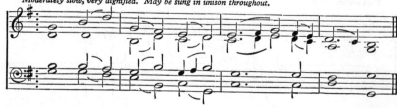

C. Wesley (1758), *and others.*

LO! he comes with clouds descending,
Once for favoured sinners slain;
Thousand thousand saints attending
Swell the triumph of his train:
Alleluya!
God appears, on earth to reign.

2*Every eye shall now behold him
Robed in glorious majesty;
Those who set at nought and sold him,
Pierced and nailed him to the tree,
Deeply wailing,
Shall their true Messiah see.

(68)

ADVENT

Descant by R. VAUGHAN WILLIAMS:
Trebles (other voices sing the melody HELMSLEY, *the organ playing the harmonies as before).*

Al - le - lu - ya, Al - - - - le -
- lu - ya, Al - le - lu - - ya, Al - - - le -
- lu - ya, Al - le - lu - ya, Al - - - - le -
- lu - ya, Al - le - lu - - ya, Al - - - le -
- lu - ya, Al - - - - le - lu - -
- ya, Al - le - lu - ya, Al - le - lu - - -
- ya, Al - - - - - - - - le - lu - - ya.

3 Those dear tokens of his passion
Still his dazzling body bears;
Cause of wondering exultation
To his countless worshippers;
With what rapture
Praise we him for all his scars!

4. Yea, amen, let all adore thee,
High on thine eternal throne;
Saviour, take the power and glory:
Claim the kingdom as thine own:
Alleluya!
Thou shalt reign, and thou alone.

ADVENT

66.

VENI EMMANUEL. (8 8. 8 8. 8 8.)

In free rhythm. Unison.

Adapted by T. HELMORE, 1811–90,
'from a French Missal'.

(70)

ADVENT

18th cent. Tr. T. A. Lacey.

Veni, veni, Emmanuel.

O COME, O come, Emmanuel!
Redeem thy captive Israel,
That into exile drear is gone
Far from the face of God's dear Son:

  Rejoice! Rejoice! Emmanuel
  Shall come to thee, O Israel.

2 O come, thou Branch of Jesse! draw
 The quarry from the lion's claw
 From the dread caverns of the grave,
 From nether hell, thy people save:

3 O come, O come, thou Dayspring bright!
 Pour on our souls thy healing light;
 Dispel the long night's lingering gloom,
 And pierce the shadows of the tomb:

4*O come, thou Lord of David's key!
 The royal door fling wide and free;
 Safeguard for us the heavenward road,
 And bar the way to death's abode:

5.*O come, O come, Adonai,
 Who in thy glorious majesty
 From that high mountain clothed with awe
 Gavest thy folk the elder law:

67

AUCTORITATE SAECULI. (L.M.)

In moderate time. Unison.

Poitiers Antiphoner, 1746.

[This hymn may also be sung to WINCHESTER NEW, 137.]

C. Coffin, 1676–1749. *S. P. V.*

Jordanis oras praevia.

ON Jordan's bank the Baptist's cry
Announces that the Lord is nigh;
Come then and hearken, for he brings
Glad tidings from the King of Kings.

2 Then cleansed be every Christian breast,
And furnished for so great a guest!
Yea, let us each our hearts prepare
For Christ to come and enter there.

3 For thou art our salvation, Lord,
Our refuge and our great reward;
Without thy grace our souls must fade,
And wither like a flower decayed.

4 Lay on the sick thy healing hand,
And make the fallen strong to stand;
Show us the glory of thy face
Till beauty springs in every place.

5. All praise, eternal Son, to thee
Whose advent sets thy people free,
Whom, with the Father, we adore,
And Holy Spirit, evermore.

A - - - men.

68

ST. THOMAS. (S.M.)
In moderate time.

Williams' Psalmody, 1770.

C. Coffin, 1676–1749. *Pr. S. P.*

Instantis adventum Dei.

THE advent of our God
    With eager hearts we greet,
And singing, haste upon the road
    His coming Reign to meet.

2 For, lo, God's Word and Son
    Came down to make us free,
And he a servant's form put on,
    To bring us liberty.

3 Daughter of Sion, rise
    To meet thy lowly King;
Let not thy heart in haste despise
    The peace he comes to bring.

4 For judgment doth befall
    The stubborn who refuse,
But God doth give his light to all
    Who cherish his Good News.

5 Then evil flee away
    Before the rising dawn!
Let this old Adam day by day
    God's image still put on.

6.* Thou Liberator true,
    All glory be to thee,
To whom in God our praise is due
    For all eternity.

69

MALDWYN. (11 11. 11 11.)
In moderate time.   Welsh Hymn Melody, harmonized by DAVID EVANS, 1874-1948.

The Kingdom.   *N. B. L.*

WITH Jesus for hero, for teacher and friend,
The world to the Purpose of God shall ascend:
We struggle and quarrel, but he brings release,
And shows us the way to his wisdom and peace.

2 His Kingdom is coming, God's will shall be done,
And kindness and justice and peace shall be won;
Then learn we that gospel of love to obey,
Till sickness and want and disputes pass away.

3. God's name shall be hallowed, his love understood—
The Father of all men, the wise and the good:
The pagans shall see him in truth as he is,
And the heart of the world shall for ever be his.

See also

511 Hark what a sound
545 Jesus shall reign
561 Lo, in the wilderness
562 Lord Christ, when first
575 Made lowly wise, we pray
602 O life that makest
634 Ring out, ye crystal
635 Rise up, O men of God
637 Say not, 'The struggle
327 Sound over all waters
310 The day of the Lord
658 The Lord will come
328 The night is ended
311 The world's great age

312 These things shall be
672 Thou Judge by whom
680 Thy Kingdom come
684 To thee whose eye
329 Turn back, O Man
687 Wake, O wake
698 When through the whirl
702 Ye servants of the Lord.
And for Advent 2.
457 Book of books
212 Prophets, teachers
645 Spread, still spread
660 The Spirit of the Lord
214 Virtue supreme

70

ES IST EIN' ROS' ENTSPRUNGEN. (7 6. 7 6. 6 7 6.)

In moderate time.   Old German Melody, harmony by M. PRAETORIUS, 1571-1621.

A full and bless - ed cure!

And peace on earth to men.

The barring of this tune is necessarily irregular; but its performance will be found to be easy if it is remembered that the time-value of a crotchet is the same throughout.

St. Germanus, 634–734. Tr. J. M. Neale.‡

Μέγα καὶ παράδοξον θαῦμα.

A GREAT and mighty wonder,
  A full and blessed cure!
The Rose has come to blossom
  Which shall for ay endure:
    Repeat the hymn again!
    'To God on high be glory,
    And peace on earth to men.'

2 The Word has dwelt among us,
  The true light from on high;
And cherubim sing anthems
  To shepherds, from the sky:

3*While thus they sing your Monarch,
  Those bright angelic bands,
Rejoice, ye vales and mountains,
  Ye oceans, clap your hands:

4 Since all he comes to succour,
  By all be he adored,
The infant born in Bethlem,
  The Saviour and the Lord:

5. And idol forms shall perish,
  And error shall decay,
And Christ shall wield his sceptre,
  Our Lord and God for ay:

(75)

71.

IRIS. (8 7. 8 7. and refrain.)

In moderate time.

French Carol Melody.

Come . . . . and

Come . . . . and

wor - ship (1st) Christ, the new - born King. . .
(2nd) Wor-ship Christ, the new - born King.

wor - ship King.

[This hymn may also be sung to LEWES, 555.
In this case, repeat the first line of the refrain.]

(Epiphany also.)

J. Montgomery, 1771–1854.

ANGELS, from the realms of glory,
  Wing your flight o'er all the earth;
Ye who sang creation's story
  Now proclaim Messiah's birth:

  Come and worship,
  Worship Christ, the new-born King.

(76)

2 Shepherds in the fields abiding,
 Watching o'er your flocks by night,
God with man is now residing;
 Yonder shines the infant Light:

3 Sages, leave your contemplations;
 Brighter visions beam afar;
Seek the great Desire of Nations;
 Ye have seen his natal star:

4*Saints before the altar bending,
 Watching long in hope and fear,
Suddenly the Lord, descending,
 In his temple shall appear:

5. Though an infant now we view him,
 He shall fill his Father's throne,
Gather all the nations to him;
 Every knee shall then bow down:

72

THIS ENDRIS NYGHT. (C.M.)

Moderately slow.   Old English Carol. 15th cent.

(*Epiphany also.*)   *T. Pestel,‡ c.* 1584–*c.* 1659.

BEHOLD the great Creator makes
 Himself a house of clay,
A robe of human flesh he takes
 Which he will wear for ay.

2 Hark, hark, the wise eternal Word
 Like a weak infant cries!
In form of servant is the Lord,
 And God in cradle lies.

3 This wonder struck the world amazed,
 It shook the starry frame;
Squadrons of spirits stood and gazed,
 Then down in troops they came.

4 Glad shepherds ran to view this sight;
 A choir of angels sings,
And eastern sages with delight
 Adore this King of Kings.

5. Join then, all hearts that are not stone,
 And all our voices prove,
To celebrate this holy one,
 The God of peace and love.

(77)

73

YORKSHIRE (OR STOCKPORT). (10 10. 10 10. 10 10.)

In moderate time, dignified.

J. WAINWRIGHT, 1723–68.

John Byrom,† 1692–1763.

CHRISTIANS, awake, salute the happy morn,
    Whereon the Saviour of the World was born;
Rise to adore the mystery of love,
Which hosts of angels chanted from above;
With them the joyful tidings first begun
Of God incarnate and the Virgin's Son.

2 Then to the watchful shepherds it was told,
    Who heard the angelic herald's voice, 'Behold,
I bring good tidings of a saviour's birth
To you and all the nations upon earth;
This day hath God fulfilled his promised word,
This day is born a saviour, Christ the Lord.'

CHRISTMAS

ALTERNATIVE VERSION

Melody in the Tenor.   Fa-burden by Martin Shaw.

[*Copyright, 1924, by Martin Shaw.*]

3 He spake; and straightway the celestial choir
   In hymns of joy, unknown before, conspire.
   The praises of redeeming love they sang,
   And heaven's whole orb with alleluyas rang:
   God's highest glory was their anthem still,
   Peace upon earth, and unto men good will.

4.*To Bethlehem straight the enlightened shepherds ran,
   To see the wonder God had wrought for man.
   He that was born upon this joyful day
   Around us all his glory shall display:
   Saved by his love, incessant we shall sing
   Eternal praise to heaven's almighty King.

(79)

CHRISTMAS

74

MENDELSSOHN. (7 7 7 7. 7 7 7 7. and refrain.)

In moderate time. Adapted from a Chorus by F. MENDELSSOHN-BARTHOLDY, 1809–47.

Unison.

Organ Pedals.

[*By permission of Novello & Co., Ltd.*]

(80)

CHRISTMAS

C. *Wesley* (1743), G. *Whitefield* (1753), M. *Madan* (1760), *and others.*

HARK! the herald angels sing
  Glory to the new-born King;
Peace on earth and mercy mild,
God and sinners reconciled:
Joyful all ye nations rise,
Join the triumph of the skies,
With the angelic host proclaim,
Christ is born in Bethlehem:

> *Hark! the herald angels sing*
> *Glory to the new-born King.*

2 Christ, by highest heaven adored,
  Christ, the everlasting Lord,
  Late in time behold him come
  Offspring of the Virgin's womb;
  Veiled in flesh the Godhead see;
  Hail the incarnate Deity!
  Pleased as man with man to dwell,
  Jesus, our Emmanuel:

3. Hail the heaven-born Prince of Peace!
  Hail the Sun of Righteousness!
  Light and life to all he brings,
  Risen with healing in his wings;
  Mild he lays his glory by,
  Born that man no more may die,
  Born to raise the sons of earth,
  Born to give them second birth:

CHRISTMAS

75

CRANHAM. (Irreg.)

In moderate time.

GUSTAV HOLST, 1874–1934.

The metre of this hymn is irregular. The music as printed is that of the first verse, and it can easily be adapted to the others.

Verses 2 and 3 run:

Our God, heaven can-not hold him Nor … earth sus-tain;
E-nough for him, whom che-ru-bim Wor-ship night and day,   A

Heaven and earth shall flee a-way When he comes to reign: In the bleak mid-
breast-ful of milk, And a man-ger-ful of hay; E-nough for him, whom
&c.

CHRISTMAS

Christina Rossetti, 1830–94.

IN the bleak mid-winter
  Frosty wind made moan;
Earth stood hard as iron,
  Water like a stone;
Snow had fallen, snow on snow,
  Snow on snow,
In the bleak mid-winter,
  Long ago.

2 Our God, heaven cannot hold him
  Nor earth sustain;
Heaven and earth shall flee away
  When he comes to reign:
In the bleak mid-winter
  A stable-place sufficed
The Lord God almighty,
  Jesus Christ.

3 Enough for him, whom cherubim
  Worship night and day,
A breastful of milk,
  And a mangerful of hay;
Enough for him, whom angels
  Fall down before,
The ox and ass and camel
  Which adore.

4 Angels and archangels
  May have gathered there,
Cherubim and seraphim
  Thronged the air:
But only his mother
  In her maiden bliss
Worshipped the Belovèd
  With a kiss.

5. What can I give him,
  Poor as I am?
If I were a shepherd
  I would bring a lamb;
If I were a wise man
  I would do my part;
Yet what I can I give him—
  Give my heart.

76

NOEL. (D.C.M.)

In moderate time.

Traditional Air, adapted by A. SULLIVAN, 1842–1900.

[By permission of Novello & Co., Ltd.]

CHRISTMAS

(After Epiphany also.)   E. H. Sears, 1810–76.

IT came upon the midnight clear,
  That glorious song of old,
From angels bending near the earth
  To touch their harps of gold:
'Peace on the earth, good will to men,
  From heaven's all-gracious King!'
The world in solemn stillness lay
  To hear the angels sing.

2 Still through the cloven skies they come,
  With peaceful wings unfurled;
And still their heavenly music floats
  O'er all the weary world;
Above its sad and lowly plains
  They bend on hovering wing;
And ever o'er its Babel sounds
  The blessèd angels sing.

3 Yet with the woes of sin and strife
  The world has suffered long;
Beneath the angel-strain have rolled
  Two thousand years of wrong;
And man, at war with man, hears not
  The love-song which they bring:
O hush the noise, ye men of strife,
  And hear the angels sing.

4*And ye, beneath life's crushing load,
  Whose forms are bending low,
Who toil along the climbing way
  With painful steps and slow,
Look now! for glad and golden hours
  Come swiftly on the wing;
O rest beside the weary road,
  And hear the angels sing.

5. For lo! the days are hastening on,
  By prophet-bards foretold,
When, with the ever-circling years,
  Comes round the age of gold;
When peace shall over all the earth
  Its ancient splendours fling,
And the whole world give back the song
  Which now the angels sing.

77

FREYLINGHAUSEN (MACHT HOCH DIE THÜR).   (8 8 8 8. 8 8 8 8. 6 5.)

In moderate time.   Melody by J. A. FREYLINGHAUSEN, 1670–1739 (slightly adapted).

CHRISTMAS

A. Domett, 1811–87.

IT was the calm and silent night!
 Seven hundred years and fifty-three
Had Rome been growing up to might,
 And now was queen of land and sea.
No sound was heard of clashing wars;
 Peace brooded o'er the hushed domain;
Apollo, Pallas, Jove, and Mars
 Held undisturbed their ancient reign,
  In the solemn midnight
   Centuries ago.

2 O strange indifference! Low and high
 Drowsed over common joys and cares:
The earth was still—but knew not why;
 The world was listening—unawares;
How calm a moment may precede
 One that shall thrill the world for ever!
To that still moment none would heed
 Man's doom was linked, no more to sever,
  In the solemn midnight
   Centuries ago.

3. It is the calm and silent night!
 A thousand bells ring out, and throw
Their joyous peals abroad, and smite
 The darkness, charmed and holy now.
The night that erst no name had worn,
 To it a happy name is given;
For in that stable lay new-born
 The peaceful Prince of Earth and Heaven,
  In the solemn midnight
   Centuries ago.

78

ADESTE FIDELES. (Irreg.)

Slow and dignified.

J. WADE, *c.* 1711–86.

Without Pedals.

Pedals.

(*Epiphany also.*)   *J. Wade, c.* 1711–86. *Tr. F. Oakeley, and others.*

Adeste fideles.

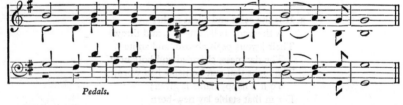

O COME, all ye faithful,
Joyful and triumphant,
O come ye, O come ye to Bethlehem;
Come and behold him,
Born the King of angels:

O come, let us adore him,
O come, let us adore him,
O come, let us adore him, Christ the Lord!

2* God of God,
Light of Light,
Lo, he abhors not the Virgin's womb;
Very God,
Begotten, not created:

3 See how the shepherds,
Summoned to his cradle,
Leaving their flocks, draw nigh to gaze;
We too will thither
Bend our joyful footsteps:

CHRISTMAS

ALTERNATIVE VERSION FOR VERSES 4 AND 6

Melody in the Tenor. — Fa-burden by MARTIN SHAW.

O come, let us a - dore him, O come, let us a - dore him, O come, let us a - dore him, a - dore him,

[Copyright, 1924, by Martin Shaw.]

4* Lo, star-led chieftains,
   Magi, Christ adoring,
Offer him incense, gold, and myrrh;
   We to the Christ-child
   Bring our hearts' oblations:

5 Child, for us sinners
   Poor and in the manger,
Fain we embrace thee, with love and
   awe;
   Who would not love thee,
   Loving us so dearly?

6 Sing, choirs of angels,
   Sing in exultation,
Sing, all ye citizens of heaven above;
   Glory to God
   In the highest:

(*Christmas Day only.*)

7. Yea, Lord, we greet thee,
   Born this happy morning,
Jesus, to thee be glory given;
   Word of the Father,
   Now in flesh appearing:

(89)

FIRST TUNE

FOREST GREEN. (D.C.M. Irreg.)

In moderate time.

English Traditional Melody.

Bp. Phillips Brooks, 1835–93.

O LITTLE town of Bethlehem,
　How still we see thee lie!
Above thy deep and dreamless sleep
　The silent stars go by.
Yet in thy dark streets shineth
　The everlasting light;
The hopes and fears of all the years
　Are met in thee to-night.

2 O morning stars, together
　Proclaim the holy birth,
And praises sing to God the King,
　And peace to men on earth;
For Christ is born of Mary;
　And, gathered all above,
While mortals sleep, the angels keep
　Their watch of wondering love.

3*How silently, how silently,
　The wondrous gift is given!
So God imparts to human hearts
　The blessings of his heaven.
No ear may hear his coming;
　But in this world of sin,
Where meek souls will receive him, still
　The dear Christ enters in.

CHRISTMAS

SECOND TUNE

CHRISTMAS CAROL. (D.C.M. Irreg.)

In moderate time.

H. WALFORD DAVIES, 1869–1941.

[*Copyright, 1905, by W. Garrett Horder.*]

4 Where children pure and happy
  Pray to the blessèd child,
Where misery cries out to thee,
  Son of the mother mild;
Where charity stands watching
  And faith holds wide the door,
The dark night wakes, the glory breaks,
  And Christmas comes once more.

5. O holy Child of Bethlehem,
  Descend to us, we pray;
Cast out our sin, and enter in,
  Be born in us to-day.
We hear the Christmas angels
  The great glad tidings tell:
O come to us, abide with us,
  Our Lord Emmanuel.

FIRST TUNE

VOM HIMMEL HOCH. (L.M.)
Slow and dignified.   Later form of melody in V. SCHUMANN's *Gesangbuch*, 1539.

SECOND TUNE

JENA (DAS NEUGEBORNE KINDELEIN). (L.M.)
In moderate time.   Later form of melody from VULPIUS' *Gesangbuch* (Jena, 1609).

CHRISTMAS

Henry More, 1614–87.

THE holy Son of God most high,
    For love of Adam's lapsèd race,
Quit the sweet pleasures of the sky
    To bring us to that happy place.

2 His robes of light he laid aside,
    Which did his majesty adorn,
And the frail state of mortals tried,
    In human flesh and figure born.

3 Whole choirs of angels loudly sing
    The mystery of his sacred birth,
And the blest news to shepherds bring,
    Filling their watchful souls with mirth.

4. The Son of God thus man became,
    That men the sons of God might be,
And by their second birth regain
    A likeness to his deity.

81

DANBURY. (5 5 5 5 5.)

In moderate time. Voices in unison.

C. ARMSTRONG GIBBS, 1889–1960.

Thou whose birth on earth An-gels sang to men, While thy stars made mirth, Sa-viour, at thy birth, This day born a-gain;

[*Copyright, 1925, by Armstrong Gibbs.*]

A. C. Swinburne, 1837–1909.

THOU whose birth on earth
    Angels sang to men,
While thy stars made mirth,
Saviour, at thy birth,
    This day born again;

2 As this night was bright
    With thy cradle-ray,
Very light of light,
Turn the wild world's night
    To thy perfect day.

3 Thou, the Word and Lord,
    In all time and space
Heard, beheld, adored,
With all ages poured
    Forth before thy face,

4*Lord, what worth in earth
    Drew thee down to die?
What therein was worth,
Lord, thy death and birth?
    What beneath thy sky?

5 Yet thy poor endure,
    And are with us yet.
Be thy name a sure
Refuge for thy poor,
    Whom men's eyes forget.

6. Bid our peace increase,
    Thou that madest morn;
Bid oppressions cease;
Bid the night be peace;
    Bid the day be born!

FIRST TUNE

WINCHESTER OLD. (C.M.)

In moderate time.

First appeared in *Este's Psalter*, 1592.

ALTERNATIVE VERSION

Melody in the Tenor.
PEOPLE'S PART.

Fa-burden by T. RAVENSCROFT in his Psalter, 1621.

CHOIR OR ORGAN.

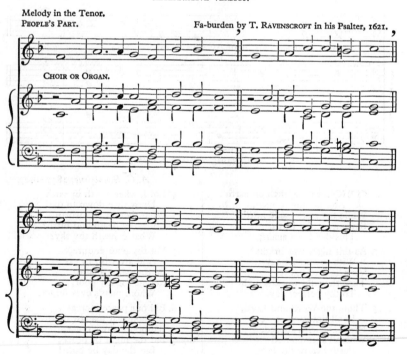

CHRISTMAS

SECOND TUNE

NORTHROP. (C.M.)

Cheerfully.

A. NORTHROP (?).

Nahum Tate, 1652–1715.

WHILE shepherds watched their
   flocks by night,
   All seated on the ground,
The angel of the Lord came down,
   And glory shone around.

2 'Fear not,' said he (for mighty dread
   Had seized their troubled mind);
'Glad tidings of great joy I bring
   To you and all mankind.

3 'To you in David's town this day
   Is born of David's line
A saviour, who is Christ the Lord;
   And this shall be the sign:

4 'The heavenly babe you there shall find
   To human view displayed,
All meanly wrapped in swathing bands
   And in a manger laid.'

5 Thus spake the seraph; and forthwith
   Appeared a shining throng
Of angels praising God, who thus
   Addressed their joyful song:

6. 'All glory be to God on high,
   And to the earth be peace;
Good will henceforth from heaven to
   men
   Begin and never cease.'

See also

The Christmas season traditionally extends throughout January, and includes the Feast of the Presentation (223) on February 2nd.

83

DIX. (7 7. 7 7. 7 7.)

In moderate time.

Abridged from a Chorale, 'Treuer Heiland', by C. KOCHER, 1786–1872.

W. Chatterton Dix, 1837–98.

As with gladness men of old
Did the guiding star behold,
As with joy they hailed its light,
Leading onward, beaming bright,
So, most gracious God, may we
Evermore be led to thee.

2 As with joyful steps they sped
To that lowly manger-bed,
There to bend the knee before
Him whom heaven and earth adore,
So may we with willing feet
Ever seek thy mercy-seat.

3 As they offered gifts most rare
At that manger rude and bare,
So may we with holy joy,
Pure, and free from sin's alloy,
All our costliest treasures bring,
Christ, to thee our heavenly King.

4 Holy Jesus, every day
Keep us in the narrow way;
And, when earthly things are past,
Bring our ransomed souls at last
Where they need no star to guide,
Where no clouds thy glory hide.

5.*In the heavenly country bright
Need they no created light;
Thou its light, its joy, its crown,
Thou its sun which goes not down:
There for ever may we sing
Alleluyas to our King.

STUTTGART. (8 7. 8 7.)

Moderately slow, majestically.

Adapted from a melody in *Psalmodia Sacra*, Gotha, 1715.

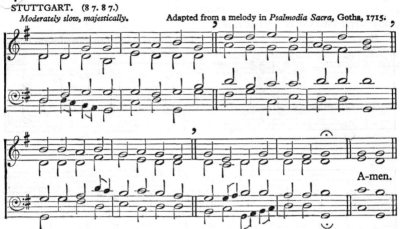

A-men.

ALTERNATIVE VERSION

Trebles sing upper part (other voices sing the melody
STUTTGART, *or harmonies as below).*

Descant by W. H. HARRIS.

CHOIR
OR
ORGAN.

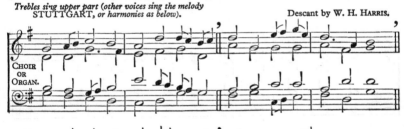

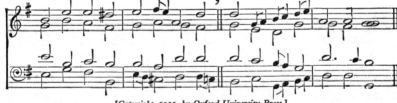

Prudentius, b. 348. *Tr. E. Caswall.*

O sola magnarum urbium.

BETHLEHEM, of noblest cities
None can once with thee compare;
Thou alone the Lord from heaven
Didst for us incarnate bear.

2 Fairer than the sun at morning
Was the star that told his birth;
To the lands their God announcing,
Hid beneath a form of earth.

3 By its lambent beauty guided
See the eastern kings appear;
See them bend, their gifts to offer,
Gifts of incense, gold, and myrrh.

4 Solemn things of mystic meaning:
Incense doth the God disclose,
Gold a royal child proclaimeth,
Myrrh a future tomb foreshows.

5. Holy Jesus, in thy brightness
To the Gentile world displayed,
With the Father and the Spirit
Endless praise to thee be paid

(97)

E

85

FIRST TUNE

LIEBSTER IMMANUEL. (11 10. 11 10.)

Slow.

Later form of melody from *Himmels-Lust*, 1679.

Bishop R. Heber, 1783–1826.

BRIGHTEST and best of the sons of the morning,
   Dawn on our darkness and lend us thine aid;
Star of the east, the horizon adorning,
   Guide where our infant Redeemer is laid.

2 Cold on his cradle the dew-drops are shining,
   Low lies his head with the beasts of the stall:
Angels adore him in slumber reclining,
   Maker and monarch and saviour of all.

EPIPHANY SEASON

SECOND TUNE

LIME STREET. (11 10. 11 10.)

With vigour. May be sung in unison.

GEOFFREY SHAW, 1879–1943.

[*This tune may also be sung in Harmony.*]

3 Say, shall we yield him, in costly devotion,
    Odours of Edom and offerings divine?
  Gems of the mountain and pearls of the ocean,
    Myrrh from the forest or gold from the mine?

4 Vainly we offer each ample oblation,
    Vainly with gifts would his favour secure;
  Richer by far is the heart's adoration,
    Dearer to God are the prayers of the poor.

5.*Brightest and best of the sons of the morning,
    Dawn on our darkness and lend us thine aid;
  Star of the east, the horizon adorning,
    Guide where our infant Redeemer is laid.

86

HILL CREST. (5 5. 5 4. D.)

In moderate time.

8. vv. 1, 4, 7.

GUSTAV HOLST, 1874–1934.

1 By weary stages The old world ages; By
4 Be-hold us bring-ing With love and sing-ing; With
7. All you in hear-ing As-sist our cheer-ing This

blood, by ra-ges, By pain-sown seeds.
great joy ring-ing And hearts new-made.
Soul un-fear-ing Who en-ters earth;

By fools and sa-ges, With death for wa-ges, Souls
The Prince, fore-spo-ken By seer and to-ken, By
On God re-ly-ing, And death de-fy-ing, He

leave their ca-ges And Man does deeds.
whom sin's bro-ken And death is stayed.
puts on dy-ing That Life have birth.

FINE.

vv. 2, 5.

DESCANT (Trebles).

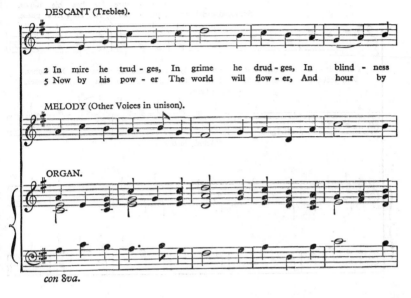

2 In mire he trud - ges, In grime he drud - ges, In blind - ness
5 Now by his pow - er The world will flow - er, And hour by

MELODY (Other Voices in unison).

ORGAN.

con 8va.

judg - es, In dark - ness gropes. His bit - ter mea - sure
hour . His realm in - crease; Now men be - night - ed

86 (*continued*)

SOPRANO and ALTO.

trea - sure He has his hopes.
light - ed To spi - rit's peace.

Yields lit - tle plea-sure; For on - ly trea-sure He has . his hopes.
Will feel them right-ed, And love be light-ed To spi - rit's peace.

TENOR and BASS.

(Melody in Bass.)

vv. 3, 6.

ff VOICES IN UNISON.

3 The hope that sail - ing When winds are fail - ing, A - bove the
6 Our God is wear - ing Man's flesh, and bear - ing Man's cares, through

ff

Ped.

rail - ing A   coast   may   rise;   The thought   that   glo - ry
car - ing What   men   may   be;   Our God   is   shar - ing His

D. S. V. 4-7.

Is not a   sto - ry, But   hea - ven o'er ye And watch - ing   eyes.
light   and   dar - ing To   help men's far - ing And set   men   free.

D. S. V. 4-7.

[*Copyright, 1928, by Gustav Holst.*]

John Masefield.

(103)

87

CRÜGER. (7 6. 7 6. D.)

Slow and dignified.

Adapted by W. H. MONK, 1823–89,
from a Chorale by J. CRÜGER, 1598–1662.

(*Other occasions also.*)

J. Montgomery, 1771–1854.

HAIL to the Lord's Anointed!
    Great David's greater Son;
Hail, in the time appointed,
    His reign on earth begun!
He comes to break oppression,
    To let the captive free;
To take away transgression,
    And rule in equity.

2 He comes with succour speedy
    To those who suffer wrong;
To help the poor and needy,
    And bid the weak be strong;
To give them songs for sighing,
    Their darkness turn to light,
Whose souls, condemned and dying,
    Were precious in his sight.

3 He shall come down like showers
    Upon the fruitful earth,
And love, joy, hope, like flowers,
    Spring in his path to birth:
Before him on the mountains
    Shall peace the herald go;
And righteousness in fountains
    From hill to valley flow.

4*Arabia's desert-ranger
    To him shall bow the knee;
The Ethiopian stranger
    His glory come to see;
With offerings of devotion
    Ships from the isles shall meet,
To pour the wealth of ocean
    In tribute at his feet.

5*Kings shall fall down before him,
    And gold and incense bring;
All nations shall adore him,
    His praise all people sing;
To him shall prayer unceasing
    And daily vows ascend;
His kingdom still increasing,
    A kingdom without end.

6. O'er every foe victorious,
    He on his throne shall rest,
From age to age more glorious,
    All-blessing and all-blest:
The tide of time shall never
    His covenant remove;
His name shall stand for ever;
    That name to us is Love.

EPIPHANY AND THE SUNDAYS AFTER

ALTERNATIVE VERSION FOR VERSE 3

Descant (Trebles). *Slow and dignified.*

Descant by R. VAUGHAN WILLIAMS.

He shall come down like show-ers

CHOIR AND PEOPLE IN UNISON WITH ORGAN.

Up - on the fruit - ful earth, And love, joy, hope, like

flow - ers, Spring in his path to birth:

Be - fore him

E*

87 (*continued*)

Shall peace the her - ald go; And right - eous - ness in foun — — — tains From hill to val - ley flow.

[*Copyright, 1925, by R. Vaughan Williams.*]

88

DENT DALE. (7 7. 7 7.)

Moderately fast.

English Traditional Melody.

C. Wesley, 1707-88.

HARK, how all the welkin rings!
  'Glory to the King of Kings,
Peace on earth and mercy mild,
  God and sinners reconciled.'

2*Joyful, all ye nations, rise,
  Join the triumph of the skies;
Universal nature say
  'Christ the Lord is born to-day.'

3*Christ, by highest heaven adored,
  Christ, the everlasting Lord,
Late in time behold him come
  Offspring of the Virgin's womb.

4*Veiled in flesh, the Godhead see!
  Hail the incarnate Deity!
Pleased as man with men to appear,
  Jesus, our Emmanuel here!

5 Hail the heavenly Prince of Peace!
  Hail the Sun of Righteousness!
Light and life to all he brings,
  Risen with healing in his wings.

6 Mild he lays his glory by,
  Born that man no more may die,
Born to raise the sons of earth,
  Born to give them second birth!

7 Come, Desire of Nations, come,
  Fix in us thy humble home;
Rise, the woman's conquering seed,
  Bruise in us the serpent's head.

8. Now display thy saving power,
  Ruined nature now restore,
Now in mystic union join
  Thine to ours, and ours to thine.

89

BONN (WARUM SOLLT ICH). (8 3 3 6. D.)

In moderate time.

JOHANN GEORG EBELING, 1637-76.

(*Other occasions also.*)   *A. G., based on* Fröhlich soll, *P. Gerhardt* (1653).

HEARTS at Christmas time were
    For a day   [jolly:
    Fled away
All our gloom and folly.
Hear, O hear, the message sung us
    In the air
    Everywhere:
Christ has come among us.

2 Come to bring a better morrow,
    Preach God's Realm
    And o'erwhelm
Selfishness and sorrow.
Men's devices spin to zero;
    He attains,
    His plan reigns:
Prophet he and hero.

3 For thy sake, then, single hearted,
    Let us use
    That good news
By thy life imparted.
Never shall our wills oppose thee;
    Noble Flower,
    Seed of power,
Hearts of men enclose thee.

4. Art and science circle o'er thee,
    Counsel, might,
    Left and right;
Wisdom rides before thee.
Plans and pleas of men are hollow:
    Son of God,
    At thy nod
We will up and follow.

WIE SCHÖN LEUCHTET DER MORGENSTERN. (8 8 7. 8 8 7. 8 4 4 8.)

Slow.   Later form of melody by P. NICOLAI (1556–1608). Harmonized by J. S. BACH, 1685–1750.

(Other occasions also.)   *P. Nicolai (1599) and J. A. Schlegel (1766). O.B.C.V.*

Wie schön leuchtet der Morgenstern.

HOW brightly beams the morning star!
    What sudden radiance from afar
        Doth glad us with its shining?
Brightness of God, that breaks our night
And fills the darkened souls with light
    Who long for truth were pining!
Newly, truly, God's word feeds us,
        Rightly leads us,
            Life bestowing.
Praise, O praise such love o'erflowing!

ALTERNATIVE VERSION

Harmonized by F. MENDELSSOHN-BARTHOLDY, 1809–47.

2 Through thee alone can we be blest;
  Then deep be on our hearts imprest
    The love that thou hast borne us;
  So make us ready to fulfil
  With ardent zeal thy holy will,
    Though men may vex or scorn us;
  Hold us, fold us, lest we fail thee.
        Lo, we hail thee,
        Long to know thee!
  All we are and have we owe thee.

3. All praise to him who came to save,
   Who conquer'd death and scorned the grave;
     Each day new praise resoundeth
   To him, the Life who once was slain,
   The friend whom none shall trust in vain,
     Whose grace for ay aboundeth;
   Sing then, ring then, tell the story
         Of his glory,
         Till his praises
   Flood with light earth's darkest mazes!

91

EIN KIND GEBOR'N. (L.M.)

Moderately fast.

Piae Cantiones, 1582.

(Other occasions also.)

P. Dearmer, 1867–1936.

IN Asia born, from Asia hailed,
Was Christ, who God for us unveiled;
The speech of God to man was he,
His life one bright epiphany.

2 And still his children come from far,
To hail from east and west his star;
In him all faiths and systems meet,
All partial truth is made complete.

3 Bright Friend, thy face shines out to-day
More real, more vivid, true and gay:
Then show thy goodly Kingdom, Christ,
The leaven, treasure, pearl unpriced!

4. True gifts we'd offer to our King:
Our myrrh as goodness we will bring,
Our incense as the truth shall rise,
Our gold be beauty's sacrifice.

92

HERMITAGE. (6 7. 6 7.)

Not too fast. Unison.

R. O. Morris, 1886–1948.

Col 8va ad lib.

Christina Rossetti, 1830–94.

LOVE came down at Christmas,
Love all lovely, Love divine;
Love was born at Christmas,
Stars and angels gave the sign.

2 Worship we the Godhead,
Love incarnate, Love divine;

Worship we our Jesus:
But wherewith for sacred sign?

3. Love shall be our token,
Love be yours and love be mine,
Love to God and all men,
Love for plea and gift and sign.

FIRST TUNE

CRASSELIUS. (13. 10. 13. 10. Irreg.)

In moderate time.

From *Dir, dir Jehova* by J. S. BACH, 1685-1750.

(Other occasions also.)

J. S. B. Monsell, 1811-75.

O WORSHIP the Lord in the beauty of holiness!
   Bow down before him, his glory proclaim;
With gold of obedience, and incense of lowliness,
   Kneel and adore him, the Lord is his name.

2 Low at his feet lay thy burden of carefulness,
   High on his heart he will bear it for thee,
Comfort thy sorrows, and answer thy prayerfulness,
   Guiding thy steps as may best for thee be.

3 Fear not to enter his courts in the slenderness
   Of the poor wealth thou wouldst reckon as thine:
Truth in its beauty, and love in its tenderness,
   These are the offerings to lay on his shrine.

4*These, though we bring them in trembling and fearfulness,
   He will accept for the name that is dear;
Mornings of joy give for evenings of tearfulness,
   Trust for our trembling and hope for our fear.

5.*O worship the Lord in the beauty of holiness!
   Bow down before him, his glory proclaim;
With gold of obedience, and incense of lowliness,
   Kneel and adore him, the Lord is his name.

93 (*continued*)

SECOND TUNE

DYMCHURCH. (13. 10. 13. 10. Irreg.)

Broadly.

GEOFFREY SHAW, 1879–1943.

[*Copyright*, 1915, *by J. Curwen & Sons, Ltd.*]

(*Other occasions also.*)

J. S. B. Monsell, 1811–75.

O WORSHIP the Lord in the beauty of holiness!
    Bow down before him, his glory proclaim;
With gold of obedience, and incense of lowliness,
    Kneel and adore him, the Lord is his name.

2 Low at his feet lay thy burden of carefulness,
    High on his heart he will bear it for thee,
Comfort thy sorrows, and answer thy prayerfulness,
    Guiding thy steps as may best for thee be.

3 Fear not to enter his courts in the slenderness
    Of the poor wealth thou wouldst reckon as thine:
Truth in its beauty, and love in its tenderness,
    These are the offerings to lay on his shrine.

4*These, though we bring them in trembling and fearfulness,
    He will accept for the name that is dear;
Mornings of joy give for evenings of tearfulness,
    Trust for our trembling and hope for our fear.

5.*O worship the Lord in the beauty of holiness!
    Bow down before him, his glory proclaim;
With gold of obedience, and incense of lowliness,
    Kneel and adore him, the Lord is his name.

94

BRAMLEY (A VIRGIN UNSPOTTED). (11 11. 11 11. and refrain.)

In moderate time.　　　　　　　　　　English Traditional Carol Melody.

FINE.

(*Other occasions also.*)　　　　　　　　　　　　　T. S. N.

THE greatness of God in his love has been shown,
　The light of his life on the nations is thrown;
And that which the Jews and the Greeks did divine
Is come in the fullness of Jesus to shine:
　　The Light of the World in the darkness has shone,
　　And grows in our sight as the ages flow on.

2 He rolls the grim darkness and sorrow away
　And brings all our fears to the light of the day;
　The idols are fallen of anger and blood,
　And God is revealed as the loving and good:

3 And, though we have sinned like the Prodigal Son,
　His love to our succour and welcome will run.
　His gospel of pardon, of love and accord,
　Will master oppression and shatter the sword:

4. The Light of the World is more clear to our sight
　As errors disperse and men see him aright:
　In lands long in shadow, his Churches arise
　And blaze for their neighbours the Way of the Wise:

(113)

95

CANTATE DOMINO. (D.L.M.)

Rather slow.

J. BARNBY, 1838–96.

[By permission of Novello & Co., Ltd.]

Arthur Penrhyn Stanley, 1815–81.

THE Lord is come, on Syrian soil,
   The child of poverty and toil;
The Man of Sorrows, born to know
Each varying shade of human woe:
His joy, his glory, to fulfil,
In earth and heaven, his Father's will;
On lonely mount, by festive board,
On bitter cross, despised, adored.

2 The Lord is come! In him we trace
   The fullness of God's truth and grace;
Throughout those words and acts divine
Gleams of the eternal splendour shine;
And from his inmost spirit flow,
As from a height of sunlit snow,
The rivers of perennial life,
To heal and sweeten nature's strife.

3. The Lord is come! In every heart
   Where truth and mercy claim a part;
In every land where right is might,
And deeds of darkness shun the light;
In every church where faith and love
Lift earthward thoughts to things above;
In every holy, happy home,
We bless thee, Lord, that thou hast come.

ST. JAMES. (C.M.)
In moderate time.

R. COURTEVILLE, d. *c.* 1772.

[This hymn may also be sung to DUNDEE, 557, with its fa-burden.]

ALTERNATIVE VERSION

The trebles sing the upper part, other voices the melody ST. JAMES
or the harmonies.

Descant by HENRY G. LEY.

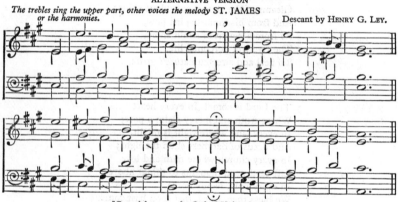

J. Morison, 1750–98 (*Scottish Paraphrases*).

THE race that long in darkness pined
   Have seen a glorious light;
The people dwell in day, who dwelt
   In death's surrounding night.

2 To hail thy rise, thou better Sun,
   The gathering nations come,
Joyous as when the reapers bear
   The harvest-treasures home.

3 To us a Child of Hope is born,
   To us a Son is given;

Him shall the tribes of earth obey,
   Him all the hosts of heaven.

4 His name shall be the Prince of Peace,
   For evermore adored;
The Wonderful, the Counsellor,
   The great and mighty Lord.

5. His power increasing still shall spread;
   His reign no end shall know:
Justice shall guard his throne above,
   And peace abound below.

See also

440 All hail the power
60 Christ is the world's
480 Crown him upon the throne
388 From the eastern mountains
64 Hills of the North, rejoice
537 In Christ there is

76 It came upon the midnight
545 Jesus shall reign
571 Lord, when the wise men
590 Not with a choir of angels
618 O worship the King
620 Our Father, while our hearts

634 Ring out, ye crystal
372 The shepherds had
668 They all were looking
669 Those who love
685 To us in Bethlem
700 Who within that stable

For Septuagesima, &c. see 'Seasons General' (*Nos.* 17–21 *and note*). 247, *Sing Alleluya, was anciently sung on the First Sunday in Lent, and is suitable from Septuagesima till the end of that day. For Quinquagesima see, among others:*

502 God is love: his the care
507 Gracious Spirit

577 Mercy, thou art
682 To Mercy, Pity, Peace

LENT

See also the General Hymns:

97

HEINLEIN (AUS DER TIEFE). (7 7. 7 7.)

Slow.

Probably by MARTIN HERBST, 1654–81.

ALTERNATIVE VERSION

Trebles sing the top line, all other voices the melody HEINLEIN.

Descant by ALAN GRAY.

G. H. Smyttan, 1822–70, and others.

FORTY days and forty nights
  Thou wast fasting in the wild;
Forty days and forty nights
Tempted still, yet unbeguiled:

2 Sunbeams scorching all the day,
Chilly dew-drops nightly shed,
Prowling beasts about thy way,
Stones thy pillow, earth thy bed.

3 Let us thy endurance share
And from earthly greed abstain,
With thee watching unto prayer,
With thee strong to suffer pain.

4*Then if evil on us press,
Flesh or spirit to assail,
Victor in the wilderness,
Help us not to swerve or fail!

5 So shall peace divine be ours;
Holier gladness ours shall be;
Come to us angelic powers,
Such as ministered to thee.

6. Keep, O keep us, Saviour dear,
Ever constant by thy side,
That with thee we may appear
At the eternal Eastertide.

(117)

98

QUITTEZ, PASTEURS.   (4 7. 4 6. 4 7. 6 4 8.)

In moderate time, not slow.

French Carol Melody.

Unison.   *Harmony.*

Varied harmonies to this tune may be found in the Oxford Book of Carols, 144.

White Lent.

P. Dearmer, 1867–1936.

NOW quit your care
   And anxious fear and worry;
For schemes are vain
   And fretting brings no gain.
To prayer, to prayer!
   Bells call and clash and hurry,
In Lent the bells do cry,
   'Come buy, come buy,
Come buy with love the love most high!'

(118)

2 Lent comes in the spring,
    And spring is pied with brightness;
        The sweetest flowers,
        Keen winds, and sun, and showers,
    Their health do bring
        To make Lent's chastened whiteness;
            For life to men brings light
                And might, and might,
            And might to those whose hearts are right.

3*To bow the head
    In sackcloth and in ashes,
        Or rend the soul,
        Such grief is not Lent's goal;
    But to be led
        To where God's glory flashes,
            His beauty to come nigh,
                To fly, to fly,
            To fly where truth and light do lie.

4*For is not this
    The fast that I have chosen?
        (The prophet spoke)
        To shatter every yoke,
    Of wickedness
        The grievous bands to loosen,
            Oppression put to flight,
                To fight, to fight,
            To fight till every wrong 's set right.

5 For righteousness
    And peace will show their faces
        To those who feed
        The hungry in their need,
    And wrongs redress,
        Who build the old waste places,
            And in the darkness shine.
                Divine, divine,
            Divine it is when all combine!

6. Then shall your light
    Break forth as doth the morning;
        Your health shall spring,
        The friends you make shall bring
    God's glory bright,
        Your way through life adorning;
            And love shall be the prize.
                Arise, arise,
            Arise! and make a paradise!

99

HERZLIEBSTER JESU. (11 11. 11 5.)   Later form of melody by J. Crüger, 1598–1662.

Very slow and solemn. May be sung in unison throughout.

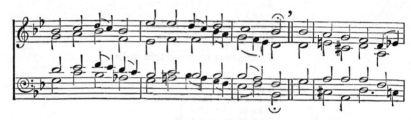

A little slower.

(*Passiontide also.*)   *J. Heermann, 1585–1647. Tr. R. Bridges.*

Herzliebster Jesu.

AH, holy Jesus, how hast thou offended,
   That man to judge thee hath in hate pretended?
By foes derided, by thine own rejected,
     O most afflicted.

2 Who was the guilty? Who brought this upon thee?
Alas, my treason, Jesus, hath undone thee.
   'Twas I, Lord Jesus, I it was denied thee:
     I crucified thee.

3 Lo, the good Shepherd for the sheep is offered;
The slave hath sinnèd, and the Son hath suffered;
   For man's atonement, while he nothing heedeth,
     God intercedeth.

LENTEN HYMNS

ALTERNATIVE VERSION

Harmonized by J. S. BACH, 1685–1750, in the *Passion according to St. Matthew.*

Very slow and solemn.

(This version may be used, in connexion with the other, in those verses only where the CHOIR SINGS ALONE. It should only be attempted by good choirs.)

4 For me, kind Jesus, was thy incarnation,
　Thy mortal sorrow, and thy life's oblation;
　　Thy death of anguish and thy bitter passion,
　　　For my salvation.

5. Therefore, kind Jesus, since I cannot pay thee,
　I do adore thee, and will ever pray thee,
　　Think on thy pity and thy love unswerving,
　　　Not my deserving.

IOO

ABRIDGE. (C.M.)
In moderate time.

I. SMITH, *c.* 1725–*c.* 1800.

ALTERNATIVE VERSION

Melody in the Tenor.

Fa-burden by GEOFFREY SHAW.

I. Williams, 1802–65.

BE thou my guardian and my guide,
  And hear me when I call;
Let not my slippery footsteps slide,
  And hold me lest I fall.

2 The world, the flesh, and Satan dwell
  Around the path I tread;
O save me from the snares of hell,
  Thou quickener of the dead.

3 And if I tempted am to sin,
  And outward things are strong,
Do thou, O Lord, keep watch within,
  And save my soul from wrong.

4. Still let me ever watch and pray,
  And feel that I am frail;
That if the tempter cross my way,
  Yet he may not prevail.

IOI

WERDE MUNTER. (7 6. 7 6. 8 8. 7 7.)

From a melody by J. SCHOP, d. c. 1664.

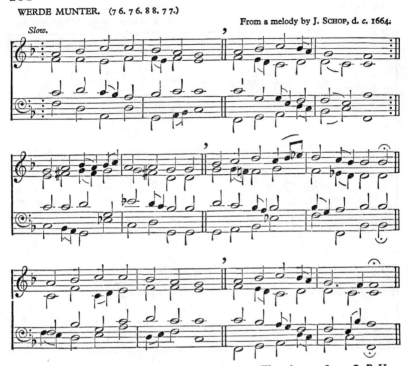

Theoctistus, c. 890. S. P. V.

Ἰησοῦ γλυκύτατε.

JESUS, name all names above;
  Jesus, best and dearest;
Jesus, fount of perfect love,
  Holiest, tenderest, nearest;
Thou the source of grace completest,
Thou the purest, thou the sweetest,
Thou the well of power divine,
Make me, keep me, seal me thine!

2 Jesus, crowned with bitter thorn,
  By mankind forsaken,
Jesus, who through scourge and scorn
  Held thy faith unshaken,
Jesus, clad in purple raiment,
For man's evils making payment:
Let not all thy woe and pain,
Let not Calvary be in vain!

3. Jesus, open me the gate
  That of old he entered
Who, in that most lost estate,
  Wholly on thee ventured;
Thou, whose wounds are ever pleading,
And thy Passion interceding,
From my weakness let me rise
To a home in paradise!

(123)

102

PETRIE. (10 10. 10 10.)

In moderate time.
Adapted from a traditional Irish Melody.

[*Copyright*, 1931, *by Martin Shaw.*]

W. H. Burleigh, 1812–71.

LEAD us, O Father, in the paths of peace:
Without thy guiding hand we go astray,
And doubts appal, and sorrows still increase;
Lead us through Christ, the true and living Way.

2 Lead us, O Father, in the paths of truth:
Unhelped by thee, in error's maze we grope,
While passion stains and folly dims our youth,
And age comes on uncheered by faith or hope.

3 Lead us, O Father, in the paths of right:
Blindly we stumble when we walk alone,
Involved in shadows of a darkening night;
Only with thee we journey safely on.

4. Lead us, O Father, to thy heavenly rest,
However rough and steep the pathway be,
Through joy or sorrow, as thou deemest best,
Until our lives are perfected in thee.

103

SONG 24. (10 10. 10 10.)

Moderately slow.

Melody by O. GIBBONS, 1583–1625.

Mrs. Frances M. Owen, 1842–83.

LIGHTEN the darkness of our life's long night.
  Through which we blindly stumble to the day.
Shadows mislead us: Father, send thy light
  To set our footsteps in the homeward way.

2 Lighten the darkness of our self-conceit—
  The subtle darkness that we love so well,
Which shrouds the path of wisdom from our feet,
  And lulls our spirits with its baneful spell.

3 Lighten our darkness when we bow the knee
  To all the gods we ignorantly make
And worship, dreaming that we worship thee,
  Till clearer light our slumbering souls awake.

4. Lighten our darkness when we fail at last,
  And in the midnight lay us down to die;
We trust to find thee when the night is past,
  And daylight breaks across the morning sky.

104

OXENBRIDGE. (10 10. 10 10. 10 10.)

In moderate time.

MARTIN SHAW, 1875-1958.

[*Copyright, 1931, by Martin Shaw.*]

J. Quarles, 1624-65, and H. F. Lyte, 1793-1847.

LONG did I toil, and knew no earthly rest,
   Far did I rove, and found no certain home;
At last I sought them in his sheltering breast,
   Who opes his arms, and bids the weary come:
With him I found a home, a rest divine,
And I since then am his, and he is mine.

2 The good I have is from his stores supplied,
   The ill is only what he deems the best;
He for my friend, I'm rich with nought beside,
   And poor without him, though of all possest:
Changes may come, I take, or I resign,
Content, while I am his, while he is mine.

3 Whate'er may change, in him no change is seen,
   A glorious Sun that wanes not nor declines,
Above the clouds and storms he walks serene,
   And on his people's inward darkness shines:
All may depart, I fret not, nor repine,
While I my Saviour's am, while he is mine.

4.*While here, alas! I know but half his love,
   But half discern him, and but half adore;
But when I meet him in the realms above
   I hope to love him better, praise him more,
And feel, and tell, amid the choir divine,
How fully I am his, and he is mine.

105

CHESHIRE. (C.M.)

Slow.

Este's Psalter, 1592.

[This hymn may also be sung to DUNDEE, 557.]

ALTERNATIVE VERSION

Melody in the Tenor.

Fa-burden by C. HYLTON STEWART.

[Copyright, 1931, by Oxford University Press.]

Richard Baxter,† 1615–91.

LORD, it belongs not to my care
    Whether I die or live;
To love and serve thee is my share,
    And this thy grace must give.

2 If life be long, I will be glad,
    That I may long obey;
If short, yet why should I be sad
    Since all receive their pay?

3 Christ leads me through no darker rooms
    Than he went through before;

He that into God's Kingdom comes
    Must enter by this door.

4 Come, Lord, when grace hath made me meet
    Thy blessèd face to see:
For if thy work on earth be sweet,
    What will thy glory be!

5.*My knowledge of that life is small,
    The eye of faith is dim;
But 'tis enough that Christ knows all,
    And I shall be with him.

(*This hymn may be begun at verse 3.*)

(127)

LENTEN HYMNS

106

SOUTHWELL. (S.M.)

Slow.

Damon's Psalter, 1579 (later form of third line).

ALTERNATIVE VERSION

Melody in the Tenor.

Fa-burden by MARTIN SHAW.

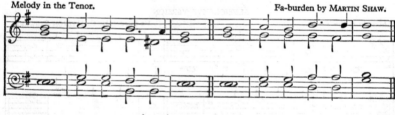

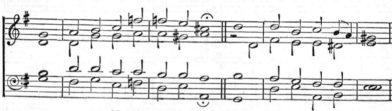

[*Copyright, 1915, by J. Curwen & Sons, Ltd.*]

Bp. Synesius, 375–430. Pr. A. W. Chatfield.
Μνώεο Χριστὲ.

LORD Jesus, think on me
And purge away my sin;
From earthborn passions set me free,
And make me pure within.

2 Lord Jesus, think on me,
With care and woe opprest;
Let me thy loving servant be,
And taste thy promised rest.

3 Lord Jesus, think on me
Amid the battle's strife;
In all my pain and misery
Be thou my health and life.

4 Lord Jesus, think on me,
Nor let me go astray;
Through darkness and perplexity
Point thou the heavenly way.

5★ Lord Jesus, think on me
When flows the tempest high:
When on doth rush the enemy,
O Saviour, be thou nigh.

6. Lord Jesus, think on me,
That, when the flood is past,
I may the eternal brightness see,
And share thy joy at last.

(128)

107

WONDER. (8 8. 7 5. Irregular.)

Moderately slow. (May be sung in unison.)

ARNOLD BAX.

1 Lord, thou hast told us that there be Two
2 The one the high - est heav - en is, The
3 Though heaven be high, the gate is low, And
4. O God! since thou de - light'st to rest With -

dwell - ings which be - long to thee, And those . . two, .
man - sions of e - ter - nal bliss; The o - - - ther's the
he that comes in there must bow; The lof - - - ty
- in the hum - ble con - trite breast, . . First . . make me

that's the won - der, Are far a - sun - der. . .
con - trite . . . . And hum - ble sprite. . . . . .
looks shall ne'er . . . . Have en - trance there. . . . . . .
so to be, ... Then dwell with me. . . . .

Thomas Washbourne, 1606–87.

F

108

HUNNYS. (C.M.)

Moderately slow.

Melody in *Seven Sobs of a Sorrowful Soul*, 1583.

J. D. Carlyle, 1759–1804.

LORD, when we bend before thy throne,
And our confessions pour,
Teach us to feel the sins we own,
And hate what we deplore.

2 Our broken spirits pitying see
And penitence impart;
Then let a kindling glance from thee
Beam hope upon the heart.

3 When we disclose our wants in prayer
May we our wills resign,
And not a thought our bosom share
That is not wholly thine.

4. Let faith each meek petition fill,
And waft it to the skies;
And teach our hearts 'tis goodness still
That grants it or denies.

109

REGNART (AUF MEINEN LIEBEN GOTT). (66. 77. 77.)

Later form of Melody by JACOB REGNART (1574).
Melody as given in the *Chorale Book for England*, 1863.

Moderately slow.

G. W. Briggs, 1875–1959.

LORD, who hast made me free,
Whose hand upholdeth me,
Thy wondrous love hath found me,
In willing bonds hath bound me;
Nor life nor death for ever
Me from thy love can sever.

2   O love, how deep, how high,
On cross of shame to die!
Such love can never fail me,
Thy grace shall still avail me;
In life thou wilt uphold me,
In death thine arms enfold me.

3   My strength is not my own:
I trust in thee alone,
And welcome each to-morrow,
Let it bring joy or sorrow;
For thou art still beside me,
Thy hand will alway guide me.

4.*   Lord of my life and guide,
In thee let me abide,
Thy way more clearly knowing,
To fuller stature growing,
Till I at last before thee
With eyes unveiled adore thee.

110

SOLOMON. (C.M.)

Adapted from the Air 'What tho' I trace', G. F. HANDEL, 1685–1759.

In moderate time.

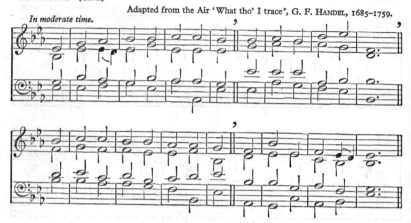

17th cent. S. P. V.

O Deus, ego amo te.

MY God, I love thee; not because
    I hope for heaven thereby,
Nor yet for fear that loving not
    I might for ever die.

2 But for that thou didst all mankind
    Upon the cross embrace;
For us didst bear the nails and spear,
    And manifold disgrace,

3 And griefs and torments numberless,
    And sweat of agony;
E'en death itself; and all for man
    Who was thine enemy.

4 Then why, O blessèd Jesus Christ,
    Should I not love thee well,
Not for the sake of winning heaven,
    Nor any fear of hell;

5 Not with the hope of gaining aught,
    Not seeking a reward;
But as thyself hast lovèd me,
    O ever-loving Lord!

6.*E'en so I love thee, and will love,
    And in thy praise will sing,
Solely because thou art my God,
    And my eternal King.

111

MAINZ (MARIA JUNG UND ZART). (6 6. 6 6.)

In moderate time.

Melody and harmony from *Psalteriolum Harmonicum*, 1642.

J. Byrom,† 1692–1763.

MY spirit longs for thee
Within my troubled breast,
Though I unworthy be
Of so divine a guest.

2 Of so divine a guest
Unworthy though I be,
Yet has my heart no rest
Unless it come from thee.

3 Unless it come from thee,
In vain I look around;
In all that I can see
No rest is to be found.

4. No rest is to be found
But in thy blessèd love:
O let my wish be crowned,
And send it from above!

112

CAITHNESS.   (C.M.)

Moderately slow.

Melody in *Scottish Psalter*, 1635.

[This hymn may also be sung to STRACATHRO, 438.]

W. Cowper, 1731–1800.

O FOR a closer walk with God,
A calm and heavenly frame;
A light to shine upon the road
That leads me to the Lamb!

2 Return, O holy Dove, return,
Sweet messenger of rest;
I hate the sins that made thee mourn,
And drove thee from my breast.

3 The dearest idol I have known,
Whate'er that idol be,
Help me to tear it from thy throne
And worship only thee.

4. So shall my walk be close with God,
Calm and serene my frame;
So purer light shall mark the road
That leads me to the Lamb.

113

STOCKTON. (C.M.)

In moderate time.

T. WRIGHT, 1763–1829.

C. Wesley, 1707–88.

O FOR a heart to praise my God,
  A heart from sin set free:
A heart that always feels thy blood
  So freely spilt for me:

2 A heart resigned, submissive, meek,
  My dear Redeemer's throne;
Where only Christ is heard to speak,
  Where Jesus reigns alone:

3 A humble, lowly, contrite heart,
  Believing, true, and clean,

Which neither life nor death can part
  From him that dwells within:

4 A heart in every thought renewed,
  And full of love divine;
Perfect, and right, and pure, and good,
  A copy, Lord, of thine.

5. Thy nature, gracious Lord, impart,
  Come quickly from above;
Write thy new name upon my heart,
  Thy new best name of Love.

114

BEDFORD. (C.M.)

Very slow and dignified.

Original form of melody by W. WEALE, d. 1727.

ALTERNATIVE VERSION

Melody in the Tenor.

Fa-burden by E. C. BAIRSTOW.

[Copyright, 1931, by Oxford University Press.]

H. H. Milman, 1791–1868.

O HELP us, Lord! Each hour of need
  Thy heavenly succour give;
Help us in thought and word and deed
  Each hour on earth we live.

2 O help us when our spirits bleed
    With contrite anguish sore,
  And when our hearts are cold and dead,
    O help us, Lord, the more.

3 O help us through the prayer of faith
    More firmly to believe;
  For still the more the servant hath,
    The more shall he receive.

4. O help us, Jesus, from on high,
    We know no help but thee;
  O help us so to live and die
    As thine in heaven to be.

(135)

115

FIRST TUNE

SUTTON VALENCE. (6 5. 6 5. D.)

In moderate time.

S. L. RUSSELL.

Sheds the se - cret tear,

Organ.

H. S. Oswald, 1751–1834. Tr. F. E. Cox.‡

Wem in Leidenstagen.

O LET him whose sorrow
  No relief can find,
Trust in God, and borrow
  Ease for heart and mind.

2 Where the mourner weeping
  Sheds the secret tear,
God his watch is keeping,
  Though none else be near.

3 God will never leave thee,
  All thy wants he knows,
Feels the pains that grieve thee,
  Sees thy cares and woes.

(136)

LENTEN HYMNS

SECOND TUNE

DUN ALUINN. (6 5. 6 5. D.)

Rather slow.

Adapted from an Irish **Traditional Melody.**

4 Raise thine eyes to heaven
   Should thy spirits quail,
When, by tempests driven,
   Sight and steering fail.

5 All our woe and trouble
   Justice will requite,
All our joys redouble
   In the eternal height.

6. Jesus, gracious Saviour,
   In the realms above
Crown us with thy favour,
   Fill us with thy love.

116

ST. MARY. (C.M.)

Prys' Psalter, 1621 (as given in Playford's *Psalms*, 1677).

Slow.

ALTERNATIVE VERSION

Melody in Bass or Tenor.

Fa-burden by GEOFFREY SHAW.

The Lamentation.   *J. Marckant (Old Version,* 1560).

O LORD, turn not away thy face
    From him that lies prostrate,
Lamenting sore his sinful life
    Before thy mercy-gate;

2 Which gate thou openest wide to those
    That do lament their sin:
Shut not that gate against me, Lord,
    But let me enter in.

3 So come I to thy mercy-gate,
    Where mercy doth abound,
Requiring mercy for my sin
    To heal my deadly wound.

4. Mercy, good Lord, mercy I ask,
    This is the total sum;
For mercy, Lord, is all my suit:
    Lord, let thy mercy come.

(138)

117

OLIVER. (C.M.)

In moderate time.

OLIVER A. KING, 1855-1923.

[*By permission of Novello & Co., Ltd.*]

[This hymn may also be sung to HARINGTON, 613.]

T. Haweis, 1734-1820, and others.

O THOU from whom all goodness flows,
  I lift my heart to thee;
In all my sorrows, conflicts, woes,
  Dear Lord, remember me.

2 When on my poor distressèd heart
    My sins lie heavily,
  Thy pardon grant, new peace impart:
    Dear Lord, remember me.

3 When trials sore obstruct my way,
    And ills I cannot flee,
  O let my strength be as my day:
    Dear Lord, remember me.

4*If, for thy sake, upon my name
    Shame and reproaches be,
  All hail reproach, and welcome shame!
    Dear Lord, remember me.

5 If worn with pain, disease, or grief
    This feeble spirit be;
  Grant patience, rest, and kind relief:
    Dear Lord, remember me.

6. So that, when comes the hour of death,
    My earthly fears may flee:
  This song of praise be my last breath—
    Thou wilt remember me.

(139)

118

ATTERCLIFFE. (C.M.)

In moderate time.

WILLIAM MATHER, 1756–1808.

C. *Wesley*, 1707–88.

SHEPHERD divine, our wants relieve
    In this our evil day;
To all thy tempted followers give
    The power to watch and pray.

2 Long as our fiery trials last,
    Long as the cross we bear,
O let our souls on thee be cast
    In never-ceasing prayer.

3*The spirit of interceding grace
    Give us in faith to claim;
To wrestle till we see thy face,
    And know thy hidden Name.

4 Till thou thy perfect love impart,
    Till thou thyself bestow,
Be this the cry of every heart,
    'I will not let thee go.'

5 I will not let thee go, unless
    Thou tell thy Name to me;
With all thy great salvation bless,
    And make me all like thee.

6. Then let me on the mountain-top
    Behold thy open face;
Where faith in sight is swallowed up,
    And prayer in endless praise.

119

DAS LEIDEN DES HERRN. (L.M.)

Very slow.

German Traditional Melody.

[This hymn may also be sung to BRESLAU, 132.]

C. W. Everest,‡ 1814–77.

TAKE up thy cross, the Saviour said,
 If thou wouldst my disciple be;
Deny thyself, the world forsake,
 And humbly follow after me.

2 Take up thy cross; let not its weight
 Fill thy weak spirit with alarm;
His strength shall bear thy spirit up,
 And brace thy heart, and nerve thine arm.

3*Take up thy cross, nor heed the shame,
 Nor let thy foolish pride rebel;
Thy Lord for thee the cross endured
 And fought the powers of death and hell.

4 Take up thy cross then in his strength,
 And calmly every danger brave;
'Twill guide thee to a better home,
 And lead to victory o'er the grave.

5 Take up thy cross, and follow Christ,
 Nor think till death to lay it down;
For only he who bears the cross
 May hope to wear the glorious crown.

6. To thee, great Lord, the One in three,
 All praise for evermore ascend;
O grant us here below to see
 The heavenly life that knows no end.

A - men.

120

WIRKSWORTH. (S.M.)

FIRST TUNE

In moderate time.

GREEN'S *Psalm Tunes*, 1724, as given in *Wesleyan Hymn Book*, 1847.

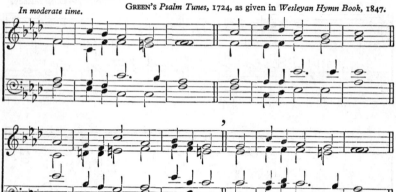

ST. EDMUND. (S.M.)

SECOND TUNE

Moderately slow.

Adapted from Hymn Melody by E. GILDING, d. 1782.

Francis Turner Palgrave, 1824–97.

THOU say'st, 'Take up thy cross,
O man, and follow me':
The night is black, the feet are slack,
Yet we would follow thee.

2 But O, dear Lord, we cry,
That we thy face could see,
Thy blessèd face one moment's space;
Then might we follow thee!

3* Dim tracts of time divide
Those golden days from me;
Thy voice comes strange o'er years of
How can I follow thee? [change;

4* Comes faint and far thy voice
From vales of Galilee;
Thy vision fades in ancient shades;
How should we follow thee?

5 Ah, sense-bound heart and blind
Is nought but what we see?
Can time undo what once was true?
Can we not follow thee?

6. Within our heart of hearts
In nearest nearness be:
Set up thy throne within thine own:—
Go, Lord: we follow thee.

I2I

MON DIEU, PRÊTE-MOI L'OREILLE. (8 8. 7 7. D.)

In moderate time, very dignified. Unison.

Composed or adapted by L. BOURGEOIS
for the 86th Psalm in the *Genevan Psalter*, 1543.

Ps. 86.

Joseph Bryan (c. 1620).

TO my humble supplication,
　Lord, give ear and acceptation;
Save thy servant, that hath none
Help nor hope but thee alone.

2 Send, O send, relieving gladness
To my soul opprest with sadness,
Which, from clog of earth set free,
Winged with zeal, flies up to thee;

3 To thee, rich in mercies' treasure,
And in goodness without measure,
Never-failing help to those
Who on thy sure help repose.

4. Heavenly Tutor, of thy kindness,
Teach my dullness, guide my blindness,
That my steps thy paths may tread,
Which to endless bliss do lead.

(143)

122

PLAISTOW. (L.M.)

Slow.

From *Magdalen Hymns, c.* 1760.

George William Russell ('*A. E.*'), 1867–1935.

WHEN the unquiet hours depart
  And far away their tumults cease,
Within the twilight of the heart
  We bathe in peace, are stilled with
    peace.

2 The fire that slew us through the day
  For angry deed or sin of sense
Now is the star and homeward ray
  To us who bow in penitence.

3*We kiss the lips of bygone pain
  And find a secret sweet in them:
The thorns once dripped with shadowy
    rain
  Are bright upon each diadem.

4*Ceases the old pathetic strife,
  The struggle with the scarlet sin:
The mad enchanted laugh of life
  Tempts not the soul that sees within.

5 No riotous and fairy song
  Allures the prodigals who bow
Within the home of law, and throng
  Before the mystic Father now,

6. Where faces of the elder years,
  High souls absolved from grief and
    sin,
Leaning from out ancestral spheres
  Beckon the wounded spirit in.

123

DRESDEN (SO GIEBST DU). (10 10. 10 10. 8 4.)

Melody from a Dresden song-book (1694) (second line slightly adapted).
Harmony from J. S. BACH, 1685–1750.

Moderately slow.

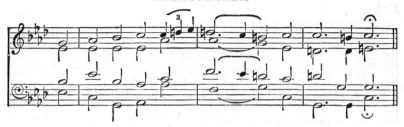

9 Slower.

[*May also be sung as a solo.*]

John Donne, 1573–1631.

WILT thou forgive that sin, where I begun,
  Which was my sin though it were done before?
Wilt thou forgive that sin, through which I run,
  And do run still, though still I do deplore?
When thou hast done, thou hast not done,
        For I have more.

2 Wilt thou forgive that sin which I have won
    Others to sin, and made my sin their door?
  Wilt thou forgive that sin which I did shun
    A year or two, but wallowed in a score?
  When thou hast done, thou hast not done,
          For I have more.

3. I have a sin of fear, that when I've spun
    My last thread, I shall perish on the shore;
  But swear by thyself, that at my death thy Son
    Shall shine, as he shines now and heretofore:
  And, having done that, thou hast done:
          I fear no more.

See also

See also the General Hymns.

124

BABYLON'S STREAMS. (L.M.)

Moderately slow, solemn.

T. CAMPIAN, c. 1575–1619.

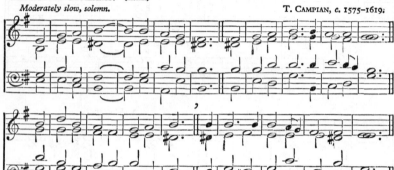

James Martineau, 1805–1900.

A VOICE upon the midnight air,
  Where Kedron's moonlit waters
Weeps forth, in agony of prayer,   [stray,
  'O Father, take this cup away!'

2 Ah, thou, who sorrowest unto death,
  We conquer in thy mortal fray;
And Earth for all her children saith,
  'O God, take not this cup away!'

3 *O Lord of sorrow, meekly die!
  Thou'lt heal or hallow all our woe;
Thy name refresh the mourner's sigh,
  Thy peace revive the faint and low.

4 Great Chief of faithful souls, arise!
  None else can lead the martyr-band,
Who teach the brave how peril flies
  When faith unarmed uplifts the hand.

5 O King of earth, the cross ascend!
  O'er climes and ages 'tis thy throne;
Where'er thy fading eye may bend
  The desert blooms, and is thine own.

6. Thy parting blessing, Lord, we pray:
  Make but one fold below, above;
And when we go the last lone way,
  O give the welcome of thy love!

125

SONG 46. (10 10.)

Slow.

First strain of Song 46, O. GIBBONS, 1583–1625.

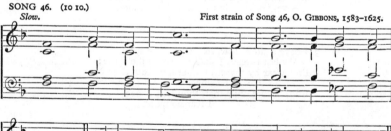

Phineas Fletcher, 1582–1650.

DROP, drop, slow tears,
  And bathe those beauteous feet,
Which brought from heaven
  The news and Prince of Peace.

2 Cease not, wet eyes,
  His mercies to entreat;

To cry for vengeance
  Sin doth never cease.

3. In your deep floods
  Drown all my faults and fears;
Nor let his eye
  See sin, but through my tears.

126

MANTEGNA. (8 6. 8 6. 8 8 8. 7. Irreg.)

Slow. Unison.

R. VAUGHAN WILLIAMS, 1872–1958.

[*Copyright,* 1931, *by R. Vaughan Williams.*]

Sidney Lanier, 1842–81.

INTO the woods my master went,
  Clean forspent, forspent;
Into the woods my master came,
Forspent with love and shame;
But the olives they were not blind to him,
The little grey leaves were kind to him,
The thorn tree had a mind to him,
When into the woods he came.

2. Out of the woods my master went,
  And he was well content;
Out of the woods my master came,
Content with death and shame.   [last,
When death and shame would woo him
From under the trees they drew him last:
'Twas on a tree they slew him, last,
When out of the woods he came.

127

FIRST TUNE

LOVE UNKNOWN. (6 6. 6 6. 4 4. 4 4.)

In moderate time. Unison.   JOHN IRELAND, 1879-1962.

Samuel Crossman, c. 1624–84.

MY song is love unknown,
  My Saviour's love to me,
Love to the loveless shown,
  That they might lovely be.
    O who am I,
      That for my sake
      My Lord should take
    Frail flesh, and die?

2 He came from his blest throne,
  Salvation to bestow;
But men made strange, and none
  The longed-for Christ would know.
    But O, my friend,
      My friend indeed,
      Who at my need
    His life did spend!

3 Sometimes they strew his way,
  And his sweet praises sing;
Resounding all the day
  Hosannas to their king.
    Then 'Crucify!'
      Is all their breath,
      And for his death
    They thirst and cry.

4 Why, what hath my Lord done?
  What makes this rage and spite?
He made the lame to run,
  He gave the blind their sight.
    Sweet injuries!
      Yet they at these
      Themselves displease,
    And 'gainst him rise.

PASSIONTIDE

SECOND TUNE

RHOSYMEDRE. (6 6. 6 6. 4 4. 4 4.)

Moderately slow.

J. D. EDWARDS, 1805–85.

5*They rise, and needs will have
    My dear Lord made away;
A murderer they save,
    The Prince of Life they slay.
        Yet cheerful he
            To suffering goes,
            That he his foes
        From thence might free.

6*In life, no house, no home
    My Lord on earth might have;
In death, no friendly tomb
    But what a stranger gave.
        What may I say?
            Heaven was his home;
            But mine the tomb
        Wherein he lay.

7. Here might I stay and sing,
    No story so divine;
Never was love, dear King,
    Never was grief like thine.
        This is my Friend,
            In whose sweet praise
            I all my days
        Could gladly spend.

128

PASSION CHORALE. (7 6. 7 6. D.)

Melody by H. L. HASSLER, 1564–1612.
Adapted and harmonized by J. S. BACH, 1685–1750.

Very slow and solemn.

ALTERNATIVE VERSION

Harmonized by J. S. BACH, in the *Passion according to St. Matthew.*

Very slow and solemn.

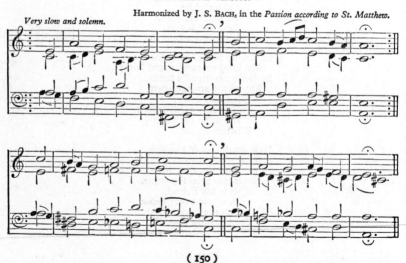

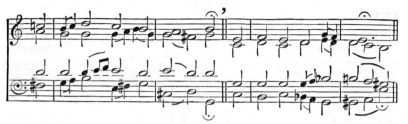

This version may be used, in connexion with the other, for verse 4, and must be sung by the CHOIR
ALONE. *It should only be attempted by good choirs.*

P. Gerhardt, 1607–76, based on Salve caput cruentatum (*probably by*
Arnulf von Loewen, 1200–50). Pr. R. Bridges.

O Haupt voll Blut und Wunden.

O SACRED head, sore wounded,
  Defiled and put to scorn;
O kingly head, surrounded
  With mocking crown of thorn:
What sorrow mars thy grandeur?
  Can death thy bloom deflower?
O countenance whose splendour
  The hosts of heaven adore!

2 Thy beauty, long-desirèd,
    Hath vanished from our sight;
  Thy power is all expirèd,
    And quenched the light of light.
  Ah me! for whom thou diest,
    Hide not so far thy grace:
  Show me, O Love most highest,
    The brightness of thy face.

3 I pray thee, Jesus, own me,
    Me, Shepherd good, for thine;
  Who to thy fold hast won me,
    And fed with truth divine.
  Me guilty, me refuse not,
    Incline thy face to me,
  This comfort that I lose not,
    On earth to comfort thee.

4*In thy most bitter passion
    My heart to share doth cry,
  With thee for my salvation
    Upon the cross to die.
  Ah, keep my heart thus movèd
    To stand thy cross beneath,
  To mourn thee, well-belovèd,
    Yet thank thee for thy death.

5.*My days are few, O fail not,
    With thine immortal power,
  To hold me that I quail not
    In death's most fearful hour:
  That I may fight befriended,
    And see in my last strife
  To me thine arms extended
    Upon the cross of life.

PASSIONTIDE

129

FIRST TUNE

PLAINSONG. (8 7. 8 7. 8 7.)   Mode iii.

SECOND TUNE

GRAFTON. (8 7. 8 7. 8 7.)
Moderately slow.
    French Church Melody,
from *Chants Ordinaires de l'Office Divin* (Paris, 1881).

Bp. Venantius Fortunatus, 530–609. *Tr. A, F.*

Pange lingua gloriosi proelium certaminis.

SING, my tongue, the glorious battle,
　　Sing the ending of the fray;
Now above the cross, the trophy,
　　Sound the loud triumphant lay:
Tell how Christ, the world's redeemer,
　　As a victim won the day.

2 Tell how, when at length the fullness
　　Of the appointed time was come,
He, the Word, was born of woman,
　　Left for us his Father's home,
Showed to men the perfect manhood,
　　Shone as light amidst the gloom.

3 Thus, with thirty years accomplished,
　　Went he forth from Nazareth,
Destined, dedicate, and willing,
　　Wrought his work, and met his death;
Like a lamb he humbly yielded
　　On the cross his dying breath.

4*Faithful cross, thou sign of triumph,
　　Now for man the noblest tree,
None in foliage, none in blossom,
　　None in fruit thy peer may be;
Symbol of the world's redemption,
　　For the weight that hung on thee!

5. Unto God be praise and glory:
　　To the Father and the Son,
To the eternal Spirit, honour
　　Now and evermore be done;
Praise and glory in the highest,
　　While the timeless ages run.

130

PLAINSONG. (L.M.) *In free rhythm.*

Melody from the *Sarum Antiphonal.*

[*Copyright, 1925, by Oxford University Press.*]

SECOND TUNE (PROPER MELODY)

ANDERNACH. (L.M.)

In moderate time, dignified. Unison.

Andernach Gesangbuch, 1608.

Vexilla regis prodeunt.

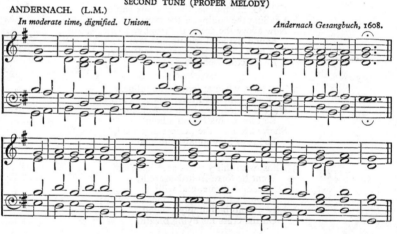

Bp. Venantius Fortunatus, 530–609. *Tr.* 1670, &c., *S. P. V.*

THE royal banners forward go,
The cross shines forth in mystic
  glow,
Where he, the Life, did death endure,
And by that death did life procure.

2 There was he slain in noble youth,
There suffered to maintain the truth,
And there, to cleanse the heart of man,
From out his side life's torrent ran.

3 Fulfilled is all his words foretold:
Then spread the banners, and unfold
Love's crowning power, that all may see
He reigns and triumphs from the tree.

4*O tree of grace, the conquering sign,
Which dost in royal purple shine,
Gone is thy shame; for, lo, each bough
Proclaims the Prince of Glory now.

5*For once thy favoured branches bore
The wealth that did the world restore,
The priceless treasure, freely spent,
To pay for man's enfranchisement.

6. Father of all, life's source and spring,
May every soul thy praises sing,
May those obey the rule of heaven
For whom the perfect life was given.

(154)

131

HORSLEY. (C.M.)
In moderate time.

W. HORSLEY, 1774–1858.

ALTERNATIVE VERSION

Melody in the Tenor.

Fa-burden by PATRICK HARVEY.

[*Copyright, 1931, by Oxford University Press.*]

Mrs. C. F. Alexander, 1818–95.

THERE is a green hill far away,
Without a city wall,
Where the dear Lord was crucified
Who died to save us all.

2 We may not know, we cannot tell,
What pains he had to bear,
But we believe it was for us
He hung and suffered there.

3*He died that we might be forgiven,
He died to make us good;
That we might go at last to heaven,
Saved by his precious blood.

4. O, dearly, dearly has he loved,
And we must love him too,
And trust in his redeeming blood
And try his works to do.

(155)

132

BRESLAU. (L.M.)

Very slow.

Melody in *As Hymnodus Sacer*, Leipzig, 1625.
Adapted and harmonized by F. MENDELSSOHN-BARTHOLDY, 1809-47.

(*Other occasions also.*) T. Kelly, 1769-1854.

WE sing the praise of him who died,
　Of him who died upon the cross;
The sinner's hope let men deride,
　For this we count the world but loss.

2 Inscribed upon the cross we see
　In shining letters, 'God is Love';
He bears our sins upon the tree;
　He brings us mercy from above.

3 The cross! it takes our guilt away;
　It holds the fainting spirit up;
It cheers with hope the gloomy day,
　And sweetens every bitter cup.

4 It makes the coward spirit brave,
　And nerves the feeble arm for fight;
It takes its terror from the grave,
　And gilds the bed of death with light;

5. The balm of life, the cure of woe,
　The measure and the pledge of love,
The sinners' refuge here below,
　The angels' theme in heaven above.

(156)

PASSIONTIDE

Melody in the Tenor.

Fa-burden by H. V. HUGHES.

[*When this setting is sung in four-part harmony, omit the small notes.*]

(*Other occasions also.*)

T. Kelly, 1769–1854.

WE sing the praise of him who died,
  Of him who died upon the cross;
The sinner's hope let men deride,
  For this we count the world but loss.

2 Inscribed upon the cross we see
    In shining letters, 'God is Love';
  He bears our sins upon the tree;
    He brings us mercy from above.

3 The cross! it takes our guilt away;
    It holds the fainting spirit up;
  It cheers with hope the gloomy day,
    And sweetens every bitter cup.

4 It makes the coward spirit brave,
    And nerves the feeble arm for fight;
  It takes its terror from the grave,
    And gilds the bed of death with light;

5. The balm of life, the cure of woe,
    The measure and the pledge of love,
  The sinners' refuge here below,
    The angels' theme in heaven above.

PASSIONTIDE

ROCKINGHAM. (L.M.)

Very slow.

Adapted by E. MILLER, 1731–1807.

ALTERNATIVE VERSION

Melody in the Tenor.

Fa-burden by GEOFFREY SHAW.

I. Watts, 1674-1748.

WHEN I survey the wondrous cross,
    On which the Prince of Glory died,
My richest gain I count but loss,
    And pour contempt on all my pride.

2 Forbid it, Lord, that I should boast
    Save in the death of Christ my God;
All the vain things that charm me most,
    I sacrifice them to his blood.

3 See from his head, his hands, his feet,
    Sorrow and love flow mingled down;
Did e'er such love and sorrow meet,
    Or thorns compose so rich a crown?

4*His dying crimson, like a robe,
    Spreads o'er his body on the tree;
Then am I dead to all the globe,
    And all the globe is dead to me.

5. Were the whole realm of nature mine,
    That were a present far too small;
Love so amazing, so divine,
    Demands my soul, my life, my all.

134

SONG 13. (7 7. 7 7.)

O. GIBBONS, 1583-1625 (original version of melody and bass).

Slow and solemn.

J. R. Wreford (1837), S. Longfellow (1848).

WHEN my love to God grows weak,
    When for deeper faith I seek,
Then in thought I go to thee,
Garden of Gethsemane.

2 There I walk amid the shades,
While the lingering twilight fades;
See that suffering, friendless one
Weeping, praying, there alone.

3 When my love for man grows weak,
When for stronger faith I seek,

Hill of Calvary, I go
To thy scenes of fear and woe.

4 There behold his agony
Suffered on the bitter tree,
See his anguish, see his faith,
Love triumphant still in death.

5. Then to life I turn again,
Learning all the worth of pain,
Learning all the might that lies
In a full self-sacrifice.

See also, among others,

135

ST. THEODULPH (VALET WILL ICH DIR GEBEN). (7 6. 7 6. D.)

Melody by M. TESCHNER, *c.* 1613. Adapted and harmonized by J. S. BACH, 1685–1750.

Very slow and solemn.

Palm Sunday.

St. Theodulph of Orleans, d. 821. *Tr.* J. M. *Neale.*‡
Gloria, laus et honor.

ALL glory, laud, and honour
  To thee, Redeemer, King,
To whom the lips of children
  Made sweet hosannas ring.

2 Thou art the King of Israel,
    Thou David's royal Son,
  Who in the Lord's name comest,
    The King and blessèd one:

3 The company of angels
    Are praising thee on high,
  And mortal men and all things
    Created make reply:

4 The people of the Hebrews
    With palms before thee went;
  Our praise and prayer and anthems
    Before thee we present:

5*To thee before thy passion
    They sang their hymns of praise;
  To thee now high exalted
    Our melody we raise:

6.*Thou didst accept their praises:
    Accept the prayers we bring,
  Who in all good delightest,
    Thou good and gracious King:

(160)

136

COME, FAITHFUL PEOPLE. (8 8 8. 7.)

Melody by C. BICKNELL, 1842–1918.

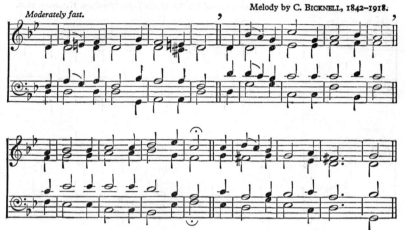

Palm Sunday.

G. Moultrie, 1829–85, and others.

COME, faithful people, come away,
Your homage to your monarch pay;
It is the feast of palms to-day:
Hosanna in the highest!

2 When Christ, the Lord of all, drew nigh
On Sunday morn to Bethany,
He called two loved ones standing by:

3 'To yonder village go,' said he,
'Where you a tethered ass shall see;
Loose it and bring it unto me':

4 The two upon their errand sped,
And brought the ass as he had said,
And on its back their clothes they spread:

5 They set him on his throne so rude;
Before him went the multitude,
And in the way their garments strewed:

6*Go, Saviour, thus to triumph borne,
Thy crown shall be the wreath of thorn,
Thy royal garb the robe of scorn:

7*They thronged before, behind, around,
They cast palm-branches on the ground,
And still rose up the joyful sound:

8*'Blessèd is Israel's King,' they cry;
'Blessèd is he that cometh nigh
In name of God the Lord most high':

9. Thus, Saviour, to thy Passion go;
Pass through the fleeting ebb and flow,
To meet the yet unconquered foe:

137

WINCHESTER NEW. (L.M.)

Slow and dignified.   Adapted from a Chorale in the *Musikalisches Handbuch*, Hamburg, 1690.

Palm Sunday.

H. H. Milman, 1791–1868.

RIDE on! ride on in majesty!
Hark, all the tribes hosanna cry;
Thine humble beast pursues his road
With palms and scattered garments strowed.

2 Ride on! ride on in majesty!
In lowly pomp ride on to die:
O Christ, thy triumphs now begin
O'er captive death and conquered sin.

3 Ride on! ride on in majesty!
The wingèd squadrons of the sky
Look down with sad and wondering eyes
To see the approaching sacrifice.

4 Ride on! ride on in majesty!
Thy last and fiercest strife is nigh;
The Father, on his sapphire throne,
Expects his own anointed Son.

5. Ride on! ride on in majesty!
In lowly pomp ride on to die;
Bow thy meek head to mortal pain,
Then take, O God, thy power, and reign.

PASSIONTIDE

ALTERNATIVE VERSION

Descant by GEOFFREY SHAW.

138

STABAT MATER. (8 8 7. D.)
Slow and solemn.
French Church Melody.

SECOND TUNE

CORNER (CHRISTI MUTTER STUND VOR SCHMERZEN). (8 8 7. D.)
Very slow and solemn.
Melody from G. CORNER, *Gesangbuch*, 1625.

Good Friday.　　　　　　　　　　　　　　　　　　*A. F.*

IN the place of sorrow, waiting,
　Stood his foes, deriding, hating,
　　While the women watched him die:
Through the six long hours' endurance
Words of pity, grief, assurance,
　Told his patient agony.

2 Undismayed, his foes forgiving,
To the last for others living,
　Lays he down his life for all;
Love heroic, love unshrinking,
Heaven and earth together linking,
　Reigns he, as the shadows fall.

3 On the cross for man presented,
Thirsting, bleeding, sore tormented,
　Hear him to the Father cry;
See his body droop and languish,
As he moves beyond the anguish
　In his last expiring sigh.

4. Truly Son of God in dying,
Safety for thyself denying,
　In the darkness thou art light:
Temples fall, but thou abidest;
O thou Spirit, highest, widest,
　Us in love to thee unite.

139

SEBASTIAN (JESU MEINES GLAUBENS ZIER). (7 8. 8 7. 8 7. 8 7.)

Melody from FREYLINGHAUSEN'S *Gesangbuch* (1714).
Harmony from J. S. BACH, 1685–1750.

Very slow and solemn.

Good Friday. (Other occasions also.)

Gabriel Gillett, 1873–1948.

IT is finished! Christ hath known
  All the life of men wayfaring,
Human joys and sorrows sharing,
  Making human needs his own.
Lord, in us thy life renewing,
  Lead us where thy feet have trod,
Till, the way of truth pursuing,
  Human souls find rest in God.

2   It is finished! Christ is slain,
  On the altar of creation,
Offering for a world's salvation
  Sacrifice of love and pain.

Lord, thy love through pain revealing,
  Purge our passions, scourge our vice,
Till, upon the tree of healing,
  Self is slain in sacrifice.

3. It is finished! Christ our King
Wins the victor's crown of glory;
Sun and stars recite his story,
  Floods and fields his triumph sing.
Lord, whose praise the world is telling,
  Lord, to whom all power is given,
By thy death, hell's armies quelling,
  Bring thy saints to reign in heaven.

140

ST. CROSS. (L.M.)
In moderate time.

J. B. DYKES, 1823-76.

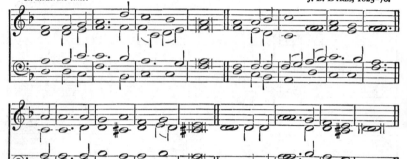

[This hymn may also be sung to DAS LEIDEN DES HERRN, 119.]

Good Friday.

F. W. Faber,‡ 1814-63.

O COME and mourn with me awhile;
Our place be at the Saviour's side;
O come, together let us mourn:
Jesus, our Lord, is crucified.

2 Seven times he spoke, seven words of love;
And for three hours his silence cried

For mercy on the souls of men:
Jesus, our Lord, is crucified.

3. O love of God! O sin of Man!
In this dread act your strength is tried;
And victory remains with Love:
Jesus, our Lord, is crucified.

141

ARFON. (7 7. 7 7. 7 7.)
Moderately slow.

Welsh Hymn Melody.

Good Friday.   J. Ellerton, 1826–93.

THRONED upon the aweful tree,
  King of grief, I watch with thee;
Darkness veils thine anguished face,
None its lines of woe can trace,
None can tell what pangs unknown
Hold thee silent and alone;

2 Silent through those three dread hours,
Wrestling with the evil powers,
Left alone with human sin,
Gloom around thee and within,
Till the appointed time is nigh,
Till the Lamb of God may die.

3 Hark that cry that peals aloud
Upward through the whelming cloud!
Thou, the Father's only Son,
Thou his own anointed one,
Thou dost ask him—can it be?
'Why hast thou forsaken me?'

4. Lord, should fear and anguish roll
Darkly o'er my sinful soul,
Thou, who once wast thus bereft
That thine own might ne'er be left,
Teach me by that bitter cry
In the gloom to know thee nigh.

For Good Friday see also Nos. 124–134 and

517 Help us to help
101 Jesus, name all names above
562 Lord Christ, when first

580 My faith looks up
117 O thou from whom
689 (II) We saw not

142

BOHEMIA (O MENSCH SIEH).   (8 8 8.)
Very slow.   Bohemian Brethren's *Gesangbuch*, 1566 (slightly adapted).

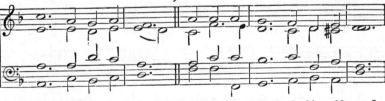

Good Friday, Easter Even.   Bp. J. R. Darbyshire, 1880–1948.

AT eve, when now he breathed no
  more,
The faithful few in anguish sore
The Lord they loved to burial bore.

2 To those who mourned him, who can say
How long the hours of sullen day,
How long the nights while hid he lay?

3 O ye who shrink beneath the blow
That death can deal, henceforth ye know
Not hopeless is your human woe.

4. For then, before their tears had ceased,
Love woke to joy the crimson east,
And Jesus rose, from death released.

143

O FILII ET FILIAE (1).   (8 8 8. and Alleluyas.)

In moderate time. Unison.

Air sur les hymnes sacrez, Paris, 1623.

Al - le - lu - ya!   Al - le - lu - ya!   Al - le - lu - ya!

Al - le - lu - ya!

NOTE.—*The opening 'Alleluyas' may be sung between each verse if preferred.*

ALTERNATIVE VERSION

O FILII ET FILIAE (2).   (8 8 8. and Alleluyas.)

Proper melody (modern version) as given in Webbe's *Motetts or Antiphons*, 1792.

In moderate time. Unison.

Al - le - lu - ya!   Al - le - lu - ya!   Al -

- le - lu - ya!

Al — — — — le - lu - ya!

16th and 17th cent. Tr. J. M. Neale.‡

O filii et filiae.

ALLELUYA, alleluya, alleluya!
Ye sons and daughters of the King,
Whom heavenly hosts in glory sing,
To-day the grave hath lost its sting:
                              Alleluya!

2 On that first morning of the week,
Before the day began to break,
The Marys went their Lord to seek:

3 A young man bade their sorrow flee,
For thus he spake unto the three:
'Your Lord is gone to Galilee':

4 That night the apostles met in fear,
Amidst them came their Lord most dear,
And greeted them with words of cheer:

5 Then for that first and best of days
To God your hearts and voices raise
In laud and jubilee and praise:

6 And thus with all the Church unite,
As evermore is just and right,
In glory to the King of Light:

Part II

7 When Thomas afterwards had heard
That Jesus had fulfilled his word,
He doubted if it were the Lord:

8 'Thomas, behold my side,' saith he,
'My hands, my feet, my body see;
And doubt not, but believe in me':

9 No longer Thomas then denied;
He saw the feet, the hands, the side;
'Thou art my Lord and God,' he cried:

10. Blessèd are they that have not seen,
And yet whose faith hath constant been;
In life eternal they shall reign:

144

AVE VIRGO VIRGINUM. (7 6. 7 6. D.)

Leisentritt's *Gesangbuch*, 1584 (rhythm of bar 7 slightly simplified).

In moderate time.

St. John Damascene, c. 750. Pr. J. M. Neale.‡
Αἴσωμεν πάντες λαοί.

COME, ye faithful, raise the strain
  Of triumphant gladness;
God hath brought his people now
  Into joy from sadness;
'Tis the spring of souls to-day;
  Christ hath burst his prison,
And from three days' sleep in death
  As a sun hath risen.

2 Now the queen of seasons, bright
  With the day of splendour,
With the royal feast of feasts,
  Comes its joy to render;
Comes to gladden Christian men,
  Who with true affection
Welcome in unwearied strains
  Jesus' resurrection.

3. Neither might the gates of death,
  Nor the tomb's dark portal,
Nor the wrappings, nor the stone,
  Hold thee as a mortal;
But to-day amidst the twelve
  Thou didst stand, bestowing
Thine own peace which evermore
  Passeth human knowing.

(170)

145

EASTER HYMN. (7 4. 7 4. D.)

Altered from melody in *Lyra Davidica*, 1708.

Slow.

[For original version of tune see 172.]

Lyra Davidica (1708), *and the Supplement* (1816).

JESUS Christ is risen to-day, *Alleluya!*
Our triumphant holy day, *Alleluya!*
Who did once, upon the cross, *Alleluya!*
Suffer to redeem our loss. *Alleluya!*

2 Hymns of praise then let us sing
Unto Christ, our heavenly King,
Who endured the cross and grave,
Sinners to redeem and save:

3. But the pains that he endured
Our salvation have procured;
Now above the sky he's King,
Where the angels ever sing:

(171)

146

GÖRLITZ (ACH GOTT VOM HIMMELREICHE).   (7 6. 7 6. D.)

Moderately fast.   Melody by M. PRAETORIUS, 1571–1621.

[This hymn may also be sung to ELLACOMBE, 193.]

St. John Damascene, c. 750. Pr. J. M. Neale.‡

Ἀναστάσεως ἡμέρα.

THE day of resurrection!
    Earth, tell it out abroad;
The Passover of gladness,
    The Passover of God!
From death to life eternal,
    From earth unto the sky,
Our Christ hath brought us over
    With hymns of victory.

2 Our hearts be pure from evil,
    That we may see aright
The Lord in rays eternal
    Of resurrection-light;
And, listening to his accents,
    May hear so calm and plain
His own 'All hail', and, hearing,
    May raise the victor strain.

(172)

3. Now let the heavens be joyful,
  And earth her song begin,
  The round world keep high triumph,
  And all that is therein;
  Let all things seen and unseen
  Their notes of gladness blend,
  For Christ the Lord hath risen,
  Our Joy that hath no end.

147

VICTORY. (8 8. 8 4.)

Slow and dignified.

First three lines adapted from a 'Gloria Patri' by
G. P. DA PALESTRINA, 1525–94. Alleluya by W. H. MONK, 1823–89.

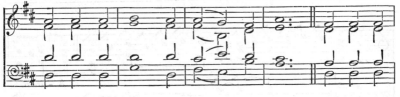

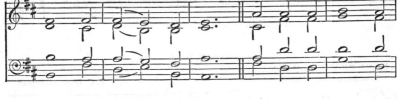

[This hymn may also be sung to VULPIUS, 154.]

Ascribed to 18th cent. Tr. F. Pott.

Finita jam sunt praelia.

THE strife is o'er, the battle done;
  Now is the Victor's triumph won;
O let the song of praise be sung:
                Alleluya!

2 Death's mightiest powers have done their worst,
  And Jesus hath his foes dispersed;
  Let shouts of praise and joy outburst:

3 On the third morn he rose again
  Glorious in majesty to reign;
  O let us swell the joyful strain:

4. Lord, by the stripes which wounded thee,
  From death's dread sting thy servants free,
  That we may live, and sing to thee:

(173)

FIRST TUNE

PLAINSONG. (L.M.) *In free rhythm.*

Melody from the *Sarum Antipnonal.*

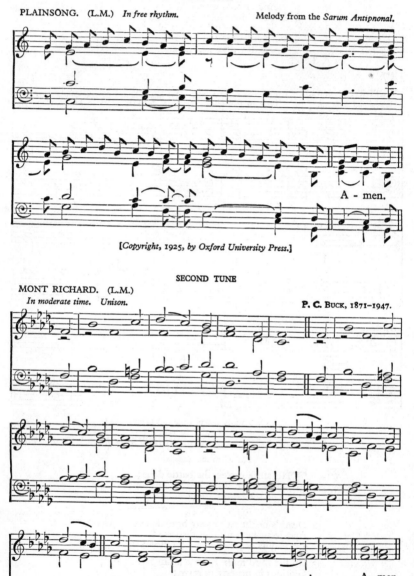

A - men.

SECOND TUNE

MONT RICHARD. (L.M.)

In moderate time.   Unison.

P. C. Buck, 1871–1947.

A - men.

4th or 5th cent. Tr. T. A. Lacey.

Sermone blando angelus.

A MESSENGER within the grave
Good cheer to wondering women
gave:
'Full soon your Master ye shall see;
He goes before to Galilee.'

2 On that fair day of Paschal joy
The sunshine was without alloy,
When, to their very eyes restored,
They looked upon the risen Lord.

3 The wounds before their eyes displayed
They see in living light arrayed,
And that they see they testify
In open witness fearlessly.

4 O Christ, the King of Gentleness,
Our several hearts do thou possess,
That we may render all our days
Thy meed of thankfulness and praise.

5*Maker of all, to thee we pray,
Fulfil in us thy joy to-day;
When death assails, grant, Lord, that we
May share the Paschal victory.

6.*To thee who, dead, again dost live,
All glory, Lord, thy people give;
All glory, as is ever meet,
To Father and to Paraclete.

149

LLANFAIR. (7 4. 7 4. D.)
In moderate time, dignified.

Melody by R. WILLIAMS (1817).

Voices in unison.

(Ascension also.)

A. P. Stanley (cento), 1815–81.

ALL the toil and sorrow done, *Alleluya!*
All the battle fought and won, *Alleluya!*
Now behind we leave the past, *Alleluya!*
Forward be our glances cast. *Alleluya!*

2 Still his words before us range,
Through the ages as they change;
Wheresoe'er the truth will lead,
He will give the light we need.

3. Evermore in heart and mind,
We our life in him will find;
To our own eternal Friend,
Evermore let us ascend.

(175)

150

FIRST TUNE

CÖTHEN (EINS IST NOT). (8 7. 8 7. 12 12. 11 11.)

In moderate time.

VOICES IN UNISON.   Melody and bass by J. S. BACH, 1685–1750.

Slightly faster.

WÜRZBURG. (8 7. 8 7. D.)

In moderate time.   Melody from *Andächtige und auserlesene Gesänger*, Würzburg, 1705.

Bp. Chr. Wordsworth, 1807–85, and others.

ALLELUYA, alleluya!
  Hearts to heaven and voices raise;
Sing to God a hymn of gladness,
  Sing to God a song of praise:
    O praise him, O praise him, who
      died and is living;
    Who died all-undaunted, his life
      for us giving;
    In him shall we rise, in our hearts
      shall he reign,
    And man to God's Kingdom at last
      shall attain.

2 He who on the cross a victim
    For the world's salvation bled,
  Jesus Christ, the King of Glory,
    Now is risen from the dead:

3 Christ is risen; we are risen!
    Shed upon us heavenly grace,
  Rain, and dew, and gleams of glory
    From the brightness of thy face:

4.*Thus we, Lord, with hearts in heaven
    Here on earth may fruitful be,
  In our daily life be gathered
    To eternal life with thee:

(The refrain is for use only with the tune 'Cöthen'.)

(177)

151

ST. FULBERT. (C.M.)

H. J. GAUNTLETT, 1805–76.

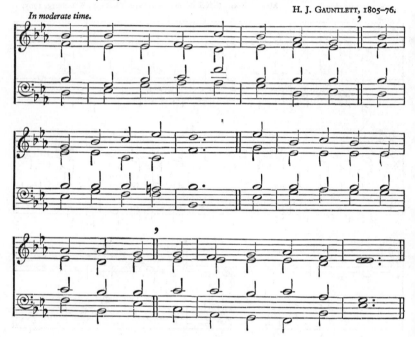

Christopher Smart, 1722–71.

AWAKE, arise! lift up thy voice,
 Which as a trumpet swell!
Rejoice in Christ! again rejoice,
 And on his praises dwell!

2 Let us not doubt, as doubted some,
 When first the Lord appeared;
But full of faith and reverence come,
 What time his voice is heard.

3 And even as John, who ran so well,
 Confess upon our knees
The Prince that locks up death and hell,
 And has himself the keys.

4*And thus through gladness and surprise
 The saints their Saviour treat;
Nor will they trust their ears and eyes
 But by his hands and feet:

5*Those hands of liberal love indeed
 In infinite degree,
Those feet still frank to move and bleed
 For millions and for me.

6. O Dead, arise! O Friendless, stand
 By seraphim adored!
O Solitude, again command
 Thy host from heaven restored!

EASTER DAY TO ASCENSION DAY

ALTERNATIVE VERSION

Melody in the Tenor.

Fa-burden by MARTIN SHAW.

[*Copyright, 1931, by Martin Shaw.*]

Christopher Smart, 1722–71.

AWAKE, arise! lift up thy voice,
　　Which as a trumpet swell!
Rejoice in Christ! again rejoice,
　　And on his praises dwell!

2 Let us not doubt, as doubted some,
　　When first the Lord appeared;
But full of faith and reverence come,
　　What time his voice is heard.

3 And even as John, who ran so well,
　　Confess upon our knees
The Prince that locks up death and hell,
　　And has himself the keys.

4*And thus through gladness and surprise
　　The saints their Saviour treat;
Nor will they trust their ears and eyes
　　But by his hands and feet:

5*Those hands of liberal love indeed
　　In infinite degree,
Those feet still frank to move and bleed
　　For millions and for me.

6. O Dead, arise!　O Friendless, stand
　　By seraphim adored!
O Solitude, again command
　　Thy host from heaven restored!

(179)

152

MIDHURST. (87 87. 75 75. 87 87.)

In moderate time.

NICHOLAS GATTY, 1874–1946.

A. T. Gurney, ?1820–87, and others.

CHRIST is risen! Christ is risen!
He hath burst his bonds in twain:
Christ is risen! Christ is risen!
Cry of gladness, soar again!
For our gain he suffered loss,
Captive, made us free;
He hath died upon the cross,
But the Life is he:

Christ is risen! Christ is risen!
He hath burst his bonds in twain:
Christ is risen! Christ is risen!
Earth and heaven prolong the strain!

(180)

2 Lo, the chains of death are broken:
 Rise we then to things above,
Joying now in every token
 Of thy triumph, Lord of Love.
He who came to earth again,
 To his friends appeared,
O'er all hearts to-day doth reign,
 Followed and revered:

3. Radiant angel-spirits thronging,
 Hail the Lord in one acclaim,
All ye souls, to God belonging,
 Join with us and praise his name:
Christ is risen, all shall rise,
 Sing on earth again;
Sing, ye saints in paradise,
 Christ is come to reign:

153

ORIENTIS PARTIBUS. (7 7. 7 7. 4.)

Moderately fast. Unison.
         Later form of Medieval French Melody.

Al - le - lu - - ya!

Michael Weisse, c. 1480–1534. Tr. C. Winkworth.

Christus ist erstanden.

CHRIST the Lord is risen again!
 Christ hath broken every chain!
Hark, the angels shout for joy,
Singing evermore on high:
    Alleluya!

2 He who gave for us his life,
 Who for us endured the strife,
 Is our Paschal lamb to-day!
 We too sing for joy, and say:

3 He who bore all pain and loss
 Comfortless upon the cross,
 Lives in glory now on high,
 Pleads for us, and hears our cry:

4. Thou, our Paschal lamb indeed,
 Christ, to-day thy people feed;
 Take our sins and guilt away,
 That we all may sing for ay:

(181)

154

VULPIUS (GELOBT SEI GOTT). (8 8 8. 4.)
In moderate time.   Unison.
Melody from M. VULPIUS' *Gesangbuch* (1609).
Harmonized by HENRY G. LEY, 1887–1962.

Al – le – lu – ya! Al – le – lu – ya! Al – le – lu – ya!

[*Copyright, 1925, by Oxford University Press.*]

C. A. Alington, 1872–1955.

GOOD Christian men rejoice and sing!
    Now is the triumph of our King!
To all the world glad news we bring:
            Alleluya!

2 The Lord of Life is risen for ay;
  Bring flowers of song to strew his way;
  Let all mankind rejoice and say:

3 Praise we in songs of victory
  That Love, that Life which cannot die,
  And sing with hearts uplifted high:

4. Thy name we bless, O risen Lord,
  And sing to-day with one accord
  The life laid down, the Life restored:

155

FIRST TUNE

CHRIST IST ERSTANDEN.   (7 8. 7 8. 4.)
Moderately slow, very dignified.   Unison.
German Melody, about 12th cent.

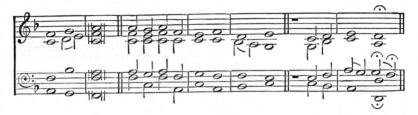

SECOND TUNE

ST. ALBINUS. (7 8. 7 8. 4.)

H. J. GAUNTLETT, 1805–76.

In moderate time.

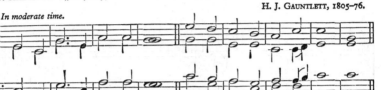

C. F. Gellert, 1715–69. Tr. F. E. Cox.

Jesus lebt, mit ihm auch ich.

JESUS lives! thy terrors now
　Can, O death, no more appal us;
Jesus lives! by this we know
　Thou, O grave, canst not enthral us:
　　　Alleluya!

2 Jesus lives! henceforth is death
　But the gate of life immortal;
This shall calm our trembling breath,
　When we pass its gloomy portal:

3 Jesus lives! for us he died;
　Then, alone to Jesus living,
Pure in heart may we abide,
　Glory to our Saviour giving:

4*Jesus lives! our hearts know well
　Nought from us his love shall sever;
Life, nor death, nor powers of hell
　Tear us from his keeping ever:

5. Jesus lives! to him the throne
　Over all the world is given;
May we go where he is gone,
　Rest and reign with him in heaven:

(183)

156

WITTENBERG (ES IST DAS HEIL). (8 7. 8 7. 8 8 7.)

Melody from *Christliche Lieder*, Wittenberg, 1524.
Adapted and harmonized by J. S. BACH, 1685–1750.

Slow.

(Ascension also.)

F. B. *Macnutt*, 1873–1949.

LET all the multitudes of light,
    Their songs in concert raising,
With earth's triumphal hymns unite,
    The risen Saviour praising.
Ye heavens, his festival proclaim!
Our King returneth whence he came,
    With victory amazing.

2 For us he bore the bitter tree,
    To death's dark realm descending;
Our foe he slew, and set us free,
    Man's ancient bondage ending.
No more the tyrant's chains oppress;
O conquering Love! thy name we bless,
    With thee to heaven ascending.

3. Jesus! to thee be endless praise,
    For this thy great salvation;
O holy Father! thine always
    Be thanks and adoration;
Spirit of life and light, to thee
Eternal praise and glory be;
    One God of all creation!

(184)

157

EASTER ALLELUYA (LASST UNS ERFREUEN). (8 8. 4 4. 8 8 and Alleluyas.)

In moderate time, dignified. Unison.   Melody from *Cölner Gesangbuch*, 1623.

Harmony.   Unison.

Harmony.

Unison.

(Other occasions also.)   T. S. N.

LET us rejoice, the fight is won,
Darkness is conquered, death undone,
    Life triumphant! Alleluya!
So age to age each nation grows
More like the heart of him who rose:
    Alleluya, alleluya,[1]
        Alleluya, alleluya, alleluya!

2 Joy comes again! all shall be well,
Friends severed now in heaven shall
    Reunited! Alleluya!   [dwell

The end of all our ways is love:
Then rise with him to things above:

3. Thou boundless power, thou God on high,
How could thy children fear to die?
    Joy immortal! Alleluya!
Thy Right rewards, thy Love forgives;
We know that our Redeemer lives:

(For a Doxology see 415.)

[1] *In Eastertide,* Christ is risen! Alleluya.

158

TREFAENAN. (8 7. 8 7. 8 8. 8 7.)

Brightly.

From a Welsh Traditional Melody.

[*Copyright, 1931, by Martin Shaw.*]

Easter Triumph. (Other occasions also.)

P. Dearmer, 1867–1936.

LIFE is good, for God contrives it,
    Deep on deep its wonder lies;
Death is good, for man survives it,
    Lives again in better guise: [him,
This they knew the night they hailed
When he came through that which
        veiled him,
            Alleluya, alleluya!
    Smiling, wonderful, and wise.

2 Failure cuts the way to triumph,
    Winter shapes the leaves of spring:
Easter came because the Master
    Loved the light of truth to bring.

Vainly priests in hatred slew him:
He came back, his loved ones knew him.
            Alleluya, alleluya!
Where, O death, is now thy sting?

3. Lord, in thee shines man's perfection—
    Kind and selfless, strong, and brave;
And thy life and resurrection
    Tells of joy beyond the grave:
All mankind is nobled through thee,
All are brothers coming to thee;
            Alleluya, alleluya!
    Thine the power to guide and save.

159

HERMANN (ERSCHIENEN IST DER HERRLICH TAG). (8 8. 8 8. 4.)

Melody by N. HERMANN, 1560.
Adapted and harmonized by J. S. BACH, 1685–1750.

In moderate time.

Al - le - lu - ya.

A. F.

LO, when the day of rest was past,
 The Lord, the Christ, was seen again;
Unknown at first, he grew to sight:
 'Mary' he said—she knew him then:
  Alleluya.

2 And dimly in the evening light
  He joined two friends who walked alone—
A stranger, till he stayed to sup;
  He brake the bread, and he was known:

3 And unto Simon he appeared,
  Who brought the joyful news apace.
Through bolted doors the presence came;
  They saw their Master face to face:

4 He was the same; his deathless form,
  Freed from dull matter, moved and spake;
The same when Thomas knew him next;
  The same who hailed them on the lake:

5*And he was seen in Galilee;
  Five hundred gathered to his call;
And he was seen by James alone;
  And next by the Apostles all:

6*Then once again he came to them,
  Embodied in etheric might,
And blessed them; as he bade farewell,
  A cloud concealed him from their sight:

7*Thus didst thou, Lord, their minds convince;
  Yet was there needed, last of all,
One more return to mortal eyes,
  To win the last apostle, Paul.

8. O Prince of Life, who once wast killed,
  Whom God has raised to his right hand,
Thou hast made known the ways of life,
  That we e'en death may understand:

(Verses 6, 7, 8 may be sung as a separate hymn.)

160

SAVANNAH (OR HERRNHUT). (7 7. 7 7.)   Melody from a MS. *Choralbuch* (Herrnhut,
Moderately fast.   *c.* 1740) as given in the *Foundery Collection*, 1742.

ALTERNATIVE VERSION

Melody in the Tenor.   Fa-burden by MARTIN SHAW.

C. *Wesley*,† 1707–88.

LOVE'S redeeming work is done;
    Fought the fight, the battle won:
Lo, our Sun's eclipse is o'er!
Lo, he sets in blood no more!

2 Vain the power of man to quell,
    Christ has burst the gates of hell;
    Death in vain forbids his rise;
    Christ has opened paradise.

3 Lives again our glorious King;
    Where, O death, is now thy sting?
    Dying once, he all doth save;
    Where thy victory, O grave?

(188)

4 Soar we now where Christ has led,
Following our exalted Head;
Made like him, like him we rise;
Ours the cross, the grave, the skies.

5. Hail the Lord of earth and heaven!
Praise to thee by both be given:
Thee we greet triumphant now;
Hail, the Resurrection thou!

161

HARWICH. (11 11. 11 11.)

In moderate time.   B. MILGROVE, 1731–1810, as given in the *Union Tune Book*, 1812.

(*Ascension also.*)   T. S. N.

REJOICE and be glad! he lives who was slain,
And Christ in the world is beginning his reign:
Love conquers, forgiving till seventy times seven,
The Kingdom is coming on earth as in heaven.

2 Rejoice and be glad! for he dwelt on this earth,
The outcast and sorrowful brought he to mirth:
He taught men, and healed men, till light on them shone;
So cease not from working, till all has been won.

3 Rejoice and be glad! for our hero is throned;
On earth as in heaven his splendour is owned:
Ascended and with us, even unto the end,
We live by his spirit, our leader and friend.

4. To God be the glory, to Christ be the praise,
To God be our service, in Christ be our ways:
O Spirit eternal, in thee be our rest,
Beyond us, within us, our goal and our guest!

162

VICTOR KING (CHRISTUS IST ERSTANDEN). (7 8. 8 8. 8 8.)

Rather quick.

German Carol. Melody from the Trier *Gesangbuch,* 1871.

(Ascension also.)

Jan Struther, 1901–53.

ROUND the earth a message runs:
Awake, awake, you drowsy ones!
Now leaps the sap in every stem
To chant the winter's requiem.
No more of sloth and dullness sing:
Sing love, sing joy, for Christ is King!

2 Round the earth a message runs:
Arise, arise, you doleful ones!
Cast off your chains, you captives all
Who long have lain in sorrow's thrall.
No more of grief and anguish sing:
Sing love, sing joy, for Christ is King!

3 Round the earth a message runs:
For shame, for shame, you brawling ones!
You shall more true adventure find
In friendliness of heart and mind.
No more of hate and envy sing:
Sing love, sing joy, for Christ is King!

4. Round the earth a message runs:
Rejoice, rejoice, you happy ones!
Now fall the gods of wrath and pain,
Now comes your Prince of Joy to reign;
To him your brave allegiance sing:
Sing love, sing joy, for Christ is King!

163

COLOGNE (CHRISTUS IST AUFERSTANDEN). (7 7. 7 7. 14 10.)

Melody from *Cölner Gesangbuch*, 1623.

Jan Struther, 1901–53.

SING, all ye Christian people!
  Swing, bells, in every steeple!
    For Christ to life is risen,
    Set free from death's dark prison.
With joyfulness, with joyfulness your alleluyas sing,
For Christ has come again to greet the spring.

2 Green now is on the larches;
  Springtime in triumph marches,
    And every day uncloses
    A host of new primroses:
Then daffodils and marybuds let us in garlands bring,
For Christ has come again to greet the spring.

3. Skylarks, the earth forsaking,
  Soar to their music-making,
    And in the roof-tree's hollow
    Now builds the trusting swallow:
So cries to him, so flies to him my soul on fearless wing,
For Christ has come again to greet the spring.

(191)

164

CHELSEA. (8 7. 8 7. 8 7. 8 7. 7 7.)

In moderate time.

JOHN IRELAND, 1879–1962.

[*This hymn may also be sung to* COBBOLD, *Appendix* 1.]

C. A. Alington, 1872–1955.

SING, brothers, sing and praise your King!
  Gone is the night of sorrow!
Have ye not heard his royal word,
  'God careth for the sparrow'?
Our watch we kept while others slept,
  We saw where Joseph laid him,
Saw women bring their offering,
  The last sad tribute paid him.
    But now from us they'll borrow
    Songs for a joyful morrow!

2. For we have heard a greater word,
    And seen a greater glory;
  Sing, brothers, sing this fair morning,
    And tell the world the story!
  We heard a voice that bade rejoice,
    Where late our Lord was lying,
  No more, it saith, shall there be death,
    Sorrow, nor pain, nor crying:
      And men from birds may borrow
      Songs for a glad to-morrow!

165

LEMON'S FARM. (6 6 6. 5. D.)

In moderate time.

MARTIN SHAW, 1875-1958.

Alternative organ accompaniment for
first bar of last verse.

&c.

[Copyright, 1929, by Martin Shaw.]

(*Ascension also.*)

John Masefield.

SING, men and angels, sing,
For God our Life and King
Has given us light and spring
  And morning breaking.
Now may Man's soul arise
As kinsman to the skies,
And God unseals his eyes
  To an awaking.

2 Sing, creatures, sing; the dust
That lives by lure and lust
  Is kindled by the thrust
    Of life undying;
This hope our Master bare
Has made all fortunes fair,
And Man can on and dare,
    His death defying.

3. After the winter snows
  A wind of healing blows,
And thorns put forth a rose
    And lilies cheer us;
Life's everlasting spring
Hath robbed death of his sting,
Henceforth a cry can bring
    Our Master near us.

(193)

H

166

NOUS ALLONS. (6 5. 6 5. D.)

Moderately fast.

French Carol Melody.

O. B. C.

TAKE heart, friends and neighbours,
  Now it's Eastertide;
Stop from endless labours,
  Worries put aside:
Men should rise from clamour,
  Evil, folly, strife,
When God's ancient glamour
  Brings the earth to life.

2 Bluebell wakes, and lily,
    Roused from drowsy hours;
  Though the wind blows chilly,
    Soon will come the flowers.

Into life he raises
  All the sleeping buds;
Meadows weave his praises,
  And the spangled woods.

3. All his truth and beauty,
    All his righteousness,
  Are our joy and duty,
    Bearing his impress:
  Look! the earth waits breathless
    After winter's strife:
  Easter shows man deathless,
    Spring leads death to life.

167

HILARITER (DIE GANZE WELT). (L.M.)

Rather fast.

Melody from *Cölner Gesangbuch*, 1623.

Hilariter. (*Other occasions also.*)

German, 1623. *Tr. O. B. C.*

THE whole bright world rejoices now,
Hilariter, hilariter;
The birds do sing on every bough,
Alleluya, alleluya!

2 Then shout beneath the racing skies,
Hilariter, hilariter,
To him who rose that we might rise,
Alleluya, alleluya!

3 And all you living things make praise,
Hilariter, hilariter;
He guideth you on all your ways,
Alleluya, alleluya!

4. He, Father, Son, and Holy Ghost,
Hilariter, hilariter,
Our God most high, our joy and boast,
Alleluya, alleluya!

168

SCHEIN (MACH'S MIT MIR GOTT). (8 7. 8 7. 8 8.)

Very slow and solemn.

Later form of melody by J. H. SCHEIN, 1586–1630.

St. John Damascene, c. 750. Tr. J. M. Neale, and others.

Αὕτη ἡ κλητή.

THOU hallowed chosen dawn of praise,
  That best and greatest shinest:
Fair Easter, queen of all the days,
  Of seasons best, divinest!
Christ rose from death; and we adore
For ever and for evermore.

2 Rise, Sion, rise, and looking forth,
  Behold thy children round thee!
From east and west, from south and north,
  Thy scattered sons have found thee,
And in thy bosom Christ adore
For ever and for evermore.

DIES IST DER TAG. (8 7. 8 7. 8 8.)

In moderate time.   Melody by P. SOHREN, *c.* 1668 (rhythm slightly adapted).

3. O ye who bear Christ's holy name,
    Give God all praise and glory:
  All ye who own his power, proclaim
    Aloud the wondrous story!
  The Love, the Wisdom, still adore
  For ever and for evermore.

See also

(197)

EASTER DAY TO TRINITY SUNDAY

169

VRUECHTEN. (6 7. 6 7. D. and refrain.)
In moderate time.

Dutch Melody (17th cent.),
Harmonized by GEOFFREY SHAW, 1879–1943.

(198)

(*And for other Festivals.*)

HOW great the harvest is
  Of him who came to save us!
The hearts of men are his,
  Our law the love he gave us.
The world lay cruel, blind,
  Nought holding, nought divining;
He came to human kind,
  And now the light is shining.

2 And though the news did seem
    Too good for man's believing,
  'Tis not an empty dream
    Too high for our achieving.
  He triumphed in the strife,
    O'er all his foes he towered;
  They killed the Prince of Life,
    But he hath death o'erpowered.

3 Then came the Father's call;
    His work on earth was ended;
  That he might light on all,
    To heaven the Lord ascended.
  To heaven so near to earth,
    Our hearts we do surrender:
  There all things find their worth
    And human life its splendour.

4 The power by which there came
    The Word of God among us
  Was love's eternal flame,
    Whose light and heat are flung us;
  That Spirit sent from God,
    Within our hearts abiding,
  Hath brought us on our road
    And still the world is guiding.

5. *In Three made manifest,
    Thou source of all our being,
  Thou loveliest, truest, best,
    Beyond our power of seeing;
  Thou power of light and love,
    Thou life that never diest—
  To thee in whom all move
    Be glory in the highest.

170

FIRST TUNE

HEATHLANDS. (7 7. 7 7. 7 7.)
In moderate time.

H. SMART, 1813–79.

[This hymn may also be sung to VOLLER WUNDER, 374.]

H. F. *Lyte*, 1793–1847.

GOD of mercy, God of grace,
Show the brightness of thy face:
Shine upon us, Saviour, shine,
Fill thy Church with light divine;
And thy saving health extend
Unto earth's remotest end.

2 Let the people praise thee, Lord;
Be by all that live adored:
Let the nations shout and sing,
Glory to their saviour King;
At thy feet their tributes pay,
And thy holy will obey.

3. Let the people praise thee, Lord;
Earth shall then her fruits afford;
God to man his blessing give,
Man to God devoted live;
All below, and all above,
One in joy, and light, and love.

ROGATIONTIDE

SECOND TUNE

CROYDON. (7 7. 7 7. 7 7.)

In moderate time.

HUBERT J. FOSS.

[*Copyright, 1931, by Oxford University Press.*]

H. F. Lyte, 1793–1847.

GOD of mercy, God of grace,
　Show the brightness of thy face:
Shine upon us, Saviour, shine,
Fill thy Church with light divine;
And thy saving health extend
Unto earth's remotest end.

2 Let the people praise thee, Lord;
Be by all that live adored:
Let the nations shout and sing,
Glory to their saviour King;
At thy feet their tributes pay,
And thy holy will obey.

3. Let the people praise thee, Lord;
Earth shall then her fruits afford;
God to man his blessing give,
Man to God devoted live;
All below, and all above,
One in joy, and light, and love.

171

LINCOLN. (C.M.)
Moderately slow.
Ravenscroft's Psalter, 1621.

ALTERNATIVE VERSION

Melody in the Tenor. Fa-burden by W. HARRISON in *Ravenscroft's Psalter.*

PEOPLE'S PART.

CHOIR OR ORGAN.

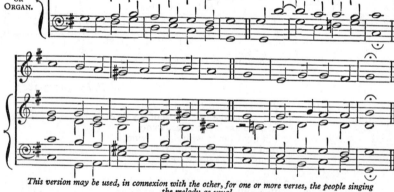

This version may be used, in connexion with the other, for one or more verses, the people singing the melody as usual.

J. Keble,† 1792–1866.

LORD, in thy name thy servants plead,
    And thou hast sworn to hear;
Thine is the harvest, thine the seed,
    The fresh and fading year.

2 Our hope, when autumn winds blew wild,
    We trusted, Lord, with thee;
And still, now spring has on us smiled,
    We wait on thy decree.

3 The former and the latter rain,
    The summer sun and air,
The green ear, and the golden grain,
    Are given us by thy care.

4 Thine too by right, and ours by grace,
    The wondrous growth unseen,
The hopes that soothe, the fears that brace,
    The love that shines serene.

5. So grant the precious things brought forth
    By sun and moon below,
That thee in thy new heaven and earth
    We never may forgo.

See also

630 Prayer is the soul's
4 Spring has now unwrapped

20 Thou art, O God
21 When spring unlocks

172

LYRA (Easter Hymn Original Version). (7 4. 7 4. D.)

Lyra Davidica, 1708.

In moderate time.

[This hymn may also be sung to LLANFAIR, 149.]

C. Wesley,‡ 1707–88.

HAIL the day that sees him rise,   *Alleluya!*
Ravished from their longing eyes;   *Alleluya!*
Christ, awhile to mortals given,   *Alleluya!*
Enters now the highest heaven!   *Alleluya!*

2 There the glorious triumph waits;
Lift your heads, eternal gates!
Wide unfold the radiant scene;
Take the King of Glory in!

3 Him though highest heaven receives,
Still he loves the earth he leaves:
Though returning to his throne,
Still he calls mankind his own.

4. Lord beyond our mortal sight,
Raise our hearts to reach thy height,
There thy face unclouded see,
Find our heaven of heavens in thee.

173

FIRST TUNE

IN BABILONE. (8 7. 8 7. D.)

Dutch Traditional Melody.

SECOND TUNE

REX GLORIAE. (8 7. 8 7. D.)

H. SMART, 1813–79.

ASCENSIONTIDE

[This hymn may also be sung to ALTA TRINITA BEATA, 669.]

Bishop Chr. Wordsworth,‡ 1807–85.

SEE the Conqueror mounts in triumph,
　See him come in royal state,
Like a laurelled king returning
　To his joyful palace gate;
Hark! the choirs of angel voices
　Joyful alleluyas sing,
And the portals wide are opened
　To receive their heavenly King.

2 Who is this that comes in glory
　　With the trump of jubilee?
Over battles, over armies,
　He has gained the victory;
He who on the cross did suffer,
　He who from the grave arose,
He has vanquished sin and Satan,
　He by death has spoiled his foes.

3 Thou hast raised our human nature
　　To the height on God's right hand;
There we sit in heavenly places,
　There with thee in glory stand;
Jesus reigns, adored by angels;
　Man with God is on the throne;
Mighty Lord, in thine ascension
　We by faith behold our own.

4.*Glory be to God the Father;
　　Glory be to God the Son,
Dying, risen, ascending for us,
　Who the heavenly realm has won;
Glory to the Holy Spirit;
　To one God in persons three;
Glory both in earth and heaven,
　Glory, endless glory be.

FIRST TUNE

A - men.

SECOND TUNE

A - men.

(205)

174

PRAETORIUS (FÜR DEIN EMPFANGEN SPEIS UND TRANK). (C.M.)

Moderately slow. Melody from the *Görlitz Gesangbuch*, 1599.

[This hymn may also be sung to ST. DAVID, 301.]

(Other occasions also.) Mrs. C. F. Alexander, 1818–95.

THE eternal gates lift up their heads,
The doors are opened wide,
The King of Glory is gone up
Unto his Father's side.

2 And ever on our earthly path
A gleam of glory lies,
A light still breaks behind the cloud
That veils thee from our eyes.

3 Lift up our hearts, lift up our minds,
And let thy grace be given,
That, while we linger yet below,
Our treasure be in heaven;

4. That, where thou art at God's right hand,
Our hope, our love may be:
Dwell in us now, that we may dwell
For evermore in thee.

175

ST. MAGNUS (NOTTINGHAM). (C.M.)

Moderately slow. Probably by J. CLARK, 1670–1707.

ASCENSIONTIDE

ALTERNATIVE VERSION

Melody in the Tenor.

Fa-burden by GEOFFREY SHAW.

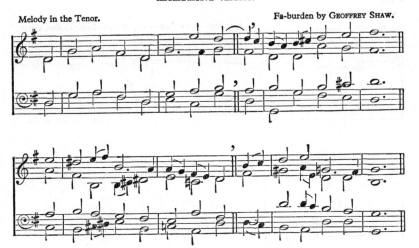

(Other occasions also.)

T. *Kelly*, 1769–1854.

THE head that once was crowned with thorns
  Is crowned with glory now:
A royal diadem adorns
  The mighty victor's brow.

2 The highest place that heaven affords
    Is his, is his by right,
  The King of kings and Lord of lords,
    And heaven's eternal Light;

3 The joy of all who dwell above,
    The joy of all below,
  To whom he manifests his love,
    And grants his name to know.

4 To them the cross, with all its shame,
    With all its grace, is given:
  Their name an everlasting name,
    Their joy the joy of heaven.

5*They suffer with their Lord below,
    They reign with him above,
  Their profit and their joy to know
    The mystery of his love.

6. The cross he bore is life and health,
    Though shame and death to him;
  His people's hope, his people's wealth,
    Their everlasting theme.

(207)

176

OLD 22ND. (D.C.M.)

In moderate time, very dignified. Melody from *Este's Psalter*, 1592 (also in *Day's Psalter*, 1563).

George Wither, 1588–1667.

To God, with heart and cheerful
A triumph song we sing; [voice,
And with true thankful hearts rejoice
In our almighty King;
Yea, to his glory we record,
Who were but dust and clay,
What honour he did us afford
On his ascending day.

2 Each door and everlasting gate
To him hath lifted been;
And in a glorious wise thereat
Our King is entered in;
Whom if to follow we regard,
With ease we safely may,
For he hath all the means prepared,
And made an open way.

3. Then follow, follow on apace,
And let us not forgo
Our Captain, till we win the place
That he hath scaled unto:
And for his honour, let our voice
A shout so hearty make,
The heavens may at our mirth rejoice,
And earth and hell may shake.

See also

177

DOWN AMPNEY. (6 6. 11. D.)

Moderately slow.

R. VAUGHAN WILLIAMS, 1872–1958.

(*Other occasions also.*)   *Bianco da Siena*, d. 1434. *Tr. R. F. Littledale.*

Discendi, Amor santo.

COME down, O Love divine,
  Seek thou this soul of mine,
And visit it with thine own ardour glowing;
  O Comforter, draw near,
  Within my heart appear,
And kindle it, thy holy flame bestowing.

2 O let it freely burn,
   Till earthly passions turn
To dust and ashes in its heat consuming;
   And let thy glorious light
   Shine ever on my sight,
And clothe me round, the while my path illuming.

3 Let holy charity
   Mine outward vesture be,
And lowliness become mine inner clothing;
   True lowliness of heart,
   Which takes the humbler part,
And o'er its own shortcomings weeps with loathing.

4. And so the yearning strong,
    With which the soul will long,
Shall far outpass the power of human telling;
    For none can guess its grace,
    Till he become the place
Wherein the Holy Spirit makes his dwelling.

(209)

178

VENI CREATOR (TALLIS). (L.M.)

Slow.

Attributed to T. TALLIS, c. 1510–85.

Last two lines (to be sung in unison).

Praise to thy e - ter-nal me - rit, Fa - ther, Son, and Ho - ly Spi - rit. A - men.

[This hymn may also be sung to the MECHLIN MELODY, 179, or to ATTWOOD'S MELODY, 181.]

(Other occasions also.)

Bishop J. Cosin, 1594–1672.
Based on Veni, creator Spiritus.

COME, Holy Ghost, our souls inspire,
And lighten with celestial fire;
Thou the anointing Spirit art,
Who dost thy sevenfold gifts impart.

2 Thy blessèd unction from above
Is comfort, life, and fire of love;
Enable with perpetual light
The dullness of our blinded sight.

3 Anoint and cheer our soilèd face
With the abundance of thy grace:
Keep far our foes, give peace at home;
Where thou art guide no ill can come.

4. Teach us to know the Father, Son,
And thee, of both, to be but one;
That through the ages all along
This may be our endless song,
Praise to thy eternal merit,
Father, Son, and Holy Spirit.

179

VENI CREATOR (MECHLIN). (L.M.)

In free rhythm. Unison.

Melody as **given** in *Vesperale Romanum cum cantu emendato*, Mechlin, 1848.

A - men.

[This hymn may also be sung to TALLIS' VENI CREATOR, 178.]

(*Other occasions also.*)

Before 10th cent. Tr. R. Bridges.

Veni, creator Spiritus.

COME, O creator Spirit, come,
And make within our hearts thy home;
To us thy grace celestial give,
Who of thy breathing move and live.

2 O Paraclete, that name is thine,
Of God most high the gift divine;
The well of life, the fire of love,
Our souls' anointing from above.

3 Thou dost appear in sevenfold dower
The sign of God's almighty power;
The Father's promise, making rich
With saving truth our earthly speech.

4 Our senses with thy light inflame,
Our hearts to heavenly love reclaim;
Our bodies' poor infirmity
With strength perpetual fortify.

5*Our mortal foe afar repel,
Grant us henceforth in peace to dwell;
And so to us, with thee for guide,
No ill shall come, no harm betide.

6.*May we by thee the Father learn,
And know the Son, and thee discern,
Who art of both; and thus adore
In perfect faith for evermore.

180

THE GOLDEN SEQUENCE.

In free rhythm.

Melody from the *Sarum Gradual.*

1. Come, thou ho - ly Par - a - clete, And from thy ce - les - tial seat
Fa - ther of the poor, draw near; Giv - er of all gifts, be here;

Send thy light and bril - lian - cy: 2. Come, of com - for - ters the best,
Come, the soul's true ra - dian - cy. Thou in la - bour rest most sweet,

Of the soul the sweet - est guest, Come in toil re - fresh - ing - ly:
Thou art sha - dow from the heat, Comfort in ad - ver - si - ty.

3. O thou light, most pure and blest, Shine with - in the in - most breast
Where thou art not, man hath nought; Ev - 'ry ho - ly deed and thought

Of thy faith - ful com - pa - ny: 4. What is soil - èd, make thou pure;
Comes from thy di - vi - ni - ty. What is ri - gid, gent - ly bend;

What is wound - ed, work its cure; What is parch - èd, fruc - ti - fy;
What is fro - zen, warm - ly tend; Strengthen what goes err - ing - ly.

5. Fill thy faith - ful, who con - fide In thy power to guard and guide;

With thy seven-fold mys - te - ry. Here thy grace and vir - tue send;

Grant sal - va - tion in the end, And in heaven fe - li - ci - ty.

13th cent.   *Tr. J. M. Neale.*

180 (*continued*)   SECOND TUNE

VENI SANCTE SPIRITUS. (7 7 7. D.)

Moderately slow.   S. WEBBE the elder, 1740–1816.

The Golden Sequence.   13th cent. Tr. *J. M. Neale.*

Veni, sancte Spiritus.

COME, thou holy Paraclete,
And from thy celestial seat
　Send thy light and brilliancy:
Father of the poor, draw near;
Giver of all gifts, be here;
　Come, the soul's true radiancy.

2 Come, of comforters the best,
Of the soul the sweetest guest,
　Come in toil refreshingly:
Thou in labour rest most sweet,
Thou art shadow from the heat,
　Comfort in adversity.

3 O thou light, most pure and blest,
Shine within the inmost breast
　Of thy faithful company:

Where thou art not, man hath nought;
Every holy deed and thought
　Comes from thy divinity.

4*What is soilèd, make thou pure;
What is wounded, work its cure;
　What is parchèd, fructify;
What is rigid, gently bend;
What is frozen, warmly tend;
　Strengthen what goes erringly.

5.*Fill thy faithful, who confide
In thy power to guard and guide,
　With thy sevenfold mystery.
Here thy grace and virtue send:
Grant salvation in the end,
　And in heaven felicity.

181

VENI, CREATOR (ATTWOOD). (8 8. 8 8. 8 8.)

Moderately slow.   T. ATTWOOD, 1765–1838.

A-men.

(*Other occasions also.*)   J. Dryden, 1631–1700. *Based on* Veni, creator Spiritus.

CREATOR Spirit, by whose aid
 The world's foundations first were laid,
Come, visit every pious mind;
Come, pour thy joys on human kind;
From sin and sorrow set us free,
And make thy temples worthy thee.

2 O source of uncreated light,
The Father's promised Paraclete,
Thrice holy fount, thrice holy fire,
Our hearts with heavenly love inspire;
Come, and thy sacred unction bring
To sanctify us while we sing.

3 Plenteous of grace, descend from high
Rich in thy sevenfold energy;
Make us eternal truths receive,
And practise all that we believe;
Give us thyself, that we may see
The Father and the Son by thee.

4.*Immortal honour, endless fame,
Attend the almighty Father's name;
The saviour Son be glorified,
Who for lost man's redemption died;
And equal adoration be,
Eternal Paraclete, to thee.

182

WICKLOW. (8 6. 8 4.)

In moderate time.

Irish Traditional Melody (slightly adapted).

(Other occasions also.)

Harriet Auber, 1773–1862.

OUR blest Redeemer, ere he breathed
  His tender last farewell,
A guide, a comforter, bequeathed
  With us to dwell.

2 He came in tongues of living flame,
  To teach, convince, subdue;
All-powerful as the wind he came,
  As viewless too.

3 He came sweet influence to impart,
  A gracious, willing guest,
While he can find one humble heart
  Wherein to rest.

4 And his that gentle voice we hear,
  Soft as the breath of even,   [fear,
That checks each fault, that calms each
  And speaks of heaven.

5 And every virtue we possess,
  And every victory won,
And every thought of holiness,
  Are his alone.

6. Spirit of purity and grace,
  Our weakness, pitying, see:
O make our hearts thy dwelling-place,
  And worthier thee.

183

FORTEM VIRILI PECTORE. (7 7. 7 7. D.)

In moderate time, with vigour.

German melody, Strasbourg, 1697.

(Other occasions also.)

F. C. Burkitt, 1864–1935.

OUR Lord, his Passion ended,
    Hath gloriously ascended,
Yet though from him divided,
He leaves us not unguided;
    All his benefits to crown
    He hath sent his Spirit down,
    Burning like a flame of fire
    His disciples to inspire.

2 God's Spirit is directing,
No more they sit expecting,
But forth to all the nation
They go with exultation;

That which God in them hath
    wrought
Fills their life and soul and thought,
So their witness now can do
Work as great in others too.

3. The centuries go gliding,
    But still we have abiding
    With us that Spirit holy
    To make us brave and lowly—
        Lowly, for we feel our need,
        God alone is strong indeed;
        Brave, for with the Spirit's aid
        We can venture unafraid.

184

O JESU MI DULCISSIME. (L.M.)

Moderately slow.

Melody from the *Clausener Gesangbuch*, 1653.

[This hymn may also be sung to RICHARD, 25, or MELCOMBE, 31.

Foundling Hospital Collection (1774).

SPIRIT of mercy, truth, and love,
    Shed thy blest influence from above,
And still from age to age convey
The wonders of this sacred day.

2 In every clime, in every tongue,
Be God's eternal praises sung;
Through all the listening earth be taught
The acts our great Redeemer wrought.

3. Unfailing Comfort, heavenly Guide,
Over thy favoured Church preside;
Still may mankind thy blessings prove,
Spirit of mercy, truth, and love.

WHITSUNTIDE

185

STROUDWATER. (C.M.)

Moderately slow.

The Psalter in Metre, 1899.
Attributed there to *Wilkins' Psalmody* (c. 1750).

(Other occasions also.)

B. R.

WHEN Christ had shown God's dawning Reign,
His Spirit came to lead,
That unto truth we might attain
And all the world be freed.

2 So, when with one accord combined
The friends of Jesus came,
They heard God's Spirit like a wind,
They saw it like a flame;

3 And they who sat within the walls
With strange new ardour blazed;
Their voices rang like trumpet calls,
And men thronged up amazed.

4 Greater than stars that swim in space,
More real than time or tide,
Is God's unseen compelling grace
Man's boundless thought to guide.

5. So urge, O Lord, our wills to-day,
Grant us the Hope divine;
Fire us with zeal; show us the way
To fill thy vast design.

(For a Doxology see 416.)

TRINITY SUNDAY

186

FIRST TUNE

PLAINSONG. (11 11. 11 5.)
In free rhythm.

Melody from the Sarum Antiphonal.

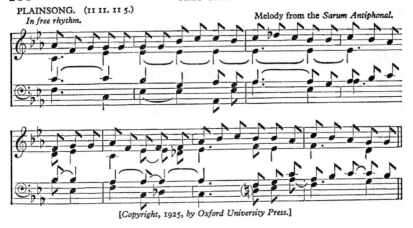

[*Copyright, 1925, by Oxford University Press.*]

SECOND TUNE

HERR, DEINEN ZORN. (11 11. 11 5.)
In moderate time, not too fast.

Later form of melody by J. CRÜGER, 1598–1662.

[This hymn may also be sung to CHRISTE FONS JUGIS, 281.]

O Pater sancte.   *c. 10th cent. Tr. E. H.*

FATHER most holy, merciful and tender;
  Jesus our Saviour, with the Father reigning;
Spirit all-kindly, advocate, defender,
    Light never waning;

2 Trinity sacred, Unity unshaken;
   Deity perfect, giving and forgiving,
Light of the angels, Life of the forsaken,
    Hope of all living;

3 Maker of all things, all thy creatures praise thee;
   Lo, all things serve thee through thy whole creation:
Hear us, Almighty, hear us, as we raise thee
    Heart's adoration.

4. To the all-ruling triune God be glory:
   Highest and greatest, help thou our endeavour,
We too would praise thee, giving honour worthy,
    Now and for ever.

(219)

187.

FIRST TUNE

NICAEA. (11 12. 12 10.)   J. B. DYKES, 1823–76.

NOTE.—*This hymn is marked to be sung at a much slower rate than usual: it may, if preferred, be sung at the more usual rate of* ♩ = 63 *and the pauses may be omitted.*

Bishop R. Heber, 1783–1826.

HOLY, holy, holy! Lord God Almighty!
Early in the morning our song shall rise to thee;
Holy, holy, holy! Merciful and mighty;
God in three persons, blessèd Trinity!

2 Holy, holy, holy! All the saints adore thee,
Casting down their golden crowns around the glassy sea;
Cherubim and seraphim falling down before thee,
Which wert, and art, and evermore shalt be.

TRINITY SUNDAY

BROMLEY COMMON. (11 12. 12 10.)

In moderate time. Unison.

MARTIN SHAW, 187-1958.

[*Copyright, 1915, by J. Curwen & Sons, Ltd.*]

3 Holy, holy, holy! Though the darkness hide thee,
Though the eye of sinful man thy glory may not see,
Only thou art holy, there is none beside thee
Perfect in power, in love, and purity.

4. Holy, holy, holy! Lord God Almighty!
All thy works shall praise thy name, in earth, and sky, and sea;
Holy, holy, holy! Merciful and mighty!
God in three persons, blessèd Trinity!

188

ST. FLAVIAN. (C.M.)

Moderately slow.

Adapted from Psalm 132 in *Day's Psalter*, 1563.

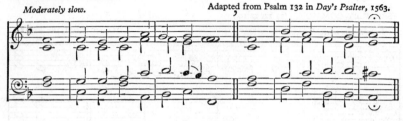

F. W. Faber, 1814-63.

MOST ancient of all mysteries,
Before thy throne we lie;
Have mercy now, most merciful,
Most holy Trinity.

2 When heaven and earth were yet unmade,
When time was yet unknown,
Thou in thy bliss and majesty
Didst live and love alone.

3 Thou wert not born; there was no fount
From which thy being flowed;
There is no end which thou canst reach
But thou art simply God.

4 How wonderful creation is,
The work which thou didst bless,
And O what then must thou be like,
Eternal loveliness!

5 O listen then, most pitiful,
To thy poor creature's heart:
It blesses thee that thou art God,
That thou art what thou art.

6.*Most ancient of all mysteries,
Still at thy throne we lie:
Have mercy now, most merciful,
Most holy Trinity.

TRINITY SUNDAY

ALTERNATIVE VERSION

Fa-burden by T. RAVENSCROFT in his Psalter, 1621
(rhythm slightly adapted).

Melody in the Tenor.

*This version may be used in connexion with the other for one or more verses,
the people singing the melody as usual.*

See also

See also Part VIII, Doxologies.

189

FIRST TUNE

BUCKLEBURY. (D.L.M.) From *Harmonia Perfecta* (1730), arranged by ALAN GRAY.
In moderate time.

SECOND TUNE

ALFRETON. (L.M.)
In moderate time.
Supplement to the New Version, 1708.

Dedication or Restoration of a Church.
J. G. Whittier, 1807–92.

ALL things are thine; no gift have we,
Lord of all gifts, to offer thee:
And hence with grateful hearts to-day
Thine own before thy feet we lay.

2 Thy will was in the builders' thought;
Thy hand unseen amidst us wrought;
Through mortal motive, scheme and plan,
Thy wise eternal purpose ran.

3 In weakness and in want we call
On thee for whom the heavens are small;
Thy glory is thy children's good,
Thy joy thy tender fatherhood.

4. O Father, deign these walls to bless;
Fill with thy love their emptiness;
And let their door a gateway be
To lead us from ourselves to thee.

190

PLAINSONG. (8 7. 8 7. 8 7.)

FIRST TUNE

In free rhythm.

Melody from the *Sarum Antiphonal.*

[*Copyright, 1925, by Oxford University Press.*]

ORIEL. (8 7. 8 7. 8 7.)

SECOND TUNE

In moderate time.

C. ETT, *Cantica Sacra,* 1840.

(*A descant to this tune will be found at 683.*)

Dedication Festival. c. 7th cent. Tr. J. M. Neale.‡

Urbs beata Jerusalem.

BLESSÈD city, heavenly Salem,
　Vision dear of peace and love,
Who, of living stones upbuilded,
Art the joy of heaven above,
And, with angel cohorts circled,
　As a bride to earth dost move!

2 From celestial realms descending,
　Bridal glory round her shed,
To his presence, decked with jewels,
　By her Lord shall she be led:
All her streets, and all her bulwarks,
　Of pure gold are fashionèd.

3 Bright with pearls her portals glitter,
　They are open evermore;
And, by virtue of his merits,
　Thither faithful souls may soar
Who for Christ's dear name in this world
　Pain and tribulation bore.

4 Many a blow and biting sculpture
　Fashioned well those stones elect,
In their places now compacted
　By the heavenly architect,
Who therewith hath willed for ever
　That his palace should be decked.

PART II

5 Christ is made the sure foundation,
　And the precious corner-stone,
Who, the two walls underlying,
　Bound in each, binds both in one,
Holy Sion's help for ever,
　And her confidence alone.

6 All that dedicated city,
　Dearly loved by God on high,
In exultant jubilation
　Pours perpetual melody:
God the One, and God the trinal,
　Singing everlastingly.

7 To this temple, where we call thee,
　Come, O Lord of Hosts, to-day;
With thy wonted loving-kindness
　Hear thy people as they pray;
And thy fullest benediction
　Shed within its walls for ay.

Doxology after either Part

8. Laud and honour to the Father;
　Laud and honour to the Son;
Laud and honour to the Spirit;
　Ever three and ever One:
Consubstantial, co-eternal,
　While unending ages run.

FIRST TUNE

SECOND TUNE

191

OLD 117TH.   (8 8. 8 8. 8 8.)

Moderately slow, dignified.

Melody in the *Genevan Psalter*, 1551
(as given in the *Scottish Psalter*, 1635).

[*May be sung throughout in unison.*]

G. *Tersteegen*, 1697–1769. *Tr. J. Wesley.*‡

Gott ist gegenwärtig.

LO, God is here! Let us adore
    And own how solemn is this place!
Let all within us feel his power,
    And silent bow before his face;
Who know his power, his grace who prove,
Serve him with awe, with reverence love.

2. Lo, God is here! Him day and night
    The united choirs of angels sing;
To him, enthroned above all height,
    Heaven's hosts their noblest praises bring;
To him may all our thoughts arise,
    In never-ceasing sacrifice.

192

EATINGTON. (C.M.)

W. CROFT, 1678–1727.

[This hymn may also be sung to RODMELL, 221.]

Commemoration or Anniversary.

F. L. Hosmer, 1840–1929.

O LIGHT, from age to age the same,
　O ever-living Word,
Here have we felt thy kindling flame,
　Thy voice within have heard.

2 Here holy thought and hymn and prayer
　Have winged the spirit's powers,
And made these walls divinely fair,
　Thy temple, Lord, and ours.

3 What visions rise above the years;
　What tender memories throng!
Till each eye fills with happy tears,
　Each heart with happy song.

4 Vanish the mists of time and sense;
　They come, the loved of yore,
And one encircling providence
　Holds all for evermore.

5 O not in vain their toil, who wrought
　To build faith's freer shrine;
Nor theirs, whose steadfast love and thought
　Have watched the fire divine.

6. Burn, holy Fire, and shine more wide!
　While systems rise and fall,
Faith, hope, and charity abide,
　The heart and soul of all.

192

FIRST TUNE

CAERLLEON. (7 6. 7 6. D.)
Dignified.

Welsh Hymn Melody, harmonized by DAVID EVANS, 1874–1948.

SECOND TUNE

ELLACOMBE. (7 6. 7 6. D.)
Brightly.

Mainz Gesangbuch, 1833.

[This hymn may also be sung to CHRISTUS DER IST MEIN LEBEN, 585.]

The Builders. (*Other occasions also.*)   *Geoffrey Dearmer.*

SING, all good people gathered;
  Your voices raise in song
Within this church that fathered
  Our ancient faith so strong,
So tried and wrought to fitness
  In scorn of fire and sword;
Sing, as these stones bear witness,
  Of men who praised the Lord.

2*Each rib from pillars springing
  A frozen fountain plays,
Above the chancel singing
  In harmony of praise;
Like tall trees ever growing
  The differing columns stand
To bear the vault down-throwing
  The shadow of God's hand.

3*At all times and unceasing,
  Work well and truly done,
In loveliness increasing
  Has mellowed here in one;
The towers and piers unshaken,
  The vaulting finely groined,
Time in his span hath taken
  And in one glory joined.

4 Of wealth and fame and power
    Those masons did not know:
'Let 's build', they said, 'a tower,
    Square to the winds that blow;
We are not men of culture,
    Yet we are here to build
Room for a king's sepulture
    And worthy of our guild.'

5 So came each beam and rafter,
    Each wingèd flight of stone.
Their deathless work lives after,
    Their names were never known:
For beauty did they plead not,
    Yet beauty they did win,
And, like a child you heed not,
    The grace of heaven crept in.

6*Here, for a workman's wages,
    This glass so surely stained
Down the long aisles of ages
    In glory has remained.
As brother works with brother,
    The glaziers worked to paint
The blue robe of the mother,
    The red robe of the saint.

7. Proud heads lie here, disowning
    All but a drooping Head;
Whole hands worked here, atoning
    For open Hands that bled;
Full hearts and living voices
    A broken Heart proclaim;
Life after death rejoices,
    And after silence, fame.

194

FIRST TUNE

DANK SEI GOTT IN DER HÖHE. (7 6. 7 6. D.)
Very slow and dignified.

Melody in J. S. BACH's *Vierstimmige*
Choralgesänge (1769) (founded on GESIUS' *Geduld die soll'n wir haben*).

Church, College, or School Commemoration.

G. W. Briggs, 1875–1959.

OUR Father, by whose servants
    Our house was built of old,
Whose hand hath crowned her children
    With blessings manifold,
For thine unfailing mercies
    Far-strewn along our way,
With all who passed before us,
    We praise thy name to-day.

2 The changeful years unresting
    Their silent course have sped,
New comrades ever bringing
    In comrades' steps to tread;
And some are long forgotten,
    Long spent their hopes and fears;
Safe rest they in thy keeping,
    Who changest not with years.

SECOND TUNE

LOUGHBOROUGH. (7 6. 7 6. D.)

In moderate time.

G. W. BRIGGS, 1875–1959.

[*Copyright, 1925, by Oxford University Press.*]

3 They reap not where they laboured,
    We reap what they have sown;
  Our harvest may be garnered
    By ages yet unknown.
  The days of old have dowered us
    With gifts beyond all praise:
  Our Father, make us faithful
    To serve the coming days.

4. Before us and beside us,
    Still holden in thine hand,
  A cloud unseen of witness,
    Our elder comrades stand:
  One family unbroken,
    We join, with one acclaim,
  One heart, one voice uplifting,
    To glorify thy name.

See also

464 Christ is our corner-stone
470 Come, kindred
495 For the might of thine arm

592 Now join, ye comrades true
602 O life that makest all things new
640 Sing praise to God

And also Part V, Thanksgiving.

PART III

THE COMMUNION OF SAINTS

THE CHURCH IN HEAVEN

195

OLD 25TH. (D.S.M.)

In moderate time.   *Day's Psalter*, 1565 (rhythm slightly adapted).

J. Montgomery, 1771–1854.

'FOR ever with the Lord!'
　Amen; so let it be;
Life from the dead is in that word;
　'Tis immortality.
Here in the body pent,
　Absent from him I roam,
Yet nightly pitch my moving tent
　A day's march nearer home.

2＊My Father's house on high,
　Home of my soul, how near
At times to faith's foreseeing eye
　Thy golden gates appear!
Ah, then my spirit faints
　To reach the land I love,
The bright inheritance of saints,
　Jerusalem above.

3 'For ever with the Lord!'
　Father, if 'tis thy will,
The promise of that faithful word
　E'en here to me fulfil.
Be thou at my right hand,
　Then can I never fail;
Uphold thou me, and I shall stand;
　Fight, and I must prevail.

4. So when my latest breath
　Shall rend the veil in twain,
By death I shall escape from death,
　And life eternal gain.
Knowing as I am known,
　How shall I love that word,
And oft repeat before the throne,
　'For ever with the Lord!'

196

DOORKEEPER. (Irreg.)

In moderate time.

MARTIN SHAW, 1875-1958.

1. I would choose to be a door-keep-er In the
2. Of all troop in not one comes out From the
3. They come with shin-ing fa-ces To the
4. There are li - lies and dai-sies In the
5.* I would be a hum-ble door-keep-er In the

House of the Lord, Rath-er than lords and
House of the Lord, Those who have won from
House of the Lord; The bro - ken hearts and
House of the Lord. The lov - er finds his
House of the Lord, Where the courts are white and

la - dies In sa-tin on the sward. To
sin and death, From age and grief ab-horred. There is
wea - ry That life has racked and scored: They come
lo - ver With a long, long re-gard. The
shin - ing In the light of the Word. When the

draw the bolts for the white souls Would be my rich re-
more room . with - in its courts Than pa - la - ces af -
hur - ry - ing . and sing - ing To sit down at his
mo - thers find . the chil - dren, Strayed from their watch and
saved souls come troop - ing For the gates to be un-

- ward: And I the hap - py doorkeep - er To the House of the Lord.
- ford; So great it is and spa - cious In the House of the Lord.
board, They are young and they are joy - ful In the House of the Lord.
ward. O the meet - ings and the greet - ings In the House of the Lord!
- barred, O bless - ed is the doorkeep - er In the House of the Lord!

[Copyright, 1931, by Martin Shaw.]

Katherine Tynan Hinkson, 1859–1931.

I WOULD choose to be a doorkeeper
  In the House of the Lord,
Rather than lords and ladies
  In satin on the sward.
To draw the bolts for the white souls
  Would be my rich reward:
And I the happy doorkeeper
  To the House of the Lord.

2 Of all troop in not one comes out
  From the House of the Lord,
Those who have won from sin and
      death,
  From age and grief abhorred.
There is more room within its courts
  Than palaces afford;
So great it is and spacious
  In the House of the Lord.

3 They come with shining faces
  To the House of the Lord;
The broken hearts and weary
  That life has racked and scored:

They come hurrying and singing
  To sit down at his board,
They are young and they are joyful
  In the House of the Lord.

4 There are lilies and daisies
  In the House of the Lord.
The lover finds his lover
  With a long, long regard.
The mothers find the children,
  Strayed from their watch and ward.
O the meetings and the greetings
  In the House of the Lord!

5.*I would be a humble doorkeeper
  In the House of the Lord,
Where the courts are white and shining
  In the light of the Word.
When the saved souls come trooping
  For the gates to be unbarred,
O blessèd is the doorkeeper
  In the House of the Lord!

(237)

197

FIRST TUNE

OLD 136TH.   (6 6. 6 6. 8 8.)

In moderate time.

Este's Psalter, 1592.

Samuel Crossman,‡ c. 1624–83.

JERUSALEM on high
  My song and city is,
My home whene'er I die,
  The centre of my bliss:
    O happy place! when shall I be,
    My God, with thee, to see thy face!

2 There dwells my Lord, my King,
  Judged here unfit to live;
There angels to him sing,
  And lowly homage give:

3 The prophets I might hear,
  The mighty men of old;
The Lord's apostles there
  I might with joy behold:

4 The bleeding martyrs, they
  Within those courts are found,
Clothèd in pure array,
  Their scars with glory crowned:

5.*Ah me! ah me! that I
  In Kedar's tents here stay;
No place like that on high;
  Lord, thither guide my way:

THE CHURCH IN HEAVEN

SECOND TUNE

CHRISTCHURCH. (6 6. 6 6. 8 8.)

Moderately fast.

C. STEGGALL, 1826–1905.

ALTERNATIVE VERSION

Trebles sing the top line, all other voices the melody CHRISTCHURCH.   Descant by ALAN GRAY.

(239)

198

EWING. (7 6. 7 6. D.)

In moderate time.

Later form of melody by A. EWING, 1830–95.

Part of Hora novissima.　　　　　*Bernard of Cluny, 12th cent. Tr. J. M. Neale.*

JERUSALEM the golden,
　With milk and honey blest,
Beneath thy contemplation
　Sink heart and voice opprest.
I know not, O I know not,
　What social joys are there,
What radiancy of glory,
　What light beyond compare.

2 They stand, those halls of Sion,
　Conjubilant with song,
And bright with many an angel,
　And all the martyr throng;
The Prince is ever with them,
　The daylight is serene,
The pastures of the blessèd
　Are decked in glorious sheen.

(240)

THE CHURCH IN HEAVEN

SECOND TUNE

PEARSALL. (7 6. 7 6. D.)

In moderate time.

R. L. DE PEARSALL, 1795–1856.

3*There is the throne of David,
  And there, from care released,
The song of them that triumph,
  The shout of them that feast;
And they who, with their Leader,
  Have conquered in the fight,
For ever and for ever
  Are clad in robes of white.

4. O sweet and blessèd country,
  Shall I ever see thy face?
O sweet and blessèd country,
  Shall I ever win thy grace?
Exult, O dust and ashes!
  The Lord shall be thy part:
His only, his for ever,
  Thou shalt be, and thou art!

See also
459 Brief life is here our portion

(241)

THE CHURCH IN HEAVEN

199

TANTUM ERGO (WEBBE). (8 7. 8 7. 8 7.)

Moderately slow, dignified.   Melody from S. WEBBE's *Motetts or Antiphons*, 1792

A-men.

ALTERNATIVE VERSION

Trebles sing the top line, all other voices the melody TANTUM ERGO.

Descant by ALAN GRAY.

THE CHURCH IN HEAVEN

[This hymn may also be sung to the PLAINSONG MELODY at 190.]

15th century. Tr. J. M. Neale.

Jerusalem luminosa.

LIGHT'S abode, celestial Salem,
  Vision dear whence peace doth spring,
Brighter than the heart can fancy,
  Mansion of the highest King;
O how glorious are the praises
  Which of thee the prophets sing!

2 There for ever and for ever
  Alleluya is outpoured;
For unending, for unbroken
  Is the feast-day of the Lord;
All is pure and all is holy
  That within thy walls is stored.

3*O how glorious and resplendent,
  Fragile body, shalt thou be,
When endued with so much beauty,
  Full of health, and strong, and free,
Full of vigour, full of pleasure
  That shall last eternally.

4 Now with gladness, now with courage,
  Bear the burden on thee laid,
That hereafter these thy labours
  May with endless gifts be paid,
And in everlasting glory
  Thou with joy may'st be arrayed.

5. Laud and honour to the Father,
  Laud and honour to the Son,
Laud and honour to the Spirit,
  Ever Three and ever One,
Consubstantial, co-eternal,
  While unending ages run.

REGNATOR ORBIS.   (10 10. 10 10.)

In moderate time. Unison.

Paris Antiphoner, 1681.

A-men.

ALTERNATIVE VERSION

Trebles (all other voices singing the melody REGNATOR ORBIS).

Descant by HAROLD E. DARKE.

THE CHURCH IN HEAVEN

Peter Abelard, 1079–1142. Tr. J. M. Neale.

O quanta qualia sunt illa sabbata.

O WHAT their joy and their glory must be,
   Those endless sabbaths the blessèd ones see!
Crown for the valiant; to weary ones rest;
God shall be all, and in all ever blest.

2 Truly Jerusalem name we that shore,
   'Vision of peace,' that brings joy evermore!
Wish and fulfilment can severed be ne'er,
Nor the thing prayed for come short of the prayer.

3 We, where no trouble distraction can bring,
   Safely the anthems of Sion shall sing;
While for thy grace, Lord, their voices of praise
Thy blessèd people shall evermore raise.

4. Low before him with our praises we fall,
   Of whom, and in whom, and through whom are all;
Of whom the Father; and through whom the Son;
In whom, the Spirit, with these ever one.

201

MENDIP. (C.M.)

In moderate time

English Traditional Melody.

I. Watts, 1674–1748.

THERE is a land of pure delight,
   Where saints immortal reign;
Infinite day excludes the night,
   And pleasures banish pain.

2 There everlasting spring abides,
   And never-withering flowers;
Death, like a narrow sea, divides
   This heavenly land from ours.

3 Sweet fields beyond the swelling flood
   Stand dressed in living green;
So to the Jews old Canaan stood,
   While Jordan rolled between.

4 But timorous mortals start and shrink
   To cross this narrow sea,
And linger shivering on the brink,
   And fear to launch away.

5*O could we make our doubts remove,
   These gloomy doubts that rise,
And see the Canaan that we love
   With unbeclouded eyes!

6. Could we but climb where Moses stood,
   And view the landscape o'er,
Not Jordan's stream, nor death's cold flood,
   Should fright us from the shore!

See also
247 Sing alleluya

(245)

THE SAINTS

202

SINE NOMINE. (10 10. 10. 4.)

Verses 1, 2, 3, and 7, 8.

In moderate time. Voices in Unison.

R. VAUGHAN WILLIAMS, 1872–1958.

(small notes vv. 2, 8.)

Harmony.

A-men.

Bishop W. W. How, 1823–97.

FOR all the saints who from their labours rest,
Who thee by faith before the world confest,
Thy name, O Jesus, be for ever blest:
        Alleluya!

2 Thou wast their rock, their fortress, and their might;
Thou, Lord, their captain in the well-fought fight;
Thou in the darkness drear their one true light:

3 O may thy soldiers, faithful, true, and bold,
Fight as the saints who nobly fought of old,
And win, with them, the victor's crown of gold:

4*O blest communion! fellowship divine!
We feebly struggle, they in glory shine;
Yet all are one in thee, for all are thine:

(246)

THE SAINTS

Harmony. Verses 4, 5, and 6.

(small notes v. 6.)

NOTE.—*Verses 4 and 6 may be sung by the* CHOIR ALONE.

5 And when the strife is fierce, the warfare long,
  Steals on the ear the distant triumph-song,
  And hearts are brave again, and arms are strong:

6 The golden evening brightens in the west;
  Soon, soon to faithful warriors cometh rest;
  Sweet is the calm of paradise the blest:

7*But lo! there breaks a yet more glorious day;
  The saints triumphant rise in bright array:
  The King of Glory passes on his way:

8.*From earth's wide bounds, from ocean's farthest coast,
  Through gates of pearl streams in the countless host,
  Singing to Father, Son, and Holy Ghost:

(247)

203

MOUNT EPHRAIM. (S.M.)
Slow.

B. MILGROVE, 1731–1810.

A - men.

[This hymn may also be sung to ST. MICHAEL, 702.]

Bp. R. Mant,† 1776–1848.

FOR thy dear saint, O Lord,
  Who strove in thee to live,
Who followed thee, obeyed, adored,
  Our grateful hymn receive.

2 For all thy saints, O Lord,
  Accept our thankful cry,
Who counted thee their great reward,
  And strove in thee to die.

3 They all in life and death,
  With thee their Lord in view,

Learned from thy Holy Spirit's breath
  To suffer and to do.

4 For this thy name we bless,
  And humbly beg that we
May follow them in holiness,
  And live and die in thee;

5.* With them the Father, Son,
  And Holy Ghost to praise,
As in the ancient days was done,
  And shall through endless days.

204

SONG 67. (C.M.)
In moderate time.

Melody by ORLANDO GIBBONS, 1583–1625.

I. Watts, 1674-1748.

GIVE me the wings of faith to rise
  Within the veil, and see
The saints above, how great their joys,
  How bright their glories be.

2 Once they were mourning here below,
  And wet their couch with tears;
They wrestled hard, as we do now,
  With sins and doubts and fears.

3 I ask them whence their victory came;
  They, with united breath,

Ascribe their conquest to the Lamb,
  Their triumph to his death.

4 They marked the footsteps that he trod,
  His zeal inspired their breast,
And, following their incarnate God,
  Possess the promised rest.

5.*Our glorious Leader claims our praise
  For his own pattern given;
While the long cloud of witnesses
  Show the same path to heaven.

205

DORKING. (C.M.)

[This hymn may also be sung to BROMSGROVE, 23.]

J. Austin,‡ 1613-69.

HAIL, glorious spirits, heirs of light,
  The high-born sons of fire,
Whose souls burn clear, whose flames
    shine bright;
  All joy, yet all desire.

2 Hail, holy saints, who long in hope,
  Long in the shadow sate,
Till our victorious Lord set ope
  Heaven's everlasting gate.

3 Hail, all ye prophets of the Name,
  Who brought that early ray,
Which from our Sun reflected came,
  And made our first fair day.

4. Hail, all you happy souls above,
  Who make that glorious ring
About the sparkling throne of love,
  And there for ever sing.

206

VISION. (8 7. 8 7. D.)
Moderately fast.

S. MASON.

[This hymn may also be sung to IN BABILONE, 173.]

THE SAINTS

Bishop Chr. Wordsworth,† 1807-85.

HARK the sound of holy voices,
　　Chanting at the crystal sea,
Alleluya, alleluya,
　　Alleluya, Lord, to thee!
Multitude, which none can number,
　　Like the stars in glory stands,
Clothed in white apparel, holding
　　Palms of victory in their hands.

2 Patriarch, and holy prophet,
　　Who prepared the way of Christ,
King, apostle, saint, confessor,
　　Martyr, and evangelist,
Saintly maiden, godly matron,
　　Widows who have watched to prayer,
Joined in holy concert, singing
　　To the Lord of all, are there.

3 Marching with thy cross their banner,
　　They have triumphed following
Thee, the captain of salvation,
　　Thee, their saviour and their king;
Gladly, Lord, with thee they suffered;
　　Gladly, Lord, with thee they died,
And by death to life immortal
　　They were born, and glorified.

4*Now they reign in heavenly glory,
　　Now they walk in golden light,
Now they drink, as from a river,
　　Holy bliss and infinite;
Love and peace they taste for ever,
　　And all truth and knowledge see
In the beatific vision
　　Of the blessèd Trinity.

5. God of God, the one-begotten
　　Light of light, Emmanuel,
In whose body joined together
　　All the saints for ever dwell;
Pour upon us of thy fullness,
　　That we may for evermore
God the Father, God the Spirit,
　　One with thee on high, adore.

A - men.

207

BALLERMA. (C.M.)
In moderate time.

Probably by F. H. BARTHÉLÉMON (1741–1808).

I. Watts, 1674–1748, and others, 18th cent.

HOW bright these glorious spirits shine!
  Whence all their white array?
How came they to the blissful seats
  Of everlasting day?

2 Lo, these are they from sufferings great
  Who came to realms of light,
And by the grace of Christ have won
  Those robes that shine so bright.

3 Now with triumphal palms they stand
  Before the throne on high,
And serve the God they love amidst
  The glories of the sky.

4 Hunger and thirst are felt no more,
  Nor sun with scorching ray;
God is their sun, whose cheering beams
  Diffuse eternal day.

5*The Lamb, which dwells amid the throne,
  Shall o'er them still preside,
Feed them with nourishment divine,
  And all their footsteps guide.

6. In pastures green he'll lead his flock
  Where living streams appear;
And God the Lord from every eye
  Shall wipe off every tear.

208

PSALM 93. (10 10. 10 10.)
Moderately slow.

Melody from *Gevevan Psalter* (1562).
Harmony adapted from C. GOUDIMEL (d. 1572).

R. *Bridges*, 1844–1930.

REJOICE, ye dead, where'er your spirits dwell;
   Rejoice that yet on earth your fame is bright,
   And that your names, remembered day and night,
Live on the lips of those who love you well.

2. 'Tis ye that conquered have the powers of hell,
   Each with the special grace of your delight:
   Ye are the world's creators, and through might
Of everlasting love ye did excel.

209

MONK'S MARCH. (Irreg.)

In moderate time. Voices in Unison.

Welsh Traditional Melody.

1. What are these that glow from a - far,
2. What are these that fly as a cloud, With
3. *Light a - bove light, and bliss be - yond bliss, Whom
4. God the Fa - ther give us grace To

These that lean o - ver the gold - en bar,
flash - ing heads and fa - ces bowed,
words can - not ut - ter, lo, who is this? As a
walk in the light of Je - sus' face;

Strong as the li - on, pure as the dove, With
In their mouths a vic - tor - ious psalm,
king with ma - ny crowns he stands, And our
God the Son give us a part In the

(253)

209 (*continued*)

o - pen arms, and hearts of love?
In their hands a robe and a palm?
names are graven up - on his hands;
hi - ding - place of Je - sus' heart;

They the bless - ed ones gone be - fore,
Wel - com - ing an - gels these that shine, He
As a priest, with God - up - lift - ed eyes,
God the Spi - rit so hold us . . up That

They the bless - ed for ev - er - more,
Your own an - gel, and yours, and mine; As the
off - ers for us his sac - ri - fice;
we may drink of Je - sus' cup;

Out . . of . . great tri - bu - la - tion they went
Who . have . hedged us, both day . and . night,
Lamb . of . . God, for sin - ners . slain, That
God . al - migh - ty, God . three in One,

Home to their home of heaven con - tent.
On the left hand and on the right.
we too may live, he lives a - gain.
God al - migh - ty, God a - lone.

A - men.

Christina Rossetti, 1830–94.

WHAT are these that glow from afar,
These that lean over the golden bar,
Strong as the lion, pure as the dove,
With open arms, and hearts of love?
They the blessèd ones gone before,
They the blessèd for evermore,
Out of great tribulation they went
Home to their home of heaven content.

2 What are these that fly as a cloud,
With flashing heads and faces bowed,
In their mouths a victorious psalm,
In their hands a robe and a palm?
Welcoming angels these that shine,
Your own angel, and yours, and mine;
Who have hedged us, both day and night,
On the left hand and on the right.

3 *Light above light, and bliss beyond bliss, [this?
Whom words cannot utter, lo, who is
As a king with many crowns he stands,
And our names are graven upon his hands;
As a priest, with God-uplifted eyes,
He offers for us his sacrifice;
As the Lamb of God, for sinners slain,
That we too may live, he lives again.

4. God the Father give us grace
To walk in the light of Jesus' face;
God the Son give us a part
In the hiding-place of Jesus' heart;
God the Spirit so hold us up
That we may drink of Jesus' cup;
God almighty, God three in One,
God almighty, God alone.

THE SAINTS

210

ALL SAINTS. (8 7. 8 7. 7 7.)

Moderately slow, dignified.

Darmstadt Gesangbuch, 1698 (slightly adapted)

ALTERNATIVE VERSION

Melody in the Tenor.

Fa-burden by HERBERT W. SUMSION.

(256)

THE SAINTS

SECOND TUNE

PSALM 146. (8 7. 8 7. 7 7.)
In moderate time. (May be sung in Unison.)

Genevan Psalter (Harmonies from Goudimel Delft edition, 1602).

H. T. Schenck, 1656–1727. Tr. F. E. Cox.

Wer sind die vor Gottes Throne.

WHO are these, like stars appearing,
      These before God's throne who
            stand?
Each a golden crown is wearing;
      Who are all this glorious band?
            'Alleluya!' hark they sing,
            Praising loud their heavenly king.

2 Who are these of dazzling brightness,
      These in God's own truth arrayed,
Clad in robes of purest whiteness,
      Robes whose lustre ne'er shall fade,
            Ne'er be touched by time's rude
                  hand: [band?
            Whence comes all this glorious

3 These are they who have contended
      For their saviour's honour long,
Wrestling on till life was ended,

Following not the sinful throng;
      These, who well the fight sustained,
      Triumph through the Lamb have
            gained.

4*These are they whose hearts were riven,
      Sore with woe and anguish tried,
Who in prayer full oft have striven
      With the God they glorified;
            Now, their painful conflict o'er,
            God has bid them weep no more.

5.*These like priests have watched and
            waited,
      Offering up to Christ their will,
Soul and body consecrated
      Day and night to serve him still:
            Now, in God's most holy place
            Blest they stand before his face.

243 For the brave

See also

244 Unknown and unrewarded

K

211

OLD 104TH. (10 10. 11 11.)

Slow and dignified.

Ravenscroft's Psalter, 1621.

A-men.

Based on Supreme quales, Arbiter, J.-B. de Santeüil (1686).
Cento. Percy Dearmer.

DISPOSER supreme, and judge of the earth,
    Who choosest for thine the meek and the poor;
To frail earthen vessels, and things of no worth,
    Entrusting thy riches which ay shall endure;

2 Like clouds are they borne to do thy great will,
    And swift as the winds about the world go;
The Word with his wisdom their spirits doth fill,
    They thunder like clouds, and the waters o'erflow.

3 They hearten the few, they armour the free,
    Thy Reign to advance, thy peace to proclaim;
The wisdom of kindness they lead men to see,
    With fire of the Spirit men's hearts they enflame.

4 O loud be their trump, and stirring the sound,
    To rouse us, O Lord, from slumber of sin;
The lights thou hast kindled in darkness around,
    O may they illumine our spirits within!

5.*All honour and praise, dominion and might,
    To thee, three in One, eternally be,
Who pouring around us the waves of thy light,
    Dost call us from darkness thy glory to see.

APOSTLES AND PROPHETS

ALTERNATIVE VERSION

Descant by ALAN GRAY.

PEOPLE'S
PART.

TREBLES
AND
ORGAN.

212

AUCTOR OMNIUM BONORUM (ALLES IST AN GOTTES SEGEN). (8 8 7. D.)

Later form of melody probably by J. B. KÖNIG (1691–1758), as given in the *Charterhouse Founder's Day Service Book*.

Moderately slow.

Apostles and Writers.

P. Dearmer, 1867–1936.

PROPHETS, teachers, true recorders,
    Pioneers, and trusty warders
        Of the truth that Christ revealed,
But for you the old estranging
Darkness had endured unchanging,
        God's great love were still concealed.

2 You assailed the haunting terrors,
    Struggled, died, to stem the errors,
        Showing God, unknown before:
When men's foolish hearts were darkened,
When few turned again and hearkened,
        Undismayed the News you bore.

3. We too, Lord, have misconstrued thee,
    Have but dimly understood thee;
        Hearing oft, we have not heard.
Make us seek the truth pure-hearted;
And, that wisdom be imparted,
        Still raise prophets for the Word.

And for all Apostles see

205 Hail, glorious spirits
197 Jerusalem on high

640 Sing praise to God
216 (I, III) The Son of God

213

CUMNOR. (7 7. 7 7. 7 7. Irreg.)   R. VAUGHAN WILLIAMS, 1872–1958.

In moderate time. Unison.   *Vv. 4 & 5.*

1. Ser-vants of God, or sons Shall I not call you, be - cause

Not as servants ye knew Your fa - ther's in - ner - most mind,

His who un - will - ing - ly sees One of his lit - tle ones lost.

V. 4, l. 1.

Ye a - light in our van; at your voice,

[Copyright, 1925, by R. Vaughan Williams.]

Matthew Arnold, 1822–88. Cento. Percy Dearmer.

2 Yours is the praise if mankind
Hath not as yet in its march
Fainted, and fallen, and died:
A feeble wavering line—
Factions divide them, their host
Threatens to break, to dissolve;

3 Then, in such hour of need,
Ye, like angels, appear,
Radiant with ardour divine:
Languor is not in your heart,
Weakness is not in your word,
Weariness not on your brow.

4 Ye alight in our van; at your voice,
Panic, despair, flee away;
Ye move through the ranks, recall
The stragglers, refresh the outworn,
Praise, re-inspire the brave:
Order, courage, return.

5. Eyes rekindling and prayers
Follow your steps as ye go.
Ye fill up the gaps in our line,
Stablish, continue our march,
On, to the bound of the waste,
On, to the City of God.

See also
640 Sing praise to God | 703 Zeal of the Lord

EVANGELISTS

MIT FREUDEN ZART. (8 7. 8 7. 8 8 7.)

In moderate time. Voices in Unison.

Later form of
Hymn Melody of the Bohemian Brethren (1566).

(Other occasions also.)

P. Dearmer, 1867–1936.

VIRTUE supreme, thy mighty stream
　Inspires the men that heed thee,
Through human word thou hast con-
　　ferred
　Thy light on us who need thee;
And best those Four, the light who bore,
Through whom we came to know one
　　Name,
　And in thy Son to read thee.

2 For these, for all, both great and small
　The path of light pursuing,
We twine the bays in joyful praise,
　Their glorious record viewing;
For Jew and Greek, for all who seek
Thy mind to know, thy ways to show,
　To thee our thanks renewing.

3 Nor shall truth cease to make increase:
　Each prophet's brave defiance,
Each thinker's quest, each critic's test,
　Each system wrought by science;
Such build thy Church, pure hearts that
　　search,
Candour for key, who trust in thee
　In full and sure reliance.

4.*Still then we ask: the false unmask,
　That truth may free and guide us.
Truth will prevail, no good can fail,
　Nor shame nor loss betide us.
In Christ unite all rays of light,
More clear each age the Gospel page;
　His radiance flames beside us.

See also

457 Book of books
212 Prophets, teachers

645 Spread, still spread
660 The Spirit of the Lord

(262)

MARTYRS

WEIMAR. (7 6. 7 6. D.)

Very slow and dignified.

Later form of melody by M. VULPIUS, 1560–1616.

St. Joseph the Hymnographer, d. 883. *Tr. J. M. Neale.*‡

Τῶν ἱερῶν ἀθλοφόρων.

LET us now our voices raise,
  Wake the day with gladness:
God himself to joy and praise
  Turns our human sadness;
Joy that martyrs won their crown,
  Opened heaven's bright portal,
When they laid the mortal down
  For the life immortal.

2 Never flinched they from the flame,
  From the torment never;
Vain the tyrant's sharpest aim,
  Vain each fierce endeavour:

For by faith they saw the land
  Decked in all its glory,
Where triumphant now they stand
  With the victor's story.

3. Up and follow, Christian men!
  Press through toil and sorrow;
Spurn the night of fear, and then,
  O the glorious morrow!
Who will venture on the strife?
  Who will first begin it?
Who will grasp the Land of Life?
  Warriors, up and win it!

216

OLD 81ST (OLD 77TH). (D.C.M.)
Slow and dignified.

Este's Psalter, 1592.
Original version appeared in *Day's Psalter, 1562.*

[This hymn may also be sung to ST. ANNE, 598.]

Martyrs, &c.   *Bishop R. Heber, 1783–1826.*

THE Son of God goes forth to war,
   A kingly crown to gain;
His blood-red banner streams afar:
   Who follows in his train?

2 Who best can drink his cup of woe,
   Triumphant over pain,
Who patient bears his cross below,
   He follows in his train.

PART II

3*The Martyr first, whose eagle eye
   Could pierce beyond the grave;
Who saw his Master in the sky,
   And called on him to save.

4*Like him, with pardon on his tongue
   In midst of mortal pain,
He prayed for them that did the wrong:
   Who follows in his train?

5*A glorious band, the chosen few
   On whom the Spirit came,
Twelve valiant Saints, their hope they knew,
   And mocked the cross and flame.

(264)

MARTYRS

ALTERNATIVE VERSION

Melody in the Bass.

Fa-burden by ERNEST BULLOCK.

[*Copyright, 1931, by Oxford University Press.*]

6*They met the tyrant's brandish'd steel,
 The lion's gory mane,
They bowed their necks the death to feel:
 Who follows in their train?

PART III

7 A noble army, men and boys,
 The matron and the maid,
Around the Saviour's throne rejoice
 In robes of light arrayed.

8. They climbed the steep ascent of heaven
 Through peril, toil, and pain:
O God, to us may grace be given
 To follow in their train.

Verses 3 and 4 refer to St. Stephen: they can be omitted, and the Apostles' verse 5 also: verse 6 can be used for Martyrs, or omitted. Parts I and III make a good hymn.

For Martyrs see also

440 All hail the power of Jesus' name
495 For the might of thine arm
206 Hark! the sound of holy voices

207 How bright these glorious spirits shine
197 Jerusalem on high
703 Zeal of the Lord

K*

SPECIAL DAYS AND OCCASIONS
ST. ANDREW

(*Nov. 30th*)

FIRST TUNE

217

OMNI DIE. (8 7. 8 7.)
In moderate time.

Melody in CORNER'S *Gesangbuch*, 1631.
Arranged by W. S. ROCKSTRO, 1823–95.

[This hymn may also be sung to REDHEAD 46, 460.]

SECOND TUNE

GOLDSCHMIDT (O, DER ALLES). (8 7. 8 7.)
Moderately slow.

From the *Chorale Book for England*, 1863.
Melody there attributed to *Geistreiches Gesangbuch*, Darmstadt, 1698.

Mrs. C. F. Alexander, 1818–95.

JESUS calls us! O'er the tumult
Of our life's wild restless sea
Day by day his sweet voice soundeth,
Saying, 'Christian, follow me':

2 As of old Saint Andrew heard it
By the Galilean lake,   [dred,
Turned from home, and toil, and kin-
Leaving all for his dear sake.

3 Jesus calls us from the worship
Of the vain world's golden store,

From each idol that would keep us,
Saying, 'Christian, love me more.'

4 In our joys and in our sorrows,
Days of toil and hours of ease,
Still he calls, in cares and pleasures,
'Christian, love me more than these.'

5. Jesus calls us! By thy mercies,
Saviour, may we hear thy call,
Give our hearts to thy obedience,
Serve and love thee best of all.

See also

481 Dear Lord and Father
211 Disposer supreme

212 Prophets, teachers
645 Spread, still spread

And Service Oversea, 299–303; *and, for Scotland, National*, 316–324.

(266)

ST. THOMAS

(Dec. 21st)

MOAB. (6 5. 6 5. 6 6 6. 5.)

Rather slow.

IEUAN GWYLLT, 1822–77.

Bp. J. R. Darbyshire, 1880–1948.

WHO dreads, yet undismayed
　　Dares face his terror;
Who errs, yet having strayed,
　　Avows his error—
Him let Saint Thomas guide,
Who stirred his fellows' pride
To move to death beside
　　Their Lord and Master.

2 Who longs for guidance clear
　　When doubts assail him,
Nor dares to move for fear
　　Lest faith should fail him—
For such the Lord's reply
To his disciple's cry:
'I am the Way,' supply
　　The light in darkness.

3. Who grieves that love lies dead
　　On fate's wheel broken;
And stands uncomforted
　　By any token—
His faith shall be restored
By Christ's compelling word
When Thomas saw the Lord,
　　And seeing worshipped.

See also

453 Believe not those who say
211 Disposer supreme
614 O thou in all thy might so far

212 Prophets, teachers
670 Thou art my life
143 (II) When Thomas afterwards

ST. STEPHEN

(Dec. 26th)

219

WELLINGTON SQUARE. (D.C.M.)
In moderate time.

GUY WARRACK.

Jan Struther, 1901–53.

WHEN Stephen, full of power and
    grace,
  Went forth throughout the land,
He bore no shield before his face,
  No weapon in his hand;
But only in his heart a flame
  And on his lips a sword
Wherewith he smote and overcame
  The foemen of the Lord.

2 When Stephen preached against the
  And by those laws was tried,   [laws
He had no friend to plead his cause,
  No spokesman at his side;
But only in his heart a flame
  And in his eyes a light
Wherewith God's daybreak to proclaim
  And rend the veils of night.

3 When Stephen, young and doomed to
  Fell crushed beneath the stones, [die,
He had no curse nor vengeful cry
  For those who broke his bones;
But only in his heart a flame
  And on his lips a prayer
That God, in sweet forgiveness' name,
  Should understand and spare.

4. Let me, O Lord, thy cause defend,
  A knight without a sword;
No shield I ask, no faithful friend,
  No vengeance, no reward;
But only in my heart a flame
  And in my soul a dream,
So that the stones of earthly shame
  A jewelled crown may seem.

See also
216 (vv. 3–4, 7–8) The Martyr first

ST. JOHN THE EVANGELIST

(Dec. 27th)

MASON ('OLD GERMAN'). (11 12. 11 12.)
In moderate time.

From J. MASON'S *Companion*, 1847,
adapted there from *Harmonia Sacra.*

J. M. C. Crum, 1872–1958.

ON the moorland of life God's Shepherd is seen,
And he waters his flock where the valley is green,
And he calleth his sheep, he knoweth them all,
And the sheep know his voice and they follow his call.

2 In the vineyard of life God planted a vine,
And its leaf doth not wither nor faileth its wine;
For the branches have all one life with the root
And are lovely with leaves and are loaded with fruit.

3 In the Passover night when Christ was betrayed,
And his own who had loved him were sorely dismayed,
When all hope in their hearts grew troubled and dim,
Then he spake of the peace of abiding in him.

4. And the love of one heart most near to the Lord's
In the Gospel has written the mystical words;
They are words of a peace the world cannot move,
Of the peace of the souls that abide in his love.

See also

457 Book of books
212 Prophets, teachers

660 The Spirit of the Lord
214 Virtue supreme

INNOCENTS' DAY

(Dec. 28th)

221

RODMELL. (C.M.)

In moderate time.

English Traditional Melody.

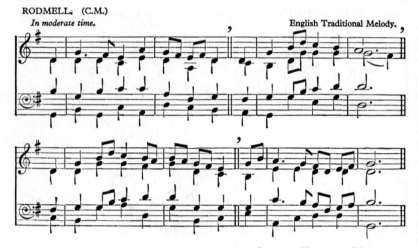

Laurence Housman, 1865–1959.

WHEN Christ was born in Bethlehem,
 Fair peace on earth to bring,
In lowly state of love he came
 To be the children's King.

2 A mother's heart was there his throne,
 His orb a maiden's breast,
Whereby he made through love alone
 His kingdom manifest.

3 And round him, then, a holy band
 Of children blest was born,
Fair guardians of his throne to stand
 Attendant night and morn.

4 And unto them this grace was given
 A saviour's name to own,
And die for him who out of heaven
 Had found on earth a throne.

5 O blessèd babes of Bethlehem,
 Who died to save our King,
Ye share the martyrs' diadem,
 And in their anthem sing!

6*Your lips, on earth that never spake,
 Now sound the eternal word;
And in the courts of love ye make
 Your children's voices heard.

7.*Lord Jesus Christ, eternal Child,
 Make thou our childhood thine;
That we with thee the meek and mild
 May share the love divine.

See also
385 Unto us a boy is born

(270)

ST. PAUL

(Jan. 25th)

BLAENCEFN. (8 7. 8 7. 8 7.)

In moderate time.

JOHN THOMAS, 1839–1922.

Geoffrey Dearmer.

'TO Damascus!' Paul had shouted:
  Now he marched in ebbing pride,
Ere the Voice from heaven had spoken;
  Fought the Silence at his side,
Fought, surrendered, came in triumph,
  By his conscience crucified.

2 Facing him was dark obtuseness,
  At his back the spur and flame
Of those deeds of persecution,
  Ere from Saul to Paul he came;
Paul, where others would have hushed it,
  Stood and shouted of his shame.

3*Died he daily yet rejoicing:
  Truth to Paul was nurtured in
Much that in itself was error,
  Since the Law itself was sin:
Thus it was where others ended
  Paul was ready to begin.

4 Paul, the least of the apostles,
  Freedom to the faith restored;
Claimed for Gentile, slave and woman,
  Christ, the deputy adored;
Made his felon-doom our symbol,
  Found the comprehensive Lord.

5. Therefore let us praise and honour
  Him who stood and fought alone,
Soldier, seaman, traveller, teacher,
  Raised in power, in weakness sown;
Through mankind in Christ he enters
  At the last unto his own.

See also

211 Disposer supreme
511 Hark what a sound

212 Prophets, teachers
213 Servants of God

223

AVE MARIA KLARE. (7 6. 7 6. 6 7 6.)
In moderate time.

Melody and harmony from
Psalteriolum Harmonicum, 1642.

Candlemas.

Jan Struther, 1901–53.

WHEN Mary brought her treasure
　Unto the holy place,
No eye of man could measure
　The joy upon her face.
　　He was but six weeks old,
Her plaything and her pleasure,
　Her silver and her gold.

2 Then Simeon, on him gazing
　With wonder and with love,
His aged voice up-raising
　Gave thanks to God above:
　　'Now welcome sweet release!
For I, my saviour praising,
　May die at last in peace.'

3 And she, all sorrow scorning,
　Rejoiced in Jesus' fame.
The child her arms adorning
　Shone softly like a flame
　　That burns the long night through,
And keeps from dusk till morning
　Its vigil clear and true.

4. As by the sun in splendour
　The flags of night are furled,
So darkness shall surrender
　To Christ who lights the world:
　　To Christ the star of day,
Who once was small and tender,
　A candle's gentle ray.

See also
94 The greatness of God

224

EPWORTH. (C.M.)
In moderate time.

Melody arranged from CHARLES WESLEY, 1757–1834.

(272)

ST. MATTHIAS

Geoffrey Dearmer.

WHEN Judas did his Lord reject
   And fell from common grace,
Matthias was the one elect
   To fill the vacant place.

2 In loyalty to make amends
   For Judas, he became
One with the Master's chosen friends,
   A witness of his name.

3 To serve his fellow men was he
   With comradeship content;
Thus did the Church with loyalty
   Stone unto stone cement.

4. Since faith with constancy is bound,
   Grant us, O Lord, that we
On earthly fellowship may found
   Our larger loyalty.

See also

211 Disposer supreme   212 Prophets, teachers

ST. DAVID

225

(March 1st)

STETTIN (NUN SEHT). (D.C.M.)
Not too slow. May be sung in Unison.

Later form of melody from the
Song Book of the Bohemian Brethren, 1566.

[This hymn may also be sung to OLD 44TH, 655.]

E. J. Newell, 1853–1916.

WE praise thy name, all-holy Lord,
   For him, the beacon-light
That shone beside our western sea
   Through mists of ancient night;
Who sent to Ireland's fainting Church
   New tidings of thy word:
For David, prince of Cambrian saints,
   We praise thee, holy Lord.

2 For all the saintly band whose prayers
   Still gird our land about,
Of whom, lest men disdain their praise,
   The voiceless stones cry out;

Our hills and vales on every hand
   Their names and deeds record:
For these, thy ancient hero host,
   We praise thee, holy Lord.

3. Grant us but half their burning zeal,
   But half their iron faith,
But half their charity of heart,
   And fortitude to death;
That we with them and all thy saints
   May in thy truth accord,
And ever in thy holy Church
   May praise thee, holy Lord.

See also for Wales, National, 316-324

ST. PATRICK (*March 17th*)
See St. Patrick's Breastplate, 528

See also for Ireland, National, 316–324

THE ANNUNCIATION
(*March 25th*)

226

DE BOODSCHAP. (9 7. 9 7. 7 7. 4 4 6.)

In moderate time.

Dutch Traditional Melody.

(Ten.) By God's most high de - cree!

THE ANNUNCIATION

O. B. C.

A MESSAGE came to a maiden young;
　　The angel stood beside her,
In shining robes and with golden tongue,
　　He told what should betide her:
　　　　The maid was lost in wonder;
　　　　Her world was rent asunder;
　　　　　　Ah! how could she
　　　　　　Christ's mother be
　　　　　By God's most high decree!

2 No greater news could a messenger bring;
　　For 'twas from that young mother
He came, who walked on the earth as a king,
　　And yet was all men's brother:
　　　　His truth has spread like leaven:
　　　　'Twill marry earth to heaven,
　　　　　　Till all agree
　　　　　　In charity
　　　　　To dwell from sea to sea.

3 He came, God's Word to the world here below;
　　And round him there did gather
A band who found that this Teacher to know
　　Was e'en to know the Father:
　　　　He healed the sick who sought him,
　　　　Forgave the foes who fought him;
　　　　　　Beside the Sea
　　　　　　Of Galilee
　　　　　He set the nations free.

4. And sometimes trumpets from Sion ring out,
　　And tramping comes, and drumming;
'Thy Kingdom come,' so we cry; and they shout,
　　'It comes!' and still 'tis coming,
　　　　Far, far ahead, to win us,
　　　　Yet with us, nay within us;
　　　　　　Till all shall see
　　　　　　That King is he,
　　　　　The Love from Galilee!

See also

368 Once in royal David's city　　　｜　　　80 The holy Son of God

ST. GEORGE

(April 23rd)

227
FALKLAND. (8 8. 8 8. 8 8.)

Moderately slow, dignified.

Melody by H. LAWES, 1596–1662.

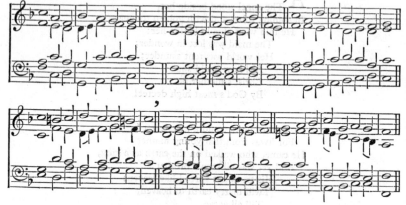

Laurence Housman, 1865–1959.

LORD God of Hosts, within whose hand
  Dominion rests on sea and land,
Before whose word of life or death
The strength of nations is but breath:
O King, enthroned all thrones above,
Give strength unto the land we love.

2 Thou, breath of life since time began,
  Breathing upon the lips of man,
Hast taught each kindred race to raise
United word to sound thy praise:
So, in this land, join, we beseech,
All hearts and lips in single speech.

3 To George our saint thou gavest grace
Without one fear all foes to face,
And to confess by faithful death
That Word of Life which was his breath.
O help us, Helper of Saint George,
To fear no bonds that man can forge.

4. Arm us like him, who in thy trust
Beat down the dragon to the dust;
So that we too may tread down sin
And with thy saints a crown may win.
Help us, O God, that we may be
A land acceptable to thee.

See also for England, National, 316–325.

ST. MARK

(April 25th)

228
BROCKHAM. (L.M.)

Moderately fast.

J. CLARK, 1670–1707.

A-men.

ST. MARK

Laurence Housman, 1865–1959.

THE saint who first found grace to pen
 The life which was the Life of men,
And shed abroad the Gospel's ray,
His fame we celebrate to-day.

2 Lo, drawn by Pentecostal fire,
His heart conceived its great desire,
When pure of mind, inspired, he heard
And with his hand set forth the Word.

3 Then, clearly writ, the Godhead shone
Serene and fair to look upon; [power
And through that record still comes
To lighten souls in death's dark hour.

4 O holy mind, for wisdom fit
Wherein that Life of lives stood writ,
May we through minds of like accord
Show forth the pattern of our Lord.

5 And so may all whose minds are dark
Be led to truth by good Saint Mark,
And after this our earthly strife
Stand written in the Book of Life.

6. Praise God who made the world so fair,
And sent his Son our saviour there,
And by his Holy Spirit wist
To teach the first evangelist.

See also

457 Book of books
212 Prophets, teachers

660 The Spirit of the Lord
214 Virtue supreme

ST. PHILIP AND ST. JAMES

(*May 1st*)

229

KING'S LANGLEY. (C.M. Irreg.)

In moderate time.

English Traditional May-Day Carol.

May Carol.

E. H.

THE winter's sleep was long and deep,
 But earth is awakened and gay;
For the life ne'er dies that from God
  doth rise,
 And the green comes after the grey.

2*So God doth bring the world to spring;
 And on their holy day [fame,
Doth the Church proclaim her apostles'
 To welcome the First of May.

3 Two saints of God went by the road
 That leadeth on to light; [call,
And they gave up all at their master's
 To work in their master's sight.

4 Would Philip's mind the Father find?
 Lo, he hath found the Way;
For to know the Son is to know the One
 Whom the earth and the heavens
  obey.

5 And, James, 'twas thine by grace divine
 To preach the Christian life, [alone,
Where our faith is shown by our works
 And love overcometh strife.

6. Lord, grant that we may brethren be,
 As Christians live in deed;
For it is but so we can learn to know
 The truth that to thee doth lead.

See also

211 Disposer supreme
  3 Lift your hidden faces

212 Prophets, teachers
  4 Spring has now unwrapped

St. Philip was one of the twelve apostles. St. James the Lord's Brother was the head of the Church in Jerusalem. The reference in v. 5 is to the Epistle General of James. For St. James the Greater, see 224.

(277)

ST. BARNABAS

(*June 11th*)

230

LONDONDERRY. (11 10. 11 10. D.)

Slow. Unison. Irish Traditional Melody, harmonized by HENRY G. LEY. 1887–1962.

[This hymn may also be sung to CHARTERHOUSE, 283.]

A. G.

TRUE Son of Man, thou crown of human valour,
By whom true men are to thy service drawn,
Fighting disease and sin and want and squalor,
We thank thee for the heralds of thy dawn.

2 Some spread thy love and freedom to the unknowing,
Some wrest the secrets hidden fast before,
Some teach, some plan the word's vast arduous sowing,
Some bear good cheer and balm from door to door.

(278)

ST. BARNABAS

3 Thus Barnabas, 'the Son of Inspiration,'
  Who cast his lands at the apostles' feet,
In fair Greek Antioch laid the great foundation,
  Till 'Christian' rang in every splendid street.

4. Forth then with Paul he went, the stately teacher,
  Like Zeus with Hermes to the simple throng.
So, Lord, may we be quickened by thy nature,
  Heartening the weak, encouraging the strong.

See also

212 Prophets, teachers | 213 Servants of God

Joses (Joseph) was called by the apostles 'Barnabas', which may be rendered as 'the man who brings encouragement and inspiration', or, as the Greek word suggests, 'the man who acts as a paraclete, coming to our side to help us'. The references in v. 3 are to Acts iv. 36–7, xi. 22–6; in v. 4 to Zeus (Jupiter), and to Hermes (Mercury) as the god of eloquence, in Acts xiv. 12.

ST. JOHN BAPTIST

(*June 24th*)

231

ISTE CONFESSOR (ANGERS). (11 11. 11 5.)
In moderate time. **To be sung in unison.**

Angers Church Melody.

A - - men.

Paulus Diaconus, 8th cent. Tr. R. Ellis Roberts.
Ut queant laxis.

LET thine example, holy John, remind us,
  Ere we can meetly sing thy deeds of wonder,
Hearts must be chastened, and the bonds that bind us
    Broken asunder!

2 E'en in thy childhood, 'mid the desert places,
  Thou hadst a refuge from the city gainèd,
Far from all slander and its bitter traces
    Living unstainèd.

3 Often had prophets in the distant ages
  Sung to announce the Daystar and to name him;
But as the Saviour, last of all the sages,
    Thou didst proclaim him.

4 Than John the Baptist, none of all Eve's daughters
  E'er bore a greater, whether high or lowly:
He was thought worthy, washing in the waters
    Jesus the holy.

5. Angels in orders everlasting praise thee,
  God, in thy triune majesty tremendous;
Hark to the prayers we penitents up-raise thee:
    Save and defend us.

See also

561 Lo, in the wilderness
67 On Jordan's bank

213 Servants of God
8 The summer days

ST. PETER

(June 29th)

OSLO. (7 6. 7 6. 8 6. 8 6.)

In moderate time. May be sung in Unison.

Norwegian Traditional Melody.

T. S. N.

LOOK up, by failure daunted,
 Ye men of good intent!
For sin and weakness haunted
 The heart of many a saint:
And chief of those who went astray
 Was he who thrice denied;
First to acclaim, he fell away:
 'I know him not,' he cried.

2 How oft are men forgiven?
 Ah, Peter, thou dost know;
Thou lovedst, and wast shriven,
 Steadfast as rock to grow.
We know not where thy wanderings led,
 Or where thy death was met;
But thou wast true to him who said,
 'Fisher, let down the net.'

3 For Paul had grasped the vision—
 A world made one in Christ,
Nor Law nor Circumcision,
 When faith alone sufficed.
Then Peter saw that God had made
 Nought common or unclean;
And James the large foundations laid
 For ages unforeseen.

4. Forth to the lands went Peter,
 His faithful wife beside,
To make the whole world sweeter
 By him he had denied,
'Lovest thou me?' Christ once had said,
 'Yea, Lord.' 'Then feed my sheep.'
We too, who hail thee from the dead,
 Thy dear commands would keep.

See also

211 Disposer supreme | 212 Prophets, teachers

ST. MARY MAGDALENE
(July 22nd)

233

PISGAH. (8 7. 8 7. D.)

Moderately slow.

DAVID EVANS, 1874–1948.

Jan Struther, 1901–53.

UNTO Mary, demon-haunted,
  With unholy dreams distraught,
By her neighbours mocked and taunted,
  Christ his healing wisdom brought.
    Banish, Lord, our minds' confusion,
      Fear and fever drive away;
    Down the valleys of illusion
      Spread the kindly light of day.

2 Mary then, with faith unswerving,
    Shared her saviour's tireless days,
  Thankfully her master serving,
    Helping him in humble ways.

Grant, O Lord, that we may never
  Grow too proud for simple things;
Let us bring to all endeavour
  Hands unwearied, heart that sings.

3. Unto her, who saw them sunder
    Valiant soul from tortured frame,
  First appeared the risen wonder,
    First the quickened Jesus came.
      Lord, when time from us has taken
        Earthly joys and earthly friends,
      Let our lonely hearts awaken
        To the joy that never ends.

Mary Magdalene is not in the Gospels identified with the sinner-woman. See Luke viii. 2.

(281)

ST. JAMES THE GREATER

(*July 25th*)

234

PADERBORN. (76. 7 6.)

In moderate time.

Melody from *Katholische Kirchengesänge*, Paderborn, 1616.

[This hymn may also be sung to CHRISTUS DER IST MEIN LEBEN, 585.]

W. Romanis, 1824–99.

LORD, who shall sit beside thee,
  Enthroned on either hand,
When clouds no longer hide thee,
  'Mid all thy faithful band?

2 Who drinks the cup of sorrow
    Thy Father gave to thee
  'Neath shadows of the morrow
    In dark Gethsemane;

3 Who on thy Passion thinking
    Can find in loss a gain,
  And dare to meet unshrinking
    Thy baptism of pain.

4 O Jesus, form within us
    Thy likeness clear and true;
  By thine example win us
    To suffer or to do.

5. This law itself fulfilleth:
    Christ-like to Christ is nigh,
  And, where the Father willeth,
    Shall sit with Christ on high.

See also

211 Disposer supreme | 212 Prophets, teachers

St. James, surnamed 'the Greater' (with reference perhaps to his stature) to distinguish him from James the son of Alphaeus, was the son of Zebedee and the brother of John. The reference in the hymn is to Mark x. 37. St. James is the only apostle whose death is recorded (Acts xii. 2); therefore a Martyr's hymn (215–16) is also appropriate.

For St. James the Lord's Brother, see 229 and 232, v. 3.

THE TRANSFIGURATION

(*Aug. 6th*)

235

TALLIS' LAMENTATION. (D.L.M.)

In moderate time.

Melody in *Day's Psalter*, 1562.

[This hymn may also be sung to CANTATE DOMINO, 95.]

Arthur Penrhyn Stanley,‡ 1815–81.

O MASTER, it is good to be
High on the mountain here with thee;
Where stand revealed to mortal gaze
The great old saints of other days;
Who once received on Horeb's height
The eternal laws of truth and right;
Or caught the still small whisper, higher
Than storm, than earthquake, or than fire.

2 O Master, it is good to be
With thee, and with thy faithful three:
Here, where the Apostle's heart of rock
Is nerved against temptation's shock;
Here, where the Son of Thunder learns
The thought that breathes, the word that burns;
Here, where on eagle's wings we move
With him whose last best creed is love.

3 O Master, it is good to be
Entranced, enwrapt, alone with thee;
Watching the glistering raiment glow,
Whiter than Hermon's whitest snow,
The human lineaments that shine
Irradiant with a light divine:
Till we too change from grace to grace
Gazing on that transfigured face.

4. O Master, it is good to be
Here on the holy mount with thee:
When darkling in the depths of night,
When dazzled with excess of light,
We bow before the heavenly voice
That bids bewildered souls rejoice,
Though love wax cold, and faith be dim,
'This is my Son! O hear ye him.'

See also
589 Not always on the Mount

ST. BARTHOLOMEW

(Aug. 24th)

236

ALCAIC ODE. (11 11. 9 10.)
In moderate time.

Melody and bass by M. A. VON LÖWENSTERN, 1594–1648.

Jan Struther, 1901–53.

O SAINT of summer, what can we sing for you?
How can we praise you, what can we bring for you?
Lost are your words, your deeds are nameless,
Saint without history, mute and fameless.

2 Said you wise sayings? No one has hoarded them.
Worked you great wonders? None has recorded them.
Only your name, time's hand defying,
Shines with the light of your faith undying.

3 So fade the words, so vanish the deeds from us
Of each lost summer, swift as it speeds from us;
We jest, we toil, we weep, but after
Slip from our memories grief and laughter.

(284)

4 Only the sun that cheered us and shone for us,
All else forgotten, ever lives on for us,
    Kindling our hearts when summer's ended—
    Soul of the summer, serene and splendid.

5. Time, take our words and do what thou wilt with them;
Death, take our hands and all that we built with them;
    Only our faith, our soul's endeavour,
    Take it, Lord, make it, Lord, shine for ever.

See also

211 Disposer supreme
 7 Summer suns are glowing

8 The summer days
691 We thank thee, Lord

ST. MATTHEW
(Sept. 21st)

237

ALFRETON. (L.M.)

In moderate time.   *Supplement to the New Version, 1708.*

W. Bright, 1824–1901.

HE sat to watch o'er customs paid,
    A man of scorned and hardening trade;
Alike the symbol and the tool
Of foreign masters' hated rule.

2 But grace within his breast had stirred;
There needed but the timely word;
It came, true Lord of Souls, from thee,
That royal summons, 'Follow me.'

3 Enough, when thou wert passing by,
To hear thy voice, to meet thine eye:
He rose, responsive to the call,
And left his task, his gains, his all.

4 O wise exchange! with these to part,
And lay up treasure in thy heart;
With twofold crown of light to shine
Amid thy servants' foremost line.

5 Come, Saviour, as in days of old;
Pass where the world has strongest hold,
And faithless care and selfish greed
Are thorns that choke the holy seed.

6. Who keep thy gifts, O bid them claim
The steward's, not the owner's name;
Who yield all up for thy dear sake,
Let them of Matthew's wealth partake.

See also

481 Dear Lord and Father

211 Disposer supreme

MICHAELMAS
(*Sept. 29th*)

QUEDLINBURG. (10 10. 10 10.)

Moderately slow.

From a Chorale by J. C. KITTEL, 1732–1809.

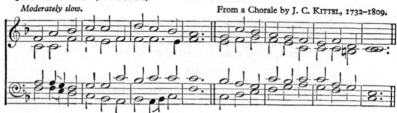

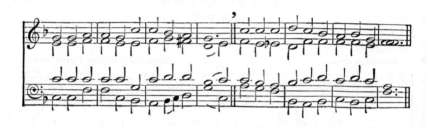

P. Dearmer, 1867–1936.

ANGELS and ministers, spirits of grace,
Friends of the children, beholding God's face,
Moving like thought to us through the beyond,
Moulded in beauty, and free from our bond!

2 Messengers clad in the swiftness of light,
Subtle as flame, as creative in might,
Helmed with the truth and with charity shod,
Wielding the wind of the purpose of God!

3 Earth's myriad creatures live after their kind,
Dumb, in the life of the body confined;
You are pure spirit, but we here below
Linked in both orders, are tossed to and fro:

4 You do God's bidding unshaken and strong,
We are distraught 'twixt the right and the wrong;
Yet would we soar as the bird from the mesh,
Freed from the weakness and wonder of flesh.

5. We too shall join you as comrades in grace,
Here but a little below you in place;
Then, when we climb from our lowness in worth,
We too shall herald good will upon earth.

239

SOLOTHURN. (L.M.)

In moderate time. Unison.   Swiss Traditional Melody.

J. M. Neale, 1818–66.

AROUND the throne of God a band
Of glorious angels always stand;
Bright things they see, sweet harps they hold,
And on their heads are crowns of gold.

2 Some wait around him, ready still
To sing his praise and do his will;
And some, when he commands them, go
To guard his servants here below.

3 Lord, give thy angels every day
Command to guide us on our way,
And bid them every evening keep
Their watch around us while we sleep.

4. So shall no wicked thing draw near,
To do us harm or cause us fear;
And we shall dwell, when life is past,
With angels round thy throne at last.

240

ENNISKERRY. (11 10. 11 10. 5.)

Slow.

INA BOYLE.

Verse 2, line 2, must be sung thus:—

Heights that soar to - ward him, depths that sink to - ward him;

Christina Rossetti, 1830–94.

SERVICE and strength, God's angels and archangels;
  His seraphs fires, and lamps his cherubim:
Glory to God from highest and from lowest,
  Glory to God in everlasting hymn
    From all his creatures.

2 Princes that serve, and Powers that work his pleasure,
  Heights that soar toward him, depths that sink toward him;
Flames fire out-flaming, chill beside his essence;
  Insight all-probing, save where scant and dim
    Toward its Creator.

3 Sacred and free, exultant in God's pleasure,
  His will their solace, thus they wait on him,
And shout their shout of ecstasy eternal,
  And trim their splendours that they burn not dim
    Toward their Creator.

4. Wherefore with angels, wherefore with archangels,
  With lofty cherubs, loftier seraphim,
We laud and magnify our God almighty,
  And veil our faces rendering love to him
    With all his creatures.

ST. LUKE

(*Oct. 18th*)

241

BRYNHYFRYD. (8 7. 8 7.)

In moderate time.

Welsh Hymn Melody. Harmonized by J. T. REES.

Bp. J. R. Darbyshire, 1880–1948.

GREAT is their joy who hide their own
    To serve another's glory:
Counting it honour to make known
    Their hero's deathless story.

2 Blessed are they who, finding joy,
    For zeal that all may share it
Gladly their days and gifts employ
    In labour to declare it.

3 Luke was of these: for love of Christ
    He dared the high endeavour
To be the Lord's evangelist,
    His grace proclaiming ever.

4 Countless the souls led by his art,
    Who tells the son's returning,
To seek, and find the Father's heart
    With love and pardon yearning.

5. Grant, Lord, that we, like him whom Paul
    Hath named the Loved Physician,
Straight to thy service at thy call
    May consecrate ambition.

See also

285 From thee all skill
212 Prophets, teachers

213 Servants of God
214 Virtue supreme

(289)

ST. SIMON AND ST. JUDE

(Oct. 28th)

242

LLANGOEDMOR. (8 8 8. D.)

In moderate time.

Welsh Hymn Melody. Harmonized by DAVID EVANS, 1874–1948.

Bp. G. K. A. Bell, 1883–1958.

CHRIST is the King! O friends rejoice;
Brothers and sisters, with one voice
Make all men know he is your choice.
Ring out ye bells, give tongue, give tongue!
Let your most merry peal be rung,
While our exultant song is sung.

2 O magnify the Lord, and raise
Anthems of joy and holy praise
For Christ's brave saints of ancient days,
Who with a faith for ever new
Followed the King, and round him drew
Thousands of faithful men and true.

3 O Christian women, Christian men,
All the world over, seek again
The Way disciples followed then.
Christ through all ages is the same:
Place the same hope in his great name,
With the same faith his word proclaim.

4. Let Love's unconquerable might
Your scattered companies unite
In service to the Lord of light:
So shall God's will on earth be done,
New lamps be lit, new tasks begun,
And the whole Church at last be one.

See also

468 City of God
211 Disposer supreme

628 Pray that Jerusalem
678 Through the night

ALL SAINTS

(Nov. 1st)

243
LOUGHBOROUGH COLLEGE. (7 7. 7 7. D.)

In moderate time, with vigour.

G. W. BRIGGS, 1875–1959.

[This hymn may also be sung to SALZBURG, 558.]

G. W. *Briggs*, 1875–1959.

FOR the brave of every race,
　All who served and fell on sleep,
Whose forgotten resting-place
　Rolling years have buried deep—
Brotherhood and sisterhood
　Of earth's age-long chivalry—
Source and giver of all good,
　Lord, we praise, we worship thee.

2 Prince and peasant, bond and free,
　Warriors wielding freedom's sword,
Bold adventurers on the sea,
　Faithful stewards of the word,
Toilers in the mine and mill,
　Toilers at the furnace-blaze,
Long forgotten, living still,
　All thy servants tell thy praise.

3 Valiantly o'er sea and land
　Trod they the untrodden way,
True and faithful to command,
　Swift and fearless to obey:

Strong in heart and hand and brain,
　Strong, yet battling for the weak,
Recked they not of their own gain,
　Their own safety scorned to seek.

4*Marvels new and manifold,
　Taught of thee, they taught their day:
Fear and bondage, long grown old,
　In thy strength they swept away:
Healed the sick and halt and lame,
　Made the doubly blind to see:
Glorious Lord, their glorious name
　Safe is treasured up with thee.

5. Evermore their life abides,
　Who have lived to do thy will:
High above the restless tides
　Stands their City on the hill:
Lord and Light of every age,
　By same sure counsel led,
Heirs of their great heritage
　In their footsteps will we tread.

(291)

244

AU FORT DE MA DÉTRESSE. (7 6. 7 6. D.)

In moderate time. Genevan Psalter, 1542 (rhythm slightly simplified).

[This hymn may also be sung to HERZLICH THUT MICH ERFREUEN, 249.]

P. Dearmer, 1867–1936.

UNKNOWN and unrewarded,
　Their very names have died—
Thy true Church through the ages,
　The remnant by thy side:
These pure in heart did see thee;
　From dross of self refined,
They spent their lives for others,
　Courageous, peaceful, kind.

2 For many learn the doctrine,
　And lose it in their rules,
And many drown thy Gospel
　In clamour of the schools;
But thy true saints have found thee
　In all things as thou art;
These followed thine example,
　The orthodox in heart.

3 Wise were they all, and simple,
　And meek, and strong, and sane,
Beloved and loving were they,
　With laughter in their train;
They turned from fame and riches
　A happier way to choose,
They understood thy Kingdom,
　They welcomed thy Good News.

4. O why so few that follow?
　And why are we so far?
Their gracious way is easy:
　Our dullness makes the bar.
O King of Saints, inspire us
　The love of self to slay,
Till, all our ranks advancing,
　We throng the narrow way!

THE CHURCH ON EARTH

LEIGHTON. (L.M.)
In moderate time.

WILLIAM LEIGHTON in *Tears or Lamentations of a Sorrowful Soul*
(1614). Harmonized by H. E. WOOLDRIDGE, 1845–1917.

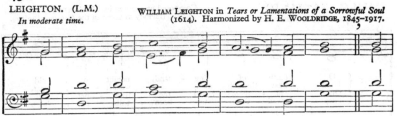

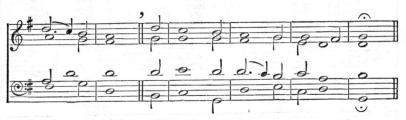

I. Watts, 1674–1748. Pr. R. Bridges.

CHRIST hath a garden walled around,
A paradise of fruitful ground,
Chosen by love and fenced by grace
From out the world's wide wilderness.

2 Like trees of spice his servants stand,
There planted by his mighty hand;
By Eden's gracious streams, that flow
To feed their beauty where they grow.

3 Awake, O wind of heaven, and bear
Their sweetest perfume through the air:
Stir up, O south, the boughs that bloom,
Till the belovèd Master come:

4. That he may come, and linger yet
Among the trees that he hath set;
That he may evermore be seen
To walk amid the springing green.

246

PSALM 68. (8 8 7. 8 8 7. D.)
In moderate time, very dignified.

Composed or adapted by M. GREITER, *c.* 1500–52
(melody as given in the *Genevan Psalter*).

1 { O Faith of Eng - land, taught of old
   Thou wast through many a wealth - y . year,
2* { Our fa - thers heard the trum - pet . call
   They bowed their stub - born wills to . learn

By faith - ful shep - herds of the . fold, The
Through many a dark - ened day of . fear, The
Through low - ly cot and king - ly . hall From
The truths that live, the thoughts that . burn, With

hallow - ing of our na - - tion;
rock of our sal - va - tion.
o - ver - sea re - sound - ing;
new re - solve a - bound - ing.

A - rise, a - rise, good Chris - tian men, Your glo - rious
A - rise, a - rise, good Chris - tian men, Your glo - rious

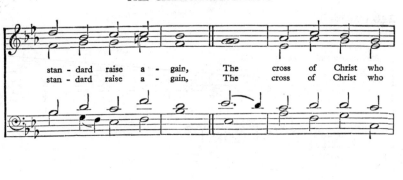

stan - dard raise a - gain, The cross of Christ who
stan - dard raise a - gain, The cross of Christ who

calls : you; : : **Who** bids you live and
guides : you; . . **Whose** arm is bared to

bids you die For his great cause, and stands on :
join the fray, Who mar - shals you in stern ar -

high To wit - ness what be - falls : you.
- ray, Fear - less, what - e'er be - tides : you.

[Continued overleaf.

246 (*continued*)

Vv. 3 and 4.
Unison.
(*Small notes 2nd time only.*)

Very broad.

NOTE.—*Verses 3 and 4 must always be sung in unison, but the organ accompaniment of verses 1 and 2 may, if preferred, be used throughout.*

T. A. Lacey, 1853–1931.

(Faith of our Fathers.)

O FAITH of England, taught of old
By faithful shepherds of the fold,
The hallowing of our nation;
Thou wast through many a wealthy year,
Through many a darkened day of fear,
The rock of our salvation.
Arise, arise, good Christian men,
Your glorious standard raise again,
The cross of Christ who calls you;
Who bids you live and bids you die
For his great cause, and stands on high
To witness what befalls you.

2*Our fathers heard the trumpet call
Through lowly cot and kingly hall
From oversea resounding;
They bowed their stubborn wills to learn
The truths that live, the thoughts that burn,
With new resolve abounding.
Arise, arise, good Christian men,
Your glorious standard raise again,
The cross of Christ who guides you;
Whose arm is bared to join the fray,
Who marshals you in stern array,
Fearless, whate'er betides you.

3 Our fathers held the faith received,
By saints declared, by saints believed,
By saints in death defended;
Through pain of doubt and bitterness,
Through pain of treason and distress,
They for the right contended.
Arise, arise, good Christian men,
Your glorious standard raise again,
The cross of Christ who bought you;
Who leads you forth in this new age
With long-enduring hearts to wage
The warfare he has taught you.

4.*Though frequent be the loud alarms,
Though still we march by ambushed arms
Of death and hell surrounded,
With Christ for chief we fear no foe,
Nor force nor craft can overthrow
The Church that he has founded.
Arise, arise, good Christian men,
Your glorious standard raise again,
The cross wherewith he signed you;
The King himself shall lead you on,
Shall watch you till the strife be done,
Then near his throne shall find you.

For countries other than England 'O Faith immortal, taught of old' may be substituted for the opening line above.

247

MARTINS. (10 10. 7.)

In moderate time. Unison.

P. C. BUCK, 1871–1947.

Mozarabic (5th–8th cent.). S. P. V.

Alleluia, piis edite laudibus.

SING alleluya forth in loyal praise,
    Ye citizens of heaven, and sweetly raise
        An endless alleluya.

2 City of God, eternal and supreme,
   On earth begin, in heaven complete the theme:

3 Ye spirits blest, God's own victorious band,
   Re-echo through your starry fatherland:

4 Thus, in one great acclaim shall ever ring
   Blithe strains which tell the virtue of our King:

5 Thee, O Creator of the world, we praise,
   And thrilling we tell out our joyous lays:

6. To thee, O Word, our merry hearts we bring;
   O Holy Spirit, jubilant we sing:

248

CAPEL. (C.M.)

In moderate time.

English Traditional Carol Melody.

[This hymn may also be sung to UNIVERSITY, 653.]

L. B. C. L. Muirhead, 1845–1925.

THE Church of God a kingdom is,
Where Christ in power doth reign,
Where spirits yearn till seen in bliss
Their Lord shall come again.

2 Glad companies of saints possess
This Church below, above;
And God's perpetual calm doth bless
Their paradise of love.

3*An altar stands within the shrine
Whereon, once sacrificed,
Is set, immaculate, divine,
The Lamb of God, the Christ.

4 There rich and poor, from countless lands,
Praise Christ on mystic rood;
There nations reach forth holy hands
To take God's holy food.

5 There pure life-giving streams o'erflow
The sower's garden-ground;
And faith and hope fair blossoms show,
And fruits of love abound.

6. O King, O Christ, this endless grace
To us and all men bring,
To see the vision of thy face
In joy, O Christ, our King.

249

FIRST TUNE

HERZLICH THUT MICH ERFREUEN. (7 6. 7 6. D.)

Moderately fast.

Founded on a German Medieval Traditional Melody.

SECOND TUNE

AURELIA. (7 6. 7 6. D.)

In moderate time.

S. S. WESLEY, 1810–76.

THE CHURCH ON EARTH

S. J. Stone, 1839–1900.

THE Church's one foundation
  Is Jesus Christ, her Lord;
She is his new creation
  By water and the word:
From heaven he came and sought her
  To be his holy bride,
With his own blood he bought her,
  And for her life he died.

2 Elect from every nation,
  Yet one o'er all the earth,
Her charter of salvation
  One Lord, one faith, one birth;
One holy name she blesses,
  Partakes one holy food,
And to one hope she presses
  With every grace endued.

3*Though with a scornful wonder
  Men see her sore opprest,
By schisms rent asunder,
  By heresies distrest,
Yet saints their watch are keeping,
  Their cry goes up, 'How long?'
And soon the night of weeping
  Shall be the morn of song.

4 'Mid toil, and tribulation,
  And tumult of her war,
She waits the consummation
  Of peace for evermore;
Till with the vision glorious
  Her longing eyes are blest,
And the great Church victorious
  Shall be the Church at rest.

5.*Yet she on earth hath union
  With God the three in One,
And mystic sweet communion
  With those whose rest is won:
O happy ones and holy!
  Lord, give us grace that we,
Like them, the meek and lowly,
  On high may dwell with thee.

See also

304 *Pioneers.* All the past
468 City of God
475 Come now, all people
485 Eternal Ruler
495 For the might of thine arm
394 Forward! be our watchword
497 Gather us in
500 Glorious things
558 Let the whole creation cry

592 Now join, ye comrades true
615 O thou not made with hands
397 Onward, Christian soldiers
628 Pray that Jerusalem
213 Servants of God
642 Soldiers of the cross
678 Through the night
687 Wake, O wake
703 Zeal of the Lord

BAPTISM

ST. STEPHEN. (C.M.)

Slow.

W. JONES, 1726–1800.

ALTERNATIVE VERSION

Melody in the Tenor.

Fa-burden by HARVEY GRACE.

H. Alford,† 1810–71.

IN token that thou shalt not fear
  Christ crucified to own,
We print the cross upon thee here,
  And stamp thee his alone.

2 In token that thou shalt not flinch
  Christ's combat to maintain,
But 'neath his banner manfully
  Firm at thy post remain;

3 In token that thou too shalt tread
  The path he travelled by,
Endure the cross, despise the shame,
  And sit thee down on high:

4. Thus outwardly and visibly
  We seal thee for his own;
And may the brow that wears his cross
  Hereafter share his crown.

(302)

251

PHILIPPINE. (L.M.)

In moderate time.　　　　　　　　　　　　R. E. ROBERTS, 1878–1940.

[*Copyright, 1925, by Oxford University Press.*]

[This hymn may also be sung to SPLENDOUR, 33, Pt. 2 (ii).]

Mrs. K. E. Roberts.

O LORD, thy people gathered here
　Uplift their joyful hearts as one,
And praise thee, with no thought of fear,
　For this bright gift, a life begun.

2 For thou art seen in every place,
　　Through all the world thy beauties shine;
　But only man may win the grace
　　To know the inward light for thine.

3 And so we trace the tender brow,
　　And pray these eyes may learn to gaze
　Through all this world of here and now
　　To find thee and to see thy ways.

4. Praise, Lord, for this sweet world we know
　　With all the joys thy children share,
　And that unknown to which we go,
　　Both now and ever 'neath thy care!

(303)

CONFIRMATION, ADULT BAPTISM, AND
SELF-DEDICATION

252

WARSAW. (6 6. 6 6. 8 8.)
In moderate time.

— CLARK (? THOMAS, 1775–1859),
as given in the *Church Hymnary*, 1928.

J. Julian, 1839–1913.

FATHER of all, to thee
  With loving hearts we pray,
Through him, in mercy given,
  The life, the truth, the way:
From heaven, thy throne, in mercy shed
Thy blessings on each bended head.

2* Father of all, to thee
  Our contrite hearts we raise,
Unstrung by sin and pain,
  Long voiceless in thy praise:
Breathe thou the silent chords along,
Until they tremble into song.

3 Father of all, to thee
  We breathe unuttered fears,
Deep-hidden in our souls,
  That have no voice but tears: [wild
Take thou our hand, and through the
Lead gently on each trustful child.

4. Father of all, may we
  In praise our tongues employ,
When gladness fills the soul
  With deep and hallowed joy:
In storm and calm give us to see
The path of peace which leads to thee.

253

ISLEWORTH. (8 8. 8 6.)
Moderately slow.

Melody by S. HOWARD, 1710–82.

(304)

Charlotte Elliott, 1789–1871.

JUST as I am, without one plea
But that thy blood was shed for me,
And that thou bidd'st me come to thee,
O Lamb of God, I come.

2 Just as I am, though tossed about
With many a conflict, many a doubt,
Fightings within, and fears without:

3 Just as I am, poor, wretched, blind;
Sight, riches, healing of the mind,
Yea, all I need, in thee to find:

4 Just as I am, thou wilt receive,
Wilt welcome, pardon, cleanse, relieve,
Because thy promise I believe:

5 Just as I am (thy love unknown
Has broken every barrier down),
Now to be thine, yea, thine alone:

6. Just as I am, of that free love
The breadth, length, depth, and height
to prove,
Here for a season, then above:

(This hymn may be begun at verse 4.)

254

DIBDIN. (C.M.)
In moderate time.

Melody in *Standard Psalm Tune-book*, 1852.
Attributed there to Dr. JACKSON.

A-men.

[This hymn may also be sung to STRACATHRO, 438.]

M. Bridges, 1800–94.

MY God, accept my heart this day,
And make it always thine,
That I from thee no more may stray,
No more from thee decline.

2 Anoint me with thy heavenly grace,
And seal me for thine own;
That I may see thy glorious face,
And worship at thy throne.

3 Let every thought, and work, and word
To thee be ever given;
Then life shall be thy service, Lord,
And death the gate of heaven.

4. All glory to the Father be,
All glory to the Son,
All glory, Holy Ghost, to thee,
While endless ages run.

FIRST TUNE

KOMM, SEELE. (7 6. 7 6. D.)

In moderate time.

From a melody by J. W. FRANCK, ? 1641–88.

J. E. Bode, 1816–74.

O JESUS, I have promised
　　To serve thee to the end;
Be thou for ever near me,
　　My master and my friend;
I shall not fear the battle
　　If thou art by my side,
Nor wander from the pathway
　　If thou wilt be my guide.

2 O let me hear thee speaking
　　In accents clear and still,
Above the storms of passion,
　　The murmurs of self-will;
O speak to reassure me,
　　To hasten or control;
O speak, and make me listen,
　　Thou guardian of my soul.

SECOND TUNE

BREMEN. (7 6. 7 6. D.) Melody adapted from STÖRL's *Würtemberg Gesangbuch*, 1710.
In moderate time.

3 O Jesus, thou hast promised
  To all who follow thee,
That where thou art in glory
  There shall thy servant be;
And, Jesus, I have promised
  To serve thee to the end;
O give me grace to follow,
  My master and my friend.

4. O let me see thy footmarks,
  And in them plant mine own;
My hope to follow duly
  Is in thy strength alone;
O guide me, call me, draw me,
  Uphold me to the end;
And then in heaven receive me,
  My Saviour and my Friend.

255 (*continued*)

THIRD TUNE

THORNBURY. (7 6. 7 6. D.)

Unison. Slow.

BASIL HARWOOD, 1859–1949.

v. 3. Harmony.

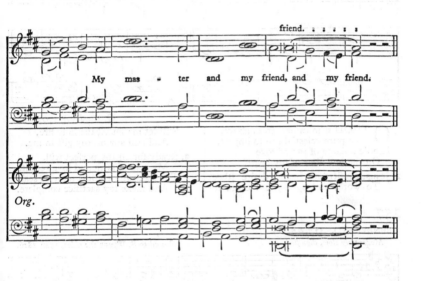

friend.

My mas - ter and my friend, and my friend.

Org.

J. E. Bode, 1816–74.

O JESUS, I have promised
  To serve thee to the end;
Be thou for ever near me,
  My master and my friend;
I shall not fear the battle
  If thou art by my side,
Nor wander from the pathway
  If thou wilt be my guide.

2 O let me hear thee speaking
  In accents clear and still,
Above the storms of passion,
  The murmurs of self-will;
O speak to reassure me,
  To hasten or control;
O speak, and make me listen,
  Thou guardian of my soul.

3 O Jesus, thou hast promised
  To all who follow thee,
That where thou art in glory
  There shall thy servant be;
And, Jesus, I have promised
  To serve thee to the end;
O give me grace to follow,
  My master and my friend.

4. O let me see thy footmarks,
  And in them plant mine own;
My hope to follow duly
  Is in thy strength alone;
O guide me, call me, draw me,
  Uphold me to the end;
And then in heaven receive me,
  My Saviour and my Friend.

256

ST. BARTHOLOMEW. (L.M.)

In moderate time.

HENRY DUNCALF (1762).

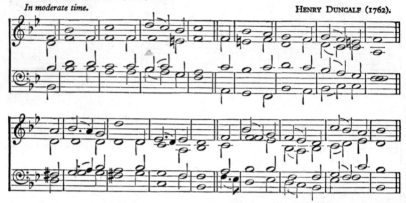

C. Wesley,† 1707–88.

O THOU who camest from above,
 The pure celestial fire to impart,
Kindle a flame of sacred love
 On the low altar of my heart.

2 Jesus, confirm my heart's desire [thee;
 To work, and speak, and think for

Still let me guard the holy fire,
 And still stir up thy gift in me.

3. Ready for all thy perfect will,
 My acts of faith and love repeat,
Till death thy endless mercies seal,
 And make my sacrifice complete.

257

BENEVENTO. (7 7. 7 7. D.)

Moderately slow, dignified.

Attributed to S. WEBBE the elder, 1740–1816.

[This hymn may also be sung to IVES, 306.]

CONFIRMATION, ADULT BAPTISM, AND SELF-DEDICATION

Frances R. Havergal, 1836–79.

TAKE my life, and let it be
  Consecrated, Lord, to thee;
Take my moments and my days,
Let them flow in ceaseless praise.
Take my hands, and let them move
At the impulse of thy love.
Take my feet, and let them be
Swift and beautiful for thee.

2 Take my voice, and let me sing
Always, only, for my King;
Take my lips, and let them be
Filled with messages from thee.

Take my silver and my gold;
Not a mite would I withhold.
Take my intellect, and use
Every power as thou shalt choose.

3. Take my will, and make it thine:
It shall be no longer mine.
Take my heart; it is thine own:
It shall be thy royal throne.
Take my love; my Lord, I pour
At thy feet its treasure-store.
Take myself, and I will be
Ever, only, all for thee.

258

HORSHAM. (7 7. 7 7.)

Slow.

English Traditional Melody.

Mrs. M. F. Maude, 1819–1913.

THINE for ever! God of love,
  Hear us from thy throne above;
Thine for ever may we be
Here and in eternity.

2 Thine for ever! O how blest
They who find in thee their rest!
Saviour, guardian, heavenly friend,
O defend us to the end.

3 Thine for ever! Lord of life,
Shield us through our earthly strife;

Thou the life, the truth, the way,
Guide us to the realms of day.

4*Thine for ever! Shepherd, keep
These thy frail and trembling sheep;
Safe alone beneath thy care,
Let us all thy goodness share.

5. Thine for ever! thou our guide,
All our wants by thee supplied,
All our sins by thee forgiven,
Led by thee from earth to heaven.

See also

259

BANGOR. (C.M.)

Moderately slow.

WILLIAM TANS'UR, *The Harmony of Zion*, 1734.

J. Montgomery, 1771–1854.

ACCORDING to thy gracious word,
  In meek humility
This will I do, my dying Lord,
  I will remember thee.

2 Thy body, broken for my sake,
  My bread from heaven shall be;
Thy testamental cup I take,
  And thus remember thee.

3 Gethsemane can I forget,
  Or there thy conflict see,
Thine agony and bloody sweat,
  And not remember thee?

4 When to the cross I turn mine eyes
  And rest on Calvary,
O Lamb of God, my sacrifice,
  I must remember thee:

5 Remember thee, and all thy pains,
  And all thy love to me;
Yea, while a breath, a pulse remains,
  Will I remember thee.

6. And when these failing lips grow dumb,
  And mind and memory flee,
When thou shalt in thy kingdom come,
  Jesus, remember me.

260

HYFRYDOL. (8 7. 8 7. D.)

Slow and dignified.

Melody by R. H. PRICHARD, 1811–87.

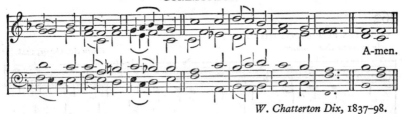

A-men.

W. Chatterton Dix, 1837–98.

ALLELUYA, sing to Jesus,
  His the sceptre, his the throne;
Alleluya, his the triumph,
  His the victory alone:
Hark! The songs of peaceful Sion
  Thunder like a mighty flood;
Jesus, out of every nation,
  Hath redeemed us by his blood.

2 Alleluya, not as orphans
  Are we left in sorrow now;
Alleluya, he is near us,
  Faith believes, nor questions how;

Though the cloud from sight received
  When the forty days were o'er, [him
Shall our hearts forget his promise,
  'I am with you evermore'?

3. Alleluya, alleluya,
  Glory be to God on high;
To the Father, and the Saviour,
  Who has gained the victory;
Glory to the Holy Spirit,
  Fount of love and sanctity;
Alleluya, alleluya,
  To the triune Majesty.

261

SONG 4. (10 10. 10 10. 10 10.)
Moderately slow.

ORLANDO GIBBONS, 1583–1625.

[This hymn may also be sung to SONG 1, 296.]

W. Bright, 1824–1901.

* AND now, O Father, mindful of the love
  That bought us, once for all, on
    Calvary's tree,
And having with us him that pleads
    above,
  We here present, we here spread forth
    to thee
That only offering perfect in thine eyes,
The one true, pure, immortal sacrifice.

2*Look, Father, look on his anointed face,
  And only look on us as found in him;
Look not on our misusings of thy grace,
  Our prayer so languid, and our faith
    so dim:
For lo! between our sins and their
    reward
We set the Passion of thy Son our Lord.

PART II   [best,
3 And then for those, our dearest and our
  By this prevailing presence we appeal;
O fold them closer to thy mercy's
    breast,   [weal:
  O do thine utmost for their souls' true
From tainting mischief keep them white
    and clear,   [persevere.
And crown thy gifts with strength to

4. And so we come; O draw us to thy feet,
  Most patient Saviour, who canst love
    us still;
And by this food, so aweful and so sweet,
  Deliver us from every touch of ill:
In thine own service make us glad and
    free,   [thee.
And grant us never more to part with

262

COELITES PLAUDANT. (11 11. 11 5.)

In moderate time. Unison.

Rouen Antiphoner, 1728.

DIVA SERVATRIX. (11 11. 11 5.)

In moderate time. Unison.

Bayeux Antiphoner, 1739.

(These two tunes to be sung consecutively to each verse.)

COMMUNION

P. Dearmer, 1867–1936.

AS the disciples, when thy Son had left them,
   Met in a love-feast, joyfully conversing,
All the stored memory of the Lord's last supper
          Fondly rehearsing;
So may we here, who gather now in friendship,
   Seek for the spirit of those earlier Churches,
Welcoming him who stands and for an entrance
          Patiently searches.

2 As, when their converse closed and supper ended,
   Taking the bread and wine they made thanksgiving,
Breaking and blessing, thus to have communion
          With Christ the living;
So may we here, a company of brothers,
   Make this our love-feast and commemoration,
That in his Spirit we may have more worthy
          Participation.

3. And as they prayed and sang to thee rejoicing,
   Ere in the night-fall they embraced and parted,
In their hearts singing as they journeyed homeward,
          Brave and true-hearted;
So may we here, like corn that once was scattered
   Over the hill-side, now one bread united,
Led by the Spirit, do thy work rejoicing,
          Lamps filled and lighted.

COMMUNION

263

DOLGELLY. (6 6. 6 6. 8 8.)

In moderate time.   Welsh Hymn Melody.

[This hymn may also be sung to RHOSYMEDRE, 127.]

J. and C. Wesley (1745).

AUTHOR of life divine,
  Who hast a table spread,
Furnished with mystic wine
And everlasting bread,
Preserve the life thyself hast given,
And feed and train us up for heaven.

2.   Our needy souls sustain
       With fresh supplies of love,
     Till all thy life we gain,
       And all thy fullness prove,
     And, strengthened by thy perfect grace,
     Behold without a veil thy face.

(316)

264

NICHT SO TRAURIG. (7 7. 7 7. 7 7.)

Slow and dignified.

J. S. BACH, 1685–1750.

[This hymn may also be sung to ARFON, 141.]

J. Conder,‡ 1789–1855.

BREAD of heaven, on thee we feed,
For thou art our food indeed;
Ever may our souls be fed
With this true and living bread,
Day by day with strength supplied
Through the life of him who died.

2. Vine of heaven, thy love supplies
This blest cup of sacrifice;
'Tis thy wounds our healing give;
To thy cross we look and live:
Thou our life! O let us be
Rooted, grafted, built on thee.

265

RENDEZ À DIEU. (9 8. 9 8. D.)

Slow and dignified.

Melody composed or adapted by L. BOURGEOIS
for Psalm 118 in the *Genevan Psalter*, 1543.

Bread of the world in mer-cy bro-ken, Wine of the soul in mer-cy shed, By whom the words of life were spo-ken, And in whose death our sins are dead: Look on the heart by sor-row bro-ken, Look on the tears by sin-ners shed, And be thy feast to us the to-ken That by thy grace our souls are fed.

Bishop R. Heber, 1783–1826.

(318)

266

BIRINGHAM. (10 10. 10 10.)

Slow.

From Rev. F. CUNNINGHAM'S *A Selection of Psalm Tunes*, 1834:

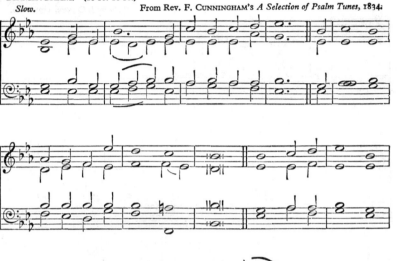

G. W. Briggs, 1875–1959.

COME, risen Lord, and deign to be our guest;
    Nay, let us be thy guests; the feast is thine;
Thyself at thine own board make manifest,
    In this our sacrament of bread and wine.

2 We meet, as in that upper room they met;
    Thou at the table, blessing, yet dost stand:
'This is my body': so thou givest yet:
    Faith still receives the cup as from thy hand.

3 One body we, one body who partake,
    One Church united in communion blest;
One name we bear, one bread of life we break,
    With all thy saints on earth and saints at rest.

4. One with each other, Lord, for one in thee,
    Who art one saviour and one living Head;
Then open thou our eyes, that we may see;
    Be known to us in breaking of the bread.

267

SCHMÜCKE DICH. (8 8. 8 8. D.)

Slow.

Melody by J. CRÜGER, 1598–1662.

NOTE.—*The original rhythm of lines 5 & 6 is as follows, and may be substituted for the above, if preferred:*

J. Franck, 1618–77. Tr. C. Winkworth.

Schmücke dich.

DECK thyself, my soul, with gladness,
Leave the gloomy haunts of sadness,
Come into the daylight's splendour,
There with joy thy praises render
Unto him whose grace unbounded
Hath this wondrous banquet founded:
High o'er all the heavens he reigneth,
Yet to dwell with thee he deigneth.

2 Now I sink before thee lowly,
Filled with joy most deep and holy,
As with trembling awe and wonder
On thy mighty works I ponder;
How, by mystery surrounded,
Depths no man hath ever sounded,
None may dare to pierce unbidden
Secrets that with thee are hidden.

PART II

3 Sun, who all my life dost brighten;
Light, who dost my soul enlighten;
Joy, the sweetest man e'er knoweth;
Fount, whence all my being floweth:
At thy feet I cry, my Maker,
Let me be a fit partaker
Of this blessèd food from heaven,
For our good, thy glory, given.

4. Jesus, Bread of Life, I pray thee,
Let me gladly here obey thee;
Never to my hurt invited,
Be thy love with love requited:
From this banquet let me measure,
Lord, how vast and deep its treasure;
Through the gifts thou here dost give me,
As thy guest in heaven receive me.

M

268

ST. SECHNALL. (10 10. 10 10.)

Rather slow. Unison.   Irish Traditional Melody. Harmonized by L. L. Dix, 1861–1935.

[This hymn may also be sung to Song 46, 125.]

7th cent. *S. P. V.*

Sancti, venite.

DRAW nigh and take the body of the Lord,
   And drink the life and grace for you outpoured.
Let us give thanks to him who makes us whole,
Preserving us in body and in soul.

2 Approach ye then with thankful hearts sincere,
And take the pledges of salvation here:
His servants, led and guarded by the Lord
For life eternal, gather round the board.

3. Offered was he for greatest and for least,
Himself the victim and himself the priest.
Your souls and bodies—less can ne'er suffice:
Offer yourselves a living sacrifice.

(322)

269

PSALM 80. (11 10. 11 10.)

In moderate time.

Scottish Psalter, 1635.

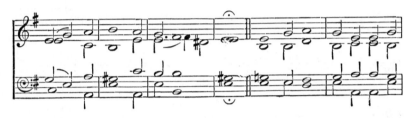

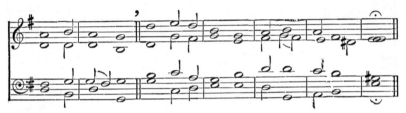

[This hymn may also be sung to CHARTERHOUSE, 283.]

J. G. Adderley, 1861–1942.

FATHER, we greet thee, God of Love, whose glory
　　Shines mirrored in the face of Jesus Christ,
Who by his perfect life of love and labour
　　And in his perfect death was sacrificed.

2 Father, we dare, by our great Brother bidden,
　　Take up the cross and humbly follow him:
Send out thy light and truth that they may lead us;
　　Show us the way amid the darkness dim.

3 Here we present ourselves, our souls and bodies,
　　Strengthened with bread, the food of every man,
Ready to love and work, but yet confessing
　　Lonely we cannot, by his grace we can.

4. Friends at his table, priests around his altar;
　　Soldiers of Christ, disciples of thy Son;
Father, we stand, prepared to do thy bidding;
　　Come, God's own Kingdom, and God's will be done.

270

ERFYNIAD. (10 10. 10 10.)

In moderate time.   Welsh Hymn Melody, harmonized by DAVID EVANS, 1874-1948.

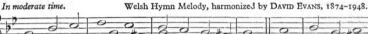

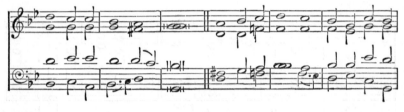

H. Bonar, 1808-89.

HERE, O my Lord, I see thee face to face;
  Here faith would touch and handle things unseen;
Here grasp with firmer hand the eternal grace,
  And all my weariness upon thee lean.

2 Here would I feed upon the bread of God;
  Here drink with thee the royal wine of heaven;
Here would I lay aside each earthly load;
  Here taste afresh the calm of sin forgiven.

3 This is the hour of banquet and of song;
  This is the heavenly table spread for me;
Here let me feast, and, feasting, still prolong
  The brief, bright hour of fellowship with thee.

4 Too soon we rise; the symbols disappear;
  The feast, though not the love, is past and gone;
The bread and wine remove, but thou art here,
  Nearer than ever, still my shield and sun.

5*I have no help but thine; nor do I need
  Another arm save thine to lean upon:
It is enough, my Lord, enough indeed,
  My strength is in thy might, thy might alone.

6.*Feast after feast thus comes and passes by,
  Yet, passing, points to the glad feast above,
Giving sweet foretaste of the festal joy,
  The Lamb's great bridal feast of bliss and love.

271

MEISTERSINGER CHORALE (DA ZU DIR DER HEILAND KAM).

(7 7. 7 7. 7 7. 4 4. 5 5.)

R. WAGNER, 1813-83.

1. Ho - ly God, we show forth here Je - sus' death, our
2. Lord, u - nite us ev - 'ry one Each to o - ther,

hearts to clear, Je - sus' life, our life to be,
through thy Son; Join us tru - ly heart to heart,

Je - sus' love, the world to free. Stay the faith - ful, win the strayed,
Let us ne'er be drawn a - part: All one bread, one bo - dy we,

Bless the liv - ing and the dead. Fa - ther lead us, Sa - viour feed us,
Bound by love to all and thee. Bless - ed Mas - ter, Bind us fas - ter;

Spi - rit be our store, Now and ev - - - - er - more.
In thy love di - vine, Love we thee . . . and thine!

[By permission of Schott & Co., Mainz and London.]

E. H.

272

O MENTES PERFIDAS. (6 6. 6 6. D.)

Moderately slow.

Melody from *Piae Cantiones*, 1582.

(For the last verse repeat the second half of this tune.)

[This hymn may also be sung to MAINZ (Maria Jung und Zart), 111.]

J. S. B. Monsell, 1811–75.

I HUNGER and I thirst;
  Jesus, my manna be:
Ye living waters, burst
  Out of the rock for me.

2 Thou bruised and broken Bread,
  My life-long wants supply;
As living souls are fed,
  O feed me, or I die.

3 Thou true life-giving Vine,
  Let me thy sweetness prove;
Renew my life with thine,
  Refresh my soul with love.

4 Rough paths my feet have trod,
  Since first their course began;
Feed me, thou Bread of God;
  Help me, thou Son of Man.

5. For still the desert lies
  My thirsting soul before;
O living waters, rise
  Within me evermore.

273

PICARDY. (8 7. 8 7. 8 7.)

Slow. Unison.

French carol tune as given in
Chanson Populaires des Provinces de France, 1860,
ed. J. FLEURY-WECKERLIN.

Liturgy of St. James. S. P. V.

Σιγησάτω πᾶσα σάρξ.

LET all mortal flesh keep silence, and with awe and welcome stand;
Harbour nothing earthly-minded; for, with blessing in his hand,
Christ our Lord with us abideth, loving homage to demand.

2 King is he, yet born a servant, Lord of all in humble guise,
Truly man, yet God revealing, God as love, to mortal eyes;
God with man, he leads and feeds us, he the power and he the prize.

3 Rank on rank the hosts immortal sweep in joy before thy face,
Shining in the light exalted, friends and loved ones in embrace,
As tne dark dissolves before thee, Light of all the human race.

4. At thy feet the seraphs cluster, veil their faces in that light,
Spirits of just men made perfect, now in timeless splendour dight,
Saints and angels, all adore thee, serve and praise thee in the height.

274

FIRST TUNE

BRYN CALFARIA. (8 7. 8 7. 4 7.)

Slow.

Melody by W. Owen, 1814–93.

Al - le - lu - ya! Al - le - lu - ya! Al - le - lu - ya!

Je - sus, true and liv - ing Bread. Je - sus, true and liv - ing Bread.

G. H. Bourne, 1840–1925.

LORD, enthroned in heavenly splendour,
First-begotten from the dead,
Thou alone, our strong defender,
Liftest up thy people's head.
Alleluya!
Jesus, true and living Bread.

2 Here our humblest homage pay we;
Here in loving reverence bow;
Here for faith's discernment pray we
Lest we fail to know thee now.
Alleluya!
Thou art here, we ask not how.

SECOND TUNE

AD PERENNIS VITAE FONTEM. (8 7. 8 7. 8 7.)

In free rhythm. Unison.

Source unknown (said to be from the *Tours Breviary*).

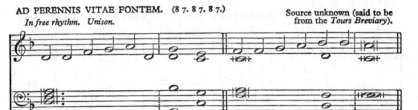

PART II

B. R.

3 Draw us in the Spirit's tether;
    For when humbly, in thy name,
Two or three are met together,
    Thou art in the midst of them:
        Alleluya!
    Touch we now thy garment's hem.

4 As the brethren used to gather
    In the name of Christ to sup,
Then with thanks to God the Father
    Break the bread and bless the cup,
        Alleluya!
    So knit thou our friendship up.

5. All our meals and all our living
    Make as sacraments of thee,
That by caring, helping, giving,
    We may true disciples be.
        Alleluya!
    We will serve thee faithfully.

COMMUNION

FARRANT. (C.M.)

Rather slow.

Adapted from an Anthem of the school of R. FARRANT, *c.* 1530–80;

ALTERNATIVE VERSION

Melody in the Tenor.

Fa-burden by MARTIN SHAW.

[*Copyright,* 1931, *by Martin Shaw.*]

(*Other occasions also.*) *The Abiding Presence.*   G. W. Briggs, 1875–1959.

O GOD, in whom we live and move,
  In whom we draw each breath,
Who fillest all the height above,
  And all the depths beneath;

2 Our hands may build thy hallowed fane,
  No bound thy presence owns;
The heaven of heavens cannot contain,
  The lowly heart enthrones.

3 Thou art about our path, where'er
  We seek to tread thy ways;
All life is sacrament and prayer,
  And every thought is praise.

(330)

COMMUNION

4 And when we gather in thy name,
    To pray with one accord,
  Around, within us, still the same,
    We find thy presence, Lord.

5 In simple faith or solemn rite,
    In head and heart and hand,
  Thou art; though hidden from our sight,
    Thou in our midst dost stand.

6. Be with us, Lord; with us abide;
    Go with us where we go;
  Changeless amid life's changing tide,
    Thy presence may we know.

276

SCHÖNSTER HERR JESU. (10 7. 10 7.)

Very slow.

Melody from *Münster Gesangbuch*, 1677.

Bishop R. Heber, 1783–1826.

O MOST merciful!
  O most bountiful!
God the Father Almighty,
By the Redeemer's
Sweet intercession,
Hear us, help us when we cry.

COMMUNION

277

VERBUM SUPERNUM.   (L.M.)

In free rhythm. Unison.

Melody from the *Antiphonarium Romanum*, Mechlin, 1848.

A - men...

SECOND TUNE

ERHALT' UNS, HERR.   (L.M.)

Very slow and solemn.

Later form of melody from KLUG, *Geistliche Lieder*, 1547.
Harmony from J. S. BACH, 1685-1750.

(332)

COMMUNION

St. Thomas Aquinas, 1227-74. Tr. cento.

O salutaris.

O SAVIOUR victim, opening wide
  The gates of life to man below,
Our foes press hard on every side:
  Thine aid supply, thy strength bestow.

2. All praise and thanks to thee ascend
   For evermore, blest One in three;
O grant us life that shall not end
   In our true native land with thee.

278

ACH GOTT UND HERR. (8 7. 8 7.)

Very slow and dignified.

Melody in *Neu-Leipziger Gesangbuch,* **1682.**
Adapted and harmonized by J. S. BACH, 1685-1750.

After the Communion.

Liturgy of Malabar. Tr. E. H.

Ḥayyēl Māran 'īdhē daphshaṭ.

STRENGTHEN for service, Lord, the hands
  That holy things have taken;
Let ears that now have heard thy songs
  To clamour never waken.

2 Lord, may the tongues which 'Holy' sang
  Keep free from all deceiving;
The eyes which saw thy love be bright,
  Thy blessèd hope perceiving.

3. The feet that tread thy hallowed courts
   From light do thou not banish;
The bodies by thy spirit fed
   With thy new life replenish.

(333)

279

ADORO TE. (10 10. 10 10.)
In free rhythm. Unison.
Proper Melody (from the Solesmes Version).

St. Thomas Aquinas, 1227–74. *Tr. Bp. J. R. Woodford.*
Adoro te devote.

THEE we adore, O hidden Saviour, thee,
Who in thy Supper with us deign'st to be;
Both flesh and spirit in thy presence fail,
Yet here thy presence we devoutly hail.

2 O blest memorial of our dying Lord,
Who living bread to men doth here afford!
O may our souls for ever feed on thee,
And thou, O Christ, for ever precious be.

3 Fountain of goodness, Jesus, Lord and God,
Cleanse us, unclean, in thy most cleansing flood;
Increase our faith and love, that we may know
The hope and peace which from thy presence flow.

4. O Christ, whom now beneath a veil we see,
May what we thirst for soon our portion be,
To gaze on thee unveiled, and see thy face,
The vision of thy glory and thy grace.

280

FIRST TUNE

PANGE LINGUA. (8 7. 8 7. 8 7.)
In free rhythm. Unison.
Melody from the *Mechlin Gradual.*

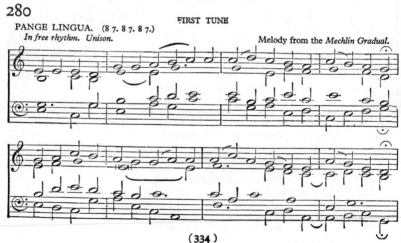

COMMUNION

A - men. .

SECOND TUNE

TANTUM ERGO (No. 2). (8 7. 8 7. 8 7.)
Very slow and solemn.

Probably by G. P. DA PALESTRINA, d. 1594.

A - - - men.

[This hymn may also be sung to ST. THOMAS, 342.]

St. Thomas Aquinas, 1227–74. Tr. cento.

Tantum ergo.

THEREFORE we, before him bending,
This great sacrament revere;
Types and shadows have their ending,
For the newer rite is here;
Faith, our outward sense befriending,
Makes the inward vision clear.

2. Glory let us give, and blessing
To the Father and the Son;
Honour, might, and praise addressing,
While eternal ages run;
Ever too his love confessing,
Who, from both, with both is one.

(335)

281

CHRISTE FONS JUGIS. (11 11. 11 5.)

Slow. May be sung in unison.

Rouen Church Melody.

S. P.

WHEREFORE, O Father, we thy humble servants
    Offer our praises, with our glad thanksgiving,
Offer ourselves, Lord, souls and bodies to thee,
    Christ's death proclaiming.

2. So, Lord, we thank thee, for that thou dost feed us,
    Members united in that mystic body—
Company blessèd of all faithful people:
    Thus we would serve thee.

See also

449 As pants the hart   253 Just as I am
496 From glory to glory   573 Love divine
508 Guide me, O thou   256 O thou who camest

Hymns for the Seasons and General Hymns are also suitable.

282

FAITHFUL. (6 6. 6 6. 7 7. 6 6 6.)
In moderate time.

From a Scottish Traditional Melody.

[*Copyright, 1931, by Martin Shaw.*]

Jan Struther, 1901–53.

GOD, whose eternal mind
  Rules the round world over,
Whose wisdom lies behind
  All that men discover:
Grant that we, by thought and speech,
May grow nearer each to each;
  Lord, let sweet converse bind
    Lover unto lover.
      Bless us, God of loving.

2   Godhead in human guise
    Once to earth returning,
  Daily through human eyes
    Joys of earth discerning:
Grant that we may treasure less
Passion than true tenderness,
  Yet never, Lord, despise
    Heart to sweetheart turning.
      Bless us, God of loving.

3   God, whose unbounded grace
    Heaven and earth pervadeth,
  Whose mercy doth embrace
    All thy wisdom madeth:
Grant that we may, hand in hand,
All forgive, all understand;
  Keeping, through time and space,
    Trust that never fadeth.
      Bless us, God of loving.

4.   God, who art three in One,
    All things comprehending,
  Wise Father, valiant Son,
    In the Spirit blending:
Grant us love's eternal three—
Friendship, rapture, constancy;
  Lord, till our lives be done,
    Grant us love unending.
      Bless us, God of loving.

(337)

283

CHARTERHOUSE. (11 10. 11 10.)

In moderate time. Unison.

DAVID EVANS, 1874–1948.

[*Copyright, 1927, by David Evans.*]

Mrs. Dorothy F. Gurney, 1858–1932.

O PERFECT Love, all human thought transcending,
Lowly we kneel in prayer before thy throne,
That theirs may be the love which knows no ending
Whom thou for evermore dost join in one.

2 O perfect Life, be thou their full assurance
Of tender charity and steadfast faith,
Of patient hope, and quiet brave endurance,
With childlike trust that fears nor pain nor death.

3. Grant them the joy which brightens earthly sorrow,
Grant them the peace which calms all earthly strife;
And to life's day the glorious unknown morrow
That dawns upon eternal love and life.

284

AFFECTION. (L.M.)

In moderate time.

Greenwood's Psalmody, Halifax, 1838.

(338)

MARRIAGE

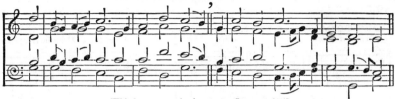

[This hymn may also be sung to ILLSLEY, 610.]

Bishop Mandell Creighton, 1843–1901.

O THOU who gavest power to love
  That we might fix our hearts on
    thee,
Preparing us for joys above
  By that which here on earth we see:

2 Thy Spirit trains our souls to know
  The growing purpose of thy will,
And gives to love the power to show
  That purpose growing larger still;

3 Larger, as love to reverent eyes
  Makes manifest another soul,
And shows to life a richer prize,
  A clearer course, a nobler goal.

4 Lord, grant thy servants who implore
  Thy blessing on the hearts they
    blend,
That from that union evermore
  New joys may blossom to the end.

5*Make what is best in each combine
  To purge all earthly dross away,
To strengthen, purify, refine,
  To beautify each coming day.

6.*So may they hand in hand advance
  Along life's path from troubles free;
Brave to meet adverse circumstance
  Because their love points up to thee.

See also

487 Father, hear the prayer
509 Happy are they
555 Lead us, heavenly Father

92 Love came down
573 Love divine
626 Praise to the Lord

See also Part VI, Thanksgiving, and Part VIII, Doxologies.

285   THE SICK: HOSPITAL SUNDAY

FARNHAM. (C.M.)
In moderate time.   From an English Traditional Melody.

Charles Kingsley, 1819–75.

FROM thee all skill and science flow,
  All pity, care, and love,
All calm and courage, faith and hope:
  O pour them from above!

2 And part them, Lord, to each and all,
  As each and all shall need
To rise, like incense, each to thee,
  In noble thought and deed.

3 And hasten, Lord, that perfect day
  When pain and death shall cease,
And thy just rule shall fill the earth
  With health, and light, and peace;

4. When ever blue the sky shall gleam,
  And ever green the sod,
And man's rude work deface no more
  The paradise of God.

286

AMSTERDAM. (7 6. 7 6. 7 8. 7 6.)

In moderate time.

From *Sacred Harmony* (1821?).

Bp. J. R. Darbyshire, 1880–1948.

LIFE and health are in the name
Of Jesus Christ our Lord:
Father, forth from thee he came
To be the healing Word.
Now our hearts rejoice to know,
Marking his life as man with men,
Nought there is of weal or woe
That lies beyond thy ken.

2 Oft, alas, in hours of pain
Sick fancies seize the mind;
Worn and tempted we complain
Thy heart is all unkind.
Then thy mercy, shining clear,
Richly our lives with blessing fills,
Shaming all our doubt and fear,
And healing all our ills.

3 Thine the gift of patient will
Affliction to endure;
Thine the gift of eager skill
That toils to find a cure.
Art to quell the fever's rage,
Faith in the potency of prayer,
Knowledge gained from age to age,
Are tokens of thy care.

4. Teach us how to use aright
These bounties of thy grace,
Bringing sweetness, health and light
In every stricken place.
May on earth thy Kingdom grow,
Knowledge and faith have common [aim,
And the fruits of mercy show
The splendour of thy name.

287

ST. MATTHEW. (D.C.M.)

In moderate time.

Probably by W. CROFT, 1678–1727 (later form of melody).

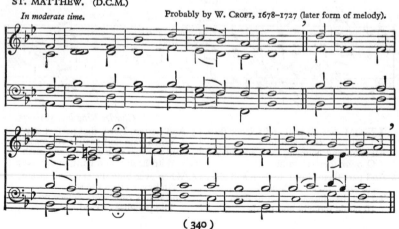

E. H. Plumptre, 1821–91.

THINE arm, O Lord, in days of old
　Was strong to heal and save;
It triumphed o'er disease and death,
　O'er darkness and the grave;
To thee they went, the blind, the dumb,
　The palsied and the lame,
The leper with his tainted life,
　The sick with fevered frame.

2 And lo! thy touch brought life and
　　health,
　Gave speech, and strength, and sight;
And youth renewed and frenzy calmed
　Owned thee the Lord of light;
And now, O Lord, be near to bless,
　Almighty as of yore,
In crowded street, by restless couch,
　As by Gennesareth's shore.

3. Be thou our great deliverer still,
　Thou Lord of life and death;
Restore and quicken, soothe and bless
　With thine almighty breath;
To hands that work, and eyes that see,
　Give wisdom's heavenly lore,
That whole and sick, and weak and strong,
　May praise thee evermore.

See also

THE LIFE BEYOND
FUNERALS AND COMMEMORATIONS

CAMBRIDGE. (6 6. 6 5. 6 5.)

Rather slowly.

CHARLES WOOD, 1866–1926.

ORGAN.

Ped.

Voices.

1. Christ who knows all his sheep Will all . in safe - ty
   take this spi - rit: We trust . thy love and

keep, He will not lose one soul, Nor ev - er
me - rit. Take home the wand - 'ring sheep, For thou hast

fail us; Nor we the prom - ised goal, Though hell as -
sought it; This soul in safe - ty keep, For thou hast

Small notes Org.

Unison.

- sail us.
bought it.
2. I know my

ORGAN.

(342)

FINE (*small notes*).

God is just; To him I whol-ly trust All that I have and am, All that I hope for: All's sure and seen to him, Which here I grope for.

3. Lord Je - sus,

N.B.—*If desired, the music for this hymn can follow verse 1 throughout.*
[*Copyright, 1925, by Oxford University Press.*]

Richard Baxter,‡ 1615–91.

CHRIST who knows all his sheep
Will all in safety keep,
He will not lose one soul,
Nor ever fail us;
Nor we the promised goal,
Though hell assail us.

2 I know my God is just;
To him I wholly trust
All that I have and am,
All that I hope for:
All's sure and seen to him,
Which here I grope for.

3. Lord Jesus, take this spirit:
We trust thy love and merit.
Take home the wandering sheep,
For thou hast sought it;
This soul in safety keep,
For thou hast bought it.

(343)

289.

MEYER (ES IST KEIN TAG). (8 8. 8 4.)

Moderately slow.

Melody in J. MEYER's *Seelenfreud*, 1692.

Commemoration.

W. *Charter Piggott*, 1872–1943.

FOR those we love within the veil,
  Who once were comrades of our way,
We thank thee, Lord; for they have won
  To cloudless day;

2 And life for them is life indeed,
  The splendid goal of earth's strait race;
And where no shadows intervene
  They see thy face.

3 Not as we knew them any more,
  Toilworn, and sad with burdened care:
Erect, clear-eyed, upon their brows
  Thy name they bear.

4 Free from the fret of mortal years,
  And knowing now thy perfect will,
With quickened sense and heightened joy,
  They serve thee still.

5 O fuller, sweeter is that life,
  And larger, ampler is the air:
Eye cannot see nor heart conceive
  The glory there;

6 Nor know to what high purpose thou
  Dost yet employ their ripened powers,
Nor how at thy behest they touch
  This life of ours.

7. There are no tears within their eyes;
  With love they keep perpetual tryst;
And praise and work and rest are one
  With thee, O Christ.

290

BATTLE. (10 10. 10 10.)

Moderately slow.

H. LAWES, 1596-1662.

[This hymn may also be sung to FFIGYSBREN, 560.]

Mrs. J. R. C. Dorr, 1825-1913.

HOW can I cease to pray for thee? Somewhere
    In God's great universe thou art to-day.
Can he not reach thee with his tender care?
    Can he not hear me when for thee I pray?

2 What matters it to him who holds within
    The hollow of his hands all worlds, all space,
That thou art done with earthly pain and sin?
    Somewhere within his ken thou hast a place.

3 Somewhere thou livest, and hast need of him;
    Somewhere thy soul sees higher heights to climb;
And somewhere still there may be valleys dim
    That thou must pass to reach the hills sublime.

4. Then all the more, e'en if thou canst not hear
    Poor human words of blessing, will I pray,
O true, brave heart! God bless thee, wheresoe'er
    In God's great universe thou art to-day!

291

PSALM 42. (8 7. 8 7. 7 7. 8 8.)

In moderate time, majestically.

Composed or adapted by
L. BOURGEOIS for *Genevan Psalter, 1551.*

All Hallows Sequence.

Adam of St. Victor, c. 1170. Tr. R. Bridges.

Supernae matris gaudia.

JOY and triumph everlasting
  Hath the heavenly Church on high;
For that pure immortal gladness
  All our feast-days mourn and sigh:
Yet in death's dark desert wild
Doth the mother aid her child,
Guards celestial thence attend us,
Stand in combat to defend us.

2 Here the world's perpetual warfare
    Holds from heaven the soul apart;
Legioned foes in shadowy terror
    Vex the Sabbath of the heart.
O how happy that estate
Where delight doth not abate!
For that home the spirit yearneth,
Where none languisheth nor mourneth.

3 There the body hath no torment,
    There the mind is free from care,
There is every voice rejoicing,
    Every heart is loving there.
Angels in that city dwell;
Them their King delighteth well:
Still they joy and weary never,
More and more desiring ever.

4.*There the seers and fathers holy,
    There the prophets glorified,
All their doubts and darkness ended,
    In the Light of Light abide.
There the saints, whose memories old
We in faithful hymns uphold,
Have forgot their bitter story
In the joy of Jesus' glory.

(346)

THE LIFE BEYOND

292

PRESSBURG (NICHT SO TRAURIG). (7 7. 7 7. 7 7.)

FREYLINGHAUSEN'S *Neues Geistreiches Gesangbuch*, 1714;
Simplified form of melody.

Slow and solemn.

P. Dearmer, 1867–1936.

NOW thy earthly work is done:
　　Ours the sorrow, thine the gain;
　　From this life's tumultuous strain
Thou hast passed, from shade to sun:

　　　Live in peace, where Christ doth shine!
　　　Tireless, deathless joy be thine!

2 We are groping, thou dost see;
　　Gone for thee are doubts and fears,
　　Gone are struggles, wrongs, and tears;
New-born spirit, thou art free:

3 Though thy voice we cannot hear,
　　Thou wilt not be far away;
　　Sometimes, when we rest or pray,
We shall know thy spirit near:

4. Friend, God bless thee! May his might
　　Gird thy soul, and give us share
　　In thy work, and joy, and prayer,
Till we join thee in the light:

(347)

293

VALIANT HEARTS. (10 10. 10 10.)

In moderate time.

GUSTAV HOLST, 1874–1934.

Small notes Organ pedals only.

Commemoration.   *J. S. Arkwright*, 1872–1954.

O VALIANT hearts, who to your glory came
    Through dust of conflict and through battle flame;
Tranquil you lie, your knightly virtue proved,
Your memory hallowed in the land you loved.

2*Proudly you gathered, rank on rank, to war,
  As who had heard God's message from afar;
All you had hoped for, all you had, you gave
To save mankind—yourself you scorned to save.

3*Splendid you passed, the great surrender made,
  Into the light that never more shall fade;
Deep your contentment in that blest abode,
Who wait the last clear trumpet-call of God.

4 Long years ago, as earth lay dark and still,
  Rose a loud cry upon a lonely hill,
While in the frailty of our human clay,
Christ, our redeemer, passed the self-same way.

5 Still stands his cross from that dread hour to this,
  Like some bright star above the dark abyss;
Still, through the veil, the Victor's pitying eyes
Look down to bless our lesser Calvaries.

6 These were his servants, in his steps they trod,
  Following through death the martyred Son of God:
Victor he rose; victorious too shall rise
They who have drunk his cup of sacrifice.

7. O risen Lord, O shepherd of our dead,
  Whose cross has bought them and whose staff has led,
In glorious hope their proud and sorrowing land
Commits her children to thy gracious hand.

(348)

THE LIFE BEYOND

ALTERNATIVE VERSION FOR VERSES 3 AND 7

VOICES IN UNISON.

ORGAN.

con 8ves ad lib.

SECOND TUNE

VALOR. (10 10. 10 10.)
In moderate time.

Adapted from a Traditional Melody.

(349)

294

FANAD HEAD. (10 8. 10 6.)

Slow.   Irish Traditional Melody. Harmonized by C. H. KITSON, 1874–1944.

Henry Vaughan the Silurist, 1622–95.

THEY are all gone into the world of light,
    And I alone sit lingering here;
Their very memory is fair and bright,
    And my sad thoughts doth clear.

2 I see them walking in an air of glory,
    Whose light doth trample on my days;
My days, which are at best but dull and hoary,
    Mere glimmering and decays.

3 Dear beauteous death! the jewel of the just,
    Shining nowhere but in the dark;
What mysteries do lie beyond thy dust,
    Could man outlook that mark!

4 And yet as angels in some brighter dreams
    Call to the soul when man doth sleep;
So some strange thoughts transcend our wonted themes,
    And into glory peep.

5. O Father of eternal life, and all
    Created glories under thee,
Resume thy spirit from this world of thrall
    Into true liberty.

295

NUN KOMM, DER HEIDEN HEILAND. (7 7. 7 7.)

Very slow. Later form of melody in Walther's *Gesangbuchlein*, 1524.

Commemoration.

J. M. Neale, 1818–66, and others.

THEY whose course on earth is o'er,
  Think they of their brethren more?
They before the throne who bow,
Feel they for their brethren now?

2 We by enemies distrest—
  They in paradise at rest;
  We the captives—they the freed;
  We and they are one indeed:

3 One in all we seek or shun,
  One, because our Lord is one;
  One in home and one in love;
  We below, and they above.

4*Those whom space on earth divides,
  Mountains, rivers, ocean-tides;
  Have they with each other part?
  Have they fellowship in heart?

5*Each to each may be unknown,
  Wide apart their lots be thrown;
  Yet in sacrament and prayer
  Each with other hath a share.

6*Saints departed, even thus
  Hold communion still with us;
  Still with us, beyond the veil,
  Praising, pleading without fail.

7. So with them our hearts we raise,
  Share their work and join their praise,
  Rendering worship, thanks, and love
  To the King of saints above.

THE LIFE BEYOND

296

SONG 1. (10 10. 10 10. 10 10.)

Moderately slow.

ORLANDO GIBBONS, 1583–1625.

G. F. Bradby, 1863–1947.

WHERE is death's sting? We were not born to die,
　　Nor only for the life beyond the grave;
All that is beautiful in earth and sky,
　　All skill, all knowledge, all the powers we have,
Are of thy giving, and in them we see
No dust and ashes, but a part of thee.

2 Laughter is thine, the laughter free from scorn,
　　And thine the smile upon a cheerful face:
Thine, too, the tears, when love for love must mourn,
　　And death brings silence for a little space.
Thou gavest, and thou dost not take away:
The parting is but here, and for a day.

(352)

3. Fullness of life, in body, mind and soul;
　　'Who saves his life shall lose it,' thou hast said:
A great adventure with a glorious goal;
　　Nothing that lives in thee is ever dead:
Brave living here: and then, beyond the grave,
More life and more adventure for the brave.

See also

459 Brief life is here our portion
463 Children of the heavenly King
347 Father, to thee we look
514 He wants not friends
155 Jesus lives!

557 Let saints on earth
115 O let him whose sorrow
208 Rejoice, ye dead
201 There is a land of pure delight
325 What heroes thou hast bred

MINISTERIAL SERVICE

297

BRUNSWICK. (8 6. 8 6. 8 6.)

In moderate time.

Adapted from G. F. HANDEL, 1685–1759.

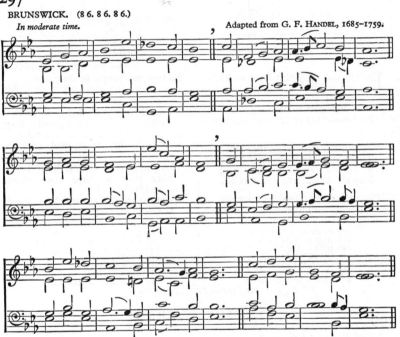

T. T. Lynch, 1818–71.

DISMISS me not thy service, Lord,
　　But train me for thy will;
For even I, in fields so broad,
　　Some duties may fulfil;
And I will ask for no reward,
　　Except to serve thee still.

2 All works are good, and each is best
　　As most it pleases thee;
Each worker pleases, when the rest
　　He serves in charity;
And neither man nor work unblest
　　Wilt thou permit to be.

3. Our Master all the work hath done
　　He asks of us to-day;
Sharing his service, every one
　　Share too his sonship may:
Lord, I would serve and be a son;
　　Dismiss me not, I pray.

N

298

DUKE STREET. (L.M.)

In moderate time.

J. HATTON, d. 1793.

(A descant to this tune will be found at 491.)

J. Montgomery,‡ 1771–1854.

POUR out thy Spirit from on high;
  Lord, thine assembled servants
    bless;
Graces and gifts to each supply,
  And clothe thy priests with righteous-
    ness.

2 Within the temple when they stand,
    To teach the truth, as taught by thee,
  Saviour, like stars in thy right hand
    May all thy Church's pastors be.

3 Wisdom, and zeal, and faith impart,
    Firmness with meekness, from above,

To bear thy people in their heart,
  And love the souls whom thou dost
    love:

4 To watch, and pray, and never faint,
    By day and night, strict guard to keep,
  To warn the sinner, cheer the saint,
    Nourish thy lambs, and feed thy
      sheep.

5. Then, when their work is finished here,
    May they in hope their charge
      resign;
  When the chief Shepherd shall appear,
    O God, may they and we be thine.

See also

304 *Pioneers.* All the past
450 Awake, awake to love
456 Blest be the day
178 Come, Holy Ghost
179 Come, O creator Spirit
485 Eternal Ruler
487 Father, hear the prayer

63 High o'er the lonely hills
391 Holy Spirit, make us strong
635 Rise up, O men of God
642 Soldiers of the cross
645 Spread, still spread
687 Wake, O wake
702 Ye servants of the Lord

See also Part IV, Social Service

299

SERVICE OVERSEA

WOODLANDS. (10 10. 10 10.)

In moderate time. Voices in unison.

W. GREATOREX, 1877–1949.

Basil Mathews, 1879–1951.

FAR round the world thy children sing their song;
  From East and West their voices sweetly blend,
Praising the Lord in whom young lives are strong,
  Jesus our guide, our hero, and our friend.

2*Guide of the pilgrim clambering to the height,
  Hero on whom our fearful hearts depend,
Friend of the wanderer yearning for the light,
  Jesus our guide, our hero, and our friend.

3 Where thy wide ocean, wave on rolling wave,
  Beats through the ages on each island shore,
They praise their Lord, whose hand alone can save,
  Whose sea of love surrounds them evermore.

4 Thy sun-kissed children on earth's spreading plain,
  Where Asia's rivers water all the land,
Sing, as they watch thy fields of glowing grain,
  Praise to the Lord who feeds them with his hand.

5 Still there are lands where none have seen thy face,
  Children whose hearts have never shared thy joy:
Yet thou would'st pour on these thy radiant grace,
  Give thy glad strength to every girl and boy.

6.*All round the world let children sing thy song,
  From East and West their voices sweetly blend;
Praising the Lord in whom young lives are strong,
  Jesus our guide, our hero, and our friend.

(355)

300

PURPOSE. (Irreg.)

In moderate time. With breadth.

MARTIN SHAW, 1875–1958.

1. God is work-ing his pur-pose out as year suc-ceeds to year;
2.* From ut-most east to ut-most west where-'er man's foot hath trod, By the
3. What can we do to work God's work, to pros-per and in-crease The
4. March we forth in the strength of God with the banner of Christ un-furled, That the
5.* All we can do is noth-ing worth un-less God blesses the deed;

God is work-ing his pur-pose out and the time is draw-ing near;
mouth of man-y mes-sen-gers goes forth the voice of God,
bro-ther-hood of all man-kind, the reign of the Prince of Peace?
light of the glo-rious gos-pel of truth may shine through-out the world;
Vain-ly we hope for the har-vest-tide till God gives life to the seed; Yet

Near-er and near-er draws the time, the time that shall sure-ly be,
'Give ear to me, ye con-ti-nents, ye isles, give ear to me,
What can we do to hasten the time, the time that shall sure-ly be,
Fight we the fight with sorrow and sin, to set their cap-tives free,
near-er and near-er draws the time, the time that shall sure-ly be,

8ves.

SERVICE OVERSEA

When the earth shall be filled with the glo - ry of God as the
That the earth may be filled with the glo - ry of God as the
When the earth shall be filled with the glo - ry of God as the
That the earth may be filled with the glo - ry of God as the
When the earth shall be filled with the glo - ry of God as the

8ves. . . . .

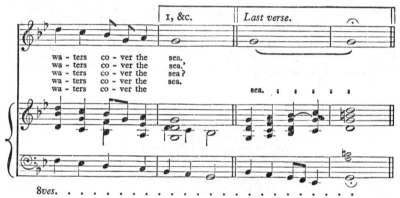

wa - ters co - ver the sea.
wa - ters co - ver the sea.'
wa - ters co - ver the sea?
wa - ters co - ver the sea.
wa - ters co - ver the sea.

1, &c. ‖ *Last verse.*

8ves. . . . . . .

A. C. Ainger, 1841–1919.

GOD is working his purpose out as year succeeds to year;
   God is working his purpose out and the time is drawing near;
Nearer and nearer draws the time, the time that shall surely be,
When the earth shall be filled with the glory of God as the waters cover the sea.

2*From utmost east to utmost west where'er man's foot hath trod,
   By the mouth of many messengers goes forth the voice of God,
   'Give ear to me, ye continents, ye isles, give ear to me,
   That the earth may be filled with the glory of God as the waters cover the sea.'

3 What can we do to work God's work, to prosper and increase
   The brotherhood of all mankind, the reign of the Prince of Peace?
   What can we do to hasten the time, the time that shall surely be,
   When the earth shall be filled with the glory of God as the waters cover the sea?

4 March we forth in the strength of God with the banner of Christ unfurled,
   That the light of the glorious gospel of truth may shine throughout the world;
   Fight we the fight with sorrow and sin, to set their captives free,
   That the earth may be filled with the glory of God as the waters cover the sea.

5.*All we can do is nothing worth unless God blesses the deed;
   Vainly we hope for the harvest-tide till God gives life to the seed;
   Yet nearer and nearer draws the time, the time that shall surely be,
   When the earth shall be filled with the glory of God as the waters cover the sea.

(357)

301

ST. DAVID. (C.M.)

In moderate time.

Later form of melody in *Ravenscroft's Psalter*, 1621.

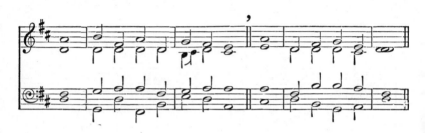

J. Montgomery, 1771–1854.

LIFT up your heads, ye gates of brass;
 Ye bars of iron, yield,
And let the King of Glory pass:
 The cross is in the field.

2 That banner, brighter than the star
 That leads the train of night,
Shines on their march, and guides from far
 His servants to the fight.

3 A holy war those servants wage;
 Mysteriously at strife,
The powers of heaven and hell engage
 For more than death or life.

4 Ye armies of the living God,
 His sacramental host,
Where hallowed footsteps never trod,
 Take your appointed post.

5 Though few and small and weak your bands,
 Strong in your captain's strength,
Go to the conquest of all lands:
 All must be his at length.

6.*Uplifted are the gates of brass,
 The bars of iron yield;
Behold the King of Glory pass:
 The cross hath won the field.

SERVICE OVERSEA

ALTERNATIVE VERSION

Trebles.

Descant by CYRIL B. ROOTHAM.

Choir and Organ.

[*Copyright, 1931, by Oxford University Press.*]

302

MARATHON. (8 7. 8 7. D.)

In moderate march time.   Unison.

R. VAUGHAN WILLIAMS, 1872–1958.

con 8va.

[*Copyright*, 1928, *by R. Vaughan Williams.*]

P. Dearmer, 1867–1936.

SERVANTS of the great adventure,
   Patriots of God's fatherland,
Fired by one supreme ambition,
   Ready for the call we stand.
Cleanse our minds, thou Love all-
    ruling,
   Steel our wills, unbind our eyes
That we see aright thy Kingdom;
   Make us daring, free, and wise.

2 Millions lie in crying darkness,
   Unredeemed, untamed, untaught,
Women prone in sealed oppression,
   Men like cattle sold and bought;
Millions grope through outworn systems;
   Many a cruel ancient faith
Binds the earth; and many a rebel
   Dooms the Christ again to death.

3 Yet men everywhere have found thee,
　　Christ, the crown of every creed;
　All the faiths and all the systems
　　To thy revelation lead;
　Thou dost guide our human groping,
　　Who hast won the hearts of men;
　Thou wilt fill the world with splendour—
　　In our hands the how and when.

4 All the world shall live in kindness,
　　Hate and war shall pass away,
　When men grow from out their blind-
　　ness,
　Wake, and see the blaze of day:
　Each but needs the truth to win him,
　　Shape the beauty of his soul,
　Fan the fire of love within him,
　　Save from self and make him whole.

PART II

5 Christ to us across the water
　　Came of old from Palestine,
　West and ever farther westward
　　Came the eastern Light to shine;
　Long and stubborn was the struggle
　　Ere our fathers' hearts were won;
　Often have we warped the message,
　　Stood like clouds before the sun.

6 But, for all our faults and failures,
　　'Tis through Christ the West has
　　　grown;
　And 'tis ours to give to others
　　What we dare not keep alone.
　Death will come, and crumbling chaos,
　　If we share not with the earth
　That which tempers might with mercy,
　　Gives to science human worth.

7 We have probed, and piled up knowledge,
　　Weighed the stars, and wrought our will,
　Marshalled fire and harnessed lightning,
　　Made men gods for good or ill:
　Only that which bred our greatness—
　　Freedom all the truth to find,
　Love revealed in one Perfection—
　　Is not fathomed by mankind.

8 Thou art building up a city
　　Pictured perfect in thy thought;
　And from glimpses of that pattern
　　All man's fairest things are wrought:
　Thou dost call as fellow-workers
　　Us, to serve thy great design:
　Thou, the artist, thou, the maker,
　　Dost to each his part assign.

Conclusion to either Part

9. Praise God for the hidden leaven,
　　For the depths yet unexplored;
　Praise him for the Realm of Heaven—
　　All ye peoples, praise the Lord!
　Sing, the round world all together,
　　With one mind and heart and mouth;
　Glorify the Lord All-Father,
　　East and West and North and South!

303

MOSCOW. (6 6 4. 6 6 6. 4.)

Moderately slow.

Adapted from F. GIARDINI, 1716–96.

Home or Oversea.

J. Marriott,‡ 1780–1825.

THOU whose almighty Word
Chaos and darkness heard,
  And took their flight;
Hear us, we humbly pray,
And where the Gospel-day
Sheds not its glorious ray
  Let there be light!

2 Thou who didst come to bring
On thy redeeming wing
  Healing and sight,
Health to the sick in mind,
Sight to the inly blind,
Ah! now to all mankind
  Let there be light!

3 Spirit of truth and love,
Life-giving, holy Dove,
  Speed forth thy flight!
Move on the waters' face,
Bearing the lamp of grace,
And in earth's darkest place
  Let there be light!

SERVICE OVERSEA

ALTERNATIVE VERSION

Trebles sing the top line, all other parts the melody MOSCOW.

Descant by ALAN GRAY.

4. Blessèd and holy Three,
   Glorious Trinity,
   Wisdom, love, might;
   Boundless as ocean tide
   Rolling in fullest pride,
   Through the world far and wide
   Let there be light!

PART IV

SOCIAL SERVICE

GENERAL

304

PIONEERS. (7. 8 8. 8 8. 7.)

Moderately fast.

Voices in unison.   MARTIN SHAW, 1875–1958.

1. All the past we leave be-
hind: We take up the task e - ter - nal, and the
burden, and the les - son, Con - quering, hold - ing, dar - ing,

(vv. 2, 3 & 4.)

ven - turing, so we go the un - known ways,

Pi - on - eers! O pi - on - eers!

Pioneers.   *Walt Whitman (cento), 1819–92.*

ALL the past we leave behind:
　　We take up the task eternal, and the burden, and the lesson,
Conquering, holding, daring, venturing, so we go the unknown ways,
　　Pioneers! O pioneers!

2　　Not for delectations sweet,
　Not the riches safe and pailing, not for us the tame enjoyment;
Never must you be divided, in our ranks you move united,
　　Pioneers! O pioneers!

3　　All the pulses of the world,
　All the joyous, all the sorrowing, these are of us, they are with us;
We to-day's procession heading, we the route for travel clearing,
　　Pioneers! O pioneers!

4.　　On and on the compact ranks,
　With accessions ever waiting, we must never yield or falter,
Through the battle, through defeat, moving yet and never stopping,
　　Pioneers! O pioneers!

305

TRES MAGI DE GENTIBUS. (7 8. 7 8. Irreg.)

In moderate time.   Melody in the *Andernach Gesangbuch*, 1608 (slightly adapted).

1. Lit - tle things that run and quail And die in

si - lence and des - pair; 2. Lit - tle things that

fight and fail And fall on sea and earth and

air; 3. All trapped and fright - ened lit - tle things, The

mouse, the con - ey, hear our prayer: 4. As we for-

give those done to us, The lamb, the lin - net,

and the hare, 5. For - give us all our

tres - pass - es, Lit - tle crea - tures ev - 'ry - where.

Animals.

James Stephens, 1882–1950.

LITTLE things that run and quail
  And die in silence and despair;

2 Little things that fight and fail
  And fall on sea and earth and air;

3 All trapped and frightened little things,
  The mouse, the coney, hear our prayer:

4 As we forgive those done to us,
  The lamb, the linnet, and the hare,

5. Forgive us all our trespasses,
  Little creatures everywhere.

306

IVES. (7 7. 7 7. D.)
Brightly.

Melody from *Plymouth Collection* (U.S.A.), 1855.

J. Russell Lowell, 1819–91.

MEN, whose boast it is that ye
Come of fathers brave and free,
If there breathe on earth a slave,
Are ye truly free and brave?
If ye do not feel the chain
When it works a brother's pain,
Are ye not base slaves indeed,
Slaves unworthy to be freed?

2 Is true freedom but to break
Fetters for our own dear sake,
And, with leathern hearts, forget
That we owe mankind a debt?
No! true freedom is to share
All the chains our brothers wear,
And, with heart and hand, to be
Earnest to make others free.

3. They are slaves who fear to speak
For the fallen and the weak;
They are slaves who will not choose
Hatred, scoffing, and abuse,
Rather than in silence shrink
From the truth they needs must think;
They are slaves who dare not be
In the right with two or three.

307

INTERCESSOR. (11 10. 11 10.)

Slow.

C. HUBERT H. PARRY, 1848–1918.

[*Copyright*, 1904, *by the Proprietors of* Hymns Ancient and Modern.]

J. G. Whittier, 1807–92.

O BROTHER man, fold to thy heart thy brother:
    Where pity dwells, the peace of God is there;
To worship rightly is to love each other,
    Each smile a hymn, each kindly deed a prayer.

2 Follow with reverent steps the great example
    Of him whose holy work was doing good:
So shall the wide earth seem our Father's temple,
    Each loving life a psalm of gratitude.

3. Then shall all shackles fall: the stormy clangour
    Of wild war music o'er the earth shall cease;
Love shall tread out the baleful fire of anger,
    And in its ashes plant the tree of peace.

308

KING'S LYNN. (7 6. 7 6. D.)

In moderate time, dignified. Unison.

English Traditional Melody.

G. K. Chesterton, 1874–1936.

O GOD of earth and altar,
  Bow down and hear our cry,
Our earthly rulers falter,
  Our people drift and die;
The walls of gold entomb us,
  The swords of scorn divide,
Take not thy thunder from us,
  But take away our pride.

2 From all that terror teaches,
    From lies of tongue and pen,
  From all the easy speeches
    That comfort cruel men,
  From sale and profanation
    Of honour and the sword,
  From sleep and from damnation,
    Deliver us, good Lord!

3. Tie in a living tether
    The prince and priest and thrall,
  Bind all our lives together,
    Smite us and save us all;
  In ire and exultation
    Aflame with faith, and free,
  Lift up a living nation,
    A single sword to thee.

(370)

309

EBENEZER (TON-Y-BOTEL). (8 7. 8 7. D.)

Moderately slow. Unison.

Welsh Hymn Melody.

[*By permission of W. Gwenlyn Evans & Son, Carnarvon.*]
[This hymn may also be sung to HYFRYDOL, 260.]

J. Russell Lowell,‡ 1819–91.

ONCE to every man and nation
  Comes the moment to decide,
In the strife of truth with falsehood,
  For the good or evil side:
Some great cause, God's new Messiah,
  Offering each the bloom or blight;
And the choice goes by for ever
  'Twixt that darkness and that light.

2 Then to side with truth is noble,
  When we share her wretched crust,
Ere her cause bring fame and profit,
  And 'tis prosperous to be just;
Then it is the brave man chooses,
  While the coward stands aside,
Till the multitude make virtue
  Of the faith they had denied.

3 By the light of burning martyrs,
  Christ, thy bleeding feet we track,
Toiling up new Calvaries ever
  With the cross that turns not back.
New occasions teach new duties;
  Time makes ancient good uncouth;
They must upward still and onward
  Who would keep abreast of truth.

4. Though the cause of evil prosper,
  Yet 'tis truth alone is strong;
Though her portion be the scaffold,
  And upon the throne be wrong,
Yet that scaffold sways the future,
  And, behind the dim unknown,
Standeth God within the shadow,
  Keeping watch above his own.

(371)

310

REMEMBER THE POOR. (Irreg.)

In moderate time. Unison.

Irish Traditional Melody (slightly adapted).

1. The day of the Lord is at hand, at hand; Its storms roll up the sky; The na - tions sleep star - ving on heaps of gold; All dream - ers toss and sigh; The night is dark - est be - fore the morn; When the pain is sor - est the child is born, And the day of the Lord at hand, at hand, The day of the Lord at hand.

2. Gath - er you, gath - er you, an - gels of God—
3*. Gath - er you, gath - er you, hounds of . hell—

Free - dom and mer - cy and truth; Come! for the earth is grown
Fam - ine, and plague, and . war; I - dle-ness, big - ot - ry,

cow - ard and old, Come down, and re - new us her youth.
cant, and mis-rule, Gath - er, and fall in the snare!

Wis - dom, self - sac - ri - fice, dar - ing, and love, : : :
Hire - ling and Mam-mon - ite, big - ot and knave, : : :

Haste to the bat - tle-field, stoop from a - bove To the day of the Lord at
Crawl to the bat - tle-field, sneak to your grave, In the day of the Lord at

hand, at hand, To the day of the Lord at hand.
hand, at hand, In the day of the Lord at hand.

4. Who would sit down and sigh for a lost age of gold,

While the Lord of all a - ges is here? True hearts will leap at the

[Continued overleaf.

(373)

310 (*continued*)

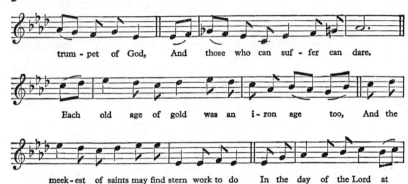

trum - pet of God, And those who can suf - fer can dare.

Each old age of gold was an i - ron age too, And the

meek - est of saints may find stern work to do In the day of the Lord at

hand, at hand, In the day of the Lord at hand.

NOTE.—*The organist must adapt the accompaniment of verse 1 to the subsequent verses.*

C. *Kingsley,* 1819–75.

THE day of the Lord is at hand, at hand;
  Its storms roll up the sky;
The nations sleep starving on heaps of gold;
  All dreamers toss and sigh;
The night is darkest before the morn;
When the pain is sorest the child is born,
  And the day of the Lord at hand.

2 Gather you, gather you, angels of God—
  Freedom and mercy and truth;
Come! for the earth is grown coward and old,
  Come down, and renew us her youth.
Wisdom, self-sacrifice, daring, and love,
Haste to the battle-field, stoop from above
  To the day of the Lord at hand.

3*Gather you, gather you, hounds of hell—
  Famine, and plague, and war;
Idleness, bigotry, cant, and misrule,
  Gather, and fall in the snare!
Hireling and Mammonite, bigot and knave,
Crawl to the battle-field, sneak to your grave,
  In the day of the Lord at hand.

4. Who would sit down and sigh for a lost age of gold,
  While the Lord of all ages is here?
True hearts will leap at the trumpet of God,
  And those who can suffer can dare.
Each old age of gold was an iron age too,
And the meekest of saints may find stern work to do
  In the day of the Lord at hand.

(374)

311

PEMBROKE. (8 6. 8 6. 8 8.)

In moderate time. Unison.

PATRICK HADLEY.

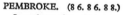

Broaden slightly.

[Copyright, 1925, by Oxford University Press.]
[This hymn may also be sung to O JESU, 532.]

P. B. Shelley, 1792–1822.

THE world's great age begins anew,
  The golden years return,
The earth doth like a snake renew
  Her winter weeds outworn:
Heaven smiles, and faiths and empires
  gleam,
Like wrecks of a dissolving dream.

2*A brighter Hellas rears its mountains
  From waves serener far;
A new Penĕus rolls his fountains
  Against the morning star.
Where fairer Tempès bloom, there sleep
Young Cyclads on a sunnier deep.

3. Another Athens shall arise,
  And to remoter time
Bequeath, like sunset to the skies,
  The splendour of its prime;
And leave, if nought so bright may live,
All earth can take or heaven can give.

(Hellas, *Greece:* Peneus, *the river running through the beautiful vale of Tempe, near Olympus:* Cyclads, *a group of islands in the Aegean Sea.*)

(375)

SOCIAL SERVICE: GENERAL

312

MERTHYR TYDVIL (DIES IRAE).   (D.L.M.)

Slow.

JOSEPH PARRY, 1841–1903.

[This hymn may also be sung to GONFALON ROYAL, 593.]

J. Addington Symonds, 1840–93.

THESE things shall be! A loftier race
  Than e'er the world hath known,
    shall rise
With flame of freedom in their souls
  And light of science in their eyes.

2 They shall be gentle, brave, and strong,
  To spill no drop of blood, but dare
All that may plant man's lordship firm
  On earth and fire and sea and air.

3 They shall be simple in their homes
  And splendid in their public ways,
Filling the mansions of the state
  With music and with hymns of praise.

4 Nation with nation, land with land,
  Inarmed shall live as comrades free;
In every heart and brain shall throb
  The pulse of one fraternity.

5. New arts shall bloom of loftier mould,
  And mightier music thrill the skies,
And every life shall be a song,
  When all the earth is paradise.

(376)

3I3

NACHTIGALL (ACH! WAN DOCH JESU, LIEBSTER MEIN).
(8 7. 8 7. D.)

Moderately fast.   Melody from *Trutz-Nachtigall* (1649).

Freedom.   *Gerald Massey*, 1828–1907.

THROUGH all the long dark night of years
    The people's cry ascendeth,
And earth is wet with blood and tears,
    But our meek sufferance endeth.
We are driven back, for our next fray
    A newer strength to borrow,
And where the vanguard camps to-day
    The rear shall rest to-morrow.

2 Though hearts brood o'er the past, our eyes
    With smiling futures glisten;
For lo, our day bursts up the skies—
    Lean out your souls and listen!
The world is rolling freedom's way
    And ripening with her sorrow.
Take heart! who bear the cross to-day
    Shall wear the crown to-morrow.

3. Build up heroic lives, and all
    Be like a sheathen sabre,
Ready to flash out at God's call,
    O chivalry of labour!
Triumph and toil are twins, though they
    Be singly born in sorrow;
And 'tis the martyrdom to-day
    Brings victory to-morrow.

314

KENDAL. (7 6. 7 6. 8 8 8. 5.)

Moderately slow. Voices in unison.   ARTHUR SOMERVELL, 1863–1937.

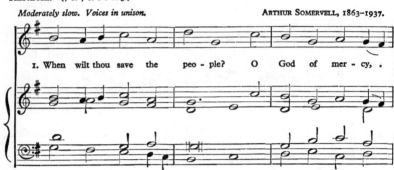

1. When wilt thou save the peo - ple? O God of mer - cy, .

when? The peo - ple, Lord, the peo - ple, Not

thrones and crowns, but men! Flowers of thy heart, O

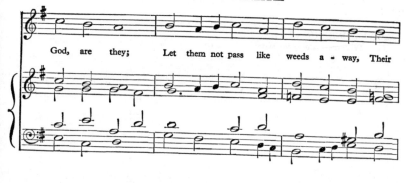

God, are they; Let them not pass like weeds a - way, Their

he - ri-tage a sun - less day: God save the peo - ple!

Ebenezer Elliott,† 1781–1849.

WHEN wilt thou save the people?
  O God of mercy, when?
The people, Lord, the people,
  Not thrones and crowns, but men!
Flowers of thy heart, O God, are they;
Let them not pass like weeds away,
Their heritage a sunless day:
    God save the people!

2 Shall crime bring crime for ever,
    Strength aiding still the strong?
  Is it thy will, O Father,
    That man shall toil for wrong?
  'No,' say thy mountains; 'No,' thy skies;
  Man's clouded sun shall brightly rise,
  And songs be heard instead of sighs:
      God save the people!

3. When wilt thou save the people?
    O God of mercy, when?
  The people, Lord, the people,
    Not thrones and crowns, but men!
  God save the people; thine they are,
  Thy children, as thy angels fair;
  From vice, oppression, and despair
      God save the people!

315

FIRST TUNE

MARYLEBONE. (Irreg.)

In moderate time. Voices in unison:

Irish Traditional Melody (rhythm slightly adapted).

1. With won - der - ful death - less dit - ties We build up the

world's great cit - ies, And out of a fab - u - lous

sto - ry We fash - ion an em - pire's glo - ry: One

man with a dream, at plea - sure, Shall go forth and

con - quer a crown; And three with a new song's

mea - sure Can tram - ple a king - dom down.

The Music-makers.

Arthur O'Shaughnessy, 1844–81.

WITH wonderful deathless ditties
　　We build up the world's great cities,
And out of a fabulous story
We fashion an empire's glory:
One man with a dream, at pleasure,
　　Shall go forth and conquer a crown;
And three with a new song's measure
　　Can trample a kingdom down.

2 A breath of our inspiration
　　Is the life of each generation;
A wondrous thing of our dreaming
Unearthly, impossible seeming—
The soldier, the king, and the peasant,
　　Are working together in one,
Till our dream shall become their present,
　　And their work in the world be done.

3. And therefore to-day is thrilling
　　With a past day's late fulfilling;
And the multitudes are enlisted
In the faith that their fathers resisted,
And, scorning the dream of to-morrow,
　　Are bringing to pass, as they may,
In the world, for its joy or its sorrow,
　　The dream that was scorned yesterday.

315 *(continued)*

SECOND TUNE

MUSIC-MAKERS. (Irreg.)

March time. Voices in unison.

SYDNEY H. NICHOLSON, 1875–1947.

1. With won-der-ful death-less

dit - ties We build up the world's great cit - ies, And

out of a fab-u-lous sto - ry We fash-ion an em - pire's

(382)

glo - ry: One man with a dream, at plea-sure, Shall go

forth and con-quer a crown; And three with a new song's

Verses 1 *and* 2.

mea - sure Can tram - ple a king - dom down.

Verse 3.

scorned yes - ter - day.

315 (*continued*)

Verse 2.

A breath of our in-spi-ra-tion Is the life of each gen-er-a-tion; A won-drous thing of our dream-ing Un-earth-ly, im-pos-si-ble seem-ing— The sol-dier, the king, and the pea-sant, Are work-ing to-geth-er in one, Till our dream shall be-come their pres-ent, And their work . . in the world be done.

Verse 3.

And there-fore to-day is thrill-ing With a past day's late ful-fill-ing; And the mul-ti-tudes are en-list-ed In the faith that their fa-thers re-sist-ed, And,

scorn - ing the dream of to-mor-row, Are bring - ing to pass, as they

may, In the world, for its joy or its sor - row, The

dream that was scorned yes - ter - day.

[*Copyright, 1919, by Stainer & Bell, Ltd.*]

The Music-makers.   *Arthur O'Shaughnessy*, 1844–81.

WITH wonderful deathless ditties
    We build up the world's great cities,
And out of a fabulous story
We fashion an empire's glory:
One man with a dream, at pleasure,
    Shall go forth and conquer a crown;
And three with a new song's measure
    Can trample a kingdom down.

2 A breath of our inspiration
    Is the life of each generation;
A wondrous thing of our dreaming
Unearthly, impossible seeming—
The soldier, the king, and the peasant,
    Are working together in one,
Till our dream shall become their present,
    And their work in the world be done.

3. And therefore to-day is thrilling
    With a past day's late fulfilling;
And the multitudes are enlisted
In the faith that their fathers resisted,
And, scorning the dream of to-morrow,
    Are bringing to pass, as they may,
In the world, for its joy or its sorrow,
    The dream that was scorned yesterday.

C

NATIONAL

316

GUILDFORD. (11 10. 11 10. 5 5. 10.)

Not too slow. Unison.

R. VAUGHAN WILLIAMS, 1872–1958.

con 8va sempre.

Verse 3. The organ part must conform.

3. Forth then, ye he - roes, pa - tri - ots, and lov - ers,

Com - rades of dan - ger, pov - er - ty, and scorn, Migh - ty in

faith of free - dom, your great mo - ther, Gi - ants refreshed in joy's new

ris - ing morn! Come and swell the song, Si - lent now so

long: Eng - land is ris - en! And the day is here!

[*Copyright, 1925, by R. Vaughan Williams.*]

Edward Carpenter, 1844-1929.

ENGLAND, arise! the long, long night is over,
   Faint in the east behold the dawn appear;
Out of your evil dream of toil and sorrow
   Arise, O England, for the day is here!
From your fields and hills,
Hark! the answer swells:
   Arise, O England, for the day is here!

2 People of England! all your valleys call you,
   High in the rising sun the lark sings clear;
Will you dream on, let shameful slumber thrall you?
   Will you disown your native land so dear?
Shall it die unheard,
That sweet pleading word?
   Arise, O England, for the day is here!

3. Forth then, ye heroes, patriots, and lovers,
   Comrades of danger, poverty, and scorn,
Mighty in faith of freedom, your great mother,
   Giants refreshed in joy's new rising morn!
Come and swell the song,
Silent now so long:
   England is risen! And the day is here!

(387)

317

FOLKINGHAM. (8 8. 8 8. 8 8.)

Moderately slow, dignified.   From the *Supplement to the New Version,* 1708.

[This hymn may also be sung to FARMBOROUGH, 689.]

Recessional.   *Rudyard Kipling, 1865–1936.*

GOD of our fathers, known of old,
  Lord of our far-flung battle-line,
Beneath whose awful hand we hold
    Dominion over palm and pine—
Lord God of Hosts, be with us yet,
Lest we forget—lest we forget!

2 The tumult and the shouting dies;
  The captains and the kings depart:
Still stands thine ancient sacrifice,
    An humble and a contrite heart.
Lord God of Hosts, be with us yet,
Lest we forget—lest we forget!

3 Far-called, our navies melt away;
  On dune and headland sinks the fire:
Lo, all our pomp of yesterday
    Is one with Nineveh and Tyre!

Judge of the Nations, spare us yet,
Lest we forget—lest we forget!

4*If, drunk with sight of power, we loose
    Wild tongues that have not thee in
      awe,
Such boastings as the Gentiles use,
    Or lesser breeds without the Law—
Lord God of Hosts, be with us yet,
Lest we forget—lest we forget!

5. For heathen heart that puts her trust
    In reeking tube and iron shard,
All valiant dust that builds on dust,
    And guarding, calls not thee to guard,
For frantic boast and foolish word—
Thy mercy on thy people, Lord!

318

NATIONAL ANTHEM. (6 6 4. 6 6 6 4.)

Moderately slow.

Thesaurus Musicus, c. **1743.**

National Anthem.   *Official Peace Version,†* **1919.**

GOD save our gracious Queen,
Long live our noble Queen,
   God save the Queen!
Send her victorious,
Happy and glorious,
Long to reign over us;
   God save the Queen!

2 One realm of races four,
Blest more and ever more,
   God save our land!
Home of the brave and free,
Set in the silver sea,
True nurse of chivalry,
   God save our land!

3. Of many a race and birth
From utmost ends of earth,
   God save us all!
Bid strife and hatred cease,
Bid hope and joy increase,
Spread universal peace,
   God save us all!

319

FIRST TUNE

THAXTED. (13. 13. 13. 13. 13. 13. Irreg.)

In moderate time. Unison.

GUSTAV HOLST, 1874–1934.

[*Copyright, 1921, by Goodwin & Tabb, Ltd.*]

The Two Fatherlands.   *Sir Cecil Spring Rice*, 1859–1918.

I VOW to thee, my country, all earthly things above,
Entire and whole and perfect, the service of my love;
The love that asks no question, the love that stands the test,
That lays upon the altar the dearest and the best;
The love that never falters, the love that pays the price,
The love that makes undaunted the final sacrifice.

2. And there's another country, I've heard of long ago,
   Most dear to them that love her, most great to them that know;
   We may not count her armies, we may not see her King;
   Her fortress is a faithful heart, her pride is suffering;
   And soul by soul and silently her shining bounds increase,
   And her ways are ways of gentleness and all her paths are peace.

SECOND TUNE

ABINGER. (13. 13. 13. 13. 13. 13. Irreg.)

Not too fast. Voices in unison.

R. VAUGHAN WILLIAMS, 1872–1958.

1. I vow to thee, my coun-try, all earth-ly things a-bove, En-tire and whole and per-fect, the ser-vice of my love; The love that

2. And there's an-oth-er coun-try, I've heard of long a-go, Most dear to them that love her, most great to them that know; We may not

[*Copyright, 1931, by R. Vaughan Williams.*]

319 (*continued*)

asks   no   ques - tion,   the love that stands   the   test,   That
count   her   ar - mies,   we   may not see   her   King ;   Her

lays   up - on the   al - tar   the   dear - est and the   best;   The
fort - ress is a   faith-ful heart,   her   pride is suf - fer - ing ;   And

love   that nev-er   fal - ters,   the   love that pays the   price,   The
soul   by soul and   si - lent-ly   her   shin-ing bounds in - crease,   And her

love that makes un - daunt - ed the fi - nal sac - ri - fice. . . . . .
ways are ways of gen-tle-ness and all her paths are peace. . . . .

The Two Fatherlands.   *Sir Cecil Spring Rice, 1859–1918.*

I VOW to thee, my country, all earthly things above,
Entire and whole and perfect, the service of my love;
The love that asks no question, the love that stands the test,
That lays upon the altar the dearest and the best;
The love that never falters, the love that pays the price,
The love that makes undaunted the final sacrifice.

2. And there's another country, I've heard of long ago,
Most dear to them that love her, most great to them that know;
We may not count her armies, we may not see her King;
Her fortress is a faithful heart, her pride is suffering;
And soul by soul and silently her shining bounds increase,
And her ways are ways of gentleness and all her paths are peace.

320

ABERDEEN. (C.M.)

In moderate time.

Melody in BREMNER's *Collection*, 1763.

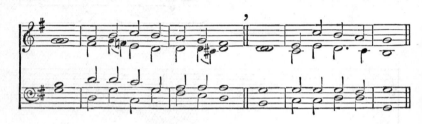

J. R. Wreford, 1800–81.

LORD, while for all mankind we pray
    Of every clime and coast,
O hear us for our native land,
    The land we love the most.

2 O guard our shores from every foe;
    With peace our borders bless;
With prosperous times our cities crown,
    Our fields with plenteousness.

3 Unite us in the sacred love
    Of knowledge, truth, and thee;
And let our hills and valleys shout
    The songs of liberty.

4. Lord of the nations, thus to thee
    Our country we commend;
Be thou her refuge and her trust,
    Her everlasting friend.

321

SUSSEX. (8 7. 8 7.)

In moderate time.

Adapted from an English Traditional Melody.

Freedom.

Thomas Campbell, 1777–1844.

MEN of England, who inherit
   Rights that cost your sires their blood!
Men whose undegenerate spirit
   Has been proved on field and flood,

2 Yet, remember, England gathers
   Hence but fruitless wreaths of fame,
If the freedom of your fathers
   Glow not in your hearts the same.

3 What are monuments of bravery,
   Where no public virtues bloom?
What avail in lands of slavery
   Trophied temples, arch and tomb?

4. We're the sons of sires that baffled
   Crowned and mitred tyranny;
They defied the field and scaffold
   For their birthrights—so will we!

322

FREEDOM. (7 6. 7 6. D.)

Not quick, broadly.

GEOFFREY SHAW, 1879–1943.

F. L. Hosmer, 1840–1929.

O BEAUTIFUL, my country!
  Be thine a nobler care
Than all thy wealth of commerce,
  Thy harvests waving fair:
Be it thy pride to cherish
  The manhood of the poor;
Be thou to the oppressèd
  Fair freedom's open door.

For thee our fathers suffered,
  For thee they toiled and prayed;
Upon thy holy altar
  Their willing lives they laid.
Thou hast no common birthright,
  Grand memories on thee shine;
The blood of pilgrim nations
  Commingled flows in thine.

SOCIAL SERVICE: NATIONAL

SECOND TUNE

HELDER (WOHLAUF THUT NICHT VERZAGEN). (7 6. 7 6. D.)

In moderate time. Melody by B. HELDER, 1585-1635.

3. O beautiful, our country!
   Round thee in love we draw;
Thine is the grace of freedom,
   The majesty of law.
Be righteousness thy sceptre,
   Justice thy diadem;
And on thy shining forehead
   Be peace the crowning gem.

(397)

323
WORCESTER. (C.M.)
In moderate time.

Playford's *Whole book of Psalms*, **1677**,
arranged by IVOR ATKINS, 1869-1953.

[*Copyright*, 1931, *by Oxford University Press.*]

ALTERNATIVE VERSION
Melody in the Tenor.

Ravenscroft's *Psalter*, 1621.
Fa-burden by THOMAS TOMKINS, 1573-1656.

[This hymn may also be sung to BURFORD, 596.]

Sir Henry Newbolt, 1862-1938.

O LORD almighty, thou whose hands
Despair and victory give,
In whom, though tyrants tread their
lands,
The souls of nations live;

2 Thou wilt not turn thy face away
From those who work thy will,
But send thy peace on hearts that pray,
And guard thy people still.

3 Remember not the days of shame,
The hands with rapine dyed,
The wavering will, the baser aim,
The brute material pride.

4 Remember, Lord, the years of faith,
The spirits humbly brave,

The strength that died defying death,
The love that loved the slave;

5*The race that strove to rule thine earth
With equal laws unbought,
Who bore for truth the pangs of birth,
And brake the bonds of thought.

6*Remember how, since time began,
Thy dark eternal mind
Through lives of men that fear not man
Is light for all mankind.

7. Thou wilt not turn thy face away
From those who work thy will,
But send thy strength on hearts that
pray
For strength to serve thee still.

(398)

324

DONNE SECOURS. (11 10. 11 10.)

Moderately slow. Unison.　　　　　　　　Psalm 12 in the *Genevan Psalter*, 1551.

R. Bridges, 1844–1930, based on F. R. Tailour (1615).

THE King, O God, his heart to thee upraiseth;
　With him the nation bows before thy face;
With high thanksgiving thee thy glad Church praiseth,
　Our strength thy spirit, our trust and hope thy grace.

2 Unto great honour, glory undeservèd,
　　Hast thou exalted us, and drawn thee nigh;
Nor, from thy judgments when our feet had swervèd,
　　Didst thou forsake, nor leave us, Lord most high.

PART II

3 In thee our fathers trusted and were savèd,
　　In thee destroyèd thrones of tyrants proud;
From ancient bondage freed the poor enslavèd;
　　To sow thy truth poured out their saintly blood.

4 Unto our minds give freedom and uprightness;
　　Let strength and courage lead o'er land and wave;
To our souls' armour grant celestial brightness,
　　Joy to our hearts, and faith beyond the grave.

5. Our plenteous nation still in power extending,
　　Increase our joy, uphold us by thy word;
Beauty and wisdom all our ways attending,
　　Good will to man and peace through Christ our Lord.

*The hymn in full is suitable for national thanksgivings: verses 2–5, or Part II, are suitable for
other occasions also.*

(399)

325

STEPNEY. (6 6 6 3. 6 6 6 4.)

In moderate time. Unison.

GUSTAV HOLST, 1874–1934.
Voices enter.

[*By permission of Stainer & Bell, Ltd.*]

Heroes.

G. K. Menzies, 1869–1954.

WHAT heroes thou hast bred,
 O England, my country!
I see the mighty dead
 Pass in line,
Each with undaunted heart
Playing his gallant part,
Making thee what thou art,
 Mother of mine!

2. Then let me take my place,
 O England, my country,
Amid the gallant race
 That is thine;
Ready to hear thy call,
Ready to give thee all,
Ready, whate'er befall,
 Mother of mine!

See also

446 *Blake's Jerusalem.* And did those feet
495 For the might of thine arm
552 Judge eternal

488 *Land of our birth*
631 Rejoice, O land
672 Thou Judge

And the National Saints, 217, 225, 227, 528.

LANGHAM. (11 10. 11 10. 10.)
Moderately slow. Unison.
GEOFFREY SHAW, 1879–1943.

Laurence Housman, 1865–1959.

FATHER eternal, ruler of creation,
   Spirit of life, which moved ere form was made,
Through the thick darkness covering every nation,
   Light to man's blindness, O be thou our aid:
      Thy Kingdom come, O Lord, thy will be done.

2 Races and peoples, lo, we stand divided,
   And, sharing not our griefs, no joy can share
By wars and tumults love is mocked, derided;
   His conquering cross no kingdom wills to bear.

3 Envious of heart, blind-eyed, with tongues confounded,
   Nation by nation still goes unforgiven,
In wrath and fear, by jealousies surrounded,
   Building proud towers which shall not reach to heaven:

4*Lust of possession worketh desolations;
   There is no meekness in the sons of earth;
Led by no star, the rulers of the nations
   Still fail to bring us to the blissful birth:

5. How shall we love thee, holy hidden Being,
   If we love not the world which thou hast made?
O give us brother-love for better seeing
   Thy Word made flesh, and in a manger laid:

ALL WATERS. (11 11. 11 11. 12. 11 11 11.)

In moderate time. Unison.

MARTIN SHAW, 1875–1958.

[Copyright, 1931, by Martin Shaw.]

(402)

INTERNATIONAL

J. G. Whittier, 1807–92.

SOUND over all waters, reach out from all lands,
The chorus of voices, the clasping of hands;
Sing hymns that were sung by the stars of the morn,
Sing songs of the angels when Jesus was born;
With glad jubilations bring hope to the nations:

The dark night is ending and dawn has begun!
Rise, hope of the ages, arise like the sun!
All speech flow to music, all hearts beat as one!

2 Sing the bridal of nations, with chorals of love,
Sing out the war vulture and sing in the dove,
Till the hearts of the peoples keep time in accord
And the voice of the world is the voice of the Lord!
Clasp hands of the nations in strong gratulations:

3. Blow, bugles of battle, the marches of peace!
East, west, north, and south, let the long quarrel cease!
Sing the song of great joy that the angels began,
Sing of glory to God and of good will to man!
Hark! joining in chorus, the heavens bend o'er us:

328

FIRST TUNE

DOWNSHIRE HILL. (10. 10 10. 10 6.)

In moderate time. Unison.

MARTIN SHAW, 1875–1958.

(v. 3.) bro - ther In ev - 'ry
(v. 4.) art . . For ev - er

Frederick Tennyson, 1807–98.

THE night is ended and the morning nears;
Awake, look up, I hear the gathering sound
Of coming cycles, like an ocean round;
I see the glory of a thousand years
Lightening from bound to bound.

2 The hour is come again; the world-wide voice
Of God shall cry into the ears of time;
Scorners shall seek, and saints shall welcome him,
And know the ancient presence, and rejoice
As in the days of prime.

3 And they that dwell apart shall know each other,
And they that hymn their solemn songs alone
Shall hear far voices mingling with their own,
And understand the utterance of a brother
In every tongue and tone.

4. That note shall soar from every living heart;
That endless note shall never die away.
God, only God, to-day as yesterday,
Thou wert from everlasting, and thou art
For ever and for ay.

328 (continued)

SECOND TUNE

TENBURY. (10. 10 10. 10 6.)

Moderately slow. Voices in unison.

HEATHCOTE STATHAM.

1. The night   is end   -   ed   and . the morn-ing nears;   A-
2. The hour   is come a-gain;   the world   -   wide voice   Of
3. And they   that dwell a-part   shall know each oth - er,   And
4. That note   shall soar . .   from ev - 'ry   liv - ing heart;   That

~ wake,   look   up,   I   hear the gath-'ring   sound   Of
God   shall   cry .   in - to   the ears   of   time;
they   that   hymn .   their so - lemn songs a - lone   Shall
end   -   less note .   shall nev - er   die a - way.

com   -   -   ing cy = cles,   like   an o - cean   round;
Scor -   ners shall seek,   and   saints   shall wel - come him,
hear   far   voi = ces   min - gling with   their   own,
God,   on - ly God,   to - day . . .   as   yes - ter - day,

INTERNATIONAL

Lyrics under the music:

I see the glo - ry of a thou-sand years Light-
And know the an - cient pres-ence, and re - joice As
And un - der - stand the utter-ance of a bro - ther In
Thou wert from ev - er - last-ing, and thou art For

- - 'ning from bound to bound.
in - - the days of prime.
ev - - 'ry tongue and tone.
ev - - er and for ay.

Frederick Tennyson, 1807–98.

THE night is ended and the morning nears;
  Awake, look up, I hear the gathering sound
  Of coming cycles, like an ocean round;
I see the glory of a thousand years
  Lightening from bound to bound.

2 The hour is come again; the world-wide voice
  Of God shall cry into the ears of time;
  Scorners shall seek, and saints shall welcome him,
And know the ancient presence, and rejoice
  As in the days of prime.

3 And they that dwell apart shall know each other,
  And they that hymn their solemn songs alone
  Shall hear far voices mingling with their own,
And understand the utterance of a brother
  In every tongue and tone.

4. That note shall soar from every living heart;
  That endless note shall never die away.
  God, only God, to-day as yesterday,
Thou wert from everlasting, and thou art
  For ever and for ay.

(405)

329

OLD 124TH. (10 10. 10 10. 10.)
Slow.

English form of melody in *Genevan Psalter* (1552?).
Harmony mostly from W. PARSONS in *Day's Psalter*, 1563.

Clifford Bax.

TURN back, O Man, forswear thy foolish ways.
   Old now is Earth, and none may count her days,
Yet thou, her child, whose head is crowned with flame,
Still wilt not hear thine inner God proclaim—
'Turn back, O Man, forswear thy foolish ways.'

2 Earth might be fair and all men glad and wise.
Age after age their tragic empires rise,
Built while they dream, and in that dreaming weep:
Would Man but wake from out his haunted sleep,
Earth might be fair and all men glad and wise.

3. Earth shall be fair, and all her people one:
Nor till that hour shall God's whole will be done.
Now, even now, once more from earth to sky,
Peals forth in joy man's old undaunted cry—
'Earth shall be fair, and all her folk be one!'

SPECIAL OCCASIONS

ABSENT FRIENDS

330

DIVA SERVATRIX. (11 11. 11 5.)

In moderate time. Unison.

Bayeux Church Melody.

Maud Bell, 1868-1957.

FATHER all-seeing, friend of all creation,
Life of thy children, still thy love revealing,
For all our loved ones, now far absent from us,
We are appealing.

2 Working or playing, Lord, be thou their leader;
And, if alarm or sickness should oppress them,
Teach them to trust thee, knowing that in all things
Thy love will bless them.

3 In all temptation be their strength and comfort;
Guide them in weakness, sanctifying, shielding;
Through him who, tempted every day as we are,
Lived without yielding.

4. When they are lonely, be thou their companion,
Hold them in safety, strengthen their endeavour;
Grant them to follow where thy voice shall call them,
Now and for ever.

ALMSGIVING

331

ST. AIDAN. (7 5. 7 5.)

In moderate time.

HERBERT POPPLE.

[*Copyright, 1931, by Oxford University Press.*]

J. G. Whittier, 1807–92.

THINE are all the gifts, O God,
Thine the broken bread;
Let the naked feet be shod,
And the starving fed.

2 Let thy children, by thy grace,
Give as they abound,
Till the poor have breathing-space
And the lost are found.

3 Wiser than the miser's hoards
Is the giver's choice;
Sweeter than the song of birds
Is the thankful voice.

4. Welcome smiles on faces sad
As the flowers of spring;
Let the tender hearts be glad
With the joy they bring.

332

WINDERMERE. (S.M.)

In moderate time.

ARTHUR SOMERVELL, 1863–1937.

Bishop W. W. How, 1823–97.

WE give thee but thine own,
Whate'er the gift may be:
All that we have is thine alone,
A trust, O Lord, from thee.

2 May we thy bounties thus
As stewards true receive,
And gladly, as thou blessest us,
To thee our first-fruits give.

ALMSGIVING

3   O hearts are bruised and dead,
     And homes are bare and cold;
  And lambs, for whom the Shepherd
    Are straying from the fold.   [bled,

4   To comfort and to bless,
    To find a balm for woe,
  To tend the lone and fatherless,
    Is angels' work below.

5   The captive to release;
    To God the lost to bring,
  To teach the way of life and peace—
    It is a Christ-like thing:

6.   And we believe thy word,
    Though dim our faith may be;
  Whate'er for thine we do, O Lord,
    We do it unto thee.

See also

340 Father, who on man dost shower
517 Help us to help

93 O worship the Lord
339 Son of God, eternal Saviour

ASSEMBLY AND DISMISSAL

333

CALVARY.   (8 7. 8 7. 8 7.)

In moderate time.   S. STANLEY, 1767–1822.

[This hymn may also be sung to GRAFTON, 129.]

Assembly.   *H. J. Buckoll*, 1803–71.

LORD, behold us with thy blessing,
  Once again assembled here;
Onward be our footsteps pressing,
  In thy love and faith and fear:
    Still protect us
  By thy presence ever near.

2. For thy mercy we adore thee,
  For this rest upon our way;
Lord, again we bow before thee;
  Speed our labours day by day:
    Mind and spirit
  With thy choicest gifts array.

(409)

333 *(continued)*

DISMISSAL. (8 7. 8 7. 8 7.)

In moderate time.

W. L. VINER, 1790–1867.

Dismissal.

PART II

1 Lord, dismiss us with thy blessing,
    Thanks for mercies past receive;
Pardon all, their faults confessing;
    Time that 's lost may all retrieve:
        May thy children
    Ne'er again thy Spirit grieve.

2. Let thy father-hand be shielding
    All who here shall meet no more;
May their seed-time past be yielding
    Year by year a richer store:
        Those returning
    Make more faithful than before.

See also
602 O life that makest all things new

(410)

FAREWELL

334

RANDOLPH. (9 8. 8 9.)

In moderate time. Unison.

Harmony. R. VAUGHAN WILLIAMS, 1872–1958.

Unison.

J. E. Rankin, 1828–1904.

GOD be with you till we meet again;
  By his counsels guide, uphold you,
  With his sheep securely fold you:
God be with you till we meet again.

2 God be with you till we meet again;
  'Neath his wings protecting hide you,
  Daily manna still provide you:
God be with you till we meet again.

3 God be with you till we meet again;
  When life's perils thick confound you,
  Put his arm unfailing round you:
God be with you till we meet again.

4 God be with you till we meet again;
  Keep love's banner floating o'er you,
  Smite death's threatening wave before you:
God be with you till we meet again.

See also
501 God be in *thy* head (*with change of pronoun*)₄

GREETING

ROYDEN. (6 6. 4 4 6, and refrain.)

With breadth.   *Voices in unison.*   MARTIN SHAW, 1875-1958.

O wel - come in our midst; Your

life with us re - new! With all our heart, From ev - 'ry part Our

love we give to you: Length to your days,

Strength to your ways! Bless - ings, bless - ings be up -

(412)

vv. 1, 2, 3. | Last verse. *rit.*

- on your head! head!

[*Copyright, 1929, by Martin Shaw.*]

S. P. B. G.

O WELCOME in our midst;
  Your life with us renew!
    With all our heart,
    From every part
  Our love we give to you:

Length to your days,
Strength to your ways!
Blessings be upon your head!

2 May faith and love be yours,
  And laughter gem your way;
    And may you find
    Clouds silver-lined,
  And all your work be play:

3 From hurt of foe, or friend,
  From envy, faction, spite,
    May you be kept,
    And live adept
  At turning dark to light:

4.*May triumph crown your plans,
  And hope maintain your youth;
    In God's dear peace
    May you increase
  And find your goal in truth:

(*Verse 1 for any new-comer. The whole (or three verses) for a new parson or teacher, or at the veginning of term. Verses 2 and 3 (and 4) may be sung at the end of term, or as a farewell.*)

See also
602 O life that makest all things new

FOR THOSE AT SEA

336

LODSWORTH. (8 8. 8 8. 8 8.)

In moderate time.

English Traditional Melody.

[This hymn may also be sung to VATER UNSER, 566.]

W. Whiting, 1825–78.

ETERNAL Father, strong to save,
Whose arm doth bind the restless wave,
Who bidd'st the mighty ocean deep
Its own appointed limits keep:
O hear us when we cry to thee
For those in peril on the sea.

2 O Saviour, whose almighty word
The winds and waves submissive heard,
Who walkedst on the foaming deep,
And calm amid its rage didst sleep:
O hear us when we cry to thee
For those in peril on the sea.

3 O sacred Spirit, who didst brood
Upon the chaos dark and rude,
Who bad'st its angry tumult cease,
And gavest light and life and peace:
O hear us when we cry to thee
For those in peril on the sea.

4. O Trinity of love and power,
Our brethren shield in danger's hour;
From rock and tempest, fire and foe,
Protect them wheresoe'er they go:
And ever let there rise to thee
Glad hymns of praise from land and sea.

(414)

FOR THOSE AT SEA

337

FIRST TUNE

CANNONS. (L.M.)

Moderately slow.

G. F. HANDEL, 1685-1759.

TRURO. (L.M.)

SECOND TUNE

In moderate time.

Psalmodia Evangelica, 1790.

(A descant to this tune will be found at 545.)

G. W. Briggs, 1875-1959.

LORD, in the hollow of thy hand
  Unfathomed lies the boundless deep,
Whose billows rage at thy command,
  And at thy bidding sink to sleep.

2 Thy way is on the pathless sea;
  On farthest coasts still thou art near;
And fearing, loving, trusting thee,
  No peril shall thy servants fear.

3 When, swept by wind and wave, they breast
  The fury of the winter gale,
On thee their valiant hearts shall rest,
  Assured that thou canst never fail.

4 When the black mantle of the night,
  Or shrouding mists, white-robed, by day,
Have veiled the perils from their sight,
  Be thou their guide upon their way.

5. Their way is sure, whate'er betide,
  Whose mind on thee, O Lord, is stayed;
In life and death still by thy side,
  They journey onward unafraid.

See also

330 Father, all-seeing
490 Fierce was the wild billow

49 Now the day is over
378 When lamps are lighted

(415)

SOCIETIES, ETC.

GENERAL

338

EXETER. (8 8 8. D.)

In moderate time.

W. JACKSON (of Exeter), 1730–1803.

[This hymn may also be sung to LLANGOEDMOR, 242.]

H. C. Shuttleworth, 1850–1900.

FATHER of men, in whom are one
All humankind beneath thy sun,
Stablish our work in thee begun.
Except the house be built of thee,
In vain the builder's toil must be:
O strengthen our infirmity!

2 Man lives not for himself alone;
In others' good he finds his own;
Life's worth in fellowship is known.
We, friends and comrades on life's way,
Gather within these walls to pray:
Bless thou our fellowship to-day.

3 O Christ, our elder brother, who
By serving man God's will didst do,
Help us to serve our brethren too.
Guide us to seek the things above,
The base to shun, the pure approve,
To live by thy free law of love.

4. In all our work, in all our play,
Be with us, Lord, our friend, our stay;
Lead onward to the perfect day:
Then may we know, earth's lesson o'er,
With comrades missed or gone before,
Heaven's fellowship for evermore.

339

YN Y GLYN. (8 7. 8 7. D.)

Moderately slow.

DAVID EVANS, 1874–1948.

[*Copyright,* 1927, *by David Evans.*]
[This hymn may also be sung to HYFRYDOL, 260.]

S. C. Lowry, 1855–1932.

SON of God, eternal Saviour,
  Source of life and truth and grace,
Son of Man, whose birth amongst us
  Hallows all our human race,
Thou, our Head, who, throned in glory,
  For thine own dost ever plead,
Fill us with thy love and pity,
  Heal our wrongs, and help our need.

2 As thou, Lord, hast lived for others,
    So may we for others live;
  Freely have thy gifts been granted,
    Freely may thy servants give.
  Thine the gold and thine the silver,
    Thine the wealth of land and sea,
  We but stewards of thy bounty,
    Held in solemn trust for thee.

3 Come, O Christ, and reign above us,
    King of Love, and Prince of Peace;
  Hush the storm of strife and passion,
    Bid its cruel discords cease;

By thy patient years of toiling,
  By thy silent hours of pain,
Quench our fevered thirst of pleasure,
  Shame our selfish greed of gain.

4 Dark the path that lies behind us,
    Strewn with wrecks and stained with
      blood;
  But before us gleams the vision
    Of the coming brotherhood.
  See the Christ-like host advancing,
    High and lowly, great and small,
  Linked in bonds of common service
    For the common Lord of all.

5.*Son of God, eternal Saviour,
    Source of life and truth and grace,
  Son of Man, whose birth amongst us
    Hallows all our human race,
  Thou who prayedst, thou who willest
    That thy people should be one,
  Grant, O grant our hope's fruition:
    Here on earth thy will be done.

See also Part IV, Social Service, and

(417)

P

FRIENDLY AND TEMPERANCE SOCIETIES

340

CHARING. (8 8. 8 7.)

Not too slow. Unison.

S. L. RUSSELL.

[*Copyright, 1931, by Oxford University Press.*]

[This hymn may also be sung to QUEM PASTORES, 540.]

(*Other occasions also.*)

E. H.

FATHER, who on man dost shower
  Gifts of plenty from thy dower,
To thy people give the power
    All thy gifts to use aright.

2 Give pure happiness in leisure,
  Temperance in every pleasure,
Wholesome use of earthly treasure,
    Bodies clean and spirits bright.

3 Lift from this and every nation
  All that brings us degradation;
Quell the forces of temptation;
    Put thine enemies to flight.

4 Be with us, thy strength supplying,
  That with energy undying,
Every foe of man defying,
    We may rally to the fight.

5 Thou who art our captain ever
  Lead us on to great endeavour;
May thy Church the world deliver,
    Give us wisdom, courage, might.

6.*Father, who hast sought and found us,
  Son of God, whose love has bound us,
Holy Spirit, in us, round us,
    Hear us, Godhead infinite!

MEDICAL GATHERINGS AND HEALTH SOCIETIES

341

SION. (8 9 8 8. D.)

In moderate time.

From MASON'S *Companion*, 1847.

A. G.

QUICK sympathy, hands that brought health
  To the sick who looked up and entreated,
A power that went forth as by stealth—
    Thus Jesus came God to reveal:
He said, 'Lo, the works that I do,
  And greater, shall yet be completed.'
Lord, we with that promise in view
    Would help to spread health and to heal.

2 For man has a virtue within,
  A force that is always restoring;
A life that to God is akin:
    We help, but 'tis God who makes whole.
We search, and we struggle again,
  Thy deep-hidden secrets exploring;
We fight in the Christ-like campaign
    Of succour for body and soul.

3. Then prosper our work to the end,
  Since thine is the will we are serving,
Thou Wisdom, Creator, and Friend,
    'Tis health to conform to thy laws.
Sustain all who work for the race,
  Give knowledge and vision unswerving,
Sincerity, kindness, and grace:
    For thine, Lord of health, is our cause.

See also

285 From thee all skill
286 Life and health

638 Shall God not share
287 Thine arm, O Lord

(419)

342

ST. THOMAS. (8 7. 8 7. 8 7.)

Moderately slow, dignified.

Melody from S. WEBBE's *Motetts or Antiphons*, 1792.

W. *Charter Piggott*, 1872–1943.

1 LORD of life, who once wast cradled
On a human mother's knee,
Fed and clothed, and taught and guided
Through the years of infancy:
Help and bless us, as we gather
With our cares and needs to thee.

2*Waking in the early morning
To the round which each day brings;
Sitting late into the evening,
Making garments, mending things:
Give us strength and cheerful patience
For these common happenings.

3 Lord, we thank thee for our children
With their faces bright and fair,
With their laughter and their temper,
Waking gladness, bringing care:
Teach us how to keep them upright,
True and gallant, everywhere.

4 Show us when to hold and curb them,
When to set them finely free,
How to keep their love and reverence
Stainless through the years to be,
How to win their adoration
And their loyalty to thee.

5. And since we have often faltered,
Missed the road and lost our way,
Known temptation, met with trouble,
Hear us mothers, as we pray;
Be thyself their guide and master,
Shape and fit them for their day.

See also
346 Lord, from whose hand

343

MILITES. (D.S.M.)

Moderately fast. Unison.   Adapted from melody in the *Foundery Collection*, 1742.

[This hymn may also be sung to FALCON STREET, 635, or ICH HALTE TREULICH, 480.]

Bishop E. A. Burroughs, 1882–1934.

LORD God, from whom all life
　　And all true gladness springs,
Whose love and care shine everywhere
　　Among earth's common things;
　　Be present while we lift
　　Our song to thee, and pay
Heart-gratitude for all things good
　　About our path to-day.

2　We praise thee for the light
　　That floats on sea and hill,
The unstinted wealth of joy and health
　　With which our pulses thrill:
　　O may the light of heaven
　　In us enkindled be,
Heaven's glory roll from soul to soul
　　And make us strong for thee.

3　We thank thee for the grace
　　In friend and brother found;
For human love that points above
　　To where all love is crowned:

O may such friendship here
　　Be to thy children given,
As shall endure, deep, fair and pure,
　　Till all be one in heaven.

4.　But most we bless thee, Lord,
　　That here thy Spirit's breath
Blows clear and strong to baffle wrong
　　And win our lives from death:
　　O may each heart accept
　　The entrance of thy power,
And take thee hence for sure defence
　　And help in evil hour.

5.*　So, when the lives, to-day
　　Within one circle brought,
Are sundered wide along the tide
　　Of human work and thought,
　　One song shall yet be ours,
　　One life, one family,
One pathway still, by vale or hill,
　　Shall lead us home to thee.

344

SCHOOL HOUSE. (11 10. 11 10.)

In moderate time. Unison.

THOMAS WOOD, 1892–1950.

[Copyright, 1931, by Oxford University Press.]

OF BOYS AND GIRLS

Steuart Wilson.

LORD, who didst send, by two and two before thee,
  Thine own disciples, those three score and ten,
That they should show the lost ones where the path was
  And bring the light to eyes of blinded men:

2*We are thy lost ones, humble guides of others,
  We are thy blind, poor leaders to the light;
Show us the Way, when ways seem past all finding,
  Teach us to guide, when all seems dark as night.

3 Make us to see the light that shines in all men,
  Help us to learn how thorns can make a crown,
Show us how love will keep ourselves from falling
  And pity lift up others who are down.

4*We must be gay when weaker hearts are weary,
  Looking ahead when tirèd eyes look back;
We must see hope when others are despairing;
  We must be guides to those who lose the track.

5 Thou art our Captain: teach us to be like thee,
  And where thou leadest we will follow on;
We do not know what orders may await us,
  Save the great order, 'Let thy will be done'.

6. It shall be done, if we be strong to follow
  The path which led thee to that aweful day;
It shall be done, if true to thy example
  We guide ourselves and others in thy Way.

(*This hymn may be begun at verse 3.*)

345

WORKING. (5 4. 5 4. 3 7. 5 7 5, and refrain.)

MARTIN SHAW, 1875-1958.

In march time.

Voices in unison.

1. Work - ing to-geth - er, Wa - ry and strong, Fair or foul wea - ther,
2. Help - ers and heed-ers, Friends of fair play, Trust-ing your lead - ers,
3. What was it caught you? What voice that called? Wood - craft that taught you,

Way short or long: Be pre - pared! For with va - lour and vir - tue, And
Swift to o - bey: Be pre - pared! Al - ways use - ful and cheer - y, And
Lore that en-thralled: Be pre - pared? So in hon - our ob - ser - vant And

OF BOYS AND GIRLS

kind-ness and skill, There is noth-ing can hurt you Or bring you to ill. Be pre-
hand-y to learn, Nev-er feel-ing too wear-y For an-y good turn, But pre-
true to the end, To God be a ser-vant, To man be a friend. Be pre-

-pared,
-pared;   One and all,   be pre-pared!
-pared,

S. P.

346

LAMBETH. (8 8. 8 8. 8 8.)

Moderately slow.

S. AKEROYDE in the *Divine Companion*, 1701.

W. *Charter Piggott*, 1872–1943.

LORD, from whose hand we take our
     charge,
   The care of childhood and of youth,
To set their feet upon life's road
   In loyalty to right and truth:
     O hear us as of thee we ask
     The strength and wisdom for our
        task.

2 That we may open doors on life,
   And share the visions that we see
Of the deep wonder of the world
   And man's heroic history,   [chord:
     And wake in them the answering
     Give us the skill and patience,
        Lord.

3 That we may use all law and rule,
   Not rudely to oppress and bind,
But as the needed discipline
   For freedom of the soul and mind,
     Equipped to face, with fearless
        eyes
     And steady faith, life's enterprise;

4 That we may understand their need,
   When comes their hour of strain and
        stress,
With sympathy to help and save
   From sordid thoughts and bitterness:
     Lord, use our struggles, conflicts,
        fears,
     To light for them the troubled years.

5. 'Tis ours to give and spend ourselves,
   Nor grudge the labour and the pain
To sow the seed of noble worth;
   Yet without thee our toil is vain:
     Great Lord of life, 'tis thine to give
     The quickening breath by which they live.

347

L'OMNIPOTENT. (11 10. 11 10.)

Moderately slow.

Melody composed or adapted by
L. BOURGEOIS for the *Genevan Psalter*, 1551.

F. L. Hosmer, 1840–1929.

FATHER, to thee we look in all our sorrow;
   Thou art the fountain whence our healing flows;
Dark though the night, joy cometh with the morrow;
   Safely they rest who on thy love repose.

2 When fond hopes fail and skies are dark before us,
   When the vain cares that vex our life increase,
Comes with its calm the thought that thou art o'er us,
   And we grow quiet, folded in thy peace.

3 Nought shall affright us, on thy goodness leaning;
   Low in the heart faith singeth still her song;
Chastened by pain we learn life's deeper meaning,
   And in our weakness thou dost make us strong.

4. Patient, O heart, though heavy be thy sorrows;
   Be not cast down, disquieted in vain;
Yet shalt thou praise him, when these darkened furrows,
   Where now he plougheth, wave with golden grain.

348

BROOKEND. (7 7. 7 3.)

Not too slow.

GUSTAV HOLST, 1874–1934.

Robert Herrick, 1591–1674.

IN this world, the Isle of Dreams,
    While we sit by sorrow's streams,
Tears and terrors are our themes
                Reciting:

2 But when once from hence we fly,
    More and more approaching nigh,
Unto young Eternity
                Uniting:

3 In that whiter Island, where
    Things are evermore sincere;
Candour here, and lustre there
                Delighting:

4 There no monstrous fancies shall
    Out of hell an horror call,
To create, or cause at all
                Affrighting.

5 There in calm and cooling sleep
    We our eyes shall never steep;
But eternal watch shall keep,
                Attending

6. Pleasures, such as shall pursue
    Me immortalized, and you;
And fresh joys, as never to
                Have ending.

(428)

349

FIRST TUNE

CHRISTE DU BEISTAND. (11 11. 11 5.)

Moderately slow.

M. VON LÖWENSTERN, 1594-1648.

Slightly slower.

Lord God al - migh - ty, Lord God al - migh - ty.

P. Pusey,‡ 1799-1855. *Based on* Christe
du Beistand, *M. von Löwenstern*, 1594-1648.

LORD of our life, and God of our salvation,
Star of our night, and hope of every nation,
Hear and receive thy Church's supplication,
Lord God almighty.

2 Lord, thou canst help when earthly armour faileth,
Lord, thou canst save when deadly sin assaileth;
Christ, o'er thy rock nor death nor hell prevaileth;
Grant us thy peace, Lord.

3*Peace in our hearts, our evil thoughts assuaging;
Peace in thy Church, where brothers are engaging;
Peace, when the world its busy war is waging:
Calm thy foes' raging.

4. Grant us thy help till backward they are driven,
Grant them thy truth, that they may be forgiven;
Grant peace on earth, and, after we have striven,
Peace in thy heaven.

(429)

349 (*continued*)

SECOND TUNE

ISTE CONFESSOR (ROUEN). (11 11 11. 5.)

In moderate time.   Rouen Church Melody.

ALTERNATIVE VERSION

The trebles sing the upper part, other voices the melody
ISTE CONFESSOR.   Descant by HARVEY GRACE.

P. Pusey,‡ 1799–1855. *Based on* Christe
du Beistand, *M. von Löwenstern,* 1594–1648.

LORD of our life, and God of our salvation,
　Star of our night, and hope of every nation,
Hear and receive thy Church's supplication,
　　Lord God almighty.

2 Lord, thou canst help when earthly armour faileth,
　Lord, thou canst save when deadly sin assaileth;
Christ, o'er thy rock nor death nor hell prevaileth;
　　Grant us thy peace, Lord.

3*Peace in our hearts, our evil thoughts assuaging;
　Peace in thy Church, where brothers are engaging;
Peace, when the world its busy war is waging:
　　Calm thy foes' raging.

4. Grant us thy help till backward they are driven,
　Grant them thy truth, that they may be forgiven;
Grant peace on earth, and, after we have striven,
　　Peace in thy heaven.

See also

465 Christ, of all my hopes the ground
478 Cometh sunshine after rain

479 Commit thou all thy griefs
118 Shepherd divine

350

NUN DANKET. (6 7. 6 7. 6 6. 6 6.)

Very slow and majestic.

Present form of melody by J. CRÜGER, 1598–1662.

A-men.

THANKSGIVING

M. Rinkart, 1586–1649. Tr. C. Winkworth.

Nun danket alle Gott.

NOW thank we all our God
  With heart and hands and voices,
Who wondrous things hath done,
In whom his world rejoices;
  Who from our mother's arms
    Hath blessed us on our way
  With countless gifts of love,
    And still is ours to-day.

2 O may this bounteous God
  Through all our life be near us,
    With ever-joyful hearts
  And blessed peace to cheer us,
    And keep us in his grace,
      And guide us when perplexed,
    And free us from all ills
      In this world and the next.

3. All praise and thanks to God
  The Father now be given,
    The Son, and him who reigns
  With them in highest heaven,
    The one eternal God,
      Whom earth and heaven adore;
    For thus it was, is now,
      And shall be evermore.

[*Continued overleaf*

350 (continued)

ALTERNATIVE VERSION

Descant by GEOFFREY SHAW.

[*By permission of Novello & Co., Ltd.*]

M. Rinkart, 1586–1649. Tr. C. Winkworth.

Nun danket alle Gott.

NOW thank we all our God
   With heart and hands and voices,
Who wondrous things hath done,
   In whom his world rejoices;
Who from our mother's arms
   Hath blessed us on our way
With countless gifts of love,
   And still is ours to-day.

2   O may this bounteous God
Through all our life be near us,
   With ever-joyful hearts
And blessèd peace to cheer us,

And keep us in his grace,
   And guide us when perplexed,
And free us from all ills
   In this world and the next.

3.   All praise and thanks to God
The Father now be given,
   The Son, and him who reigns
With them in highest heaven,
   The one eternal God,
Whom earth and heaven adore;
   For thus it was, is now,
And shall be evermore.

351

LAUDATE DOMINUM. (5 5. 5 5. 6 5. 6 5.)

Moderately slow.

Melody by H. J. GAUNTLETT, 1805-76.

[This hymn may also be sung to ST. JOSEPH, 441, by substituting ♩♩ for ♩. at line 3, second bar.]

Ps. 150.   *Sir H. W. Baker,* 1821-77.

O PRAISE ye the Lord!
  Praise him in the height;
Rejoice in his word,
  Ye angels of light;
Ye heavens, adore him
  By whom ye were made,
And worship before him,
  In brightness arrayed.

2 O praise ye the Lord!
  Praise him upon earth,
In tuneful accord,
  Ye sons of new birth;
Praise him who hath brought you
  His grace from above,
Praise him who hath taught you
  To sing of his love.

3 O praise ye the Lord,
  All things that give sound;
Each jubilant chord,
  Re-echo around;
Loud organs, his glory
  Forth tell in deep tone,
And sweet harp, the story
  Of what he hath done.

4. O praise ye the Lord!
  Thanksgiving and song
To him be outpoured
  All ages along:
For love in creation,
  For heaven restored,
For grace of salvation,
  O praise ye the Lord!

Specially suitable for occasions of thanksgiving are

439 All creatures of our God
441 All hail to the Power
443 *Old Hundredth.* All people
149 All the toil
448 Angels holy
492 Fill thou my life
408 From all that dwell
496 From glory to glory
19 Hark, my soul, how everything
553 King of glory
556 Let all the world
558 Let the whole creation cry
590 Not with a choir of angels
592 Now join, ye comrades

609 O sing to the Lord
618 O worship the King
387 Of the father's heart begotten
623 Praise, my soul, the King of heaven
624 Praise the Lord! Ye heavens, adore him
626 Praise to the Lord, the Almighty
631 Rejoice, O land
632 Rejoice! the Lord is King
644 Songs of praise
398 The God of Abraham
657 The Lord of Heaven confess
684 To thee whose eye
701 Ye holy angels bright

And also Part VIII, Doxologies.

PART VI

FOR CHILDREN

Hymns suitable for Young People are marked ° in the Index of First Lines; and the Hymns themselves are so marked in the Small Edition.

Adult hymns should be freely used. See the Preface also, and the note after No. 386.

This section is not intended for older children, but for the youngest. A few hymns are marked for older folk also.

Services for the Young in which three hymns are sung may conveniently conclude with one of the Doxologies in Part VIII.

352

A LITTLE CHILD. (Irreg.)

In moderate time.   Flemish Traditional Melody, arranged by JULIUS RÖNTGEN, 1855–1933.

(*Christmas and New Year.*)   *Old Flemish Carol. Tr. R. C. Trevelyan.*

A LITTLE child on the earth has been born;
He came to the earth for the sake of us all.

2 He came to earth, but no home did he find;
He came to earth, and its cross did he bear.

3. He came to earth for the sake of us all,
And wishes us all a Happy New Year.

(437)

353

CRADLE SONG. (11 11. 11 11.)

In moderate time. Unison.

Melody by W. J. KIRKPATRICK, 1838–1921.

Anon.

AWAY in a manger, no crib for a bed,
The little Lord Jesus laid down his sweet head.
The stars in the bright sky looked down where he lay,
The little Lord Jesus asleep on the hay.

2 The cattle are lowing, the baby awakes,
But little Lord Jesus no crying he makes.
I love thee, Lord Jesus! Look down from the sky,
And stay by my bedside till morning is nigh.

3. Be near me, Lord Jesus; I ask thee to stay
Close by me for ever, and love me, I pray.
Bless all the dear children in thy tender care,
And fit us for heaven, to live with thee there.

354

GLENFINLAS. (6 5. 6 5.)

In moderate time. Unison.

K. G. FINLAY.

Treasure.

Jan Struther, 1901–53.

DAISIES are our silver,
    Buttercups our gold:
This is all the treasure
    We can have or hold.

2 Raindrops are our diamonds
    And the morning dew;
While for shining sapphires
    We've the speedwell blue.

3 These shall be our emeralds—
    Leaves so new and green;
Roses make the reddest
    Rubies ever seen.

4 God, who gave these treasures
    To your children small,
Teach us how to love them
    And grow like them all.

5 Make us bright as silver:
    Make us good as gold;
Warm as summer roses
    Let our hearts unfold.

6. Gay as leaves in April,
    Clear as drops of dew—
God, who made the speedwell,
    Keep us true to you.

355

WAINWRIGHT. (L.M.)

In moderate time.

Later form of melody by RICHARD WAINWRIGHT, 1758–1825.

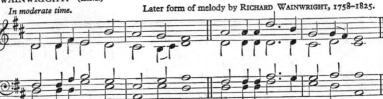

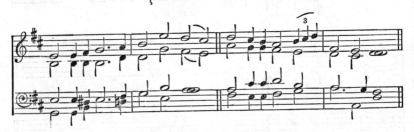

(*Morning.*)

Ascribed to Rebecca J. Weston (1885).

FATHER, we thank thee for the night,
 And for the pleasant morning light;
For rest and food and loving care,
And all that makes the day so fair.

2. Help us to do the things we should,
 To be to others kind and good;
In all we do at work or play
To grow more loving every day.

356

GENTLE JESUS. (7 7. 7 7.)

In moderate time.

MARTIN SHAW, 1875–1958.

C. *Wesley*, 1807–88.

GENTLE Jesus, meek and mild,
Look upon a little child;
Pity my simplicity,
Suffer me to come to thee.

2 Fain I would to thee be brought,
Dearest God, forbid it not;
Give me, dearest God, a place
In the kingdom of thy grace.

PART II

3 Lamb of God, I look to thee;
Thou shalt my example be:
Thou art gentle, meek and mild,
Thou wast once a little child.

4. Fain I would be as thou art;
Give me thy obedient heart:
Thou art pitiful and kind,
Let me have thy loving mind.

357

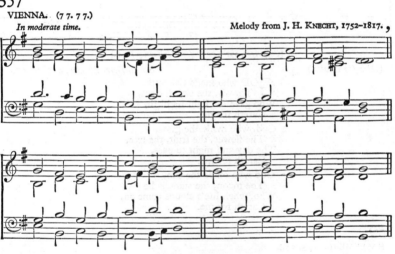

VIENNA. (7 7. 7 7.)
In moderate time.
Melody from J. H. KNECHT, 1752–1817.

G. W. *Briggs*, 1875–1959.

GOD my Father, loving me,
Gave his Son, my friend to be:
Gave his Son, my form to take,
Bearing all things for my sake.

2 Jesus still remains the same
As in days of old he came;
As my brother by my side,
Still he seeks my steps to guide.

3 How can I repay thy love,
Lord of all the hosts above?
What have I, a child, to bring
Unto thee, thou heavenly King?

4. I have but myself to give:
Let me to thy glory live;
Let me follow, day by day,
Where thou showest me the way.

358

PLATT'S LANE. (5 6. 6 4.)

In moderate time. Unison.

EVELYN SHARPE.

[*Copyright, 1929, by Oxford University Press.*]

(*Also for adults.*)

Sarah Betts Rhodes, c. 1830–90.

Gᴏᴅ who made the earth,
   The air, the sky, the sea,
Who gave the light its birth,
   Careth for me.

2 God, who made the grass,
   The flower, the fruit, the tree,
The day and night to pass,
   Careth for me.

3. God who made the sun,
   The moon, the stars, is he
Who, when life's clouds come on,
   Careth for me.

359

HASLEMERE. (5 5. 5 5.)

In moderate time. Unison.

Source unknown.

FOR CHILDREN

Florence Hoatson.

GOD whose name is Love,
  Happy children we:
Listen to the hymn
  That we sing to thee.

2 Help us to be good,
  Always kind and true,
In the games we play
  Or the work we do.

3. Bless us every one
  Singing here to thee.
God whose name is Love,
  Loving may we be!

360

SPRINGTIME.   (8 3. 8 3. 7 7. 8 7.)

In moderate time. Unison.

G. W. BRIGGS, 1875-1959.

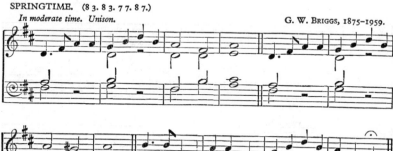

[*Copyright, 1929, by Oxford University Press.*]

(*Spring.*) (*Older classes also.*)

G. W. *Briggs*, 1875-1959.

HARK! a hundred notes are swelling
    Loud and clear.
'Tis the happy birds are telling
    Spring is here!
Nature, decked in brave array,
Casts her winter robes away;
All earth's little folk rejoicing
    Haste to greet the glad new day.

2. Lord and life of all things living,
    Come to me:
Thou delightest but in giving;
    Give to me:
Spring of joyous life thou art:
Thine own joy to me impart:
Let my praises be the outburst
    Of the springtime in my heart.

(443)

361

BILSDALE. (D.C.M. Irreg.)

In moderate time. Unison.

GORDON SLATER.

(*Older classes also.*)

G. W. Briggs, 1875–1959.

I LOVE God's tiny creatures
   That wander wild and free,
The coral-coated lady-bird,
   The velvet humming-bee;
Shy little flowers in hedge and dyke
   That hide themselves away:
God paints them, though they are so small,
   God makes them bright and gay.

2. Dear Father, who hast all things made,
   And carest for them all,
There's none too great for thy great love,
   Nor anything too small:
If thou canst spend such tender care
   On things that grow so wild,
How wonderful thy love must be
   For me, thy loving child.

(444)

362

FARNABY. (7 7. 7 7.)

In moderate time. Unison.

Adapted from an English Traditional Melody.

(*Nativity.*)

Eleanor Smith.†, 1858–1942.

I N another land and time,
  Long ago and far away,
There was once a baby born
On the first glad Christmas day.

2 Words of truth and deeds of love
   Filled his life from day to day,
So that all the world was blessed
On the first glad Christmas day.

3. Little children did he love
     With a tender love alway:
So should little children be
Always glad for Christmas day.

363

WESTRIDGE. (8 5. 8 3.)

Not too quick. Unison.

MARTIN SHAW, 1875–1958.

[*Copyright, 1929, by Oxford University Press.*]

Walter J. Mathams, 1853–1931.

J ESUS, friend of little children,
  Be a friend to me;
Take my hand, and ever keep me
Close to thee.

2 Teach me how to grow in goodness,
   Daily as I grow:
Thou hast been a child, and surely
Thou dost know.

3. Never leave me, nor forsake me;
     Ever be my friend;
For I need thee, from life's dawning
To its end.

364

SHIPSTON. (8 7. 8 7.)

In moderate time.

English Traditional Melody.

(*Evening.*)

Mrs. Mary Duncan, 1814–40.

JESUS, tender shepherd, hear me,
  Bless thy little lamb to-night;
Through the darkness be thou near me;
  Watch my sleep till morning light.

2. All this day thy hand has led me,
  And I thank thee for thy care;
Thou hast clothed me, warmed and fed me;
  Listen to my evening prayer.

365

CAMBER. (6 5. 6 5.)

Rather slowly. Unison.

MARTIN SHAW, 1875–1958.

Mrs. J. A. Carney (1845), and Percy Dearmer, 1867–1936.

LITTLE drops of water,
  Little grains of sand,
Make the mighty ocean
  And the beauteous land.

2 Little deeds of kindness,
  Little words of love,
Make our earth an Eden,
  Like the heavens above.

3 Little seeds of mercy
  Sown by youthful hands,
Grow to bless the nations
  Far in other lands.

4. Glory then for ever
  Be to God on high,
Beautiful and loving,
  To eternity.

366

INNOCENTS. (7 7. 7 7.)

Moderately fast.

Composed or adapted by J. SMITH, 1800–73.

Jane E. Leeson, 1807–82.

LOVING Shepherd of thy sheep,
  Keep thy lamb, in safety keep;
Nothing can thy power withstand,
None can pluck me from thy hand.

2 I would bless thee every day,
  Gladly all thy will obey,
Like thy blessèd ones above,
Happy in thy precious love.

3 Loving Shepherd, ever near,
  Teach thy lamb thy voice to hear;
Suffer not my steps to stray
From the straight and narrow way.

4. Where thou leadest I would go,
  Walking in thy steps below,
Till before my Father's throne
I shall know as I am known.

367

BULSTRODE. (7 6. 7 6.)

In moderate time. Unison.

EVELYN SHARPE.

S. P.

O DEAR and lovely Brother,
 The Son of God alone,
When we love one another
 We are thy very own.

2. In heaven thy face is hidden,
 Too near for us to see;
And each of us is bidden
 To share that heaven with thee.

368

IRBY. (8 7. 8 7. 7 7.)

In moderate time. May be sung in unison.

H. J. GAUNTLETT, 1805–76.

(*Nativity.*)

Mrs. C. F. Alexander, 1818–95.

O NCE in royal David's city
 Stood a lowly cattle shed,
Where a mother laid her baby
 In a manger for his bed:
Mary was that mother mild,
Jesus Christ her little child.

2 He came down to earth from heaven,
 Who is God and Lord of all,
And his shelter was a stable,
 And his cradle was a stall;
With the poor, and mean, and lowly,
Lived on earth our Saviour holy.

3*And through all his wondrous childhood
   He would honour and obey,
  Love and watch the lowly maiden,
    In whose gentle arms he lay:
  Christian children all must be
  Mild, obedient, good as he.

4*For he is our childhood's pattern:
   Day by day like us he grew,
  He was little, weak, and helpless,
    Tears and smiles like us he knew;
  And he feeleth for our sadness,
  And he shareth in our gladness.

5. And our eyes at last shall see him,
   Through his own redeeming love,
  For that child so dear and gentle
    Is our Lord in heaven above;
  And he leads his children on
  To the place where he is gone.

369

IN DER WIEGEN. (7 6. 7 6. D.)

Moderately slow.

Melody from CORNER's *Geistliche Nachtigall*, 1649.

[This hymn may also be sung to ELLACOMBE, 193.]

(Also for adults.)

P. *Dearmer*, 1867–1936.

REMEMBER all the people
Who live in far-off lands
In strange and lovely cities,
  Or roam the desert sands,
Or farm the mountain pastures,
  Or till the endless plains
Where children wade through rice-fields
  And watch the camel-trains:

2 Some work in sultry forests
  Where apes swing to and fro,
Some fish in mighty rivers,
  Some hunt across the snow.

Remember all God's children,
  Who yet have never heard
The truth that comes from Jesus,
  The glory of his word.

3. God bless the men and women
  Who serve him oversea;
God raise up more to help them
  To set the nations free,
Till all the distant people
  In every foreign place
Shall understand his Kingdom
  And come into his grace.

370

WHITE LADIES ASTON. (7 7. 7 7.)

Rather slow. Voices in unison.

IVOR ATKINS, 1869–1953.

[Copyright, 1931, by Oxford University Press.]

[This hymn may also be sung to BOYCE, 375.]

Jane E. Leeson, 1807–82.

SAVIOUR, teach me, day by day,
Love's sweet lesson to obey;
Sweeter lesson cannot be,
Loving him who first loved me.

2 With a child's glad heart of love
At thy bidding may I move,
Prompt to serve and follow thee,
Loving him who first loved me.

3 Teach me thus thy steps to trace,
Strong to follow in thy grace,
Learning how to love from thee,
Loving him who so loved me.

4. Love in loving finds employ,
In obedience all her joy;
Ever new that joy will be,
Loving him who first loved me.

(450)

371

ST. HUGH. (C.M.)

Brightly. English Traditional Melody.

R. S. Hawker of Morwenstow, 1803–75.

SING to the Lord the children's hymn,
His gentle love declare,
Who bends amid the seraphim
To hear the children's prayer.

2 He at a mother's breast was fed,
Though God's own son was he;
He learnt the first small words he said
At a meek mother's knee.

3 He held us to his mighty breast,
The children of the earth;
He lifted up his hands and blessed
The babes of human birth.

4. Lo! from the stars his face will turn
On us with glances mild;
The angels of his presence yearn
To bless the little child.

372

BERWICK STREET. (7 6. 7 6. 7 6. Irreg.)

In moderate time. Unison.

MARTIN SHAW, 1875–1958.

[*Copyright, 1929, by Oxford University Press.*]

Christina Rossetti, 1830–94.

THE shepherds had an angel,
   The wise men had a star;
But what have I, a little child,
   To guide me home from far,
Where glad stars sing together
   And singing angels are?

2 Lord Jesus is my guiding star,
   My beacon-light in heaven;
He leads me step by step along
   The path of life uneven;
He, true light, leads me to that land
   Whose day shall be as seven.

3*Those shepherds through the lonely night
   Sat watching by their sheep,
Until they saw the heavenly host
   Who neither tire nor sleep,
All singing 'Glory, glory'
   In festival they keep.

4.*Christ watches me, his little lamb,
   Cares for me day and night,
That I may be his own in heaven:
   So angels clad in white
Shall sing their 'Glory, glory'
   For my sake in the height.

(452)

FOR CHILDREN

373

IN MEMORIAM. (7 6. 7 6. D.)

In moderate time. Unison.

JOHN STAINER, 1840–1901
(slightly adapted by permission).

* The chord in brackets does not refer to the words printed below, but is inserted to enable those who wish to sing the tune to the words for which it was originally written.   The bass note D on the last beat is, of course, only to be used in this connexion, otherwise the first bass note is E.

Anon.

THE wise may bring their learning,
　The rich may bring their wealth,
And some may bring their greatness,
　And some their strength and health:
We, too, would bring our treasures
　To offer to the King;
We have no wealth or learning—
　What shall we children bring?

2. We'll bring the many duties
　We have to do each day;
We'll try our best to please him,
　At home, at school, at play:
And better are these treasures
　To offer to our King
Than richest gifts without them;
　Yet these a child may bring.

(453)

FOR CHILDREN

374

VOLLER WUNDER. (7 7. 7 7. 7 7.)

In moderate time.

J. G. EBELING, 1637–70.

(Morning or Evening.)

F. T. *Palgrave*, 1824–97.

THOU who once on mother's knee
Wast a little one like me,
When I wake, or go to bed,
Lay thy hands upon my head;
Let me feel thee very near,
Jesus Christ, our Saviour dear.

2. Be beside me in the light,
Be close by me through the night;
Make me gentle, kind, and true,
Do what I am bid to do;
Help and cheer me when I fret,
And forgive when I forget.

375

BOYCE. (7 7. 7 7.)

In moderate time. May be sung in unison.

W. BOYCE, 1710–79.

(454)

FOR CHILDREN

(Morning.)

W. Canton, 1845–1926.

THROUGH the night thy angels kept
  Watch beside me while I slept;
Now the dark has passed away,
Thank thee, Lord, for this new day.

2 North and south and east and west
  May thy holy name be blest;
Everywhere beneath the sun,
As in heaven, thy will be done.

3. Give me food that I may live;
  Every naughtiness forgive;
Keep all evil things away
From thy little child this day.

376

DANIEL. (L.M.)

In moderate time. Unison.

Irish Traditional Melody.

(Also for adults.)

J. M. C. Crum, 1872–1958.

TO God who makes all lovely things
  How happy must our praises be!
Each day a new surprise he brings
  To make us glad his world to see.

2 How plentiful must be the mines
  From which he gives his gold away;
In March he gives us celandines,
  He gives us buttercups in May.

3 He grows the wheat and never stops;
  There's none can count the blades of green;
And up among the elm-tree tops
  As many thousand leaves are seen.

4 And when the wheat is bound in sheaves
  He sends his wind among the trees,
And down come all the merry leaves
  In yellow-twinkling companies.

5*On winter nights his quiet flakes
  Come falling, falling all the night,
And when the world next morning wakes
  It finds itself all shining white.

6*He makes the sea that shines afar
  With waves that dance unceasingly;
And every single little star
  That twinkles in the evening sky.

7. He made the people that I meet,
  The many people, great and small,
In home and school, and down the street,
  And he made me to love them all.

(455)

377

STOWEY. (7 4. 7 4. Irreg.)

In moderate time. Voices in unison.

Adapted from an English Traditional Melody.

Jan Struther, 1901–53.

WHEN a knight won his spurs, in the stories of old,
He was gentle and brave, he was gallant and bold;
With a shield on his arm and a lance in his hand
For God and for valour he rode through the land.

2 No charger have I, and no sword by my side,
Yet still to adventure and battle I ride,
Though back into storyland giants have fled,
And the knights are no more and the dragons are dead.

3. Let faith be my shield and let joy be my steed
'Gainst the dragons of anger, the ogres of greed;
And let me set free, with the sword of my youth,
From the castle of darkness the power of the truth.

(456)

378

BUTLER. (C.M.)

Not too fast.

English Traditional Melody.

The Ships.

M. M. *Penstone*, 1859–1910.

WHEN lamps are lighted in the town,
　The boats sail out to sea;
The fishers watch when night comes down,
　They work for you and me.

2 We little children go to rest;
　Before we sleep, we pray
That God will bless the fishermen
　And bring them back at day.

3 The boats come in at early dawn,
　When children wake in bed;
Upon the beach the boats are drawn,
　And all the nets are spread.

4. God hath watched o'er the fishermen
　Far on the deep dark sea,
And brought them safely home again,
　Where they are glad to be.

379

GAMBLE. (6 5. 6 5. D.)

In moderate time. Unison. Adapted from a melody in *John Gamble's Collection*, 1659.

(*Nativity.*)   *William Canton*, 1845–1926.

WHEN the herds were watching
   In the midnight chill,
Came a spotless lambkin
   From the heavenly hill.

2 Snow was on the mountains
   And the wind was cold,
When from God's own garden
   Dropped a rose of gold.

3 When 'twas bitter winter,
   Homeless and forlorn
In a star-lit stable
   Christ the babe was born.

4. Welcome, heavenly lambkin;
   Welcome, golden rose;
Alleluya, baby
   In the swaddling clothes!

(458)

380

SUO-GÂN. (6 6. 6 6.)

Rather slow. Voices in unison.

Verse 1.

Welsh Traditional Melody.

Verse 2. (A little quicker.)

Winter.

S. P.

WINTER creeps,
Nature sleeps;
Birds are gone,
Flowers are none,
Fields are bare,
Bleak the air,
Leaves are shed:
All seems dead.

2. God's alive!
Grow and thrive,
Hidden away,
Bloom of May,
Robe of June!
Very soon
Nought but green
Will be seen!

FOR CHILDREN

FIVE SHORT CAROLS

381

THE BIRDS. (10 2. 10 2. 8 8 6.)

Rather quick.

Czech Traditional Carol.

[*Copyright, 1928, by Martin Shaw.*]

(*This tune may be sung throughout in unison, the organ playing the harmonies.*)

The Birds Carol.

O. B. C. from the Czech.

FROM out of a wood did a cuckoo fly,
  Cuckoo,
He came to a manger with joyful cry,
  Cuckoo;
He hopped, he curtsied, round he flew,
And loud his jubilation grew,
  Cuckoo, cuckoo, cuckoo.

2 A pigeon flew over to Galilee,
  Vrercroo,
He strutted, and cooed, and was full of glee,
  Vrercroo,
And showed with jewelled wings unfurled,
His joy that Christ was in the world,
  Vrercroo, vrercroo, vrercroo.

(460)

3. A dove settled down upon Nazareth,
   Tsucroo,
   And tenderly chanted with all his breath,
   Tsucroo:
   'O you,' he cooed, 'so good and true,
   My beauty do I give to you—
   Tsucroo, tsucroo, tsucroo.'

382

NORTHUMBRIA. (8 7. 8 7.)

Moderately slow.

Verse 1. *Unison.*

English Traditional Melody.

Verses 2 and 4. *Harmony.*

1st time. | 2nd time.

Verse 3 (Choir unaccompanied). (Or may be sung in two parts by trebles, one part singing the melody, the other the treble part; the organ playing the accompaniment.)

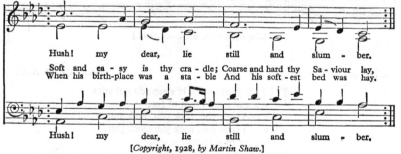

Hush! my dear, lie still and slum - ber.

Soft and ea - sy is thy cra - dle; Coarse and hard thy Sa - viour lay,
When his birth-place was a sta - ble And his soft - est bed was hay.

Hush! my dear, lie still and slum - ber.

[*Copyright, 1928, by Martin Shaw.*]

(*A fuller arrangement of this tune may be found in the* Oxford Book of Carols, No. 130.)

Cradle Song.   *Isaac Watts, 1674–1748.*

HUSH! my dear, lie still and slumber;
     Holy angels guard thy bed!
Heavenly blessings without number
Gently falling on thy head.

2 How much better thou'rt attended
     Than the Son of God could be
When from heaven he descended,
     And became a child like thee.

3 Soft and easy is thy cradle;
     Coarse and hard thy Saviour lay,
When his birthplace was a stable
     And his softest bed was hay.

4. May'st thou live to know and fear him,
     Trust and love him all thy days:
Then go dwell for ever near him,
     See his face and sing his praise.

383

ROCKING. (10 7. 8 8. 7 7.)
Rather slow.

Melody 'Hajej Nynej'
as sung in Czechoslovakia (origin unknown).

[*Copyright, 1931, by Martin Shaw.*]

Rocking Carol.   *Czech. Tr. O. B. C.*

LITTLE Jesus, sweetly sleep, do not stir;
We will lend a coat of fur,
We will rock you, rock you, rock you,
We will rock you, rock you, rock you:
See the fur to keep you warm,
Snugly round your tiny form.

2. Mary's little baby, sleep, sweetly sleep,
Sleep in comfort, slumber deep;
We will rock you, rock you, rock you,
We will rock you, rock you, rock you:
We will serve you all we can,
Darling, darling little man.

(462)

384

THE FIRST NOWELL. (Irreg.)

In moderate time.

English Traditional Carol Melody.

REFRAIN.

(*Christmas, Epiphany.*)

Old Carol.

THE first Noel the angel did say
Was to certain poor shepherds in fields as they lay;
In fields where they lay, keeping their sheep,
In a cold winter's night that was so deep:

Noel, noel, noel, noel,
Born is the King of Israel!

2 Then wise men, guided by a star,
Came from the eastern countries far;
To seek for a king was their intent,
And to follow the star wheresoever it went:

3. This star drew nigh to the north-west;
O'er Bethlehem it took its rest,
And there it did both stop and stay
Right over the place where Jesus lay:

385

OMEGA AND ALPHA (PUER NOBIS NASCITUR). (7 6. 7 7.)   From *Piae Cantiones*, 1582.

Moderately fast. Unison.   Arranged by GEOFFREY SHAW, 1879–1943.

(*A varied accompaniment for each verse will be found in the* Oxford Carol Book, No. 92.)

15th-century Carol. Tr. O. B. C.

Puer nobis nascitur.

UNTO us a boy is born!
   King of all creation,
Came he to a world forlorn,
   The Lord of every nation.

2 Cradled in a stall was he
   With sleepy cows and asses;
But the very beasts could see
   That he all men surpasses.

3 Herod then with fear was filled:
   'A prince', he said, 'in Jewry!'

All the little boys he killed
   At Bethlem in his fury.

4 Now may Mary's son, who came
   So long ago to love us,
Lead us all with hearts aflame
   Unto the joys above us.

5.*He the Source and he the End!
   Let the organ thunder,
While our happy voices rend
   The jocund air asunder!

386   SUNDAY KINDERGARTEN

GREETING. (5 5. 6 5.)   **I**

In moderate time. Unison.   MARTIN SHAW, 1875–1958.

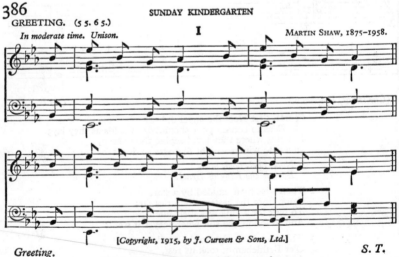

[*Copyright*, 1915, *by J. Curwen & Sons, Ltd.*]

Greeting.   S. T.

Good day to you all, good day to each one,
Good day to you, teachers! our school has begun.

(464)

OPPIDANS MEWS. (6 5. 6 5.)

II

Brightly.

MARTIN SHAW, 1875–1958.

1. Here we come with glad - ness, Gifts of love to bring,
2. Small may be the offer - ing, But the Lord will use
3. More and more for Je - sus May we glad - ly give;

Prais - ing him who loves us, Christ our sa - viour King.
Ev - 'ry gift we bring him; None will he re - fuse.
Giv - ing, giv - ing, giv - ing, Is the way to live.

[Copyright, 1915, by J. Curwen & Sons, Ltd.]

Collection March.

Julia H. Johnston, 1849–1919.

HERE we come with gladness,
Gifts of love to bring,
Praising him who loves us,
Christ our saviour King.

2 Small may be the offering,
But the Lord will use
Every gift we bring him;
None will he refuse.

3. More and more for Jesus
May we gladly give;
Giving, giving, giving,
Is the way to live.

(465)

386 *(continued)*

III

BIRTHDAY. (12 12. 8 10.)
In moderate time.

MARTIN SHAW, 1875–1958.

[*Copyright, 1915, by J. Curwen & Sons, Ltd.*]

Birthdays.

S. T.

WE wish you many happy returns of the day!
We hope you may be healthy and strong all the way:
Strong to do right, slow to do wrong,
And thoughtful for others all the day long.

Or, if there is no birthday, the following may be substituted:

FAIRLIGHT. (5 5. 8 6. D.)
At a gentle pace.

GEOFFREY SHAW, 1879–1943.

1. Who has seen the wind? Nei-ther you nor I; But
when the trees bow down their heads . The wind is pass-ing

SUNDAY KINDERGARTEN

by. . . The wind is pass-ing by. . .

2. Who has seen the wind? Nei-ther I nor you; . . But

when the leaves hang trem-bling, . The wind is pass-ing

through. The wind is pass-ing through. . . .

Christina Rossetti, 1840–94.

Or the opening verses of 358, 359, 362, 363.

386 (*continued*)

IV

CHILDREN ALL. (8 8. 8 6.)

Not too quick.

Voices in unison.

MARTIN SHAW, 1875–1958.

Our ba - bies' names are on the roll:

We love to see them writ - ten there; God give them

health in heart and soul : And in their bod - ies fair.

The Roll.   *S. T.*

OUR babies' names are on the roll:
 We love to see them written there;
God give them health in heart and soul
 And in their bodies fair.

2. All boys and girls belong to him,
 And baby children big and small:
God make them strong in life and limb,
 God bless the children all.

See also 382, Watts' Cradle Song.

V

MANOR STREET. (10 6. D.)

Rather fast. Voices in unison.

MARTIN SHAW, 1875–1958.

Praise him, praise him, all his chil-dren praise him! He is love, he is love. Thank him, thank him, all his chil-dren thank him! He is love, he is love.

Praise.

S. P. V.

PRAISE him, praise him, all his children praise him!
He is love, he is love.

2 Thank him, thank him, all his children thank him!
He is love, he is love.

3 Love him, love him, all his children love him!
He is love, he is love.

4. Crown him, crown him, all his children crown him!
He is love, he is love.

(469)

386 (continued)

VI

GOOD-BYE. (7 6. 8 6, and refrain.)

In moderate time. Unison.

MARTIN SHAW, 1875–1958.

Good-bye! Our school is o - ver, And we must go a - way;

Good-bye to you! We'll try to be true, And brave, and kind, and gay.

Good - bye, good - bye, good - bye.

[*Copyright, 1915, by J. Curwen & Sons, Ltd.*]

Good-bye Song. S. T.

Young children can learn the opening verses of hymns like 135, All glory, laud; 145, Jesus Christ is risen to-day; 78, O come, all ye faithful; 82, While shepherds watched. See also the Graces and Doxologies in Part VIII, and the hymns marked ° in the Index.
For collections of hymns for young people, see the Table of Hymns Arranged in the Music Edition.

387 DIVINUM MYSTERIUM. (8 7. 8 7. 8 7 7.)

Moderately fast. Unison.

Melody from *Piae Cantiones*, 1582.

Christmastide.

Prudentius, b. 348. *Tr. R. F. Davis.*

Corde natus ex parentis.

O F the Father's heart begotten,
    Ere the world from chaos rose,
He is Alpha: from that fountain
    All that is and hath been flows;
He is Omega, of all things
    Yet to come the mystic close:
      Evermore and evermore.

2 By his word was all created;
    He commanded and 'twas done;
Earth and sky and boundless ocean,
    Universe of three in one,
All that sees the moon's soft radiance,
    All that breathes beneath the sun:

3 This is he, whom seer and sibyl
    Sang in ages long gone by;
This is he of old revealèd
    In the page of prophecy;
Lo! he comes, the promised saviour;
    Let the world his praises cry:

4 Sing, ye heights of heaven, his praises;
    Angels and archangels, sing!
Wheresoe'er ye be, ye faithful,
    Let your joyous anthems ring,
Every tongue his name confessing,
    Countless voices answering:

5 *Now let old and young uniting
    Chant to thee harmonious lays,
Maid and matron hymn thy glory,
    Infant lips their anthem raise,
Boys and girls together singing
    With pure heart their song of praise:

6.*Let the storm and summer sunshine,
    Gliding stream and sounding shore,
Sea and forest, frost and zephyr,
    Day and night their Lord adore;
Let creation join to laud thee
    Through the ages evermore:

(This hymn may be begun at verse 4.)

388

LAUS TIBI CHRISTE. (6 5. 6 5. D.)

Moderately slow, dignified.

From a 14th-century German Processional Melody:

[This hymn may also be sung to KING'S WESTON, 392.]

PROCESSIONAL

G. Thring, 1823–1903.

FROM the eastern mountains
   Pressing on they come,
Wise men in their wisdom,
   To his humble home;
Stirred by deep devotion,
   Hasting from afar,
Ever journeying onward,
   Guided by a star.

2 There their Lord and Saviour
   Meek and lowly lay,
Wondrous light that led them
   Onward on their way,
Ever now to lighten
   Nations from afar,
As they journey homeward
   By that guiding star.

3 Thou who in a manger
   Once hast lowly lain,
Who dost now in glory
   O'er all kingdoms reign,
Gather in the heathen,
   Who in lands afar
Ne'er have seen the brightness
   Of thy guiding star.

4 Gather in the outcasts,
   All who've gone astray;
Throw thy radiance o'er them,
   Guide them on their way;
Those who never knew thee,
   Those who've wandered far,
Guide them by the brightness
   Of thy guiding star.

5*Onward through the darkness
   Of the lonely night,
Shining still before them
   With thy kindly light,
Guide them, Jew and Gentile,
   Homeward from afar,
Young and old together,
   By thy guiding star.

6.*Until every nation,
   Whether bond or free,
'Neath thy star-lit banner,
   Jesus, follows thee,
O'er the distant mountains
   To that heavenly home
Where nor sin nor sorrow
   Evermore shall come.

389

PLAINSONG. (Irreg.)

Chorus.

Melody from the *Sarum Processional.*

Chanter.

* This note is omitted in verse 7.

PROCESSIONAL

Festivals.

Bp. Venantius Fortunatus, c. 530–609. *Cento, S. P. V.*

Salve, festa dies.

Easter

*H*AIL *thee, Festival Day! blest day that art hallowed for ever;*
Day whereon Christ arose, breaking the kingdom of death.

Ascension

*H*AIL *thee, Festival Day! blest day that art hallowed for ever;*
Day when the Christ ascends, high in the heavens to reign.

Whitsunday

*H*AIL *thee, Festival Day! blest day that art hallowed for ever;*
Day whereon God from heaven shone in the world with his grace.

Dedication Festival

*H*AIL *thee, Festival Day! blest day that art hallowed for ever;*
Day when the Church, like a bride, welcomes the helpmate of all.

2*Lo, the fair beauty of earth, from the death of the winter arising!
Every good gift of the year now with its Master returns:

3 He who was nailed to the cross is Lord and the ruler of all men;
All things created on earth sing to the glory of God:

4*Daily the loveliness grows, adorned with the glory of blossom;
Heaven her gates unbars, flinging her increase of light:

5*Christ in his triumph ascends, who hath vanquished the devil's dominion;
Fitly the light gives him praise—meadows and ocean and sky:

6*Lo, in the likeness of fire, on them that await his appearing,
He, whom the Lord had foretold, suddenly, swiftly, descends:

7 You who have put on Christ are indeed his mystical body.
If you have kept his faith, longed to become as your Lord:

8 God the All-Father, the Lord, who rulest the earth and the heavens,
Guard us from harm without, cleanse us from evil within:

9 Jesus the health of the world, enlighten our minds, thou Redeemer,
Son of the Father supreme, only-begotten of God:

10 Paraclete, Spirit of Life, now flow in us, fount of our being,
Light that dost lighten all, life that in all dost abide:

11. Praise to the Giver of Good! Thou Love who art author of concord,
Pour out thy balm on our souls, order our ways in thy peace:

PROCESSIONAL

390

SALVE FESTA DIES. (Irreg.)

With vigour. Unison.

REFRAIN.

R. VAUGHAN WILLIAMS, 1872–1958.

(Small notes optional.)

1st time.

2nd time.

vv. 2 & 4.

PROCESSIONAL

Repeat Refrain after each verse.   *vv. 3 & 5.*

For any Sunday. (*Not necessarily Processional.*)   P. Dearmer, 1867–1936.

WELCOME, *Day of the Lord, the first and the best of the seven,
Day whereon Christ arose, brought us the promise of life.*

2 Day of refreshing and rest, that was won by the Church for the weary
   Working at labour unblest, slaves with no break in their toil:

3*Day of hilarity bright, of health and serene recreation;
   Kindred and friends unite, fathers and children can play:

4 Day that we set apart for all that is highest within us,
   Freed from the workshop and mart, finding the lovely and true:

5. Day for the worship of God, in fellowship sacred and joyful,
   Prayer and the heavenly food, comfort and knowledge and praise:

PROCESSIONAL

391 HEILIGER GEIST. (7 7. 7 4. 4. 4.)   Melody from CORNER's *Geistliche Nachtigall*, 1649.
Moderately slow.   Harmonized by HENRY G. LEY, 1887-1962.

Al - le - - - lu - ya, Al - le - lu - ya, Al - le - lu - ya!

The following harmonization may be used for one or more verses†

Al - le - - - lu - ya, Al - le - lu - ya, Al - le - lu - ya!

PROCESSIONAL

Based on Veni, sancte Spiritus. *S. P. V.*

HOLY Spirit, make us strong!
Radiant powers to thee belong;
Bless us, as we raise our song:
Alleluya!

2 Come to them who suffer dearth:
With thy gifts of priceless worth
Lighten all who dwell on earth:

3 Thou the heart's most precious guest,
Thou of strengtheners the best,
Give to us ascent and rest:

4 Come! in thee our work is sweet;
Wings art thou to weary feet,
Shelter from the noon-day heat:

5 Blessèd Sun, still rising higher,
Knowledge, counsel, might, inspire,
Understanding, wisdom's fire:

6 All good by thine aid is wrought,
Skilful deed and candid thought;
All we know from thee is brought:

7*Cleanse us, Lord, from greed of gain;
O'er our selfish conflicts reign;
Heal disease, defect, and pain:

8*Touch our hearts with flame divine;
All our thoughts to thee incline;
Mould our wills to follow thine:

9*Grant us, Lord, who cry to thee,
Steadfast for thy cause to be;
Give us hope and charity:

10.*May we live in holiness,
Through our lives bring happiness,
Help thy Kingdom to progress:

392

KING'S WESTON. (6 5. 6 5. D.)

With vigour. Unison.

R. VAUGHAN WILLIAMS, 1872–1958.

Con 8va.

A-men.

[Copyright, 1925, by R. Vaughan Williams.]

PROCESSIONAL

Caroline M. Noel, 1817–77, and others.

AT the name of Jesus
　　Every knee shall bow,
Every tongue confess him
　　King of glory now;
'Tis the Father's pleasure
　　We should call him Lord,
Who from the beginning
　　Was the mighty Word.

2 Humbled for a season
　　To receive a name
From the lips of sinners
　　Unto whom he came,
Faithfully he bore it,
　　Spotless to the last,
Brought it back victorious
　　When through death he passed.

3 Bore it up triumphant
　　With its human light,
Through all ranks of creatures,
　　To the central height,
To the throne of Godhead,
　　To the Father's breast;
Filled it with the glory
　　Of that perfect rest.

4 Name him, brothers, name him—
　　Strong your love as death—
But with awe and wonder,
　　And with bated breath;
He is God the Saviour,
　　He is Christ the Lord,
Ever to be worshipped,
　　Evermore adored.

5*In your hearts enthrone him;
　　There let him subdue
All that is not holy,
　　All that is not true:
Crown him as your captain
　　In temptation's hour;
Let his will enfold you
　　In its light and power.

6*Brothers, this Lord Jesus
　　Dwells with us again,
In his Father's wisdom
　　O'er the earth to reign;
For all wreaths of empire
　　Meet upon his brow,
And our hearts confess him
　　King of glory now.

7. Glory then to Jesus,
　　Who, the Prince of Light,
To a world in darkness
　　Brought the gift of sight;
Praise to God the Father;
　　In the Spirit's love
Praise we all together
　　Him who reigns above.

R

393

STALHAM. (C.M.)
In moderate time.
English Traditional Melody.

DUNSTAN. (C.M.)
Moderately slow.
From an English Traditional Melody.

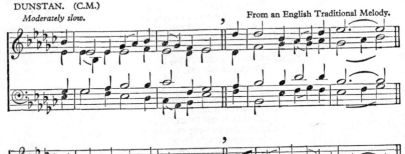

The Psalm of Sion.

Cento from W. Prid‡ (1585).

C ITY of Peace, our mother dear,
The throne of God on high,
O sacred city, queen and wife
Of Christ eternally!

2 My heart doth long to see thy face;
My soul doth still desire
Thy glorious beauty to behold;
My mind is set on fire.

3 O comely queen, in glory clad,
In honour and degree,
All fair thou art, exceeding bright;
No spot there is in thee.

4 O peerless dame and daughter fair
Of love without annoy,
Triumph! for in thy beauty brave
The King doth greatly joy.

(482)

THIRD TUNE

BARDISLEY. (C.M.)

In moderate time.

English Traditional Melody.

[This hymn may also be sung to St. Austin, 395.]

5 Thy port, thy shape, thy stately grace,
    Thy favour fair indeed,
Thy pleasant hue and countenance
    All others doth exceed.

6 O then thrice happy should my state
    In happiness remain,
If I might once thy glorious realm
    And princely place attain.

7 And view thy gallant gates, thy walls,
    Thy streets and dwellings wide,
Thy noble troop of citizens
    And mighty King beside.

PART II

8 Of stones full precious are thy towers;
    Thy gates of pearl are told;
There is that alleluya sung
    In streets of beaten gold.

9 Those stately towers manifold
    On squarèd stones do rise,
With sapphires decked and lofty frames
    Enclosèd castlewise.

10 Into the gates shall none approach
    But honest, pure and clean;
No spot, no filth, no loathsome thing
    Shall enter in, or mean.

11 City of Peace, our mother dear,
    The comfort of us all,

How sweet thou art and delicate!
    No thing shall thee befall.

12 O, blessèd are the pure in heart!
    Their Sovran they shall see;
And they most happy heavenly wights
    That of his household be.

13 Wherefore, O Lord, dissolve my bonds,
    My chains and fetters strong;
For I have dwelt within the tents
    Of wanderers over long.

14 And grant, O God, for Christ his sake,
    That, once devoid of strife,
I may thy holy hill attain
    To dwell in all my life.

15. He is the King of Kings, beset
    Amidst his servants right;
And they, his happy household all,
    Do serve him day and night.

(For another version see 395.)

394
BLENCATHRA. (6 5. 6 5. Ter.)

With vigour.

ARTHUR SOMERVELL, 1863–1937.

REFRAIN. *Voices in unison.*

Organ.

Alternative pedals.

H. Alford,† 1810–71.

FORWARD! be our watchword,
  Steps and voices joined;
Seek the things before us,
  Not a look behind;
Burns the fiery pillar
  At our army's head;
Who shall dream of shrinking,
  By our Captain led?
      Forward through the desert,
        Through the toil and fight;
      Jordan flows before us,
        Sion beams with light.

2 Glories upon glories
  Hath our God prepared,
By the souls that love him
  One day to be shared;
Eye hath not beheld them,
  Ear hath never heard;
Nor of these hath uttered
  Thought or speech a word.
      Forward, marching eastward,
        Where the heaven is bright,
      Till the veil be lifted,
        Till our faith be sight.

3 Far o'er yon horizon
  Rise the city towers;
Where our God abideth,
  That fair home is ours:
Flash the streets with jasper,
  Shine the gates with gold;
Flows the gladdening river,
  Shedding joys untold:
      Thither, onward thither,
        In the Spirit's might;
      Pilgrims to your country,
        Forward into light.

4*Into God's high temple
  Onward as we press,
Beauty spreads around us,
  Born of holiness;
Arch, and vault, and carving,
  Lights of varied tone,
Softened words and holy,
  Prayer and praise alone;
      Every thought up-raising
        To our city bright,
      Where the tribes assemble
        Round the throne of light.

5*Nought that city needeth
  Of these aisles of stone;
Where the Godhead dwelleth
  Temple there is none;
All the saints that ever
  In these courts have stood
Are but babes, and feeding
  On the children's food.
      On, through sign and token!
        Stars amidst the night,
      Forward through the darkness,
        Forward into light.

6.*To the Father's glory
  Loudest anthems raise;
To the Son and Spirit
  Echo songs of praise;
To the Lord almighty,
  Blessèd three in One,
Be by men and angels
  Endless honour done.
      Weak are earthly praises,
        Dull the songs of night;
      Forward into triumph,
        Forward into light!

A - men.

PROCESSIONAL

395
ST. AUSTIN. (C.M.)

In moderate time.

English Traditional Melody.

(This tune may also be used for Parts 2 and 3.)

'F. B. P.' *(late 16th or early 17th cent.)*.

JERUSALEM, my happy home,
  When shall I come to thee?
When shall my sorrows have an end?
  Thy joys when shall I see?

2 O happy harbour of the saints!
    O sweet and pleasant soil!
  In thee no sorrow may be found,
    No grief, no care, no toil.

3*In thee no sickness may be seen,
    No hurt, no ache, no sore;
  There is no death nor ugly dev'l,
    There 's life for evermore.

4*No dampish mist is seen in thee,
    No cold nor darksome night;
  There every soul shines as the sun;
    There God himself gives light.

5 There lust and lucre cannot dwell;
    There envy bears no sway;
  There is no hunger, heat, nor cold,
    But pleasure every way.

6 Jerusalem, Jerusalem,
    God grant I once may see
  Thy endless joys, and of the same
    Partaker ay to be!

(486)

SOUTHILL. (C.M.)
In moderate time.
English Traditional Melody.

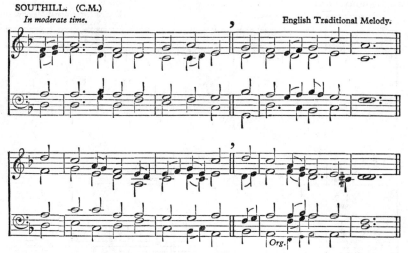

(This tune may also be used for Parts 1 and 3.)

PART II

7 Thy walls are made of precious stones,
    Thy bulwarks diamonds square;
    Thy gates are of right orient pearl;
    Exceeding rich and rare;

8 Thy turrets and thy pinnacles
    With carbuncles do shine;
    Thy very streets are paved with gold,
    Surpassing clear and fine;

9 Thy houses are of ivory,
    Thy windows crystal clear;
    Thy tiles are made of beaten gold—
    O God that I were there!

10 Within thy gates no thing doth come
    That is not passing clean,
    No spider's web, no dirt, no dust,
    No filth may there be seen.

11 Ah, my sweet home, Jerusalem,
    Would God I were in thee!
    Would God my woes were at an end,
    Thy joys that I might see!

[Continued overleaf]

395 (*continued*)

NEWBURY. (C.M.)

In moderate time.

English Traditional Melody.

PART III

(If sung separately, may begin with verse 1.)

12 Thy saints are crowned with glory great;
    They see God face to face;
    They triumph still, they still rejoice:
    Most happy is their case.

13 We that are here in banishment,
    Continually do mourn;
    We sigh and sob, we weep and wail,
    Perpetually we groan.

14 Our sweet is mixed with bitter gall,
    Our pleasure is but pain,
    Our joys scarce last the looking on,
    Our sorrows still remain.

15 But there they live in such delight,
    Such pleasure and such play,
    As that to them a thousand years
    Doth seem as yesterday.

PROCESSIONAL

Moderately slow.

Melody from HOLDROYD's *Spiritual Man's Companion*, 1753.

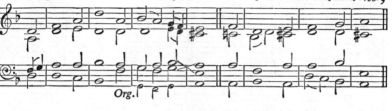

NOTE.—*Any of these four tunes can be used to any one part.*

PART IV

16 Thy vineyards and thy orchards are
　　Most beautiful and fair,
　　Full furnishèd with trees and fruits,
　　Most wonderful and rare;

17 Thy gardens and thy gallant walks
　　Continually are green;
　　There grow such sweet and pleasant
　　　flowers
　　As nowhere else are seen.

18 There's nectar and ambrosia made,
　　There's musk and civet sweet;
　　There many a fair and dainty drug
　　Is trodden under feet.

19 There cinnamon, there sugar grows,
　　There nard and balm abound:
　　What tongue can tell, or heart conceive,
　　The joys that there are found!

20 Quite through the streets with silver
　　　sound
　　The flood of life doth flow,
　　Upon whose banks on every side
　　The wood of life doth grow.

21 There trees for evermore bear fruit,
　　And evermore do spring;
　　There evermore the angels sit,
　　And evermore do sing.

22*There David stands with harp in hand
　　As master of the choir:
　　Ten thousand times that man were blest
　　That might this music hear.

23*Our Lady sings Magnificat
　　With tune surpassing sweet;
　　And all the virgins bear their parts,
　　Sitting about her feet.

24*Te Deum doth Saint Ambrose sing,
　　Saint Austin doth the like;
　　Old Simeon and Zachary
　　Have not their songs to seek.

25*There Magdalene hath left her moan,
　　And cheerfully doth sing
　　With blessèd saints, whose harmony
　　In every street doth ring.

26.*Jerusalem, my happy home,
　　Would God I were in thee!
　　Would God my woes were at an end,
　　Thy joys that I might see!

(For another version see 393.)

(489)

396

MADDERMARKET. (11 11. 11 9.)

Parts 1, 2, 4, and Conclusion.

In moderate time. Unison.

MARTIN SHAW, 1875-1958.

[*Copyright*, 1929, *by Oxford University Press.*]

Onward ever. (For the Young, and others.)   P. Dearmer, 1867–1936.

PART I (A).

O FATHER above us, our father in might,
  All live by thy love, as the flowers in the light;
Our father and mother and maker art thou.
        Forward!
    Forward ever, forward now!

2 In thee move the infinite stars on their rounds,
    The planets, the sun, and the moon in their bounds,
      As they kindle and glitter and sparkle and glow:
          Onward!
      Onward ever, onward go!

3 The flowers in our gardens of every gay hue,
    The meadows and sky-world, the green and the blue,
      All show us thy mind, for thou makest them so:

4 The plants are all breathing, the stones are alive,
    The atoms are busy as bees in a hive,
      And forces invisible spin to and fro:

5 And thou art the maker of beautiful things,
    Of roses and daisies and butterflies' wings,
      And mountains and forests, and water and snow:

(490)

B.

6 The cloud-mists rise up from the sea, by thy hand,
   And bring life to all, as they water the land,
      Then back to the ocean as rivers they flow:

7 All creatures are thine in the world and beyond,
   The bee at the pollen, the fish in the pond,
      The fox in his burrow, the bird on the bough:

8 The lambs and the calves and the foals that are born,
   The beans and potatoes, the roots and the corn,
      The apple and cherry trees, row after row:

9 And thine are the herds of the cattle and sheep,
   And lions, and monsters who surge in the deep,
      And sea-birds who float on the winds as they blow:

C.

10 Thine, Lord, are the men in the mills and the mines,
   The factories, offices, stations, and lines,
      The airplanes and steamers that pass to and fro:

11 The smith at his anvil, the cook by her fire,
   The builders, the painters, the men in the choir,
      The diggers and weavers, and women who sew:

12 And children who play by the sea on the sand,
   Who sing in their schools, and who dance on the land,
      And toss up the hay that the labourers mow:

Part II

13 O Father in heaven, our father on earth,
   Thou makest new life in each seed and each birth;
      The inventor, designer and artist art thou.
         Forward!
      Forward ever, forward now!

14 We thank thee for happiness, healthiness, love,
   For thoughts and for whispers that come from above,
      For good things we think of and good things we do:

         Onward!
      Onward ever, onward go!

15 We thank thee for games, and for friendship and fun,
   And the strength in our limbs when we wrestle and run,
      And all that is good and delightful and true:

16 Yes, we praise thee for goodness and beauty and truth;
   And we pray we may learn in the days of our youth
      To love all the gifts that from thee overflow:

[Continued overleaf

396 (*continued*)

ALDEBY. (11 11. 11 9.)

In moderate time.   Unison.

MARTIN SHAW, 1875–1958.

Part III

17 O Father of goodness, thou art in each one;
   And only our darkness can shadow the sun;
      That sun shining always unclouded art thou.
         Forward!
         Forward ever, forward now!

18 As we forgive others, forgive us our debts,
   Preserve us from evil, from anger and threats,
      And all that is mean and deceitful and low:

         Onward!
         Onward ever, onward go!

19 From cruelty, slander, and keeping things back,
   From white lies and grey lies and lies that are black,
      And every temptation to draw the long bow:

20 And keep us from making a fuss of our woes,
   From sulks and from fretfulness, rudeness and blows;
      To peace make us quick, and to quarrelling slow:

21 O give us the grace not to wrangle or fight,
   And give us the wisdom to know what is right,
      And when to say Yes, and the way to say No:

22 So, active and healthy in body and mind,
   And sweet to each other, unselfish and kind,
      And always more faithful to thee we would grow:

23 And as we grow older, Lord, help us to learn,
   That wisdom and truth we may always discern,
      And follow with patience the way thou wilt show:

[Continued overleaf.

396 (continued)

MADDERMARKET. (11 11. 11 9.)

Parts 1, 2, 4, and Conclusion.

In moderate time. Unison.

MARTIN SHAW, 1875–1958.

[*Copyright, 1929, by Oxford University Press.*]

PART IV

24 O Father of wisdom and friendship and peace,
As men become wiser thy Reign makes increase;
Our guide and inspirer and guardian art thou.
Forward!
Forward ever, forward now!

25 We pray for our fathers and mothers, who give
Our food and our clothes and the homes where we live:
O teach us to pay them the debt that we owe:

Onward!
Onward ever, onward go!

26 On brothers and sisters, relations and friends,
Each helper and teacher, and each one who spends
Her time on the children, thy blessing bestow:

27 And we pray for our rulers in Church and in State,
    For all, for the wise and the learned and great,
       For neighbour and stranger, for friend and for foe:

28 May all men their freedom and happiness win;
    May union between all the nations begin;
       The Kingdom of Heaven may all come to know:

29 And show us thy light when our notions are wrong,
    Make the ill to be well, and the weak to be strong,
       And all that is evil and false overthrow:

Conclusion

30 ***So we lift up our hands and we sing out thy praise,
    While the banners go forward, and lights are ablaze,
       And the organ peals out, and the trumpeters blow:

31 O God in whose working we live and we move,
    Through Jesus we know that thy nature is love.
       O teach us, O lead us, the way we should go:

32 We praise thee, O Father of infinite might,
    We thank thee for life and for love and for light,
       We pray thee thy treasure on all to bestow:

33. Our Father thou art whom all creatures obey,
    Thy Son to all people on earth shows the way,
       Thy Spirit gives light to our minds here below:

(This may be sung as one long processional such as may be needed on massed festivals: or some only of the Parts may be sung, ending with the Conclusion. Each or any Part may have the star verse *** 30 (with action) sung at the end. Short hymns can be made of any section, A, B, or C, or of any Part, with or without the Conclusion.

Even those who cannot read can still sing the refrain to each verse, 'Onward ever, onward go,' while others sing the verses.)

397

PRINCE RUPERT. (6 5. 6 5. Ter.)

With vigour.

GUSTAV HOLST, 1874–1934, from an old English March.

Alto and Bass.
Christ   the   roy - al Mas - ter

For - - ward   in - to bat - tle

PROCESSIONAL

S. Baring-Gould, 1834–1924.

ONWARD, Christian soldiers!
　　Marching as to war,
With the cross of Jesus
　Going on before.
　　Christ the royal Master
　　　Leads against the foe;
　Forward into battle,
　　See, his banners go:

　　Onward, Christian soldiers,
　　　Marching as to war,
　　With the cross of Jesus
　　　Going on before.

2*At the sign of triumph
　Satan's legions flee;
On then, Christian soldiers,
　On to victory!
Hell's foundations quiver
　At the shout of praise;
Brothers, lift your voices,
　Loud your anthems raise:

3*Like a mighty army
　Moves the Church of God;
Brothers, we are treading
　Where the saints have trod;
We are not divided,
　All one body we,
One in hope and doctrine,
　One in charity:

4 Crowns and thrones may perish,
　Kingdoms rise and wane,
But the Church of Jesus
　Constant will remain;
Gates of hell can never
　'Gainst that Church prevail;
We have Christ's own promise,
　And that cannot fail:

5. Onward, then, ye people,
　Join our happy throng,
Blend with ours your voices
　In the triumph song;
Glory, laud, and honour
　Unto Christ the King;
This through countless ages
　Men and angels sing:

398

LEONI. (6 6. 8 4. D.)
With vigour.

Adapted from a Hebrew Melody by M. LEONI, 1770.

A-men.

T. Olivers,‡ 1725–99. Based on the Yigdal.

THE God of Abraham praise
Who reigns enthroned above,
Ancient of everlasting days,
And God of love:
To him uplift your voice,
At whose supreme command
From earth we rise, and seek the joys
At his right hand.

2* Though nature's strength decay,
And earth and hell withstand,
To Canaan's bounds we urge our way
At his command.
The watery deep we pass,
With Jesus in our view;
And through the howling wilderness
Our way pursue.

3 The goodly land we see,
With peace and plenty blest;
A land of sacred liberty
And endless rest;
There milk and honey flow,
And oil and wine abound,
And trees of life for ever grow,
With mercy crowned.

4 There dwells the Lord our King,
The Lord our Righteousness,
Triumphant o'er the world and sin,
The Prince of Peace;
On Sion's sacred height
His kingdom he maintains,
And glorious with his saints in light
For ever reigns.

5   Before the great Three-One
     They all exulting stand,
And tell the wonders he hath done
     Through all their land:
   The listening spheres attend,
    And swell the growing fame,
And sing, in songs which never end,
    The wondrous name.

6*   The God who reigns on high
    The great archangels sing,
And 'Holy, holy, holy,' cry,
     'Almighty King!
   Who was, and is, the same,
    And evermore shall be:
Eternal Father, great "I AM",
    We worship thee.'

7.*   The whole triumphant host
    Give thanks to God on high;
'Hail! Father, Son, and Holy Ghost,'
    They ever cry:
   Hail! Abraham's God, and mine!
    (I join the heavenly lays)
All might and majesty are thine,
    And endless praise.

The following also, among others, are suitable for use in processions

(499)

PART VIII

VERSES AND DOXOLOGIES

GRACES AND OTHER VERSES

399

STONETHWAITE. (3 8. 6 5. 6 3.)

Rather slow. Unison.

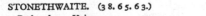

ARTHUR SOMERVELL, 1863–1937.

[Copyright, 1931, by Oxford University Press.]

St. Richard of Chichester, c. 1197–1253.

DAY by day,
 Dear Lord, of thee three things I pray:
  To see thee more clearly,
  Love thee more dearly,
  Follow thee more nearly,
   Day by day.

400

STRASSBURG. (C.M.)

Not too slow. Unison.

Melody from the *Strassburger Kirchengesang-Buch*, 1616.

(500)

Morning.

G. W. Briggs, 1875–1959.

DEAR Father, keep me through this day
  Obedient, kind and true:
That, always loving thee, I may
  Seek all thy will to do.

401

WULFRUN. (8 8 8.)

In moderate time.

G. W. BRIGGS, 1875–1959.

George Herbert,† 1593–1633.

ENRICH, Lord, heart, mouth, hands in me,
  With faith, with hope, with charity:
That I may run, rise, rest with thee.

402

PADDOCKS. (7 7. 7 7. 7 7.)

Simply, and not too fast. Voices in unison.

GEOFFREY SHAW, 1879–1943.

Here a lit - tle child I stand,

Heav - ing up my ei - ther hand;

Cold as pad - docks though they be,

Here I lift them up to thee,

For a ben - i - son to fall

On our meat and on us all. A - men.

Herrick's Grace.

Robert Herrick, 1591–1674.

HERE a little child I stand,
  Heaving up my either hand;
Cold as paddocks though they be,
Here I lift them up to thee,
For a benison to fall
On our meat and on us all. Amen.

(Paddocks are frogs and toads: a benison is a blessing.)

403

PACHELBEL (WAS GOTT THUT). (8 8. 8 8 8.)

Rather slow.

Adapted from a melody in the Nürnberg *Gesangbuch*, 1690.

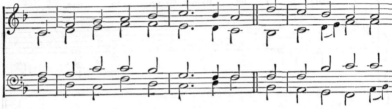

Grace before Meals.

G. W. Briggs, 1875-1959.

OUR Father, for our daily bread
  Accept our praise and hear our prayer.
By thee all living souls are fed:
  Thy bounty and thy loving care
  With all thy children let us share.

404

To be sung to BATTISHILL, 538.

E. Rutter Leatham, 1870–1939.

THANK you for the world so sweet;
  Thank you for the food we eat;
Thank you for the birds that sing:
  Thank you, God, for everything!

405

To be sung to MAGDALENA, 591.

Anon.

WE thank thee, loving Father,
  For all thy tender care,
For food and clothes and shelter
And all the world so fair.

DOXOLOGIES, ETC.

For the Conclusion of a Service or of Part of a Service

Some of these, such as 407, 408, 410, 411, 412, 414, 418, are suitable also for the beginning of a service, as are also verses from many other hymns.

406

(350)

To be sung to NUN DANKET, 350.

ALL praise and thanks to God
  The Father now be given,
The Son, and him who reigns
  With them in highest heaven;
The one eternal God,
  Whom earth and heaven adore;
For thus it was, is now,
  And shall be evermore. Amen.

407

To be sung to O SEIGNEUR, 696, or NUNC DIMITTIS, 50.

G. D.

BE, Lord, the happy guide
  Our earthly ways beside,
  As onward we are faring:
Thou art the Word, but since
Thou didst become our Prince,
  Be not of us despairing.
Enclose us as the robe
Of air about our globe,
  And be our inspiration;
That life on earth begun
Beneath our daily sun
  Be crowned in man's creation.

(505)

408

To be sung to ILLSLEY, 610, or WAREHAM, 631.

Ps. 117.

I. Watts, 1674–1748.

FROM all that dwell below the skies
  Let the Creator's praise arise:
Let the Redeemer's name be sung
Through every land by every tongue.

Eternal are thy mercies, Lord;
Eternal truth attends thy word:
Thy praise shall sound from shore to shore,
Till suns shall rise and set no more.

409

To be sung to COELITES PLAUDANT, 262.

L. Housman, 1865–1959.

HONOUR and glory, power and salvation,
  Be in the highest unto him who reigneth
Changeless in heaven over earthly changes,
        Triune, eternal.

410

To be sung to DUNDEE (or FRENCH), 557.

Ps. 121.

Scottish Psalter (1650).

I TO the hills will lift mine eyes,
  From whence doth come mine aid.
My safety cometh from the Lord,
  Who heaven and earth hath made.

2. Thy foot he'll not let slide, nor will
  He slumber that thee keeps.
Behold, he that keeps Israel,
  He slumbers not, nor sleeps.

411

To be sung to BIRMINGHAM, 266.

J. C. Earle, 1821–99.

I WILL arise and to my Father go;
  This very hour the journey is begun:
I start to reach the blissful goal, and lo,
  My spirit at one bound her race has run.
For seeking God and finding him are one;
He feeds the rillets that towards him flow:
  It is the Father who first seeks the son,
And moves all heavenward movement, swift or slow

412

To be sung to St. Patrick, 528.

A. G.

IN God rejoice! his good endures;
 To all he gives, from all receives:
The urge and end of world desire,
 He shapes, foresees, informs, achieves:
Our great Companion understands
 And man's bewildering sorrow shares:
Praise him, the Poet who creates;
 Praise him, the Patience who forbears!

413

L.M.

To be sung to Old 100th, 443.

PRAISE God, from whom all blessings flow;
 Praise him, all creatures here below;
Praise him above, ye heavenly host;
Praise Father, Son, and Holy Ghost.

414

To be sung to Laus Tibi, 388.

T. B. Browne, 1805–74.

PRAISE the Lord of heaven; praise him in the height;
 Praise him, all ye angels; praise him, stars and light;
For the name of God is excellent alone:
On the earth his footstool, over heaven his throne.

415

To be sung to Easter Alleluya, 157.

THROUGH north and south and east and west
 May God's immortal name be blest:
    Alleluya, alleluya!
Till everywhere beneath the sun
His Kingdom comes, his will is done:
 Alleluya, alleluya, alleluya, alleluya, alleluya!

416

C.M.

To be sung to MARTYRDOM, 449, or WILTSHIRE, 677.

(449, 677)

TO Father, Son, and Holy Ghost,
   The God whom we adore,
Be glory, as it was, is now,
   And shall be evermore.

417

S.M.

To be sung to ST. THOMAS, 68, or DRUMCONDRA, 601.

S. P. (601)

TO thee, who makest all,
   High praise and glory be,
Who Goodness, Truth, and Beauty art
   Through all eternity.

A - men.

418

To be sung to PRAISE, 624, or HYFRYDOL, 260, or AUSTRIAN HYMN, 500.

(624)

WORSHIP, honour, glory, blessing,
   Lord, we offer to thy name;
Young and old, thy praise expressing,
   Join their Saviour to proclaim.
As the saints in heaven adore thee,
   We would bow before thy throne;
As thine angels serve before thee,
   So on earth thy will be done.

A - men.

See also

and the Table of Hymns Arranged in the Music Edition
('Amen' is generally suitable after Doxologies.)

PART IX

CANTICLES, ETC.

419

Venite. Ps. 95.

O COME, let us sing unto the Lord : let us heartily rejoice in the strength of our salvation.

Let us come before his presence with thanksgiving : and show ourselves glad in him with psalms.

For the Lord is a great God : and a great King above all gods.

In his hand are all the corners of the earth : and the strength of the hills is his also.

The sea is his, and he made it : and his hands prepared the dry land.

PART II

O COME, let us worship, and fall down : and kneel before the Lord our maker.

For he is the Lord our God : and we are the people of his pasture, and the sheep of his hand.

Doxology

Glory be to the Father, and to the Son : and to the Holy Ghost;

As it was in the beginning, is now and ever shall be : world without end. Amen.

420

Te Deum.   *4th or 5th century. Original Version.*

WE praise thee, O God : we acknowledge thee to be the Lord.

All the earth doth worship thee : the Father everlasting.

To thee all angels cry aloud : the heavens, and all the powers therein.

To thee cherubin and seraphin : continually do cry,

Holy, holy, holy : Lord God of Sabaoth;

Heaven and earth are full of the majesty : of thy glory.

The glorious company of the apostles : praise thee.

The goodly fellowship of the prophets : praise thee.

The noble army of martyrs : praise thee.

The holy Church throughout all the world : doth acknowledge thee;

The Father : of an infinite majesty;

Thine honourable, true : and only Son;

Also the Holy Ghost : the Comforter.

Part II

THOU art the King of Glory : O Christ.
Thou art the everlasting Son : of the Father.

When thou tookest upon thee to deliver man : thou didst not abhor the Virgin's womb.

When thou hadst overcome the sharpness of death : thou didst open the Kingdom of Heaven to all believers.

Thou sittest at the right hand of God : in the glory of the Father.

We believe that thou shalt come : to be our judge.

We therefore pray thee, help thy servants : whom thou hast redeemed with thy precious blood.

Make them to be numbered with thy Saints : in glory everlasting.

421

Benedicite. Apocrypha, Bk. 9.

O ALL ye works of the Lord :
Bless ye the Lord[1]:
Praise him, and magnify him for ever,

O ye heavens :
O all ye powers of the Lord :
O ye sun and moon :
O ye stars of heaven :
O ye showers and dew :
O ye winds of God :
O ye fire and heat :
O ye winter and summer :
O ye ice and snow :
O ye nights and days :
O ye lightnings and clouds :

Part II

O YE mountains and hills :
O all ye green things upon the earth :
O ye seas and floods :
O ye whales, and all that move in the waters :
O all ye fowls of the air :
O all ye beasts and cattle :
O ye children of men :

Part III

O LET *Israel*[2] bless the Lord :
O ye priests of the Lord :
O ye servants of the Lord :
O ye spirits and souls of the righteous :
O ye holy and humble men of heart :
* O give thanks unto the Lord, because he is gracious : for his mercy endureth for ever.
* O all ye that worship the Lord, bless the God of gods, praise him, and give him thanks : for his mercy endureth for ever.

[1] *The Minister may say,* 'Bless ye the Lord'; *the People,* 'Praise him', &c.
[2] Or *the World,* or *England,* &c.

422

Benedictus. St. Luke 1 : 68.

BLESSED be the Lord God of Israel : for he hath visited and redeemed his people;
And hath raised up a mighty salvation for us : in the house of his servant David;
As he spoke by the mouth of his holy prophets : which have been since the world began;

* That we should be saved from our enemies : and from the hands of all that hate us;

* To perform the mercy promised to our forefathers : and to remember his holy covenant;

* To perform the oath which he sware to our forefather Abraham : that he would give us;

That we being delivered out of the hands of our enemies : might serve him without fear;

In holiness and righteousness before him : all the days of our life.

PART II

And thou, child, shalt be called the Prophet of the Highest : for thou shalt go before the face of the Lord to prepare his ways;

To give knowledge of salvation unto his people : for the remission of their sins,

Through the tender mercy of our God : whereby the day-spring from on high hath visited us;

To give light to them that sit in darkness, and in the shadow of death : and to guide our feet into the way of peace.

423

Jubilate. Ps. 100.

O BE joyful in the Lord, all ye lands : serve the Lord with gladness, and come before his presence with a song.

Be ye sure that the Lord he is God : it is he that hath made us, and not we ourselves; we are his people, and the sheep of his pasture.

O go your way into his gates with thanksgiving, and into his courts with praise : be thankful unto him, and speak good of his name.

For the Lord is gracious, his mercy is everlasting : and his truth endureth from generation to generation.

424

Magnificat. St. Luke 1 : 46.

MY soul doth magnify the Lord : and my spirit hath rejoiced in God my saviour.
For he hath regarded : the lowliness of his hand-maiden.

For behold, from henceforth : all generations shall call me blessed.

For he that is mighty hath magnified me : and holy is his name.

And his mercy is on them that fear him : throughout all generations.

He hath showed strength with his arm : he hath scattered the proud in the imagination of their hearts.

He hath put down the mighty from their seat : and hath exalted the humble and meek.

He hath filled the hungry with good things : and the rich he hath sent empty away.

He remembering his mercy hath holpen his servant Israel : as he promised to our forefathers, Abraham and his seed, for ever.

425

Cantate. Ps. 98.

O SING unto the Lord a new song : for he hath done marvellous things.

With his own right hand, and with his holy arm : hath he gotten himself the victory.

The Lord declared his salvation : his righteousness hath he openly showed in the sight of the heathen.

He hath remembered his mercy and truth toward the house of Israel : and all the ends of the world have seen the salvation of our God.

Show yourselves joyful unto the Lord, all ye lands : sing, rejoice, and give thanks.

* Praise the Lord upon the harp : sing to the harp with a psalm of thanksgiving.

* With trumpets also and shawms : O show yourselves joyful before the Lord the King.

* Let the sea make a noise, and all that therein is : the round world, and they that dwell therein.

Let the floods clap their hands, and let the hills be joyful together before the Lord : for he cometh to judge the earth.

With righteousness shall he judge the world : and the people with equity.

426

Nunc dimittis. St. Luke 2 : 29.

L ORD, now lettest thou thy servant depart in peace : according to thy word.

For mine eyes have seen : thy salvation,

Which thou hast prepared : before the face of all people;

To be a light to lighten the Gentiles : and to be the glory of thy people Israel.

427

Deus Misereatur. Ps. 67.

G OD be merciful unto us, and bless us : and show us the light of his countenance, and be merciful unto us :

That thy way may be known upon earth : thy saving health among all nations.

Let the people praise thee, O God : yea, let all the people praise thee.

O let the nations rejoice and be glad : for thou shalt judge the folk righteously, and govern the nations upon earth.

Let the people praise thee, O God : yea, let all the people praise thee.

Then shall the earth bring forth her increase : and God, even our own God, shall give us his blessing.

God shall bless us : and all the ends of the world shall fear him.

428

Dominus regit me. Ps. 23.

THE Lord is my shepherd : therefore can I lack nothing.

He shall feed me in a green pasture : and lead me forth beside the waters of comfort.

He shall convert my soul : and bring me forth in the paths of righteousness, for his name's sake.

Yea, though I walk through the valley of the shadow of death, I will fear no evil : for thou art with me; thy rod and thy staff comfort me.

Thou shalt prepare a table before me against them that trouble me : thou hast anointed my head with oil, and my cup shall be full.

But thy loving-kindness and mercy shall follow me all the days of my life : and I will dwell in the house of the Lord for ever.

429

Miserere mei, Deus. Ps. 51.

HAVE mercy upon me, O God, after thy great goodness : according to the multitude of thy mercies do away mine offences.

Wash me throughly from my wickedness : and cleanse me from my sin.

For I acknowledge my faults : and my sin is ever before me.

But lo, thou requirest truth in the inward parts : and shalt make me to understand wisdom secretly.

* Thou shalt purge me with hyssop, and I shall be clean : thou shalt wash me, and I shall be whiter than snow.

* Thou shalt make me hear of joy and gladness : that the bones which thou hast broken may rejoice.

* Turn thy face from my sins : and put out all my misdeeds.

* Make me a clean heart, O God : and renew a right spirit within me.

* Cast me not away from thy presence : and take not thy holy Spirit from me.

O give me the comfort of thy help again : and stablish me with thy free Spirit.

Then shall I teach thy ways unto the wicked : and sinners shall be converted unto thee.

Deliver me from blood-guiltiness, O God, thou that art the God of my health : and my tongue shall sing of thy righteousness.

Thou shalt open my lips, O Lord : and my mouth shall show thy praise.

For thou desirest no sacrifice, else would I give it thee : but thou delightest not in burnt-offerings.

The sacrifice of God is a troubled spirit : a broken and contrite heart, O God, shalt thou not despise.

430

Dilexi, quoniam. Ps. 116.

I AM well pleased : that the Lord hath heard the voice of my prayer;

That he hath inclined his ear unto me : therefore will I call upon him as long as I live.

The snares of death compassed me round about : and the pains of hell gat hold upon me.

I shall find trouble and heaviness, and I will call upon the name of the Lord : O Lord, I beseech thee, deliver my soul.

s

430 (*continued*)

Gracious is the Lord, and righteous : yea, our God is merciful.

The Lord preserveth the simple : I was in misery, and he helped me.

Turn again then unto thy rest, O my soul : for the Lord hath rewarded thee.

And why, thou hast delivered my soul from death : mine eyes from tears, and my feet from falling.

I will walk before the Lord : in the land of the living.

* What reward shall I give unto the Lord : for all the benefits that he hath done unto me?

* I will receive the cup of salvation : and call upon the name of the Lord.

* I will pay my vows unto the Lord, in the sight of all his people : in the courts of the Lord's house, even in the midst of thee, O Jerusalem. Praise the Lord.

431

Gloria in excelsis.   *Greek, c. 4th century.*

GLORY be to God on high, and in earth peace, good will towards men. We praise thee, we bless thee, we worship thee, we glorify thee, we give thanks to thee for thy great glory, O Lord God, heavenly King, God the Father Almighty.

O Lord, the only-begotten Son Jesu Christ; O Lord God, Lamb of God, Son of the Father, that takest away the sins of the world, have mercy upon us. Thou that takest away the sins of the world, have mercy upon us. Thou that takest away the sins of the world, receive our prayer. Thou that sittest at the right hand of God the Father, have mercy upon us.

For thou only art holy; thou only art the Lord; thou only, O Christ, with the Holy Ghost, art most high in the glory of God the Father. Amen.

432

FAMOUS MEN (Canticle).

432 (continued)

know - ledge. Such as found out mu-si-cal tunes

and re - ci - ted ver-ses in wri - ting: All these were

hon - oured in their gen - er - a - tions, and were the glo - - ry of their

times. And some there be which have

Ecclesiasticus 44.

433

GOD IS SPIRIT. (Canticle.)

In the time of slow reading. Note values dependent on syllabic values.

MARTIN SHAW, 1875–1958.

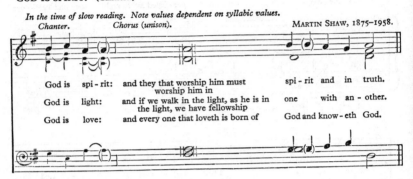

God is	spi - rit:	and they that worship him must worship him in
God is	light:	and if we walk in the light, as he is in the light, we have fellowship
God is	love:	and every one that loveth is born of

spi - rit and in truth.

one with an - other.

God and know-eth God.

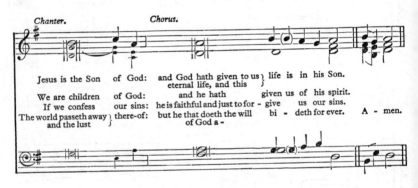

Jesus is the Son	of God:	and God hath given to us } eternal life, and this }	life is in his Son.
We are children	of God:	and he hath	given us of his spirit.
If we confess	our sins:	he is faithful and just to for - give	us our sins.
The world passeth away } and the lust }	there-of:	but he that doeth the will of God a -	bi - deth for ever. A - men.

[Copyright, 1931, by Martin Shaw.]

We believe:

God is spirit : and they that worship him must worship him in spirit and in truth.

God is light : and if we walk in the light, as he is in the light, we have fellowship one with another.

God is love : and every one that loveth is born of God and knoweth God.

Jesus is the Son of God : and God hath given to us eternal life, and this life is in his Son.

We are children of God : and he hath given us of his spirit.

If we confess our sins : he is faithful and just to forgive us our sins.

The world passeth away and the lust thereof : but he that doeth the will of God abideth for ever. Amen.

434

ALL CREATURES. (Canticle.)

In the time of slow reading. Unison.

Set to a Parisian Tone and an original
tune by MARTIN SHAW, 1875-1958.

1. O most high, almighty, good Lord God : to thee belong
praise, glory, honour, and all bless-ing.

Org.

2. Prais-ed be my Lord } all his crea-tures:
God, with } and specially our brother the sun, who brings us the day and who brings us the light.

mf Harmony.

3. Fair is he, and shining } ry great splen-dour : O Lord, he signifies
with a ve- } to us thee.

Unison.

4. Prais - ed be my Lord for our sis - ter the moon :
5. Prais - ed be my Lord for our bro - ther the wind :

and for the stars, the which he has set clear and love - - ly in hea - ven.
and for air and cloud, calms, and all weather by the life all crea - tures.
which thou upholdest in

[*Copyright, 1926, by Martin Shaw.*]

(519)

434 (continued)

mf Harmony.

6. Praisèd be my Lord for our   sis - ter wa - ter:

who is very serviceable unto us, and humble and pre - - cious and clean.

f Unison.

7. Prais - ed be my Lord for our brother fire, through whom   in   the   dark - ness:
thou givest us light

8. Prais - ed be my Lord for our mother the earth, the which doth us   and   keep us:
sustain

v. 8.

and he is bright and pleasant and very   migh - ty   and strong.
and bringeth forth divers fruits, and flowers of many   col - ours, and grass.

PART II

mp Harmony.

9. Praisèd be my Lord for
all those who pardon { for   his   love's   sake:
one another

and who endure
weakness and   tri - bu - la - tion:

CANTICLES, ETC.

10. Bless - ed are they who peaceably shall en - dure: for thou, O most Highest, shalt give them a crown.

11. *Praisèd be my Lord for our sister the death of the bo - dy:

blessed are they who are found walking by thy most ho - ly will.

Doxology to either part.

12. Praise ye and bless ye the Lord and give thanks un - to him:

and serve him with great hu - mi - li - ty. Al - le - lu - ya, al - le - lu - ya!

The Song of the Creatures. St. Francis (1225). Tr. Matthew Arnold.

(521)

BOOK II

PART X

GENERAL

See also

435

SELNECKER (NUN LASST UNS GOTT DEM HERREN). (7 7. 7 7.)

In moderate time.   Later form of melody in SELNECKER's *Christliche Psalmen*, 1587.

Resurrection.   E. H.

A BRIGHTER dawn is breaking,
  And earth with praise is waking;
For thou, O King most highest,
The power of death defiest;

2 And thou hast come victorious,
With risen body glorious,
Who now for ever livest,
And life abundant givest.

3 O free the world from blindness,
And fill the world with kindness;
Give sinners resurrection,
Bring striving to perfection;

4. In sickness give us healing,
In doubt thy clear revealing,
That praise to thee be given
In earth as in thy heaven.

(522)

436   EIN' FESTE BURG.   (8 7. 8 7. 6 6. 6 6 7.)

Very slow and solemn.   Present form of melody by M. LUTHER, 1483–1546.

Martin Luther, 1483–1546.   *Tr. Thomas Carlyle.*

Ein' feste Burg.

A SAFE stronghold our God is still,
  A trusty shield and weapon;
He'll help us clear from all the ill
  That hath us now o'ertaken.
    The ancient prince of hell
    Hath risen with purpose fell;
    Strong mail of craft and power
    He weareth in this hour;
    On earth is not his fellow.

2 With force of arms we nothing can,
  Full soon were we down-ridden;
But for us fights the proper Man,
  Whom God himself hath bidden.
    Ask ye, Who is this same?
    Christ Jesus is his name,
    The Lord Sabaoth's Son;
    He, and no other one,
    Shall conquer in the battle.

3*And were this world all devils o'er,
  And watching to devour us,
We lay it not to heart so sore;
  Not they can overpower us.
    And let the prince of ill
    Look grim as e'er he will,
    He harms us not a whit;
    For why?—-his doom is writ;
    A word shall quickly slay him.

4.*God's word, for all their craft and force,
  One moment will not linger,
But, spite of hell, shall have its course;
  'Tis written by his finger.
    And though they take our life,
    Goods, honour, children, wife,
    Yet is their profit small:
    These things shall vanish all:
    The City of God remaineth!

437

EVENTIDE. (10 10. 10 10.)

Slow.

W. H. MONK, 1823–89.

[This hymn may also be sung to CONGLETON, 622.]

H. F. Lyte, 1793–1847.

ABIDE with me; fast falls the eventide:
The darkness deepens; Lord, with me abide!
When other helpers fail, and comforts flee,
Help of the helpless, O abide with me.

2 Swift to its close ebbs out life's little day;
Earth's joys grow dim, its glories pass away;
Change and decay in all around I see;
O thou who changest not, abide with me.

3 I need thy presence every passing hour;
What but thy grace can foil the tempter's power?
Who like thyself my guide and stay can be?
Through cloud and sunshine, O abide with me.

4 I fear no foe with thee at hand to bless;
Ills have no weight, and tears no bitterness.
Where is death's sting? Where, grave, thy victory?
I triumph still, if thou abide with me.

5. Hold thou thy cross before my closing eyes;
Shine through the gloom, and point me to the skies:
Heaven's morning breaks, and earth's vain shadows flee;
In life, in death, O Lord, abide with me!

(524)

GENERAL

ALTERNATIVE VERSION FOR VERSE 3

CHOIR AND PEOPLE.

Descant by R. VAUGHAN WILLIAMS.

DESCANT. (*Trebles.*)

I need thy pres-ence ev-'ry pass-ing hour;

Organ.

What but thy grace can foil the temp-ter's power? Who like thy-self my guide and stay can be?

[*Continued overleaf.*

437 (*continued*)

Thro' cloud and sun-shine, O . . . a-bide . . . . . . with me.

H. F. Lyte, 1793–1847.

ABIDE with me; fast falls the eventide:
 The darkness deepens; Lord, with me abide!
When other helpers fail, and comforts flee,
Help of the helpless, O abide with me.

2 Swift to its close ebbs out life's little day;
 Earth's joys grow dim, its glories pass away;
 Change and decay in all around I see;
 O thou who changest not, abide with me.

3 I need thy presence every passing hour;
 What but thy grace can foil the tempter's power?
 Who like thyself my guide and stay can be?
 Through cloud and sunshine, O abide with me.

4 I fear no foe with thee at hand to bless;
 Ills have no weight, and tears no bitterness.
 Where is death's sting? Where, grave, thy victory?
 I triumph still, if thou abide with me.

5. Hold thou thy cross before my closing eyes;
 Shine through the gloom, and point me to the skies:
 Heaven's morning breaks, and earth's vain shadows flee;
 In life, in death, O Lord, abide with me!

438 STRACATHRO. (C.M.)

In moderate time.

Melody by CHARLES HUTCHESON, 1792–1860, from *Christian Vespers*, Glasgow, 1832.

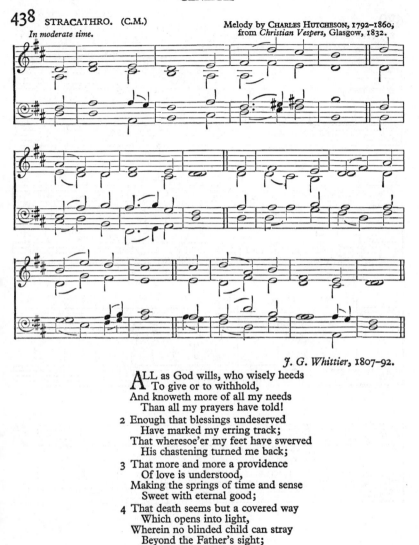

J. G. Whittier, 1807–92.

ALL as God wills, who wisely heeds
    To give or to withhold,
And knoweth more of all my needs
    Than all my prayers have told!

2 Enough that blessings undeserved
    Have marked my erring track;
That wheresoe'er my feet have swerved
    His chastening turned me back;

3 That more and more a providence
    Of love is understood,
Making the springs of time and sense
    Sweet with eternal good;

4 That death seems but a covered way
    Which opens into light,
Wherein no blinded child can stray
    Beyond the Father's sight;

5*That care and trial seem at last,
    Through memory's sunset air,
Like mountain ranges overpast,
    In purple distance fair;

6*That all the jarring notes of life
    Seem blending in a psalm,
And all the angles of its strife
    Slow rounding into calm.

7. And so the shadows fall apart,
    And so the west winds play;
And all the windows of my heart
    I open to the day.

(527)

439

ST. FRANCIS. (8 8. 4 4. 8 8, and Alleluyas.)

Brightly. (*May be sung in harmony throughout.*)

G. W. BRIGGS, 1875–1959.

A - men.

[This hymn may also be sung to EASTER ALLELUYA, 157.]

W. H. Draper, 1855–1933, based on St. Francis, 1182–1226.

ALL creatures of our God and King,
   Lift up your voice and with us sing
   Alleluya, alleluya!
Thou burning sun with golden beam,
Thou silver moon with softer gleam:

     O praise him, O praise him,
     Alleluya, alleluya, alleluya!

2 Thou rushing wind that art so strong,
   Ye clouds that sail in heaven along,
     O praise him, alleluya!
   Thou rising morn, in praise rejoice,
   Ye lights of evening, find a voice:

3 Thou flowing water, pure and clear,
   Make music for thy Lord to hear,
     Alleluya, alleluya!
   Thou fire so masterful and bright,
   That givest man both warmth and light:

4*Dear mother earth, who day by day
   Unfoldest blessings on our way,
     O praise him, alleluya!
   The flowers and fruits that in thee grow,
   Let them his glory also show:

5*And all ye men of tender heart,
   Forgiving others, take your part,
     O sing ye, alleluya!
   Ye who long pain and sorrow bear,
   Praise God and on him cast your care:

6*And thou, most kind and gentle death,
   Waiting to hush our latest breath,
     O praise him, alleluya!
   Thou leadest home the child of God,
   And Christ our Lord the way hath trod:

7. Let all things their Creator bless,
   And worship him in humbleness,
     O praise him, alleluya!
   Praise, praise the Father, praise the Son,
   And praise the Spirit, three in One:

See also
434 O most high

440

MILES LANE. (C.M.)

In moderate time.

W. Shrubsole, 1760–1806.
(Modern form of second line.)

crown him, crown him, crown him, crown him Lord of all.

E. Perronet (1780), *and others.*

ALL hail the power of Jesus' name;
  Let angels prostrate fall;
Bring forth the royal diadem
  To crown him Lord of all.

2 Crown him, ye martyrs of your God,
    Who from his altar call;
  Praise him whose way of pain ye trod,
    And crown him Lord of all.

3 Ye prophets who our freedom won,
    Ye searchers, great and small,
  By whom the work of truth is done,
    Now crown him Lord of all.

4*Sinners, whose love can ne'er forget
    The wormwood and the gall,
  Go spread your trophies at his feet,
    And crown him Lord of all.

5*Bless him, each poor oppressèd race
    That Christ did upward call;
  His hand in each achievement trace,
    And crown him Lord of all.

6. Let every tribe and every tongue
    To him their hearts enthral:
  Lift high the universal song,
    And crown him Lord of all.

GENERAL

ALTERNATIVE VERSION

[*Copyright, 1931, by Oxford University Press.*]

441

ST. JOSEPH. (10 10. 10 10.)

In moderate time.

JOSEPH PARRY, 1841–1903.

[*By permission of Hughes & Son, Wrexham.*]

B. R.

ALL hail to the Power who giveth men might,
All praise to the God too great for our sight!
O Spirit concealed, not vainly we call—
Thy face is revealed as Father of all.

2. Enlighten our minds, thou author of light,
Thou love undiscouraged, thou charity bright,
That we, all our days, whatever befall,
May show thee our praise, thou Father of all.

(532)

442

MEINE HOFFNUNG. (8 7. 8 7. 3 3 7.)

Moderately slow.   Later form of melody by J. NEANDER, 1650–80.

J. *Neander*, 1650–80. *Pr. R. Bridges.*

Meine Hoffnung stehet feste.

ALL my hope on God is founded;
    He doth still my trust renew.
Me through change and chance he guideth,
    Only good and only true.
        God unknown,
        He alone
    Calls my heart to be his own.

2 Pride of man and earthly glory,
    Sword and crown betray his trust;
What with care and toil he buildeth,
    Tower and temple, fall to dust.
        But God's power,
        Hour by hour,
    Is my temple and my tower.

3 God's great goodness ay endureth,
    Deep his wisdom, passing thought:
Splendour, light, and life attend him,
    Beauty springeth out of nought.
        Evermore,
        From his store
    New-born worlds rise and adore.

4*Daily doth the almighty giver
    Bounteous gifts on us bestow;
His desire our soul delighteth,
    Pleasure leads us where we go.
        Love doth stand
        At his hand;
    Joy doth wait on his command.

5.*Still from man to God eternal
    Sacrifice of praise be done,
High above all praises praising
    For the gift of Christ his Son.
        Christ doth call
        One and all:
    Ye who follow shall not fall.

443

OLD HUNDREDTH. (L.M.)

Melody from *Genevan Psalter*, 1551.
(English form of final line.)

Slow and dignified.

ALTERNATIVE VERSION

People's Part.

Fa-burden by J. DOWLAND, *Ravenscroft's Psalter*, 1621.

Choir or Organ.

(534)

GENERAL

A SIMPLER ALTERNATIVE VERSION

PEOPLE'S PART.

Fa-burden by J. DOWLAND, 1562–1626.

CHOIR OR ORGAN.

NOTE.—*These alternative versions may be used in connexion with the first for one or more verses, the people singing the melody as usual.*

Ps. 100.

W. Kethe, Daye's Psalter (1560–1), and Scottish Psalter (1650).

ALL people that on earth do dwell,
    Sing to the Lord with cheerful voice;
Him serve with mirth, his praise forth tell,
    Come ye before him, and rejoice.

2 The Lord, ye know, is God indeed;
    Without our aid he did us make;
We are his folk, he doth us feed,
    And for his sheep he doth us take.

3 O enter then his gates with praise;
    Approach with joy his courts unto;
Praise, laud, and bless his name always,
    For it is seemly so to do.

4 For why, the Lord our God is good:
    His mercy is for ever sure;
His truth at all times firmly stood,
    And shall from age to age endure.

5. To Father, Son, and Holy Ghost,
    The God whom heaven and earth adore,
From men and from the angel-host
    Be praise and glory evermore.

A - men.

444

ROYAL OAK. (7 6. 7 6, and refrain.)

Fast. Voices in unison.

Adapted from an English Traditional
Melody by MARTIN SHAW, 1875–1958.

1. All things bright and beau - ti - ful, All crea - tures great and

small, All things wise and won - der - ful, The

Lord God made them all. 2. Each lit - tle flower that

o - pens, Each lit - tle bird that sings, He

D.C.

made their glow - ing col - ours, He made their ti - ny wings:

[*Copyright*, 1915, *by J. Curwen & Sons, Ltd.*]
NOTE.—*The pause (⌢) is for the last time only.*

Mrs. C. F. Alexander,‡ 1818–95.

*A*LL *things bright and beautiful,*
   All creatures great and small,
All things wise and wonderful,
   The Lord God made them all.

2 Each little flower that opens,
      Each little bird that sings,
   He made their glowing colours,
      He made their tiny wings:

3 The purple-headed mountain,
      The river running by,
   The sunset and the morning,
      That brightens up the sky:

4 The cold wind in the winter,
      The pleasant summer sun,
   The ripe fruits in the garden,
      He made them every one:

5*The tall trees in the greenwood,
      The meadows for our play,
   The rushes by the water
      To gather every day:

6. He gave us eyes to see them,
      And lips that we might tell
   How great is God Almighty,
      Who has made all things well.

(537)

445 JACKSON. (C.M.)
In moderate time.

T. JACKSON, 1715–81;

Edward J. Brailsford, 1841–1921.

ALL things which live below the sky,
  Or move within the sea,
Are creatures of the Lord most high,
  And brothers unto me.

2 I love to hear the robin sing,
    Perched on the highest bough;
  To see the rook with purple wing
    Follow the shining plough.

3 I love to watch the swallow skim
    The river in his flight;
  To mark, when day is growing dim,
    The glow-worm's silvery light;

4 The sea-gull whiter than the foam,
    The fish that dart beneath;
  The lowing cattle coming home;
    The goats upon the heath.

5*God taught the wren to build her nest,
    The lark to soar above,
  The hen to gather to her breast
    The offspring of her love.

6*Beneath his heaven there's room for all;
    He gives to all their meat;
  He sees the meanest sparrow fall
    Unnoticed in the street.

7. Almighty Father, King of Kings,
    The lover of the meek,
  Make me a friend of helpless things,
    Defender of the weak.

(538)

446

JERUSALEM. (D.L.M.)
Slow but with animation.

C. HUBERT H. PARRY, 1848–1918.

1. And did those feet in an - cient time Walk up - on England's moun - tains green? And was the ho - ly Lamb of

446 (*continued*)

God On Eng-land's plea-sant pas — tures seen? And did the

poco cres.

coun — te-nance di-vine Shine forth up-on our cloud-ed

f

poco rit.

hills? And was Je-ru-sa-lem build-ed here A-mong those

dark sa-tan-ic mills?

f a tempo. *ff*

mf

2. Bring me my bow of burn-ing gold! Bring me my

mf

ar-rows of de-sire! Bring me my spear! O clouds, un-

446 (*continued*)

-fold! Bring me my cha-ri-ot of fire! I will not cease from men-tal fight, Nor shall my sword sleep in my hand, Till we have built Je-ru-sa-lem In Eng-land's

green and plea - sant land.

Jerusalem.

William Blake, 1757–1827.

AND did those feet in ancient time
   Walk upon England's mountains green?
And was the holy Lamb of God
   On England's pleasant pastures seen?
And did the countenance divine
   Shine forth upon our clouded hills?
And was Jerusalem builded here
   Among those dark satanic mills?

2. Bring me my bow of burning gold!
   Bring me my arrows of desire!
Bring me my spear! O clouds, unfold!
   Bring me my chariot of fire!
I will not cease from mental fight,
   Nor shall my sword sleep in my hand,
Till we have built Jerusalem
   In England's green and pleasant land.

447

MUNDAYS. (10 10. 10 6.)

In moderate time.

MARTIN SHAW, 1875–1958.

[*Copyright, 1931, by Martin Shaw.*]

Jean Ingelow, 1820–97.

AND didst thou love the race that loved not thee?
And didst thou take to heaven a human brow?
Dost plead with man's voice by the marvellous sea?
Art thou his kinsman now?

1 O God, O kinsman loved, but not enough,
    O Man, with eyes majestic after death,
  Whose feet have toiled along our pathways rough,
    Whose lips drawn human breath:

2 By that one likeness which is ours and thine,
    By that one nature which doth hold us kin,
  By that high heaven where, sinless, thou dost shine
    To draw us sinners in;

3 By thy last silence in the judgment hall,
    By long foreknowledge of the deadly tree,
  By darkness, by the wormwood and the gall,
    I pray thee visit me.

4. Come, lest this heart should, cold and cast away,
    Die ere the guest adored she entertain:
  Lest eyes which never saw thine earthly day
    Should miss thy heavenly reign.

[*The first verse may be sung as a solo.*]

448

FLANDERS. (8 7. 8 7. 8 7. 7 7.)

In moderate time.

Flemish Traditional Melody.

John Stuart Blackie,†️ 1809-95.

ANGELS holy, high and lowly,
   Sing the praises of the Lord;
Earth and sky, all living nature,
   Starry temples azure-floored,
Man, the stamp of thy creator,
   Praise ye, praise ye God the Lord:

   Praise ye, praise ye God the Lord,
   Praise ye, praise ye God the Lord.

2 Ocean hoary, tell his glory;
   Cliffs, where tumbling seas have
      roared,
Mighty mountains, purple breasted,
   Crag where eagle's pride hath soared,
Peaks cloud-cleaving, snowy-crested,
   Praise ye, praise ye God the Lord:

3 Rolling river, praise him ever,
   From the mountain's deep vein
      poured;
Silver fountain, clearly gushing,
   Sing the praises of the Lord;
Troubled torrent, madly rushing,
   Praise ye, praise ye God the Lord:

4. Youth, whose morning smiles at warn-
      ing,
   Age, in counsel deeply stored,
Each glad soul its free course winging,
   Praise him, Father, Friend, and Lord,
Each glad voice its free song singing,
   Praise the great and mighty Lord:

(The first verse may be sung as a solo.)

T

449

MARTYRDOM. (C.M.)

R. A. SMITH's *Sacred Music*, 1825.
Possibly a Scottish Traditional Melody.

A - men.

ALTERNATIVE VERSION

Melody in the Tenor.

Fa-burden by GEOFFREY SHAW.

Ps. 42.

N. Tate and N. Brady, New Version (1696).

AS pants the hart for cooling streams
    When heated in the chase,
So longs my soul, O God, for thee,
    And thy refreshing grace.

2 For thee, my God, the living God,
    My thirsty soul doth pine:
O when shall I behold thy face,
    Thou Majesty divine?

3 Why restless, why cast down, my soul?
    Hope still, and thou shalt sing
The praise of him who is thy God,
    Thy health's eternal spring.

4. To Father, Son, and Holy Ghost,
    The God whom we adore,
Be glory, as it was, is now,
    And shall be evermore.

450 BRUNSWICK. (8 6. 8 6. 8 6.)
In moderate time.

Adapted from G. F. HANDEL, 1685–1759.

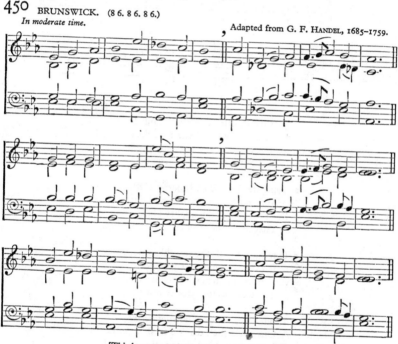

[This hymn may also be sung to ARABIA, 454.]

AWAKE, awake to love and work!
    The lark is in the sky,
The fields are wet with diamond dew,
    The world's awake to cry
Their blessings on the Lord of life,
    As he goes meekly by.

2 Come, let thy voice be one with theirs,
    Shout with their shout of praise;
See how the giant sun soars up,

G. A. Studdert-Kennedy, 1883–1929.
    Great lord of years and days;
So let the love of Jesus come,
    And set thy soul ablaze,

3. To give, and give, and give again,
    What God has given thee;
To spend thyself, nor count the cost;
    To serve right gloriously
The God who gave all worlds that are
    And all that are to be.

451

SAMSON. (L.M.)
In moderate time.

Adapted from HANDEL, 1685–1759.

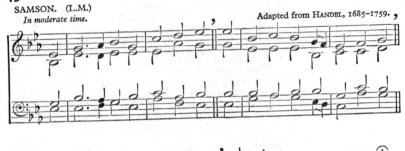

I. Watts, 1674–1748.

AWAKE, our souls! away, our fears!
   Let every trembling thought be gone!
Awake, and run the heavenly race,
   And put a cheerful courage on.

2 True, 'tis a strait and thorny road,
   And mortal spirits tire and faint;
But they forget the mighty God,
   That feeds the strength of every saint.

3 O mighty God! thy matchless power
   Is ever new and ever young;
And firm endures, while endless years
   Their everlasting circles run.

4 From thee, the ever-flowing spring,
   Our souls shall drink a fresh supply;
While such as trust their native strength
   Shall melt away, and droop, and die.

5. Swift as the eagle cuts the air,
   We'll mount aloft to thine abode;
On wings of love our souls shall fly,
   Nor tire along the heavenly road.

452

KINGSLAND. (6 6. 6 6.)

In moderate time.

Dr. WILLIAM BOYCE, 1710–79.

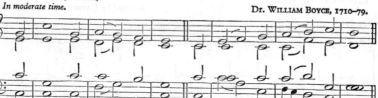

Science.

Sir Ronald Ross, 1857–1932.

BEFORE thy feet I fall,
    Lord, who made high my fate;
For in the mighty small
    Thou show'st the mighty great.

2 Lo, while we ask the stars
    To learn the will of God,
His answer unawares
    Strikes sudden from the sod.

3 He is the Lord of light;
    He is the thing that is;
He sends the seeing sight;
    And the right mind is his.

4. Henceforth I will resound
    But praises unto thee;
Though I was beat and bound,
    Thou gav'st me victory.

See also

285 From thee all skill and science flow
567 Lord of health
571 Lord, when the wise men came

606 O Lord of hosts
312 These things shall be
214 Virtue supreme

(549)

453

LLANLLYFNI. (D.S.M.)
Moderately slow.

Adapted by DAVID JENKINS, 1849–1915.

[If an S.M. tune is preferred for this hymn it may be sung to CARLISLE, 458.]

Courage.

Anne Brontë,† 1820–49.

BELIEVE not those who say
  The upward path is smooth,
Lest thou shouldst stumble in the way
  And faint before the truth.

2 It is the only road
    Unto the realms of joy;
But he who seeks that blest abode
    Must all his powers employ.

3 Arm, arm thee for the fight!
    Cast useless loads away;
Watch through the darkest hours of
      night;
  Toil through the hottest day.

4 To labour and to love,
    To pardon and endure,
To lift thy heart to God above
    And keep thy conscience pure,—

5 Be this thy constant aim,
    Thy hope, thy chief delight;
What matter who should whisper blame,
    Or who should scorn or slight,

6. If but thy God approve,
    And if, within thy breast,
Thou feel the comfort of his love,
    The earnest of his rest.

(550)

454 ARABIA. (8 6. 8 6. 8 6.)

In moderate time.

W. WILSON (?), 1833.

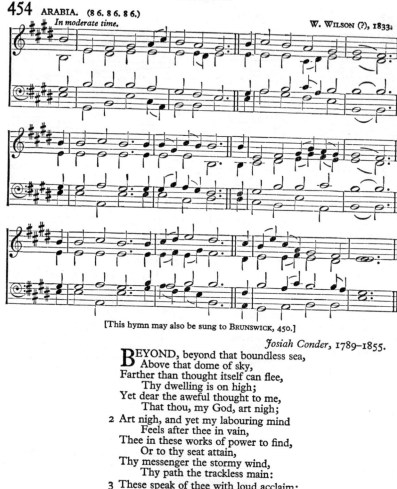

[This hymn may also be sung to BRUNSWICK, 450.]

Josiah Conder, 1789–1855.

BEYOND, beyond that boundless sea,
    Above that dome of sky,
Farther than thought itself can flee,
    Thy dwelling is on high;
Yet dear the aweful thought to me,
    That thou, my God, art nigh;

2 Art nigh, and yet my labouring mind
    Feels after thee in vain,
Thee in these works of power to find,
    Or to thy seat attain,
Thy messenger the stormy wind,
    Thy path the trackless main:

3 These speak of thee with loud acclaim:
    They thunder forth thy praise,
The glorious honour of thy name,
    The wonders of thy ways:
But thou art not in tempest-flame,
    Nor in day's glorious blaze.

4*We hear thy voice when thunders roll
    Through the wide fields of air;
The waves obey thy dread control,
    Yet still thou art not there.
Where shall I find him, O my soul,
    Who yet is everywhere?

5. O not in circling depth or height,
    But in the conscious breast;
Present to faith, though veiled from sight,
    There doth his Spirit rest.
O come, thou Presence infinite!
    And make thy creature blest.

(551)

455

FRANCONIA. (S.M.)
In moderate time.

W. H. HAVERGAL, 1793–1870
(founded on a melody by J. B. KÖNIG).

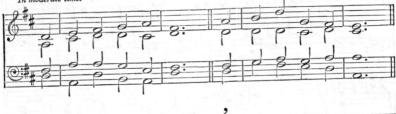

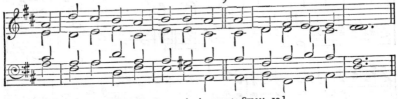

[This hymn may also be sung to SELMA, 10.]

J. Keble, 1792–1866, and others.

BLEST are the pure in heart,
For they shall see our God;
The secret of the Lord is theirs,
Their soul is Christ's abode.

2 The Lord, who left the heavens
Our life and peace to bring,
To dwell in lowliness with men,
Their pattern and their King;

3 Still to the lowly soul
He doth himself impart,
And for his dwelling and his throne
Chooseth the pure in heart.

4. Lord, we thy presence seek;
May ours this blessing be:
Give us a pure and lowly heart,
A temple meet for thee.

See also
523 How blest are they

456

TIVERTON. (C.M.)

In moderate time.

— GRIGG, in *John Rippon's*
Selection of Psalm and Hymn Tunes, c. 1795.

[This hymn may also be sung to UNIVERSITY, 653.]

The Pilgrim.   *P. B. Clayton, based on John Bunyan, 1628–88.*

BLEST be the day when moved I was
  A pilgrim for to be,
And blessèd also be the cause
  That thereto movèd me.

2 Blest work, that drove me back to pray,
  To strive to be sincere;
To take my cross up day by day
  With love that casts out fear.

3 Yet long it is since I began
  And little have I done:
God give me grace to play the man
  And heed my heart and tongue;

4 To show the road from doubt to faith,
  For feet beside mine own
To climb from self to rarer breath,
  Unknown and yet well-known.

5*With Master Fearing, may I fear
  My God, and be afraid
Of doing anything while here
  That may have him betrayed.

6*With Servant Great-heart, who arose
  The children's guide to be,
For those who trust me, I'd oppose
  Each Giant enemy.

7 He that me seeks shall now be sought:
  Surrendered here I stand,
A truant eager to be taught
  His purpose for my hand.

8. Life, like an unencumbered flood,
  Leaps to the sea and sky:
At last, beyond the Slough of mood,
  Master, thy man am I.

457

DESSAU (LIEBSTER JESU). (7 8. 7 8. 8 8.)
Very slow and quiet.

Later form of
Melody by J. R. AHLE, 1625–73.

Scripture.   *P. Dearmer, 1867–1936.*

BOOK of books, our people's strength,
  Statesman's, teacher's, hero's treasure,
Bringing freedom, spreading truth,
  Shedding light that none can measure—
    Wisdom comes to those who know thee,
    All the best we have we owe thee.

2 Thank we those who toiled in thought,
  Many diverse scrolls completing,
Poets, prophets, scholars, saints,
  Each his word from God repeating;
    Till they came, who told the story
    Of the Word, and showed his glory.

3. Praise we God, who hath inspired
  Those whose wisdom still directs us;
Praise him for the Word made flesh,
  For the Spirit which protects us.
    Light of Knowledge, ever burning,
    Shed on us thy deathless learning.

See also

570 Lord, thy word abideth
212 Prophets, teachers
645 Spread, still spread

660 The Spirit of the Lord
214 Virtue supreme
699 Where is thy God

458

CARLISLE. (S.M.)
Moderately slow, dignified.

C. LOCKHART, 1745–1815.

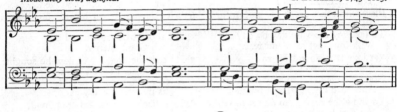

DESCANT TO THE ABOVE TUNE

Trebles (other voices sing the melody CARLISLE,
the organ playing the harmonies as above).

SYDNEY H. NICHOLSON, 1875–1947.

[*Copyright, 1931, by Oxford University Press.*]

Edwin Hatch, 1835–89.

BREATHE on me, Breath of God,
　Fill me with life anew,
That I may love what thou dost love,
　And do what thou wouldst do.

2　Breathe on me, Breath of God,
　　Until my heart is pure,
Until with thee I will one will,
　To do and to endure.

3　Breathe on me, Breath of God,
　　Blend all my soul with thine,
Until this earthly part of me
　Glows with thy fire divine.

4.　Breathe on me, Breath of God,
　　So shall I never die,
But live with thee the perfect life
　Of thine eternity.

(554)

459

FIRST TUNE

DEVONSHIRE. (7 6. 7 6.)
In moderate time.

English Traditional Melody.

ST. ALPHEGE. (7 6. 7 6.)   SECOND TUNE
In moderate time.

H. J. GAUNTLETT, 1805–76.

Part of Hora novissima.   *Bernard of Cluny, 12th cent. Tr. J. M. Neale.*

B RIEF life is here our portion,
    Brief sorrow, short-lived care;
The life that knows no ending,
    The tearless life, is there.

2 For thee, O dear, dear country,
    Mine eyes their vigils keep;
For very love, beholding
    Thy happy name, they weep.

3 There grief is turned to pleasure,
    Such pleasure as below
No human voice can utter,
    No human heart can know.

4*And now we fight the battle,
    But then shall wear the crown
Of full and everlasting
    And passionless renown.

PART II

5*Thou hast no shore, fair ocean!
    Thou hast no time, bright day!
Dear fountain of refreshment
    To pilgrims far away!

6 Strive, man, to win that glory;
    Toil, man, to gain that light;
Send hope before to grasp it,
    Till hope be lost in sight.

7 The morning shall awaken,
    The shadows shall decay,
And each true-hearted servant
    Shall shine as doth the day.

8. Then all the halls of Sion
    For ay shall be complete,
And, in the Land of Beauty,
    All things of beauty meet.

See also, 198 Jerusalem the golden

(555)

460 LAUS DEO (REDHEAD No. 46). (8 7. 8 7.)

In moderate time.

R. REDHEAD, 1820–1901.

DESCANT TO THE ABOVE TUNE

Trebles (other voices sing the melody LAUS DEO, *the organ playing the harmonies as above).*

PERCY WHITLOCK.

Bishop R. Mant, 1776–1848.

BRIGHT the vision that delighted
    Once the sight of Judah's seer;
Sweet the countless tongues united
    To entrance the prophet's ear.

2 Round the Lord in glory seated,
    Cherubim and seraphim
Filled his temple, and repeated
    Each to each the alternate hymn:

3 'Lord, thy glory fills the heaven;
    Earth is with its fullness stored;
Unto thee be glory given,
    Holy, holy, holy, Lord.'

4 Heaven is still with glory ringing,
    Earth takes up the angels' cry,
'Holy, holy, holy,' singing,
    'Lord of hosts, the Lord most high.'

5*With his seraph train before him,
    With his holy Church below,
Thus conspire we to adore him,
    Bid we thus our anthem flow:

6.*'Lord, thy glory fills the heaven;
    Earth is with its fullness stored;
Unto thee be glory given,
    Holy, holy, holy, Lord.'

461

GALLIARD. (7 7. 7 7.)

In moderate time.

Adapted from a Melody
by J. DOWLAND, 1562–1626.

[*Copyright, 1925, by Martin Shaw.*]

William Blake, 1757–1827.

CAN I see another's woe,
 And not be in sorrow too?
Can I see another's grief,
And not seek for kind relief?

2 Can I see a falling tear,
 And not feel my sorrow's share?
 Can a father see his child
 Weep, nor be with sorrow filled?

3 God doth give his joy to all;
 He becomes an infant small,
 He becomes a man of woe,
 He doth feel the sorrow too.

4 Think not thou canst sigh a sigh,
 And thy Maker is not by;
 Think not thou canst weep a tear,
 And thy Maker is not near.

5. O! he gives to us his joy
 That our grief he may destroy:
 Till our grief is fled and gone,
 He doth sit by us and moan.

(557)

462

TREFAENAN. (8 7. 8 7. 8 8. 8 7.)

Not too quick. Unison.

Welsh Traditional Melody.

He hath made them, He hath made them, He hath made them, ev - 'ry one.
And he loves them, And he loves them, And he loves them, ev - 'ry one.

Johann W. Hey, 1789–1854. *Tr. H. W. Dulcken.*‡
Weisst du wie viel Sternlein.

CAN you count the stars that brightly
Twinkle in the midnight sky?
Can you count the clouds, so lightly
O'er the meadows floating by?
God, the Lord, doth mark their number
With his eyes that never slumber;
He hath made them, every one.

2. Do you know how many children
Rise each morning blithe and gay?
Can you count their jolly voices,
Singing sweetly day by day?
God hears all the happy voices,
In their pretty songs rejoices;
And he loves them, every one.

463

MELLING. (7 7. 7 7.)

With vigour.

From *A New Set of Sacred Music*
by JOHN FAWCETT, 1830.

J. Cennick, 1718–55.

CHILDREN of the heavenly King,
As ye journey sweetly sing;
Sing your Saviour's worthy praise,
Glorious in his works and ways.

2 We are travelling home to God
In the way the fathers trod;
They are happy now, and we
Soon their happiness shall see.

3. Fear not, brethren, joyful stand
On the borders of your land;
Jesus Christ, your Father's Son,
Bids you undismayed go on.

4. Lord, obediently we go,
Gladly leaving all below;
Only thou our leader be,
And we still will follow thee.

464

FIRST TUNE

RAMOTH. (6 6. 6 6. 8 8.)
In moderate time.

J. R. JONES, 762–1822.

SECOND TUNE

HAREWOOD. (6 6. 6 6. 8 8.)
In moderate time.

SAMUEL SEBASTIAN WESLEY, 1810–76.

J. Chandler, 1806–76, based on Angularis fundamentum (190, 11), *7th cent.*

CHRIST is our corner-stone:
On him alone we build;
With his true saints alone
The courts of heaven are filled;
On his great love
Our hopes we place
Of present grace
And joys above.

2 O then with hymns of praise
These hallowed courts shall ring;
Our voices we will raise
The three in One to sing,
And thus proclaim
In joyful song,
Both loud and long,
That glorious name.

3 Here, gracious God, do thou
For evermore draw nigh;
Accept each faithful vow,
And mark each suppliant sigh;
In copious shower
On all who pray
Each holy day
Thy blessings pour.

4. Here may we gain from heaven
The grace which we implore;
And may that grace, once given,
Be with us evermore,
Until that day
When all the blest
To endless rest
Are called away.

465

LONG MYND. (7 7. 7 7.)
In moderate time.

R. S. THATCHER, 1888–1957.

[*Copyright*, 1931, *by Oxford University Press.*]
[This hymn may also be sung to ABERYSTWYTH, 542.]

R. *Wardlaw*, 1779–1853.

CHRIST, of all my hopes the ground,
Christ, the spring of all my joy,
Still in thee may I be found,
Still for thee my powers employ;
Let thy love my heart inflame,
Keep thy fear before my sight,
Be thy praise my highest aim,
Be thy smile my chief delight.

2. When affliction clouds my sky
And the wintry tempests blow,
Let thy mercy-beaming eye
Sweetly cheer the night of woe;
When new triumphs of thy name
Swell the raptured songs above,
May I feel the kindred flame—
Full of zeal, and full of love!

466

GUTE BÄUME BRINGEN. (6 5. 6 5. D.)
Moderately fast.

Later form of melody by P. SOHREN, d. c. 1692.

GENERAL

Galilee.   P. Dearmer, 1867–1936.

CHRISTIAN, do you see him,
　　There in Galilee,
As the people throng him?
　Healer, prophet he!
Christian, up and follow:
　His the perfect school.
Learn to make men happy
　By the Golden Rule.

2 Christian, do you hear him?
　　God would have us glad—
Watching like a mother
　Over good and bad.
Christian, learn to succour
　Stranger, friend, or foe;
Ask but if they need you,
　Then in mercy go.

3 Christian, do you heed him?
　　'Let your light so shine.'
Let men in your doings
　Trace the ray divine.

Christian, share your blessings:
　Thus you show to men
God the Father's kindness—
　They will worship then.

4 Christian, do you mark him?
　'Ye shall perfect be.'
Follow the ideal
　Far as man can see.
Christian, far above you
　Truth and Right are set;
Love them for their own sake,
　Say, 'What lack I yet?'

5. Christian, then obey him!
　First the Kingdom seek:
God will add the treasure;
　He enthrones the meek.
Christian, spurn self-seeking;
　Then on you will fall
Happiness of sonship,
　Love uniting all.

467 ROBYN. (7 7. 7 3.)
In moderate time.
Adapted by GEOFFREY SHAW, 1879–1943, from a
melody by WILLIAM CORNYSSHE, early 16th century.

[*Copyright, 1931, by Oxford University Press.*]

Charlotte Elliott, 1789–1871.

CHRISTIAN, seek not yet repose;
　Hear thy guardian angel say,
'Thou art in the midst of foes:
　　Watch and pray!'

2 Gird thy heavenly armour on,
　Wear it ever, night and day;
Ambushed lies the evil one:
　　Watch and pray!

3 Hear the victors who o'ercame;
　Still they mark each warrior's way;
All with one sweet voice exclaim:
　　'Watch and pray!'

4 Hear, above all, hear thy Lord,
　Him thou lovest to obey;
Hide within thy heart his word:
　　'Watch and pray!'

5. Watch, as if on that alone
　Hung the issue of the day;
Pray, that help may be sent down:
　　Watch and pray!

(563)

468

RICHMOND. (C.M.)
Moderately slow.

Adapted from T. HAWEIS, 1734–1820,
by S. WEBBE (the younger), 1770–1843.

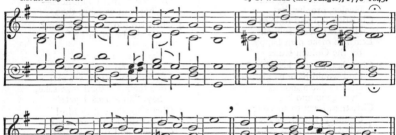

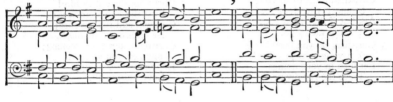

ALTERNATIVE VERSION

Melody in the Tenor.

Fa-burden by MARTIN SHAW.

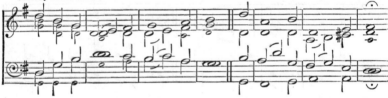

[*If this setting is sung in unaccompanied four-part harmony, omit the small notes.*]

God's City.

CITY of God, how broad and far
Outspread thy walls sublime!
The true thy chartered freemen are
Of every age and clime.

2 One holy Church, one army strong,
One steadfast, high intent;
One working band, one harvest-song,
One King omnipotent.

3 How purely hath thy speech come down
From man's primeval youth!

S. Johnson, 1822–82.

How grandly hath thine empire grown
Of freedom, love, and truth!

4 How gleam thy watch-fires through the night
With never-fainting ray!
How rise thy towers, serene and bright,
To meet the dawning day!

5 In vain the surge's angry shock,
In vain the drifting sands:
Unharmed upon the eternal Rock
The eternal City stands.

See also

475 Come now, all people   615 O thou not made with hands

(564)

469

EXON. (8 4. 8 4. 8 4.)

In moderate time. May be sung in unison.

Thomas Armstrong.

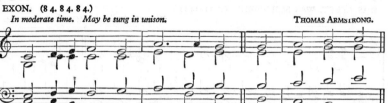

G. A. Studdert-Kennedy, 1883–1929.

CLOSE by the heedless worker's side,
  Still patient stands
The carpenter of Nazareth,
  With piercèd hands
Outstretched to plead unceasingly
  His love's demands;

2 Longing to pick the hammer up
    And strike a blow;
  Longing to feel his plane swing out,
    Steady and slow,
  The fragrant shavings falling down
    Silent as snow.

3. Because this is my work, O Lord,
    It must be thine;
  Because it is a human task
    It is divine.
  Take me, and brand me with thy cross,
    Thy slave's proud sign.

470

WAS LEBET, WAS SCHWEBET. (12 11. 12 11.)

In moderate time.

From the *Rheinhardt MS.*, Üttingen, 1754:

P. B. Clayton.

COME, kindred, upstand in the valour of Jesus,
    And praise him and plight him the troth of true men.
His yoke we are breasting together will ease us
    When back at the pick and the lathe and the pen.

2 How honest his harness! O be ye then humble
    To know that he gives us a thing to be done!
Let us laugh at each set-back, and learn from each stumble
    With his hand to help us, his light leading on.

3 The mists that lie round us are thinning and breaking,
    The road it runs up to the dawn on the hills.
Trudge on with your tools to your great undertaking
    To lighten the burden of Everyman's ills.

PART II

4 Trudge on, singing praise for a spirit twice gifted
    Through lads in the line from their Lord on his tree.
As strong stars at midnight, his lamp they uplifted,
    And strode to their task like tall ships running free.

5. We are debtors to them, who with lamps ever burning
    Forgather this instant in heed to his call.
Reunion they brought us by never returning,
    And, homeless, they builded a house for us all.

(566)

471 SALONICA. (4 10. 10 10 4.)

Moderately fast. Unison.

J. S. SCOTT.

Jane Borthwick, 1813–97.

COME, labour on!
Who dares stand idle on the harvest plain,
While all around him waves the golden grain,
And to each servant doth the master say,
'Go, work to-day'?

2 Come, labour on!
Away with gloomy doubt and faithless fear!
No arm so weak but may do service here:
By hands the feeblest can our God fulfil
His righteous will.

3 Come, labour on!
No time for rest, till glows the western sky,
Till the long shadows o'er our pathway lie,
And a glad sound comes with the setting sun,
'Servant, well done!'

4. Come, labour on!
The toil is pleasant and the harvest sure;
Blessèd are those who to the end endure:
How full their joy, how deep their rest shall be,
O Lord, with thee!

472 CHEERFUL. (C.M.)

Moderately fast.

MARTIN SHAW, 1875–1958.

Org.

[*Copyright, 1915, by J. Curwen & Sons, Ltd.*]
[This hymn may also be sung to ST. HUGH, 371.]

I. *Watts*, 1674–1748.

COME, let us join our cheerful songs
  With angels round the throne;
Ten thousand thousand are their tongues
  But all their joys are one.

2 'Worthy the Lamb that died,' they cry,
  'To be exalted thus';
'Worthy the Lamb,' our lips reply,
  'For he was slain for us.'

3 Jesus is worthy to receive
  Honour and power divine;
And blessings more than we can give
  Be, Lord, for ever thine.

4. The whole creation join in one
  To bless the sacred name
Of him that sits upon the throne,
  And to adore the Lamb.

473 LOUEZ DIEU. (7 7. 7 7.)

In moderate time.

Melody of Psalm 136, *Genevan Psalter*, 1562.

[This hymn may also be sung to TUNBRIDGE, 474.]

J. Newton,† 1725–1807.

COME, my soul, thy suit prepare:
  Jesus loves to answer prayer;
He himself has bid thee pray,
Therefore will not say thee nay.

2 Thou art coming to a king,
  Large petitions with thee bring;
For his grace and power are such
None can ever ask too much.

3 Show me, Lord, what I must do;
  Every hour my strength renew;
Let me live a life of faith,
Let me die thy people's death.

4. While I am a pilgrim here,
  Let thy love my spirit cheer;
Be my guide, my guard, my friend;
Lead me to my journey's end.

474

TUNBRIDGE. (7 7. 7 7.)
Moderately slow.

J. CLARK, 1670–1707.

[This hymn may also be sung to SAVANNAH, 160.]

The Call.

George Herbert, 1593–1633.

COME, my way, my truth, my life:
  Such a way as gives us breath,
Such a truth as ends all strife,
  Such a life as killeth death.

2 Come, my light, my feast, my strength:
  Such a light as shows a feast,
Such a feast as mends in length,
  Such a strength as makes his guest.

3. Come, my joy, my love, my heart:
  Such a joy as none can move,
Such a love as none can part,
  Such a heart as joys in love.

475

MELCHIOR (LOBT GOTT). (8 7. 8 7. 8 8 7.)

With vigour.

Melody by M. VULPIUS, *c.* 1560–1616.

A. G.

COME now, all people, keep high mirth,
    Let all unite to share it;
Tell Christ's Good News through all the earth,
    Let every creature hear it:
Till all obey the Inner Light,
In each decision choose aright,
    And bring to pass God's Kingdom.

2. This is the goal of man's desire,
    God's shining joyful City,
Where every tribe and tongue 's afire
    With faith and love and pity.
Then let us share all lovely things,
And serve the light; for so each brings
    Here on this earth God's Kingdom.

476

DAVID'S HARP. (8 8. 8 8. 8 8.)

Moderately slow.

ROBERT KING in *The Divine Companion*, 1722.

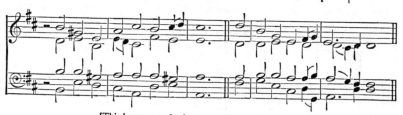

[This hymn may also be sung to FOLKINGHAM, 317.]

C. Wesley,† 1707–88.

COME, O thou Traveller unknown,
  Whom still I hold, but cannot see;
My company before is gone,
  And I am left alone with thee;
With thee all night I mean to stay,
And wrestle till the break of day.

2 I need not tell thee who I am,
    My misery or sin declare;
  Thyself hast called me by my name;
    Look on thy hands, and read it there!
  But who, I ask thee, who art thou?
  Tell me thy name, and tell me now.

3 Yield to me now, for I am weak,
    But confident in self-despair;
  Speak to my heart, in blessings speak,
    Be conquered by my instant prayer.
  Speak, or thou never hence shalt move,
  And tell me if thy name is Love.

4. 'Tis Love! 'tis Love! Thou died'st for me!
    I hear thy whisper in my heart!
  The morning breaks, the shadows flee;
    Pure universal love thou art;
  To me, to all, thy mercies move:
  Thy nature and thy name is Love.

477

NEANDER. (8 7. 8 7. 8 7.)

Moderately slow, dignified.

From Chorale 'Unser Herrscher', by J. NEANDER, 1650-80.

A-men.

ALTERNATIVE VERSION

Trebles sing the top line, all other parts the melody NEANDER.

Descant by ALAN GRAY.

Resurrection.

J. Hupton, 1762–1849, and others.

COME, ye people, raise the anthem,
　Cleave the sky with shouts of praise;
Sing to him, the Good Physician,
　Who from death the world doth raise;
Shepherd, Prophet, Word incarnate,
　Him the heart of man obeys.

2 Lo, for us and our salvation
　Hatred, scorn, and death he bore;
He, to bring mankind to freedom,
　Died that we might die no more;
Then, arising, showed his glory,
　Prince of Life for evermore.

3 Now in that celestial country
　His the honour, his the might,
'Mid the circling alleluyas
　Welling from the sons of light;

He the King and he the Captain,
　Victor in the hard-won fight.

4*Bring your harps and bring your incense,
　Sweep the string and sound the lay;
Let the earth proclaim his wonders,
　King of that eternal day;
He, the Lamb once slain, is risen,
　He was dead, yet lives for ay.

5. Laud and honour to the Father,
　Laud and honour to the Son,
Laud and honour to the Spirit,
　In the Godhead ever one.
God of life and resurrection,
　Honour, praise, to thee be done.

478

IN NATALI DOMINI. (7 7. 7 7. 7 7 7.)

Not too slow. Unison.

Melody from the Andernach *Gesangbuch,* 1608
(with emendations from the Cologne *Gesangbuch,* 1619).

Hope.

P. Gerhardt, 1607–76. Tr. C. Winkworth.‡

Auf den Nebel folgt die Sonn'.

COMETH sunshine after rain,
   After sorrow joy again;
After storms of bitter grief
Dawneth God's own sure relief:
   And my soul, who from her height
   Sank to realms of darkest night,
   Wingeth up to heaven her flight.

2 None was ever left a prey,
   None was ever turned away,
   Who had given himself to God,
   And on him had cast his load;
      Who in God his hope hath placed
      Shall not life in sorrow waste;
      Fullest joy he yet shall taste.

3 Though to-day may not fulfil
   All your hopes, have patience still,
   For perchance to-morrow's sun
   Sees a happier day begun:
      As God willeth march the hours,
      Bringing joy at last in showers:
      God is ours; all things are ours.

4.*So the passing years employ,
   Greeting life and death with joy,
   Till at last you meet the grave
   With a heart still glad and brave.
      Whom the Almighty doth defend,
      Whom the Highest counts his friend,
      Cannot perish in the end.

479

DINBYCH. (D.S.M.)

In moderate time.

J. PARRY, 1841–1903 (abridged).

[This hymn may also be sung to ICH HALTE TREULICH STILL, 480.]

Confidence.

P. *Gerhardt*, 1607–76. *Tr. J. Wesley*, 1703–91.
Befiehl du deine Wege.

COMMIT thou all thy griefs
  And ways into his hands,
To his sure truth and tender care
  Who earth and heaven commands.
  Who points the clouds their course,
  Whom winds and seas obey,
He shall direct thy wandering feet,
  He shall prepare thy way.

2 No profit canst thou gain
  By self-consuming care;
To him commend thy cause; his ear
  Attends the softest prayer.
  Through waves, and clouds, and storms,
  He gently clears thy way;
Wait thou his time; so shall the night
  Soon end in joyous day.

3* Leave to his sovran sway
  To choose and to command;
So shalt thou, wondering, own his way,
  How wise, how strong his hand.
  Far, far above thy thought
  His counsel shall appear,
When fully he the work hath wrought
  That caused thy needless fear.

4. Father, thy ceaseless truth,
  Thine everlasting love,
Sees all thy children's wants, and knows
  What best for each will prove.
  Let us, in life, in death,
  Thy steadfast truth declare,
And publish with our latest breath
  Thy love and guardian care.

480

ICH HALTE TREULICH STILL, (D.S.M.)

Brightly.

Attributed to J S. BACH, 1685–1750.

Diadems.   *A. F.*

CROWN him upon the throne
    Of justice and of right,
In him the love of God is shown,
    To shine in human light:
    He reigns, the Son of Man,
    All grace divine is his:
Pierce through the creeds, his features scan,
    And see him as he is.

2   Crown him the Lord of Love,
    And spread his Kingdom wide.
In him the world shall onward move,
    His love shall be the guide.
    Alone it can prevail
    Above our fears and cares;
He stands like friends who never fail,
    His faith in us like theirs.

3   Crown him the Lord of Peace,
    Whose will, so long undone,
Obeyed shall make all war to cease
    And man to be at one.
    His Realm shall spread like fire;
    For now he stands revealed,
The end of every heart's desire,
    Of each good cause the shield.

4   Crown him the Lord of Truth:
    The past he leaves behind
And reigns in his eternal youth,
    And rules the honest mind.
    More light than they could bear
    Who first his message heard,
More light than we can dream or dare,
    Shall break forth from his word.

5.   Crown him the Lord, and still
    Press on where he doth lead;
Be strong to do the Father's will:
    Then is he Lord indeed!
    His gospel-life make yours,
    Hold fast his simple way:
One crown we give that bright endures,
    When we his mind obey.

481

FIRST TUNE

REPTON. (8 6. 8 8 6.)

In moderate time. Voices in unison.

C. HUBERT H. PARRY, 1848–1918 (from *Judith*).

[By permission of Novello & Co., Ltd.]

(It is suggested that the melody line be played in the accompaniment for the first verse.)

SECOND TUNE

NICOLAUS (LOBT GOTT). (8 6. 8 8 6.)

Slow.

NICHOLAUS HERMANN, 1485–1561.
Arranged and harmonized by J. S. BACH, 1685–1750.

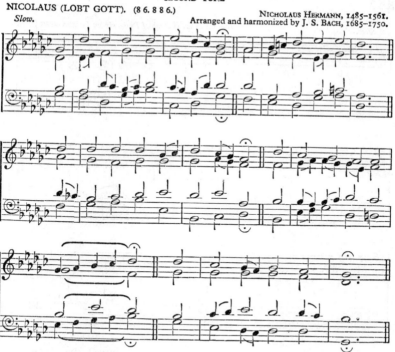

J. G. Whittier, 1807–92.

DEAR Lord and Father of mankind,
  Forgive our foolish ways!
Re-clothe us in our rightful mind,
In purer lives thy service find,
  In deeper reverence praise.

2 In simple trust like theirs who heard,
  Beside the Syrian sea,
The gracious calling of the Lord,
Let us, like them, without a word
  Rise up and follow thee.

3 O Sabbath rest by Galilee!
  O calm of hills above,
Where Jesus knelt to share with thee
The silence of eternity,
  Interpreted by love!

4 Drop thy still dews of quietness,
  Till all our strivings cease;
Take from our souls the strain and stress,
And let our ordered lives confess
  The beauty of thy peace.

5.*Breathe through the heats of our desire
  Thy coolness and thy balm;
Let sense be dumb, let flesh retire;
Speak through the earthquake, wind, and fire,
  O still small voice of calm!

482

CROWLE. (C.M.)
Slow.

Melody from *A Book of Psalmody* by JAMES GREEN (1724).

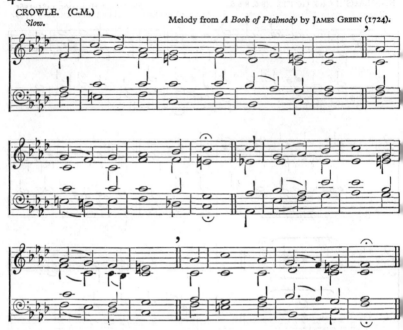

E. *Sherman Oakley*, 1865–1934.

ENDURING Soul of all our life,
  In whom all beings blend,
Unchanging Peace 'mid storm and strife,
  Our Parent, Home, and End.

2 Through thee the worlds, with all they bear,
    Their mighty courses run;
  Through thee the heavens are passing fair,
    And splendour clothes the sun.

3 The thoughts that move the heart of man
    And lift his soul on high,
  The skill that teaches him to plan
    With wondrous subtlety:

4 These are thy thoughts, almighty Mind,
    This skill is thine, O Lord,
  Who dost by hidden influence bind
    All powers in sweet accord.

5*No noble work was e'er begun
    Which came not first from heaven;
  No loving deed was ever done
    Without thine impulse given.

6. O fill me now, thou living Power,
    With energy divine;
  Thus shall my will from hour to hour
    Become, not mine, but thine.

(580)

483

FIFTH MODE MELODY. (8 4. 8 6. D.)

Moderately slow.

Melody by Thomas Tallis, *c.* 1510–85.

Ps. 119.

R. Bridges, 1844–1930.

ENTER thy courts, thou word of life,
  My joy and peace;
Let the glad sound therein be heard,
  Bid plaintive sadness cease.
Comfort my heart, thou truth most fair;
  O enter in,
Chasing despair and earthborn care,
  My woe and slothful sin.

2 Glad was the time when I would sing
  Thy heavenly praise;
Happy my heart when thou wert nigh
  Directing all my ways.

O let thy light, thy joy again
  Return to me;
Nor in disdain from me refrain,
  Who lift my soul to thee.

3. In heaven and earth thy law endures,
  Thy word abides:
My troubled flesh trembleth in awe,
  My heart in terror hides.
Yet still on thee my hope is set;
  On thee, O Lord,
I will await, and not forget
  The promise of thy word.

484

DECREE. (10 10. 10 10.)

Moderately slow.

English Traditional Melody.

Begin v. 4 here.

[This hymn may also be sung to FARLEY CASTLE, 22.]

R. Bridges, 1844–1930.

ETERNAL Father, who didst all create,
In whom we live, and to whose bosom move,
To all men be thy name known, which is Love,
Till its loud praises sound at heaven's high gate.

2 Perfect thy Kingdom in our passing state,
That here on earth thou mav'st as well approve
Our service, as thou ownest theirs above,
Whose joy we echo and in pain await.

3 Grant body and soul each day their daily bread:
And should in spite of grace fresh woe begin,
Even as our anger soon is past and dead
Be thy remembrance mortal of our sin:

4. By thee in paths of peace thy sheep be led,
And in the vale of terror comforted.

485 SONG 1. (10 10. 10 10. 10 10.)

Moderately slow.

O. GIBBONS, 1583–1625.

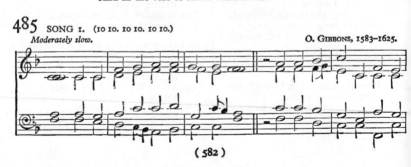

(582)

J. W. Chadwick, 1840–1904.

ETERNAL Ruler of the ceaseless round
    Of circling planets singing on their way;
Guide of the nations from the night profound
    Into the glory of the perfect day;
Rule in our hearts, that we may ever be
Guided and strengthened and upheld by thee.

2 We are of thee, the children of thy love,
    The brothers of thy well-belovèd Son;
Descend, O Holy Spirit, like a dove
    Into our hearts, that we may be as one:
As one with thee, to whom we ever tend;
As one with him, our brother and our friend.

3 We would be one in hatred of all wrong,
    One in our love of all things sweet and fair,
One with the joy that breaketh into song,
    One with the grief that trembleth into prayer,
One in the power that makes the children free
To follow truth, and thus to follow thee.

4.*O clothe us with thy heavenly armour, Lord,
    Thy trusty shield, thy sword of love divine;
Our inspiration be thy constant word;
    We ask no victories that are not thine:
Give or withhold, let pain or pleasure be;
Enough to know that we are serving thee.

(583)

486

GUN HILL. (5 5. 6 5. 8 7. 8 7.)

In moderate time. Unison.

MARTIN SHAW, 1875-1958.

[Copyright, 1929, by Oxford University Press.]

S. P. from Goethe, 1749-1832.

EVERYTHING changes,
But God changes not;
The power never changes
That lies in his thought:

Splendours three, from God proceeding,
May we ever love them true,
Goodness, Truth, and Beauty heeding
Every day, in all we do.

2 Truth never changes,
And Beauty's her dress,
And Good never changes,
Which those two express:

3 Perfect together
And lovely apart,
These three cannot wither;
They spring from God's heart:

4. Some things are screening
God's glory below;
But this is the meaning
Of all that we know:

487

GOTT WILL'S MACHEN. (8 7. 8 7.)

In moderate time.

J. L. STEINER, 1688-1761.

[This hymn may also be sung to SUSSEX, 321.]

Mrs. L. M. Willis, 1824–1908, and others.

FATHER, hear the prayer we offer:
    Not for ease that prayer shall be,
But for strength that we may ever
    Live our lives courageously.

2 Not for ever in green pastures
    Do we ask our way to be;
But the steep and rugged pathway
    May we tread rejoicingly.

3 Not for ever by still waters
    Would we idly rest and stay;
But would smite the living fountains
    From the rocks along our way.

4. Be our strength in hours of weakness,
    In our wanderings be our guide;
Through endeavour, failure, danger,
    Father, be thou at our side.

488 LLANGOLLEN (LLEDROD). (L.M.)

With vigour.   May be sung in unison.

Welsh Hymn Melody.

Rudyard Kipling, 1865–1936.

Land of our birth, we pledge to thee
Our love and toil in the years to be;
When we are grown and take our place
As men and women with our race.

FATHER in heaven who lovest all,
  O help thy children when they call,
That they may build from age to age
An undefilèd heritage.

2 Teach us to bear the yoke in youth,
With steadfastness and careful truth;
That in our time thy grace may give
The truth whereby the nations live.

3 Teach us to rule ourselves alway,
Controlled and cleanly night and day;
That we may bring, if need arise,
No maimed or worthless sacrifice.

4 Teach us to look in all our ends
On thee for judge, and not our friends;
That we, with thee, may walk uncowed
By fear or favour of the crowd.

5 Teach us the strength that cannot seek,
By deed or thought, to hurt the weak;
That, under thee, we may possess
Man's strength to comfort man's distress.

6. Teach us delight in simple things,
And mirth that has no bitter springs;
Forgiveness free of evil done,
And love to all men 'neath the sun.

Land of our birth, our faith, our pride,
For whose dear sake our fathers died;
O Motherland, we pledge to thee, [*to be!*
Head, heart, and hand through the years

489 WHITE GATES. (8 8. 8 3.)

In moderate time.

R. VAUGHAN WILLIAMS, 1872–1958.

(586)

G. Thring, 1823–1903.

FIERCE raged the tempest o'er the deep,
  Watch did thine anxious servants keep,
But thou wast wrapped in guileless sleep,
      Calm and still.

2 'Save, Lord, we perish !' was their cry,
  'O save us in our agony!'
Thy word above the storm rose high,
      'Peace, be still.'

3 The wild winds hushed; the angry deep
  Sank, like a little child, to sleep;
The sullen billows ceased to leap,
      At thy will.

4. So, when our life is clouded o'er,
  And storm-winds drift us from the shore,
Say, lest we sink to rise no more,
      'Peace, be still.'

490 ST. ISSEY. (6 4. 6 4. D.)
In moderate time.   English Traditional Melody.

J. M. Neale,‡ 1818–66.

Ζοφερᾶς τρικυμίας.

FIERCE was the wild billow,
  Dark was the night;
Oars laboured heavily,
  Foam glimmered white;
Trembled the mariners,
  Peril was nigh:
Then said the Lord of Lords,
  'Peace! It is I.'

2 Ridge of the mountain-wave,
  Lower thy crest!
Wail of the hurricane,
  Be thou at rest!
Sorrow can never be,
  Darkness must fly,
Where saith the Light of Light,
  'Peace! It is I.'

3. Jesus, deliverer,
    Near to us be;
  Soothe thou my voyaging
    Over life's sea:
  Thou, when the storm of death
    Roars, sweeping by,
  Whisper, O Truth of Truth,
    'Peace! It is I.'

(587)

491

FIRST TUNE

DUKE STREET. (L.M.)
In moderate time.

J. HATTON, d. 1793.

ALTERNATIVE VERSION

Trebles sing the top line, all other parts the melody
DUKE STREET.

Descant by ALAN GRAY.

SECOND TUNE

MONTESANO. (L.M.)
In moderate time.

A. LEECH-WILKINSON.

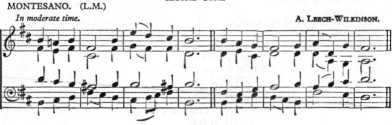

GENERAL

[Copyright, 1931, by Oxford University Press.]

J. S. B. Monsell, 1811–75.

FIGHT the good fight with all thy might,
Christ is thy strength, and Christ thy right;
Lay hold on life, and it shall be
Thy joy and crown eternally.

2 Run the straight race through God's good grace,
Lift up thine eyes, and seek his face;
Life with its way before us lies,
Christ is the path, and Christ the prize.

3 Cast care aside, upon thy Guide
Lean, and his mercy will provide;
Lean, and the trusting soul shall prove
Christ is its life, and Christ its love.

4. Faint not nor fear, his arms are near,
He changeth not, and thou art dear;
Only believe, and thou shalt see
That Christ is all in all to thee.

492 ABBEY. (C.M.)

In moderate time.

Scottish Psalter, 1615.

Praise.

H. Bonar, 1808–89.

FILL thou my life, O Lord my God,
In every part with praise,
That my whole being may proclaim
Thy being and thy ways.

2 Not for the lip of praise alone,
Nor e'en the praising heart,
I ask, but for a life made up
Of praise in every part:

3 Praise in the common words I speak,
Life's common looks and tones,

In intercourse at hearth or board
With my belovèd ones.

4 Fill every part of me with praise:
Let all my being speak
Of thee and of thy love, O Lord,
Poor though I be and weak.

5. So shall no part of day or night
From sacredness be free;
But all my life, in every step,
Be fellowship with thee.

(589)

493 LEW TRENCHARD. (7 7. 7 7. Irreg.)

In moderate time.

From an English Traditional Melody.

V. 1 only.

[*By permission of A. W. Ridley & Co.*]

Laurence Binyon, 1869–1943.

FOR mercy, courage, kindness, mirth,
 There is no measure upon earth:
Nay, they wither, root and stem,
If an end be set to them.

2. Overbrim and overflow,
If your own heart you would know;
For the spirit born to bless
Lives but in its own excess.

494 ENGLAND'S LANE. (7 7. 7 7. 7 7.)

Moderately fast. Unison.

Adapted by GEOFFREY SHAW, 1879–1943,
from an English Melody.

[*This tune may also be sung in harmony*.]
[This hymn may also be sung to RATISBON, 24.]

F. S. Pierpoint,† 1835-1917.

FOR the beauty of the earth,
For the beauty of the skies,
For the love which from our birth
Over and around us lies:
Father, unto thee we raise
This our sacrifice of praise.

2 For the beauty of each hour
Of the day and of the night,
Hill and vale, and tree and flower,
Sun and moon and stars of light:

3 For the joy of ear and eye,
For the heart and brain's delight,

For the mystic harmony
Linking sense to sound and sight:

4 For the joy of human love,
Brother, sister, parent, child,
Friends on earth, and friends above,
For all gentle thoughts and mild:

5.*For each perfect gift of thine
To our race so freely given,
Graces human and divine,
Flowers of earth and buds of heaven:

495   CORMAC.   (14. 14. 14. 14.   Irreg.)
With vigour. Unison.

Irish Traditional Melody.

C. Silvester Horne, 1865-1914.

FOR the might of thine arm we bless thee, our God, our fathers' God;
Thou hast kept thy pilgrim people by the strength of thy staff and rod;
Thou hast called us to the journey which faithless feet ne'er trod;
For the might of thine arm we bless thee, our God, our fathers' God.

2 For the love of Christ constraining, that bound their hearts as one;
For the faith in truth and freedom in which their work was done;
For the peace of God's evangel wherewith their feet were shod;
For the might of thine arm we bless thee, our God, our fathers' God.

3 We are watchers of a beacon whose light must never die;
We are guardians of an altar that shows thee ever nigh;
We are children of thy freemen who sleep beneath the sod;
For the might of thine arm we bless thee, our God, our fathers' God.

4. May the shadow of thy presence around our camp be spread;
Baptize us with the courage thou gavest to our dead;
O keep us in the pathway their saintly feet have trod;
For the might of thine arm we bless thee, our God, our fathers' God.

(591)

496

SHEEN. (14 14. 14 15.)
In moderate time.

GUSTAV HOLST, 1874–1934.

Liturgy of St. James, Tr. C. W. H.

Ἀπὸ δόξης εἰς δόξαν πορευόμενοι.

FROM glory to glory advancing, we praise thee, O Lord;
    Thy name with the Father and Spirit be ever adored.

2 From strength unto strength we go forward on Sion's highway,
    To appear before God in the city of infinite day.

3 Thanksgiving, and glory and worship, and blessing and love,
    One heart and one song have the saints upon earth and above.

4. Evermore, O Lord, to thy servants thy presence be nigh;
    Ever fit us by service on earth for thy service on high.

497 BILLESLEY. (10 10. 10 10. 4.)

MICHAEL MULLINAR.

Moderately fast.

[Copyright, 1927, by Oxford University Press.]

George Matheson, 1842–1906.

GATHER us in, thou love that fillest all;
   Gather our rival faiths within thy fold.
Rend each man's temple-veil and bid it fall,
   That we may know that thou hast been of old;
        Gather us in.

2 Gather us in: we worship only thee;
   In varied names we stretch a common hand;
In diverse forms a common soul we see;
   In many ships we seek one spirit-land;
        Gather us in.

3 Each sees one colour of thy rainbow-light,
   Each looks upon one tint and calls it heaven;
Thou art the fullness of our partial sight;
   We are not perfect till we find the seven;
        Gather us in.

4*Thine is the mystic life great India craves,
   Thine is the Parsee's sin-destroying beam,
Thine is the Buddhist's rest from tossing waves,
   Thine is the empire of vast China's dream;
        Gather us in.

5*Thine is the Roman's strength without his pride,
   Thine is the Greek's glad world without its graves,
Thine is Judæa's law with love beside,
   The truth that censures and the grace that saves;
        Gather us in.

6. Some seek a Father in the heavens above,
   Some ask a human image to adore,
Some crave a Spirit vast as life and love:
   Within thy mansions we have all and more;
        Gather us in.

498

CHILSWELL. (10 10. 10 10.)
In moderate time.   Unison.

GUSTAV HOLST, 1874–1934.

[This hymn may also be sung to ERFYNIAD, 270.]

R. Bridges, 1844–1930.

GIRD on thy sword, O man, thy strength endue,
  In fair desire thine earthborn joy renew.
Live thou thy life beneath the making sun
Till Beauty, Truth, and Love in thee are one.

2 Through thousand ages hath thy childhood run:
  On timeless ruin hath thy glory been:
  From the forgotten night of loves fordone
  Thou risest in the dawn of hopes unseen.

Harmony for v. 3 (or any other verses).

3 Higher and higher shall thy thoughts aspire,
 Unto the stars of heaven, and pass away,
 And earth renew the buds of thy desire
 In fleeting blooms of everlasting day.

4. Thy work with beauty crown, thy life with love;
 Thy mind with truth uplift to God above:
 For whom all is, from whom was all begun,
 In whom all Beauty, Truth, and Love are one.

499

WATER-END. (6 5. 6 5. Irreg.)

Brightly. Voices in unison.

GEOFFREY SHAW, 1879–1943.

1. Glad that I live am I, That the sky is blue;

simile.

Glad for the coun - try lanes And the fall of dew.

2. Af - ter the sun the rain, Af - ter the rain the sun;

This is the way of life, Till the work be done:

3. All that we need to do, Be we low or high, Is to

see that we grow Near - er . . . . the sky.

Lizette Woodworth Reese, 1856–1935.

500

AUSTRIAN HYMN. (8 7. 8 7. D.)
Moderately slow.

F. J. HAYDN, 1732–1809.

(For alternative version with descant see following page.)

J. Newton, 1725–1807.

GLORIOUS things of thee are spoken,
Sion, city of our God!
He whose word cannot be broken
Formed thee for his own abode:
On the Rock of Ages founded,
What can shake thy sure repose?
With salvation's walls surrounded,
Thou may'st smile at all thy foes.

2 See, the streams of living waters,
Springing from eternal love,
Well supply thy sons and daughters,
And all fear of want remove.
Who can faint while such a river
Ever flows their thirst to assuage—
Grace which, like the Lord the giver,
Never fails from age to age?

3. Saviour, if of Sion's city
I, through grace, a member am,
Let the world deride or pity,
I will glory in thy name:
Fading is the worldling's pleasure,
All his boasted pomp and show;
Solid joys and lasting treasure
None but Sion's children know.

(598)

GENERAL

ALTERNATIVE VERSION

ALTERNATIVE VERSION

Trebles:

Descant by T. H. INGHAM:

CHOIR AND ORGAN.

501

CONSTANTIA. (Irreg.)

Moderately slow.

R. O. MORRIS.

1. God be in my head, And in my un - der - stand - ing;

2. God be in mine eyes, And in my look - ing; 3. God be in my

mouth, And in my speak - ing; 4. God be in my heart, And in my

think - ing; 5. God be at mine end, And at my de - part - ing.

(The pronoun may be changed.)

Horae B. V. Mariae,
London, 1514.

(600)

SECOND TUNE

DAVID. (Irregular.)
Rather slow.

G. W. BRIGGS, 1875–1959.

1. God be in my head, And in my un-der-stand-ing;

2. God be in mine eyes, And in my look-ing; 3. God be in my mouth, And in my speak-ing; 4. God be in my heart, And in my think-ing; 5. God be at mine end, And at my de-part-ing.

Rather more slowly and quietly. rall.

Horae B. V. Mariae,
London, 1514.

502

THEODORIC. (6 6 6. 6 6. 5 5. 3. 9.)

In moderate time. Voices in unison.

Melody from *Piae Cantiones*, 1582.
Arranged by GUSTAV HOLST, 1874–1934.

1. God is love: his the care,
Tend - ing each, ev - 'ry - where. God is love— all is there!
Je - sus came to show him, That man - kind might know him:

[*Copyright, 1924, by Gustav Holst.*]

A. F.

GOD is love: his the care,
　Tending each, everywhere.
God is love—all is there!
　　Jesus came to show him,
　　That mankind might know him:

Sing aloud, loud, loud!
Sing aloud, loud, loud!
　　God is good!
　　God is truth! God is beauty! Praise him!

2 None can see God above;
　All have here man to love;
　Thus may we Godward move,
　　Finding him in others,
　　Holding all men brothers:

3 Jesus lived here for men,
　Strove and died, rose again,
　Rules our hearts, now as then;
　　For he came to save us
　　By the truth he gave us:

4.★To our Lord praise we sing—
　Light and life, friend and king,
　Coming down love to bring,
　　Pattern for our duty,
　　Showing God in beauty!

(603)

503

LONDON NEW. (C.M.)
Slow and dignified.

Playford's Psalms, 1671. Adapted
from NEWTOUN in *Scottish Psalter*, 1635.

ALTERNATIVE VERSION

Melody in the Tenor.

Fa-burden by MARTIN SHAW.

(When this setting is sung in four-part harmony, omit the small notes.)

Providence. *W. Cowper*, 1731–1800.

GOD moves in a mysterious way
   His wonders to perform;
He plants his footsteps in the sea,
   And rides upon the storm.

2 Deep in unfathomable mines
   Of never-failing skill
He treasures up his bright designs,
   And works his sovran will.

3 Ye fearful saints, fresh courage take,
   The clouds ye so much dread
Are big with mercy, and shall break
   In blessings on your head.

4 Judge not the Lord by feeble sense,
   But trust him for his grace;
Behind a frowning providence
   He hides a smiling face.

5 His purposes will ripen fast,
   Unfolding every hour;
The bud may have a bitter taste,
   But sweet will be the flower.

6.*Blind unbelief is sure to err,
   And scan his work in vain;
God is his own interpreter,
   And he will make it plain.

504

PRAYERS. (6 6. 6 6. D. Irregular.)

Moderately fast. *Voices in unison.*

R. H. MILFORD. 1903-60.

1. God, who cre - a - ted me Nim - ble and light of limb, In
2. *Je - sus, King and Lord, Whose are my foes to fight,
3. *Spi - rit of love and truth, Breath - ing in gross - er clay, The

Ped.

three e - le-ments free, To run, to ride, . . to swim;
Gird me with thy sword, . Swift and sharp . . and bright;
light and flame of youth, De-light of men in the fray,

Not when the sense is dim, But now from the heart of joy,
Thee would I serve if I might, And con - quer if . . I can:
Wis - dom in strength's de-cay; From pain, strife, wrong to be free,

(* *If singers find starting on the 2nd beat in verses 2 and 3 too difficult, they may start on the 1st beat, though this is not desirable*.)

H. C. Beeching, 1859–1919.

GOD, who created me
   Nimble and light of limb,
In three elements free,
   To run, to ride, to swim;
Not when the sense is dim,
   But now from the heart of joy,
I would remember him:
   Take the thanks of a boy.

2 Jesus, King and Lord,
   Whose are my foes to fight,
Gird me with thy sword,
   Swift and sharp and bright;
Thee would I serve if I might,
   And conquer if I can:
From day-dawn till night,
   Take the strength of a man.

3. Spirit of love and truth,
   Breathing in grosser clay,
The light and flame of youth,
   Delight of men in the fray,
Wisdom in strength's decay;
   From pain, strife, wrong to be free,
This best gift I pray:
   Take my spirit to thee.

505

FIRST TUNE

BRAINT. (2. 8 8 8. 8 8.)
Slow. Unison.

Welsh Hymn Melody.
Harmonies from DAVID EVANS, 1874–1948.

S. P., based on Abp. Trench, 1807–86.

GOOD cheer!
Let all men know that all men move
Beneath God's canopy of love,
As broad as the blue sky above:
For life is good; doubt, fear, and pain,
And troubles, all are shadows vain.

2   Good cheer!
All flows, all grows; the darkest way,
For those who will the Guide obey,
Shall move unto the perfect day,
When all that's hid shall be made plain,
And death itself will not remain.

3.   Good cheer!
We cannot fail who know that love—
Blessing, not cursing—rules above,
And that in this we live and move.
God's Realm must grow, all else must wane,
And we the Good at last will gain.

(608)

SECOND TUNE

GLAN'RAFON. (2. 8 8 8. 8 8.)

In moderate time.

DAVID DAVIES, 1810–75.

(*If sung to 'Glan'rafon' the last four syllables of the last line must be repeated.*)

S. P., based on Abp. Trench, 1807–86.

G OOD cheer!
Let all men know that all men move
Beneath God's canopy of love,
As broad as the blue sky above:
For life is good; doubt, fear, and pain,
And troubles, all are shadows vain.

2   Good cheer!
All flows, all grows; the darkest way,
For those who will the Guide obey,
Shall move unto the perfect day,
When all that 's hid shall be made plain,
And death itself will not remain.

3.   Good cheer!
We cannot fail who know that love—
Blessing, not cursing—rules above,
And that in this we live and move.
God's Realm must grow, all else must wane,
And we the Good at last will gain.

(609)

x

506

JESU, JESU DU MEIN HIRT. (7 7. 7 7. 7 7.)

In moderate time.

P. HEINLEIN, 1626–86.

[This hymn may also be sung to DIX, 83.]

The Eternal Spirit.

T. T. Lynch, 1818–71.

GRACIOUS Spirit, dwell with me:
I myself would gracious be,
And with words that help and heal
Would thy life in mine reveal,
And with actions bold and meek
Would for Christ my Saviour speak.

2 Truthful Spirit, dwell with me:
I myself would truthful be,
And with wisdom kind and clear
Let thy life in mine appear,
And with actions brotherly
Speak my Lord's sincerity.

3 Mighty Spirit, dwell with me:
I myself would mighty be,
Mighty so as to prevail
Where unaided man must fail;
Ever by a mighty hope
Pressing on and bearing up.

4. Holy Spirit, dwell with me:
I myself would holy be;
Separate from sin, I would
Choose and cherish all things good;
And whatever I can be,
Give to him who gave me thee.

507

CAPETOWN. (7 7. 7 5.)

Moderately slow.

Adapted from a Chorale by F. FILITZ, 1804–76.

ALTERNATIVE VERSION

Melody in the Tenor.

Fa-burden by H. GOSS CUSTARD.

Charity.

Bp. Chr. Wordsworth, 1807–85.

GRACIOUS Spirit, Holy Ghost,
   Taught by thee, we covet most
Of thy gifts at Pentecost,
   Holy, heavenly love.

2 Love is kind, and suffers long,
Love is meek, and thinks no wrong,
Love than death itself more strong;
   Therefore give us love.

3 Prophecy will fade away,
Melting in the light of day;

Love will ever with us stay;
   Therefore give us love.

4 Faith and hope and love we see,
Joining hand in hand agree;
But the greatest of the three,
   And the best, is love.

5. From the overshadowing
Of thy gold and silver wing
Shed on us, who to thee sing,
   Holy, heavenly love.

508

FIRST TUNE

LLANILAR. (8 7. 8 7. 4 7.)
Moderately slow.

Welsh Hymn Melody.

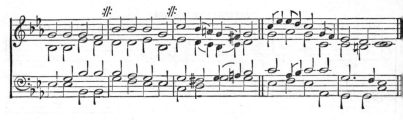

SECOND TUNE

CAERSALEM. (8 7. 8 7. 4 7.)
Moderately slow.

R. Edwards, 1797–1862.

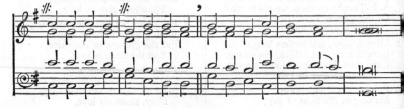

GENERAL

W. Williams, 1717–91. Tr. P. and W. Williams.‡

Arglwydd arwain trwy'r anialwch.

GUIDE me, O thou great Redeemer,
  Pilgrim through this barren land;
I am weak, but thou art mighty;
  Hold me with thy powerful hand:
    Bread of heaven,
Feed me till I want no more.

2 Open now the crystal fountain,
  Whence the healing stream doth flow;
Let the fire and cloudy pillar

Lead me all my journey through:
  Strong deliverer,
Be thou still my strength and shield.

3. When I tread the verge of Jordan,
  Bid my anxious fears subside;
Death of death, and hell's destruction,
  Land me safe on Canaan's side:
    Songs and praises
I will ever give to thee.

509

BINCHESTER.   (C.M.)
In moderate time.

W. CROFT, 1678–1727.

R. Bridges, 1844–1930, based on O quam juvat. *C. Coffin* (1736).

HAPPY are they, they that love God,
  Whose hearts have Christ confest,
Who by his cross have found their life,
  And 'neath his yoke their rest.

2 Glad is the praise, sweet are the songs,
  When they together sing;
And strong the prayers that bow the ear
  Of heaven's eternal King.

3 Christ to their homes giveth his peace,
  And makes their loves his own:
But ah, what tares the evil one
  Hath in his garden sown.

4 Sad were our lot, evil this earth,
  Did not its sorrows prove
The path whereby the sheep may find
  The fold of Jesus' love.

5. Then shall they know, they that love him,
  How all their pain is good;
And death itself cannot unbind
  Their happy brotherhood.

510

FREUEN WIR UNS. (7 7. 7 7.)
In moderate time.

M. WEISSE, c. 1480–1534.

[This hymn may also be sung to SAVANNAH, 160.]

W. Cowper, 1731–1800.

HARK, my soul! it is the Lord;
'Tis thy saviour, hear his word;
Jesus speaks, and speaks to thee:
'Say, poor sinner, lov'st thou me?

2 'I delivered thee when bound,
And, when wounded, healed thy wound;
Sought thee wandering, set thee right,
Turned thy darkness into light.

3*'Can a woman's tender care
Cease towards the child she bare?
Yes, she may forgetful be,
Yet will I remember thee.

4 'Mine is an unchanging love,
Higher than the heights above,
Deeper than the depths beneath,
Free and faithful, strong as death.

5 'Thou shalt see my glory soon,
When the work of grace is done;
Partner of my throne shalt be;
Say, poor sinner, lov'st thou me?'

6. Lord, it is my chief complaint
That my love is weak and faint;
Yet I love thee, and adore;
O for grace to love thee more!

511

ST. OSYTH. (11 10. 11 10.)
With vigour. Unison.

Thomas Wood, 1892–1950.

[*Copyright, 1925, by Oxford University Press.*]

[This hymn may also be sung to Londonderry, 230, 611.]

F. W. H. Myers, 1843–1901.

HARK what a sound, and too divine for hearing,
  Stirs on the earth and trembles in the air!
Is it the thunder of the Lord's appearing?
  Is it the music of his people's prayer?

2 Surely he cometh, and a thousand voices
  Shout to the saints, and to the deaf are dumb;
Surely he cometh, and the earth rejoices,
  Glad in his coming who hath sworn, 'I come.'

3 This hath he done, and shall we not adore him?
  This shall he do, and can we still despair?
Come, let us quickly fling ourselves before him,
  Cast at his feet the burden of our care.

4. Yea, through life, death, through sorrow and through sinning
  He shall suffice me, for he hath sufficed:
Christ is the end, for Christ was the beginning,
  Christ the beginning, for the end is Christ.

512

OLD 107TH. (D.C.M.)

Moderately slow, dignified. *May also be sung in unison.*

Scottish Psalter, 1635,
based on the *Genevan Psalter.*

[This hymn may also be sung in C.M. to KING'S NORTON, 547.]

I. Watts, 1674–1748, and others.

HAST thou not known, hast thou not heard,
　That firm remains on high
The everlasting throne of him
　Who formed the earth and sky?
Art thou afraid his power shall fail
　When comes thy evil day?
And can an all-creating arm
　Grow weary or decay?

2 He gives the conquest to the weak,
 Supports the fainting heart,
And courage in the evil hour
 His heavenly aids impart.
His truth for ever stands secure;
 He stays the troubled mind,
He saves the oppressed, he feeds the poor,
 Pours eyesight on the blind.

3. Mere human power shall fast decay,
 And youthful vigour cease;
But they who wait upon the Lord
 In strength shall still increase.
They with unwearied feet shall tread
 The path of life divine,
With growing ardour onward move,
 With growing brightness shine.

513

WARWICK. (C.M.)

In moderate time.

SAMUEL STANLEY, 1767–1822.

[This hymn may also be sung to BUTLER, 378.]

John Bunyan, 1628–88.

HE that is down needs fear no fall,
 He that is low no pride;
He that is humble ever shall
 Have God to be his guide.

2 I am content with what I have,
 Little be it or much;
And, Lord, contentment still I crave
 Because thou savest such.

3. Fullness to such a burden is
 That go on pilgrimage;
Here little, and hereafter bliss
 Is best from age to age.

514

CAMERONIAN MIDNIGHT HYMN. (L.M.)

In moderate time.

Scottish Hymn Melody.

Richard Baxter,† 1615–91.

HE wants not friends that hath thy love,
And may converse and walk with thee,
And with thy saints here and above,
With whom for ever I must be.

2 In the blest fellowship of saints
Is wisdom, safety and delight;
And when my heart declines and faints,
It 's raisèd by their heat and light.

3 As for my friends, they are not lost;
The several vessels of thy fleet,
Though parted now, by tempests tost,
Shall safely in the haven meet.

4 Still we are centred all in thee,
Members, though distant, of one Head;
In the same family we be,
By the same faith and spirit led.

5 Before thy throne we daily meet
As joint-petitioners to thee;
In spirit we each other greet,
And shall again each other see.

6.*The heavenly hosts, world without end,
Shall be my company above;
And thou, my best and surest friend,
Who shall divide me from thy love?

(618)

515

MONKS GATE. (11 11. 12 11.)

Brightly.

Adapted from an English Traditional Melody.

Pilgrim Song.

P. Dearmer, 1867–1936,
after J. Bunyan, 1628–88.

HE who would valiant be
    'Gainst all disaster,
Let him in constancy
    Follow the Master.
There 's no discouragement
Shall make him once relent
His first avowed intent
    To be a pilgrim.

2 Who so beset him round
    With dismal stories,
Do but themselves confound—
    His strength the more is.
No foes shall stay his might,
Though he with giants fight:
He will make good his right
    To be a pilgrim.

3. Since, Lord, thou dost defend
    Us with thy Spirit,
We know we at the end
    Shall life inherit.
Then fancies flee away!
I'll fear not what men say,
I'll labour night and day
    To be a pilgrim.

516

PLEADING SAVIOUR. (8 7. 8 7. D.)
In moderate time.

Plymouth Collection (U.S.A.), 1855.

SECOND TUNE

ENGADINE. (8 7. 8 7. D.)

Adapted from a melody in *Canzuns Spirituaelas* (Upper Engadine), 1765.
In moderate time. (*May be sung in unison or in 2 parts. Tenor part is ad lib.*)

W. Charter Piggott, 1872–1943.

HEAVENLY Father, may thy blessing
  Rest upon thy children now,
When in praise thy name they hallow,
  When in prayer to thee they bow:
In the wondrous story reading
  Of the Lord of truth and grace,
May they see thy love reflected
  In the light of his dear face.

2 May they learn from this great story
  All the arts of friendliness;
Truthful speech and honest action,
  Courage, patience, steadfastness;
How to master self and temper,
  How to make their conduct fair;
When to speak and when be silent,
  When to do and when forbear.

3. May his spirit wise and holy
  With his gifts their spirits bless,
Make them loving, joyous, peaceful,
  Rich in goodness, gentleness,
Strong in self-control, and faithful,
  Kind in thought and deed; for he
Sayeth, 'What ye do for others
  Ye are doing unto me'.

517

DUNFERMLINE. (C.M.)

Moderately slow.

Scottish Psalter, 1615.

ALTERNATIVE VERSION

Trebles (all other voices sing the melody DUNFERMLINE).

Descant by ROBIN MILFORD.

Charles Wesley, 1707–88.

HELP us to help each other, Lord,
　　Each other's cross to bear,
Let each his friendly aid afford
　　And feel his brother's care.

2 Up into thee, our living head,
　　Let us in all things grow,
Till thou hast made us free indeed,
　　And spotless here below.

3. Touched by the loadstone of thy love,
　　Let all our hearts agree;
And ever toward each other move,
　　And ever move toward thee.

518

OAKRIDGE LYNCH. (6 5. 6 5.)
Moderately slow.　　　　　　　MARTIN SHAW, 1875–1958.

[*Copyright,* 1925, *by Martin Shaw.*]

Village Hymn.　　　　　　*Norman Gale,* 1862–1948.

HERE in the country's heart
　　Where the grass is green,
Life is the same sweet life
　　As it e'er hath been.

2 Trust in a God still lives,
　　And the bell at morn
Floats with a thought of God
　　O'er the rising corn.

3. God comes down in the rain,
　　And the crop grows tall—
This is the country faith,
　　And the best of all.

5I9 MISERERE MEI. (4 8. 8 4.)

Slow.

Melody from
Seven Sobs of a Sorrowful Soul, 1585 (slightly adapted).

' Slower.

W. Canton, 1845–1926.

HOLD thou my hands!
  In grief and joy, in hope and fear,
Lord, let me feel that thou art near:
  Hold thou my hands!

2   If e'er, by doubts
Of thy good Fatherhood depressed,
I cannot find in thee my rest,
  Hold thou my hands!

3   Hold thou my hands—
These passionate hands too quick to smite,
These hands so eager for delight:
  Hold thou my hands!

4.   And when at length,
With darkened eyes and fingers cold,
I seek some last loved hand to hold,
  Hold thou my hands!

520 HARTS. (7 7. 7 7.)

In moderate time.

B. MILGROVE, 1731–1810.

The Eternal Spirit.

S. Longfellow, 1819–92.

HOLY Spirit, truth divine,
  Dawn upon this soul of mine;
Word of God, and Inward Light,
Wake my spirit, clear my sight.

2 Holy Spirit, love divine,
  Glow within this heart of mine;
Kindle every high desire.
Perish self in thy pure fire!

(624)

3 Holy Spirit, power divine,
  Fill and nerve this will of mine;
  By thee may I strongly live,
  Bravely bear, and nobly strive.

4 Holy Spirit, right divine,
  King within my conscience reign;
  Be my law, and I shall be
  Firmly bound, for ever free.

5*Holy Spirit, peace divine,
  Still this restless heart of mine;
  Speak to calm this tossing sea,
  Stayed in thy tranquillity.

6.*Holy Spirit, joy divine,
  Gladden thou this heart of mine;
  In the desert ways I sing,
  Spring, O Well, for ever spring!

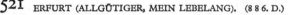

521 ERFURT (ALLGÜTIGER, MEIN LEBELANG). (8 8 6. D.)

In moderate time.   G. P. WEIMAR, 1734–1800.

Ps. 147.   *Christopher Smart,* 1722–71.

HOSANNA! Music is divine,
  When in the praise the psalmists join
    And each good heart is warm;
  Yea, joy is sweetest so renewed,
  And all the rites of gratitude
    Are rapture to perform.

2 For God is magnitude immense;
  His prowess is omnipotence
    That knows no date or end,
  His wisdom infinitely great;
  And all duration, depth and height,
    His mysteries transcend.

3*He the blue heaven in beauty shrouds,
  And balances the plumy clouds
    Which for the rain he wrings;

He causes the mild dew to drop,
And grass upon the mountain top
    In tufted verdure springs.

4*He laid the verdant turf to graze,
  That earth the due supplies might raise
    Of annual food and wealth;
  And fragrant herbs and flowers profuse
  The seasons on the field produce
    For pleasure and for health.

5.*He shall the broken heart repair,
  And for all sickness and despair
    A cure in Christ provide;
  And heal the wounded and the bruised,
  His oil into their sores infused,
    And soothing balm applied.

(Verses 3, 4 and 5 may be sung as a separate hymn.)

(625)

522

KILMARNOCK. (C.M.)
In moderate time.

NEIL DOUGALL, 1776–1862.

Confidence.

J. *Addison*,‡ 1672–1719.

HOW are thy servants blest, O Lord!
How sure is their defence!
Eternal wisdom is their guide,
Their help omnipotence.

2 In foreign realms and lands remote,
Supported by thy care,
Through burning climes they pass un-
hurt,
And breathe in tainted air.

3 From all their griefs and dangers, Lord,
Thy mercy sets them free,

While in the confidence of prayer
Their souls take hold on thee.

4 In midst of dangers, fears, and death,
Thy goodness we'll adore;
And praise thee for thy mercies past,
And humbly hope for more.

5. Our life, while thou preserv'st that life,
Thy sacrifice shall be;
And death, when death shall be our lot,
Shall join our souls to thee.

523

GLENLUCE. (C.M.)
In moderate time.

Scottish Psalter, 1635.
(Later version of melody.)

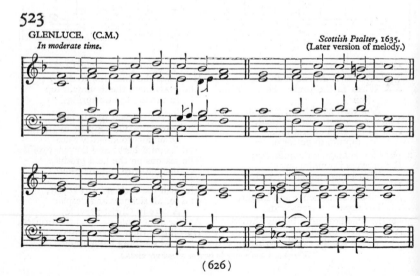

Purity.

W. H. Bathurst, 1796–1877.

HOW blest are they whose hearts are pure,
From guile their spirits free:
To them shall God himself reveal,
His glory they shall see.

2 Their simple souls upon his word,
In fullest light of love,
Place all their trust, and ask no more
Than guidance from above.

3 They who in faith, unmixed with doubt,
The engrafted word receive,
Whom the first sign of heavenly power
Persuades, and they believe.

4 They, as they walk this painful world,
See hidden glories rise;
Our God the sunshine of his love
Unfolds before their eyes.

5. For them far greater things than these
Does Christ the Lord prepare,
Whose bliss no heart of man can reach,
No human voice declare.

524

KENT. (L.M.)
In moderate time.

J. F. LAMPE, 1703–51.

[This hymn may also be sung to LLANGOLLEN, 488.]

Sir H. Wotton,‡ 1568–1639.

HOW happy is he born and taught,
That serveth not another's will;
Whose armour is his honest thought,
And simple truth his utmost skill;

2 Whose passions not his masters are;
Whose soul is still prepared for death,
Untied unto the world by care
Of public fame or private breath;

3 Who God doth late and early pray
More of his grace than goods to lend;
And walks with man from day to day
As with a brother and a friend.

4. This man is freed from servile bands
Of hope to rise, or fear to fall;
Lord of himself, though not of lands;
And having nothing, yet hath all.

525
DURHAM. (C.M.)
In moderate time.

Ravenscroft's Psalter, 1621.

Ps. 84.

J. Milton, 1608-74.

HOW lovely are thy dwellings fair!
 O Lord of Hosts, how dear
Thy pleasant tabernacles are,
 Where thou dost dwell so near.

2 My soul doth long and almost die
 Thy courts, O Lord, to see;
My heart and flesh aloud do cry,
 O living God, for thee.

3 Happy who in thy house reside,
 Where thee they ever praise!
Happy whose strength in thee doth bide,
 And in their hearts thy ways!

4 They journey on from strength to strength
 With joy and gladsome cheer,
Till all before our God at length
 In Sion do appear.

5. For God, the Lord, both sun and shield,
 Gives grace and glory bright;
No good from them shall be withheld
 Whose ways are just and right.

526

OLD 137TH. (D.C.M.)
Moderately slow.

Day's Psalter, 1563.

John Mason, c. 1645–94.

HOW shall I sing that majesty
　Which angels do admire?
Let dust in dust and silence lie;
　Sing, sing, ye heavenly choir.
Thousands of thousands stand around
　Thy throne, O God most high;
Ten thousand times ten thousand sound
　Thy praise; but who am I?

Thy brightness unto them appears,
　Whilst I thy footsteps trace;
A sound of God comes to my ears,
　But they behold thy face.
They sing because thou art their sun;
　Lord, send a beam on me;
For where heaven is but once begun
　There alleluyas be.

3*Enlighten with faith's light my heart,
　Inflame it with love's fire;
Then shall I sing and bear a part
　With that celestial choir.
I shall, I fear, be dark and cold,
　With all my fire and light;
Yet when thou dost accept their gold,
　Lord, treasure up my mite.

4. How great a being, Lord, is thine,
　Which doth all beings keep!
Thy knowledge is the only line
　To sound so vast a deep.
Thou art a sea without a shore,
　A sun without a sphere;
Thy time is now and evermore,
　Thy place is everywhere.

527

FIRST TUNE

ST. BOTOLPH. (C.M.)
In moderate time.　　　　　　　　　　　　GORDON SLATER.

[*Copyright, 1929, by Oxford University Press.*]

J. Newton,† 1725–1807.

HOW sweet the name of Jesus sounds
　　In a believer's ear!
It soothes his sorrows, heals his wounds,
　　And drives away his fear.

2 It makes the wounded spirit whole,
　　And calms the troubled breast;
'Tis manna to the hungry soul,
　　And to the weary, rest.

3 Dear name! the rock on which I build,
　　My shield and hiding-place,
My never-failing treasury filled
　　With boundless stores of grace.

4 Jesus! my shepherd, brother, friend,
　　My prophet, priest, and king,
My lord, my life, my way, my end,
　　Accept the praise I bring.

5 Weak is the effort of my heart,
　　And cold my warmest thought;
But when I see thee as thou art,
　　I'll praise thee as I ought.

6.*Till then I would thy love proclaim
　　With every fleeting breath;
And may the music of thy name
　　Refresh my soul in death.

SECOND TUNE

ST. PETER. (C.M.)
In moderate time.

A. R. REINAGLE, 1799–1877.

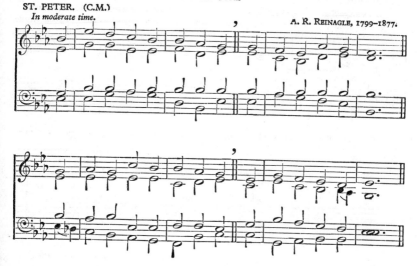

ALTERNATIVE VERSION

Melody in the Tenor.

Fa-burden by EDGAR C. ROBINSON.

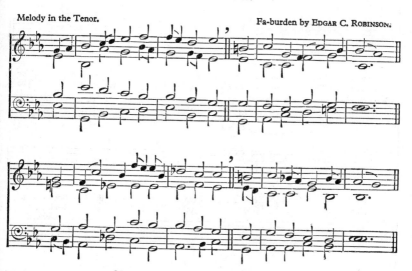

528

ST. PATRICK. (D.L.M.)*

Aτompιuʒ ınbıu.

Slow and dignified. Voices in unison.

From an Ancient Irish Hymn Melody.

1. I bind un-to... my-self.. to-day The strong name
of... the Trin-i-ty, By in-vo-ca-tion
of the same, The three in. One,.. and One in three.

2. I bind un-to... my-self... to-day 'The
3. I bind un-to... my-self... to-day The

vir-tues of.... the star-lit and hea-ven,
pow-er of God... to hold and lead,...

* *This refers to the complete tune only as given for verses 2, 3, and 5.*

GENERAL

The glo- rious sun's life- giv- ing ray,.. The
His eye... to.. watch, his might to stay,.. His

white- ness of... the moon at e- ven, The flash- ing
ear to. heark- - en to my need... The wis- dom

of the.. light- ning free, The whir- ling wind's.. tem-
of my.. God to teach, His hand to guide,.. his

- pes- tuous shocks, The sta- ble.. earth, the deep salt
shield to ward; The word.. of.. God to give me

sea,.. A- round the.. old... e- ter- nal rocks;
speech, His heaven- ly.. host... to be my guard.

(633)

528 *(continued)*

PART II

MORLEY. (8 8. 8 8. D. Trochaic.)

Unison.   Ancient Irish Melody.   Harmonized by C. BURKE.

4. Christ be with me, Christ with-in me, Christ be-hind me, Christ before me, Christ be-side me, Christ to win me, Christ to
com - fort and re - store me, Christ be - neath me, Christ a-
- bove me, Christ in qui - et, Christ in dan - ger, Christ in
hearts of all that love me, Christ in mouth of friend and stran - ger.

GENERAL

Doxology to either part.

5. I bind un-to... my-self the name, The strong name of.. the Trin-i-ty; By in-vo-ca-tion of the same, The three in.. One, and One in three, Of whom all na-ture hath cre-a-tion; E-ter-nal Fa-ther, Spi-rit, Word: Praise to the Lord of my sal-va-tion: Sal-va-tion is... of Christ the Lord.

St. Patrick's Breastplate.

Ascr. to St. Patrick, c. 372–466.
Tr. Mrs. C. F. Alexander.

529

KINGSFOLD. (D.C.M.)

In moderate time.

From an English Traditional Melody.

H. Bonar, 1808–89.

I HEARD the voice of Jesus say,
  'Come unto me and rest;
Lay down, thou weary one, lay down
  Thy head upon my breast.'
I came to Jesus as I was,
  Weary, and worn, and sad;
I found in him a resting-place,
  And he has made me glad.

2 I heard the voice of Jesus say,
  'Behold, I freely give
The living water, thirsty one:
  Stoop down, and drink, and live.'
I came to Jesus, and I drank
  Of that life-giving stream;
My thirst was quenched, my soul revived,
  And now I live in him.

3. I heard the voice of Jesus say,
  'I am this dark world's light:
Look unto me, thy morn shall rise,
  And all thy day be bright.'
I looked to Jesus, and I found
  In him my star, my sun;
And in that light of life I'll walk
  Till travelling days are done.

In verses 2 and 3 lines 5 and 6 run thus:

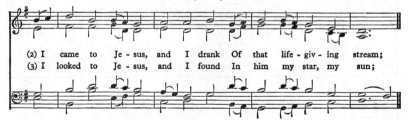

(2) I came to Je-sus, and I drank Of that life-giv-ing stream;
(3) I looked to Je-sus, and I found In him my star, my sun;

530 CULROSS. (C.M.)
Moderately slow.

Scottish Psalter, 1634.

Trust.

J. G. Whittier, 1807–92.

I KNOW not what the future hath
  Of marvel or surprise;
Assured of this, that life and death
  His mercy underlies.

2 And if my heart and flesh are weak
    To bear an untried pain,
  The bruisèd reed he will not break,
    But strengthen and sustain.

3 And so beside the silent sea
    I wait the muffled oar:
  No harm from him can come to me,
    On ocean or on shore.

4. I know not where his islands lift
    Their fronded palms in air:
  I only know I cannot drift
    Beyond his love and care.

531 CROMER. (L.M.)
In moderate time.

J. A. LLOYD, 1815–74.

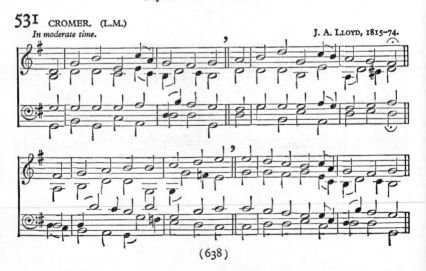

Wealth.   *Lucy Larcom,* 1826–93.

I LEARNED it in the meadow path,
  I learned it on the mountain stairs—
The best things any mortal hath
  Are those which every mortal shares.

2 The air we breathe, the sky, the breeze,
    The light without us and within,
  Life with its unlocked treasuries,
    God's riches are for all to win.

3 The grass is softer to my tread,
    Because it rests unnumbered feet;

Sweeter to me the wild rose red,
  Because she makes the whole world
    sweet.

4 And up the radiant peopled way
    That opens into worlds unknown,
  It will be life's delight to say,
    'Heaven is not heaven for me alone.'

5. Wealth won by other's poverty—
    Not such be mine! Let me be blest
  Only in what they share with me,
    And what I share with all the rest.

532

O JESU. (8 6. 8 6. 8 8.)
Moderately slow.

J. B. REIMANN, 1702–49.

Peace.   *S. Longfellow,* 1819–92.

I LOOK to thee in every need,
  And never look in vain;
I feel thy strong and tender love,
  And all is well again:
The thought of thee is mightier far
Than sin and pain and sorrow are.

2*Discouraged in the work of life,
    Disheartened by its load,
  Shamed by its failures or its fears,
    I sink beside the road;
  But let me only think of thee,
  And then new heart springs up in me.

3 Thy calmness bends serene above,
    My restlessness to still;
  Around me flows thy quickening life,
    To nerve my faltering will:
  Thy presence fills my solitude;
  Thy providence turns all to good.

4. Embosomed deep in thy dear love,
    Held in thy law, I stand;
  Thy hand in all things I behold,
    And all things in thy hand;
  Thou leadest me by unsought ways,
  And turn'st my mourning into praise.

533 GESIUS (HEUT' TRIUMPHIRET). (8 8. 8 8. 8 8.)

Moderately slow.

B. GESIUS, 1555–1614.
Adapted and harmonized by J. S. BACH, 1685–1750.

[This hymn may also be sung to LAMBETH, 346.]

Bishop R. Heber, 1783–1826.

I PRAISED the earth, in beauty seen,
With garlands gay of various green;
I praised the sea, whose ample field
Shone glorious as a silver shield;
And earth and ocean seemed to say,
'Our beauties are but for a day.'

2 I praised the sun, whose chariot rolled
On wheels of amber and of gold;
I praised the moon, whose softer eye
Gleamed sweetly through the summer sky;
And moon and sun in answer said,
'Our days of light are numberèd.'

3. O God, O good beyond compare,
If thus thy meaner works are fair,
If thus thy beauties gild the span
Of ruined earth and sinful man,
How glorious must the mansion be
Where thy redeemed shall dwell with thee!

534

MONK STREET. (10 4. 10 4. 10 4. 10 10.)

In moderate time.

GUSTAV HOLST, 1874-1934.

The Supreme Values.   *Thomas Heywood, c. 1650, and Percy Dearmer, 1867-1936.*

I SOUGHT thee round about, O thou my God,
    To find thy abode;
I said unto the earth, 'Speak, art thou he?'
    She answered me
She was not; and I asked of creatures all
    In general
Contained therein: they with one voice proclaim
That none amongst them challenged such a name.

2 But now, my God, by thy illumining grace,
    Thy glorious face
So far forth as thou wilt discovered be,
    Methinks I see;
And though invisible and infinite
    To human sight,
Thou in thy Goodness, Beauty, Truth, appearest,
In which to our frail senses thou art nearest.

3. O make us apt to seek and quick to find,
    Thou God most kind;
Give us love, hope, and faith in thee to trust,
    Thou God most just;
Remit all our offences, we entreat,
    Most good, most great;
Grant that our willing though unworthy quest
May through thy grace admit us 'mongst the blest.

535
ST. DENIO. (11 11. 11 11.)
In moderate time.   Welsh Hymn Melody.

W. Chalmers Smith, 1824–1908.

IMMORTAL, invisible, God only wise,
In light inaccessible hid from our eyes,
Most blessèd, most glorious, the ancient of days,
Almighty, victorious, thy great name we praise.

2 Unresting, unhasting, and silent as light,
Nor wanting, nor wasting, thou rulest in might;
Thy justice like mountains high soaring above,
Thy clouds which are fountains of goodness and love.

3 To all life thou givest, to both great and small;
In all life thou livest, the true life of all;
We blossom and flourish as leaves on the tree,
And wither and perish; but nought changeth thee.

4. Great Father of glory, pure Father of light,
Thine angels adore thee, all veiling their sight;
All laud we would render: O help us to see
'Tis only the splendour of light hideth thee.

536

BISHOPTHORPE (OR ST. PAUL'S). (C.M.)

In moderate time.

Attributed to J. CLARK, 1670–1707.

J. G. Whittier, 1807–92.

IMMORTAL love for ever full,
   For ever flowing free,
For ever shared, for ever whole,
   A never-ebbing sea!

2 Our outward lips confess the name,
   All other names above;
Love only knoweth whence it came
   And comprehendeth love.

3 We may not climb the heavenly steeps
   To bring the Lord Christ down;
In vain we search the lowest deeps,
   For him no depths can drown;

4 But warm, sweet, tender, even yet
   A present help is he;
And faith has still its Olivet,
   And love its Galilee.

5*The healing of his seamless dress
   Is by our beds of pain;
We touch him in life's throng and press,
   And we are whole again.

6*Through him the first fond prayers are said
   Our lips of childhood frame;
The last low whispers of our dead
   Are burdened with his name.

7.*Alone, O Love ineffable,
   Thy saving name is given;
To turn aside from thee is hell,
   To walk with thee is heaven.

(643)

537 ST. BERNARD. (C.M.)
Moderately slow.

Adapted from a melody in *Tochter Sion* (Cöln, 1741).

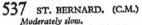

[This hymn may also be sung to ST. JAMES, 96.]

John Oxenham, 1852–1941.

IN Christ there is no East or West,
In him no South or North,
But one great fellowship of love
Throughout the whole wide earth.

2 In him shall true hearts everywhere
Their high communion find,
His service is the golden cord
Close-binding all mankind.

3 Join hands, then, brothers of the faith,
Whate'er your race may be!
Who serves my Father as a son
Is surely kin to me.

4. In Christ now meet both East and West,
In him meet South and North,
All Christly souls are one in him,
Throughout the whole wide earth.

538 BATTISHILL. (7 7. 7 7.)
In moderate time.

Adapted from a melody by JONATHAN BATTISHILL, 1738–1801.

School-days.

W. *Charter Piggott,* 1872–1943.

IN our work and in our play,
    Jesus, be thou ever near;
Guarding, guiding all the day,
    Keep us in thy presence dear.

2 Thou, who at thy mother's knee
    Learned to hearken and obey,
Then, work done, ran happily
    With the children to their play;

3 And by Joseph's bench did stand,
    Holding his edged tools, as he
Guiding them with skilful hand,
    Made a carpenter of thee;

4*Help us, that with eager mind
    We may learn both fact and rule,
Patient, diligent and kind
    In the comradeship of school.

5 Help us, too, in sport and game
    Gallantly to play our part;
Win or lose, to keep the same
    Dauntless spirit and brave heart.

6. May we grow like him in grace,
    True in mind and pure of soul,
Meeting life with steadfast face,
    Run its race and reach the goal.

539

FITZWILLIAM. (8 8. 8 6.)

In moderate time.

From an English Traditional Melody.

Stopford A. Brooke, 1832–1916.

IT fell upon a summer day,
    When Jesus walked in Galilee,
The mothers from a village brought
    Their children to his knee.

2 He took them in his arms, and laid
    His hands on each remembered head;
'Suffer these little ones to come
    To me,' he gently said.

3 'Forbid them not; unless ye bear
    The childlike heart your hearts within,
Unto my Kingdom ye may come,
    But may not enter in.'

4 Master, I fain would enter there;
    O let me follow thee, and share
Thy meek and lowly heart, and be
    Freed from all worldly care.

5 Of innocence, and love, and trust,
    Of quiet work, and simple word,
Of joy, and thoughtlessness of self,
    Build up my life, good Lord.

6*All happy thoughts, and gentle ways,
    And loving-kindness daily given,
And freedom through obedience gained,
    Make in my heart thy heaven.

7*O happy thus to live and move!
    And sweet this world, where I shall find
God's beauty everywhere, his love,
    His good in all mankind.

8.*Then, Father, grant this childlike heart,
    That I may come to Christ, and feel
His hands on me in blessing laid,
    Love-giving, strong to heal.

540

QUEM PASTORES LAUDAVERE. (8 8 8. 7.)

In moderate time.

Melody from a 14th-century German MS.

P. Dearmer, 1867–1936, based on J. M. Neale, 1816–66.

JESUS, good above all other,
  Gentle child of gentle mother,
In a stable born our brother,
      Give us grace to persevere.

2 Jesus, cradled in a manger,
  For us facing every danger,
  Living as a homeless stranger,
      Make we thee our King most dear.

3 Jesus, for thy people dying,
  Risen Master, death defying,
  Lord in heaven, thy grace supplying,
      Keep us to thy presence near.

4 Jesus, who our sorrows bearest,
  All our thoughts and hopes thou sharest,
  Thou to man the truth declarest;
      Help us all thy truth to hear.

5. Lord, in all our doings guide us;
  Pride and hate shall ne'er divide us;
  We'll go on with thee beside us,
      And with joy we'll persevere!

GENERAL

541

PEACEFIELD. (7 7. 7 7.)

Slow.

Ancient Irish Lullaby, harmonized by DAVID F. R. WILSON, 1871–1957.

Unity.

Charles Wesley, 1707–88.

JESUS, Lord, we look to thee;
Let us in thy name agree;
Show thyself the Prince of Peace;
Bid our strife for ever cease.

2 Make us of one heart and mind,
Courteous, pitiful, and kind,
Lowly, meek, in thought and word,
Altogether like our Lord.

3 Let us each for other care,
Each the other's burden bear;
To thy Church the pattern give,
Show how true believers live.

4. Free from anger and from pride,
Let us thus in God abide;
All the depths of love express,
All the height of holiness.

542

ABERYSTWYTH. (7 7. 7 7. D.)

Slow.

Composed or adapted by JOSEPH PARRY, 1841–1903.

[By permission of Hughes & Son, Wrexham.]

Charles Wesley, 1707–88.

JESU, lover of my soul,
  Let me to thy bosom fly,
While the nearer waters roll,
  While the tempest still is high:
Hide me, O my Saviour, hide,
  Till the storm of life is past;
Safe into the haven guide,
  O receive my soul at last.

2 Other refuge have I none;
  Hangs my helpless soul on thee;
Leave, ah! leave me not alone,
  Still support and comfort me.

(648)

GENERAL

ALTERNATIVE VERSION

Trebles sing the top line, all other voices the melody

ABERYSTWYTH.

Descant by ALAN GRAY.

All my trust on thee is stayed,
  All my help from thee I bring;
Cover my defenceless head
  With the shadow of thy wing.

3. Plenteous grace with thee is found,
    Grace to cover all my sin;
  Let the healing streams abound;
    Make and keep me pure within.
  Thou of life the fountain art;
    Freely let me take of thee;
  Spring thou up within my heart,
    Rise to all eternity.

(649)

543

BELSIZE. (6 5. 6 5.)

Moderately slow.

MARTIN SHAW, 1875–1958.

Last verse.

[*Copyright, 1915, by J. Curwen & Sons, Ltd.*]

G. R. *Prynne*, 1818–1903.

JESUS, meek and gentle,
  Son of God most high,
Pitying, loving Saviour,
  Hear thy children's cry.

2 Pardon our offences,
    Loose our captive chains,
  Break down every idol
    Which our soul detains.

3 Give us holy freedom,
    Fill our hearts with love,
  Draw us, holy Jesus,
    To the realms above.

4 Lead us on our journey,
    Be thyself the way
  Through terrestrial darkness
    To celestial day.

5. Jesus, meek and gentle,
    Son of God most high,
  Pitying, loving Saviour,
    Hear thy children's cry.

544

JESU MEINE FREUDE. (6 6 5. 6 6 5. 7 8 6.)

German Traditional Melody adapted by J. CRÜGER, 1598–1662.
Further adapted and harmonized by J. S. BACH, 1685–1750.

Slow and dignified.

Security.

J. Franck, 1618–77. Tr. C. Winkworth.‡

Jesu, meine Freude.

JESUS, priceless treasure,
Source of purest pleasure,
Truest friend to me;
Long my heart hath panted,
Till it well-nigh fainted,
Thirsting after thee.
Thine I am, O spotless Lamb,
I will suffer nought to hide thee,
Ask for nought beside thee.

2 In thine arm I rest me;
Foes who would molest me
Cannot reach me here.
Though the earth be shaking,
Every heart be quaking,

God dispels our fear;
Sin and hell in conflict fell
With their heaviest storms assail us:
Jesus will not fail us.

3. Hence, all thoughts of sadness!
For the Lord of gladness,
Jesus, enters in:
Those who love the Father,
Though the storms may gather,
Still have peace within;
Yea, whate'er we here must bear,
Still in thee lies purest pleasure,
Jesus, priceless treasure!

(651)

545
TRURO. (L.M.)
In moderate time.

Psalmodia Evangelica, 1790.

ALTERNATIVE VERSION

Melody in the Tenor.

Fa-burden by GEOFFREY SHAW.

I. Watts, 1674–1748.

JESUS shall reign where'er the sun
    Does his successive journeys run;
His kingdom stretch from shore to shore
Till moons shall wax and wane no more.

2 People and realms of every tongue
    Dwell on his love with sweetest song,
    And infant voices shall proclaim
    Their early blessings on his name.

3 Blessings abound where'er he reigns;
    The prisoner leaps to lose his chains;
    The weary find eternal rest,
    And all the sons of want are blest.

4. Let every creature rise and bring
    Peculiar honours to our King;
    Angels descend with songs again,
    And earth repeat the long amen.

546

SWANWICK. (5 4. 5 4.)

Moderately slow. Voices in unison.

MARTIN SHAW, 1875-1958.

[*Copyright, 1931, by Martin Shaw.*]

Edith Williams.

JESUS, so lowly,
  Child of the earth;
Christen me wholly,
  Bring me new birth.

2 Jesus, so lonely,
    Weary and sad,
  Teach me that only
    Love maketh glad.

3 Jesus, so broken,
    Silent and pale:
  Be this the token
    Love will not fail.

4. Jesus, victorious,
    Mighty and free:
  Teach me how glorious
    Death is to be.

547

FIRST TUNE

KING'S NORTON. (C.M.)
Slow.

J. CLARK, 1670-1707.

WINDSOR. (C.M.)
Slow.

SECOND TUNE

Melody from *Este's Psalter*, 1592,
rhythm from the *Scottish Psalter*, 1615.

c. 12th cent. *Tr. E. Caswall* (1858).

Dulcis Jesu Memoria

JESU! the very thought of thee
  With sweetness fills my breast;
But sweeter far thy face to see
  And in thy presence rest.

2 Nor voice can sing, nor heart can frame,
  Nor can the memory find,
A sweeter sound than thy blest name,
  O saviour of mankind!

3 O hope of every contrite heart,
  O joy of all the meek,
To those who fall, how kind thou art,
  How good to those who seek!

4 But what to those who find? Ah! this
  Nor tongue nor pen can show;
The love of Jesus, what it is
  None but his loved ones know.

(654)

GENERAL

ALTERNATIVE VERSION

Trebles (*the other voices singing the melody* WINDSOR).

Descant by HAROLD E. DARKE.

[*Copyright, 1931, by Oxford University Press.*]

5 Jesus, our only joy be thou,
  As thou our prize wilt be;
Jesus, be thou our glory now,
  And through eternity.

PART II

6 O Jesus, King most wonderful,
  Thou conqueror renowned,
Thou sweetness most ineffable,
  In whom all joys are found:

7 When once thou visitest the heart,
  Then truth begins to shine;
Then earthly vanities depart;
  Then kindles love divine.

8 O Jesus, light of all below,
  Thou fount of life and fire,
Surpassing all the joys we know,
  And all we can desire:

9 May every heart confess thy name,
  And ever thee adore;
And, seeking thee, itself inflame
  To seek thee more and more.

10 Thee may our tongues for ever bless,
  Thee may we love alone;
And ever in our lives express
  The image of thine own.

PART III

11 O Jesus, thou the beauty art
  Of angel worlds above;
Thy name is music to the heart,
  Enchanting it with love.

12. Stay with us, Lord, and with thy light
  Illume the soul's abyss;
Scatter the darkness of our night,
  And fill the world with bliss.

548

THE ROSY SEQUENCE. (L.M.)

In speaking rhythm.　　　　　　　　　　*Sarum Gradual*, 1527, 1528, and 1532.

1. Je - su! the ve - ry thought is sweet! In that dear name all heart-joys meet;

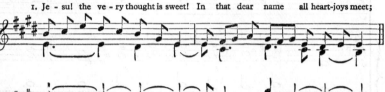

But sweet-er than the hon - ey far The glimp - ses of . . his pres-ence are.

2. No word is sung more sweet than this: No name is heard more full of bliss:

No thought brings sweeter com-fort nigh, Than Je - sus, Son of God most high.

548 (continued)

No let - ters write its bless - ed - ness: A - lone who hath thee
in his heart Knows, love of Je - sus, what thou art.

6. I seek for Je - sus in re - pose, When round my heart the sha-dows close;
7. As Ma - ry in the morn-ing gloom Sought out her Mas - ter at the tomb,

A-broad, and when I shut the door, I long for Je - sus . . . ev-er-more.
So now, with love's most earnest cry, I seek with heart . and . . . not with eye.

8. Je - sus, to God the Fa-ther gone, Is seat - ed on the heavenly throne;
9. We fol - low Je - sus now, and raise The voice of prayer, the hymn of praise,

My heart hath al-so passed from me, That where he is . . . there it may be.
That he at last may make us meet With him to gain . . the heaven-ly seat.

The Rosy Sequence. (*Sarum Gradual,* 1527.) *Cento from* Dulcis Jesu Memoria (547).
Tr. J. M. Neale‡ (1854).

JESU! the very thought is sweet!
In that dear name all heart-joys meet;
But sweeter than the honey far
The glimpses of his presence are.

2 No word is sung more sweet than this:
No name is heard more full of bliss:
No thought brings sweeter comfort nigh,
Than Jesus, Son of God most high.

3 Jesus, the hope of souls forlorn,
How good to them for sin that mourn;
To them that seek thee, O how kind;
But what art thou to them that find?

4 Jesus, thou sweetness, pure and blest,
Truth's fountain, light of souls distrest,
Surpassing all that heart requires,
Exceeding all that soul desires!

5 No tongue of mortal can express,
No letters write its blessedness:
Alone who hath thee in his heart
Knows, love of Jesus, what thou art.

6 I seek for Jesus in repose,
Where round my heart the shadows close;
Abroad, and when I shut the door,
I long for Jesus evermore.

7 As Mary in the morning gloom
Sought out her Master at the tomb,
So now, with love's most earnest cry,
I seek with heart and not with eye.

8 Jesus, to God the Father gone,
Is seated on the heavenly throne;
My heart hath also passed from me,
That where he is there it may be.

9. We follow Jesus now, and raise
The voice of prayer, the hymn of praise,
That he at last may make us meet
With him to gain the heavenly seat.

(659)

549

FIRST TUNE

PLAINSONG. (L.M.)
In free rhythm.

Melody from *Sarum Antiphonal.*

[*Copyright, 1931, by Oxford University Press.*]

SECOND TUNE

DULCIS JESU MEMORIA. (L.M.)
In moderate time.

Proper Melody from *Cöln Gesangbuch*, 1619.

GENERAL

Cento from Dulcis Jesu Memoria (547). *Pr. Ray Palmer* (1859).

JESUS, thou joy of loving hearts,
　　Thou fount of life, thou light of men,
From the best bliss that earth imparts
　　We turn unfilled to thee again.

2 Thy truth unchanged hath ever stood;
　　Thou savest those that on thee call:
To them that seek thee thou art good,
　　To them that find thee, all in all.

3 We taste thee, O thou living bread,
　　And long to feast upon thee still;
We drink of thee, the fountain-head,
　　And thirst our souls from thee to fill.

4 Our restless spirits yearn for thee,
　　Where'er our changeful lot is cast,
Glad when thy gracious smile we see,
　　Blest when our faith can hold thee fast.

5. O Jesus, ever with us stay:
　　Make all our moments calm and bright;
Chase the dark night of sin away;
　　Shed o'er the world thy holy light.

550

OSBORNE.　(C.M.)

In moderate time.

HENRY CAREY, 1692 ?–1743 (slightly adapted).

Ray Palmer, 1808–87.

JESUS, these eyes have never seen
　　That radiant form of thine;
The veil of sense hangs dark between
　　Thy blessèd face and mine.

2 I see thee not, I hear thee not,
　　Yet art thou oft with me;
And earth hath ne'er so dear a spot
　　As where I meet with thee.

3 Yet, though I have not seen, and still
　　Must rest in faith alone,
I love thee, dearest Lord, and will,
　　Unseen, but not unknown.

4. When death these mortal eyes shall seal
　　And still this throbbing heart,
The rending veil shall thee reveal
　　All glorious as thou art.

(661)

551

SIMEON. (L.M.)
Moderately slow.

S. STANLEY, 1767–1822.

W. Cowper, 1731–1800.

JESUS, where'er thy people meet,
  There they behold thy mercy-seat;
Where'er they seek thee, thou art found,
And every place is hallowed ground.

2 For thou, within no walls confined,
  Inhabitest the humble mind;
  Such ever bring thee where they come,
  And, going, take thee to their home.

3 Dear shepherd of thy chosen few,
  Thy former mercies here renew;
  Here to our waiting hearts proclaim
  The sweetness of thy saving name.

4 Here may we prove the power of prayer,
  To strengthen faith and sweeten care;
  To teach our faint desires to rise,
  And bring all heaven before our eyes.

5. Lord, we are few, but thou art near;
  Nor short thine arm, nor deaf thine ear;
  O rend the heavens, come quickly down,
  And make a thousand hearts thine own!

552

RHUDDLAN. (8 7. 8 7. 8 7.)
Moderately slow.

Welsh Traditional Melody.

Commonwealth.

Henry Scott Holland, 1847–1918.

JUDGE eternal, throned in splendour,
  Lord of lords and King of kings,
With thy living fire of judgment
  Purge this realm of bitter things:
Solace all its wide dominion
  With the healing of thy wings.

2 Still the weary folk are pining
    For the hour that brings release,
  And the city's crowded clangour
    Cries aloud for sin to cease,
  And the homesteads and the woodlands
    Plead in silence for their peace.

3. Crown, O God, thine own endeavour;
    Cleave our darkness with thy sword;
  Feed the faint and hungry heathen
    With the richness of thy word;
  Cleanse the body of this empire
    Through the glory of the Lord.

(663)

553

GWALCHMAI. (7 4. 7 4. D.)
In moderate time.

J. D. JONES, 1827–70.

Praise.

George Herbert, 1593–1633.

KING of glory, King of peace,
    I will love thee;
And that love may never cease,
    I will move thee.
Thou hast granted my request,
    Thou hast heard me;
Thou didst note my working breast,
    Thou hast spared me.

2 Wherefore with my utmost art
    I will sing thee,
And the cream of all my heart
    I will bring thee.
Though my sins against me cried,
    Thou didst clear me;
And alone, when they replied,
    Thou didst hear me.

3. Seven whole days, not one in seven,
    I will praise thee;
In my heart, though not in heaven,
    I can raise thee.
Small it is, in this poor sort
    To enrol thee:
E'en eternity's too short
    To extol thee.

(664)

554

ALBERTA. (10 4. 10 4. 10 10.)
In moderate time. Unison.

WILLIAM H. HARRIS.

J. H. Newman, 1801-90.

LEAD, kindly Light, amid the encircling gloom,
  Lead thou me on;
The night is dark, and I am far from home,
  Lead thou me on.
Keep thou my feet; I do not ask to see
The distant scene; one step enough for me.

2 I was not ever thus, nor prayed that thou
  Should'st lead me on;
I loved to choose and see my path; but now
  Lead thou me on.
I loved the garish day, and, spite of fears,
Pride ruled my will: remember not past years.

3. So long thy power hath blest me, sure it still
  Will lead me on
O'er moor and fen, o'er crag and torrent, till
  The night is gone,
And with the morn those angel faces smile,
Which I have loved long since, and lost awhile.

(665)

554 (*continued*)

SECOND TUNE

LUX BENIGNA. (10 4. 10 4. 10 10.)

Slow.

J. B. DYKES, 1823–76.

(*Another tune to this hymn will be found in the Appendix.*)

J. H. Newman, 1801–90.

LEAD, kindly Light, amid the encircling gloom,
　　　Lead thou me on;
The night is dark, and I am far from home,
　　　Lead thou me on.
Keep thou my feet; I do not ask to see
The distant scene; one step enough for me.

2 I was not ever thus, nor prayed that thou
　　　Should'st lead me on;
I loved to choose and see my path; but now
　　　Lead thou me on.
I loved the garish day, and, spite of fears,
Pride ruled my will: remember not past years.

3. So long thy power hath blest me, sure it still
　　　Will lead me on
O'er moor and fen, o'er crag and torrent, till
　　　The night is gone,
And with the morn those angel faces smile,
Which I have loved long since, and lost awhile.

(666)

555

LEWES. (8 7. 8 7. 8 7.)
In moderate time.

J. RANDALL, 1715–99.

J. Edmeston, 1791–1867.

LEAD us, heavenly Father, lead us
　O'er the world's tempestuous sea;
Guard us, guide us, keep us, feed us,
　For we have no help but thee;
Yet possessing every blessing
　If our God our Father be.

2 Saviour, breathe forgiveness o'er us;
　　All our weakness thou dost know,
Thou didst tread this earth before us,
　　Thou didst feel its keenest woe;
Lone and dreary, faint and weary,
　　Through the desert thou didst go.

3. Spirit of our God, descending,
　　Fill our hearts with heavenly joy,
Love with every passion blending,
　　Pleasure that can never cloy:
Thus provided, pardoned, guided,
　　Nothing can our peace destroy.

(667)

555 *(continued)*

SECOND TUNE

MANNHEIM. (8 7. 8 7. 8 7.)
Moderately slow.

Altered from Chorale by F. FILITZ, 1804–76.

J. Edmeston, 1791–1867.

LEAD us, heavenly Father, lead us
　　O'er the world's tempestuous sea;
Guard us, guide us, keep us, feed us,
　　For we have no help but thee;
Yet possessing every blessing
　　If our God our Father be.

2 Saviour, breathe forgiveness o'er us;
　　All our weakness thou dost know,
Thou didst tread this earth before us,
　　Thou didst feel its keenest woe;
Lone and dreary, faint and weary,
　　Through the desert thou didst go.

3. Spirit of our God, descending,
　　Fill our hearts with heavenly joy,
Love with every passion blending,
　　Pleasure that can never cloy:
Thus provided, pardoned, guided,
　　Nothing can our peace destroy.

HIGH ROAD. (10 4. 6 6. 6 6. 10 4.)

Moderately fast.

MARTIN SHAW, 1875–1958.

[Copyright, 1915, by J. Curwen & Sons, Ltd.]
(If desired, the 1st verse can be repeated after the 2nd.)

Antiphon.

George Herbert, 1593–1633.

LET all the world in every corner sing,
 My God and King!
  The heavens are not too high,
  His praise may thither fly;
  The earth is not too low,
  His praises there may grow.
Let all the world in every corner sing,
 My God and King!

2. Let all the world in every corner sing,
 My God and King!
  The Church with psalms must shout,
  No door can keep them out;
  But, above all, the heart
  Must bear the longest part.
Let all the world in every corner sing,
 My God and King!

(669)

557

DUNDEE (or FRENCH). (C.M.)
Moderately slow. Scottish Psalter, 1615, as given in *Ravenscroft's Psalter,*

C. Wesley, 1707–88, *and others.*

LET saints on earth in concert sing
With those whose work is done;
For all the servants of our King
In earth and heaven are one.

2 One family, we dwell in him,
One Church, above, beneath;
Though now divided by the stream,
The narrow stream of death.

3 One army of the living God,
To his command we bow;
Part of his host hath crossed the flood,
And part is crossing now.

4 E'en now to their eternal home
There pass some spirits blest,
While others to the margin come,
Waiting their call to rest.

5. Jesus, be thou our constant guide;
Then, when the word is given,
Bid Jordan's narrow stream divide,
And bring us safe to heaven.

GENERAL

(This version may be used in connexion with the other for one or more verses, the people singing the melody as usual.)

558

SALZBURG. (7 7. 7 7. D.)

Melody from J. HINTZE, 1622–1702.
Harmony from J. S. BACH, 1685–1750.

Moderately slow, dignified.

[This hymn may also be sung to IVES, 306.]

Stopford A. Brooke, 1832–1916.

LET the whole creation cry,
'Glory to the Lord on high!'
Heaven and earth, awake and sing,
'God is good and therefore King.'
Praise him, all ye hosts above,
Ever bright and fair in love;
Sun and moon, uplift your voice,
Night and stars, in God rejoice!

(672)

GENERAL

Melody in the Tenor.

Fa-burden by GEOFFREY SHAW.

2 Warriors fighting for the Lord,
  Prophets burning with his word,
  Those to whom the arts belong,
  Add their voices to the song.
  Kings of knowledge and of law,
  To the glorious circle draw;
  All who work and all who wait,
  Sing, 'The Lord is good and great!'

3. Men and women, young and old,
  Raise the anthem manifold,
  And let children's happy hearts
  In this worship bear their parts;
  From the north to southern pole
  Let the mighty chorus roll:
  Holy, holy, holy One,
  Glory be to God alone!

559

KEINE SCHÖNHEIT HAT DIE WELT. (7 7. 7 7.)

In moderate time.

SCHEFFLER'S *Seelenlust*, 1657.

The Spirit.

S. *Johnson*, 1822–82.

LIFE of ages, richly poured,
   Love of God, unspent and free,
Flowing in the prophet's word
   And the people's liberty!

2 Never was to chosen race
   That unstinted tide confined:
Thine are every time and place,
   Fountain sweet of heart and mind;

3 Breathing in the thinker's creed,
   Pulsing in the hero's blood,
Nerving noblest thought and deed,
   Freshening time with truth and good;

4 Consecrating art and song,
   Holy book and pilgrim way,
Quelling strife and tyrant wrong,
   Widening freedom's sacred sway.

5. Life of ages, richly poured,
   Love of God, unspent and free,
Flowing in the prophet's word
   And the people's liberty!

560

FFIGYSBREN. (10 10. 10 10.)

In moderate time.

Welsh Hymn Melody.

[This hymn may also be sung to FARLEY CASTLE, 22.]

H. Montagu Butler, 1833–1918.

'LIFT up your hearts!' We lift them, Lord, to thee;
Here at thy feet none other may we see:
'Lift up your hearts!' E'en so, with one accord,
We lift them up, we lift them to the Lord.

2 Above the level of the former years,
The mire of sin, the slough of guilty fears,
The mist of doubt, the blight of love's decay,
O Lord of Light, lift all our hearts to-day!

3*Above the swamps of subterfuge and shame,
The deeds, the thoughts, that honour may not name,
The halting tongue that dares not tell the whole,
O Lord of Truth, lift every Christian soul!

4 Lift every gift that thou thyself hast given;
Low lies the best till lifted up to heaven:
Low lie the bounding heart, the teeming brain,
Till, sent from God, they mount to God again.

5. Then, as the trumpet-call in after years,
'Lift up your hearts!', rings pealing in our ears,
Still shall those hearts respond with full accord,
'We lift them up, we lift them to the Lord!'

(**675**)

561

ALLEIN GOTT IN DER HÖH' SEI EHR'. (8 7. 8 7. 8 8 7.)

Slow and dignified. Adapted from an Easter Gloria, 1524 (later form of the melody).

Very broad.

P. Dearmer, 1867–1936.

LO, in the wilderness a voice
   'Make straight the way' is crying:
When men are turning from the light,
   And hope and love seem dying,
The prophet comes to make us clean:
'There standeth one you have not seen,
   Whose voice you are denying.'

2 God give us grace to hearken now
   To those who come to warn us,
Give sight and strength, that we may kill
   The vices that have torn us,
Lest love professed should disappear
In creeds of hate, contempt, and fear,
   That crash and overturn us.

3. When from the vineyard cruel men
   Cast out the heavenly powers
And Christendom denies its Lord,
   The world in ruin cowers.
Now come, O God, in thy great might!
Unchanged, unchanging is thy right,
   Unswayed thy justice towers.

562 WÄCHTERLIED. (8 7. 8 7. 8 8 7.)

Slow.

Adapted from a 16th-century German Melody.

[This hymn may also be sung to LUTHER'S HYMN, 672, *or* NUN FREUT EUCH, 640, *or* MIT FREUDEN ZART, 214.]

W. Russell Bowie.

LORD Christ, when first thou cam'st to men,
　　Upon a cross they bound thee,
And mocked thy saving kingship then
　　By thorns with which they crowned thee:
And still our wrongs may weave thee now
New thorns to pierce that steady brow,
　　And robe of sorrow round thee.

2 O aweful love, which found no room
　　In life where sin denied thee,
And, doomed to death, must bring to doom
　　The power which crucified thee,
Till not a stone was left on stone,
And all a nation's pride, o'erthrown,
　　Went down to dust beside thee!

3 New advent of the love of Christ,
　　Shall we again refuse thee,
Till in the night of hate and war
　　We perish as we lose thee?
From old unfaith our souls release
To seek the Kingdom of thy peace,
　　By which alone we choose thee.

4. O wounded hands of Jesus, build
　　In us thy new creation;
Our pride is dust, our vaunt is stilled,
　　We wait thy revelation:
O love that triumphs over loss,
We bring our hearts before thy cross,
　　To finish thy salvation.

(678)

563

DER TAG BRICHT AN. (L.M.)

Slow and solemn.

Melody probably by M. VULPIUS, *c.* 1560–1616 (?).

Ray Palmer,† 1808–87.

LORD, my weak thought in vain would climb
　　To search the starry vault profound;
In vain would wing her flight sublime,
　　To find creation's utmost bound.

2 But vainer yet that thought must prove
　　To search thy great eternal plan,
Thy sovran counsels, born of love
　　Long ages ere the world began.

3 When my dim reason would demand
　　Why that, or this, thou dost ordain,
By some vast deep I seem to stand,
　　Whose secrets I must ask in vain.

4 When doubts disturb my troubled breast,
　　And all is dark as night to me,
Here, as on solid rock, I rest—
　　That so it seemeth good to thee.

5. Be this my joy, that evermore
　　Thou rulest all things at thy will;
Thy sovran wisdom I adore,
　　And calmly, sweetly, trust thee still.

(679)

564

UFFINGHAM: (L.M.)

Slow.

J. CLARK, 1670-1707.

O. Wendell Holmes, 1809-94.

LORD of all being, throned afar,
Thy glory flames from sun and star;
Centre and soul of every sphere,
Yet to each loving heart how near!

2 Sun of our life, thy quickening ray
Sheds on our path the glow of day;
Star of our hope, thy softened light
Cheers the long watches of the night.

3 Our midnight is thy smile withdrawn,
Our noontide is thy gracious dawn,
Our rainbow arch thy mercy's sign;
All, save the clouds of sin, are thine.

4 Lord of all life, below, above,
Whose light is truth, whose warmth is love,
Before thy ever-blazing throne
We ask no lustre of our own.

5. Grant us thy truth to make us free,
And kindling hearts that burn for thee,
Till all thy living altars claim
One holy light, one heavenly flame.

(680)

565

SLANE. (10 11. 11 12.)

In moderate time.　　　　　　　　　　　　　　　Irish Traditional Melody.

All-Day Hymn.　　　　　　　　　　　　　　　*Jan Struther*, 1901–53.

LORD of all hopefulness, Lord of all joy,
　　Whose trust, ever child-like, no cares could destroy,
　Be there at our waking, and give us, we pray,
　Your bliss in our hearts, Lord, at the break of the day.

2 Lord of all eagerness, Lord of all faith,
　Whose strong hands were skilled at the plane and the lathe,
　Be there at our labours, and give us, we pray,
　Your strength in our hearts, Lord, at the noon of the day.

3 Lord of all kindliness, Lord of all grace,
　Your hands swift to welcome, your arms to embrace,
　Be there at our homing, and give us, we pray,
　Your love in our hearts, Lord, at the eve of the day.

4. Lord of all gentleness, Lord of all calm,
　Whose voice is contentment, whose presence is balm,
　Be there at our sleeping, and give us, we pray,
　Your peace in our hearts, Lord, at the end of the day.

(681)

566

VATER UNSER. (8 8. 8 8. 8 8.)
Very slow and solemn.

Later form of melody in V. SCHUMANN's *Gesangbuch*, 1539.
Harmony from J. S. BACH, 1685–1750.

G. W. *Briggs*, 1875–1959.

L ORD of all majesty and might,
Whose presence fills the unfathomed deep,
Wherein uncounted worlds of light
Through countless ages vigil keep;
Eternal God, can such as we,
Frail mortal men, know aught of thee?

2 Beyond all knowledge thou art wise,
With wisdom that transcends all thought:
Yet still we seek with straining eyes,
Yea, seek thee as our fathers sought;
Nor will we from the quest depart
Till we shall know thee as thou art.

(682)

GENERAL

ALTERNATIVE VERSION

Melody in the Tenor.   Fa-burden by SYDNEY H. NICHOLSON.

[*Copyright, 1931, by Oxford University Press.*]

3*Frail though our form, and brief our day,
  Our mind has bridged the gulf of years,
Our puny balances can weigh
  The magnitude of starry spheres:
    Within us is eternity;
    Whence comes it, Father, but from thee?

4 For, when thy wondrous works we scan,
  And Mind gives answer back to mind,
Thine image stands revealed in man;
  And, seeking, he shall surely find.
    Thy sons, our heritage we claim:
    Shall not thy children know thy name?

5. We know in part: enough we know
  To walk with thee, and walk aright;
And thou shalt guide us as we go,
  And lead us into fuller light,
    Till, when we stand before thy throne,
    We know at last as we are known.

(683)

567

IL BUON PASTOR. (8 7. 8 7 7.)
Moderately fast. Unison.

Adapted from a melody in *Canzuns Spirituaelas*
(Upper Engadine), 1765.

B. R.

LORD of health, thou life within us,
  Strength of all that lives and grows,
Love that meets our hearts to win us,
  Beauty that around us glows,
  Take the praise that brims and flows!

2 Praise for all our work and leisure,
  Mirth and games and jollity,
Study, science, all the treasure
  That is stored by memory,
  Skill of mind and hand and eye;

3 Praise for joys, for sorrows even,
  All that leads us up to thee;
Most of all that out from heaven
  Came thy Son to set us free,
  Came to show us what to be.

4. May our work be keen and willing;
  Make us true to thee and wise;
Help us now, each moment filling,
  Skill and service be our prize,
  Till to thy far hills we rise.

568

RISBY. (8 8. 8 8. 8 6.)

In moderate time. May be sung in unison.

J. B. ROOPER.

[*Copyright, 1925, by Oxford University Press.*]

Donald Hankey, 1884–1916.

LORD of the strong, when earth you trod,
You calmly faced the angry sea,
The fierce unmasked hypocrisy,
 The traitor's kiss, the rabble's hiss,
The aweful death upon the tree:
  All glory be to God.

2 Lord of the weak, when earth you trod,
Oppressors writhed beneath your scorn;
The weak, despised, depraved, forlorn,
 You taught to hope and know the scope
Of love divine for all who mourn:
  All glory be to God.

3 Lord of the rich, when earth you trod,
To Mammon's power you never bowed,
But taught how men with wealth endowed
 In meekness' school might learn to rule
The demon that enslaves the proud:
  All glory be to God.

4 Lord of the poor, when earth you trod,
The lot you chose was hard and poor;
You taught us hardness to endure,
 And so to gain through hurt and pain
The wealth that lasts for evermore:
  All glory be to God.

5.* Lord of us all, when earth you trod,
The life you led was perfect, free,
Defiant of all tyranny:
 Now give us grace that we may face
Our foes with like temerity,
  And glory give to God.

569

NEED. (8 8. 8 8. 8 10.)

Moderately slow.

HARRY FARJEON, 1878–1948.

[*Copyright, 1931, by Oxford University Press.*]

Need.   *Eleanor Farjeon.*

LORD, thou who gav'st me all I have,
  My mind's delight, my body's
      power,
All that in coming to the grave
  I must let fall like summer's flower,
One thing thou didst to me accord,
I still may keep: my need of thee, O Lord.

2 Thou didst that everlasting gift
  Upon my cradled sleep bestow,
That I in life might never lift
  My head, might nothing do or know
Which in itself could perfect be,
Unless, O Lord, I turned my face to thee.

3 No joy wherein thou hast no part,
  Nor love but thou the soul of it,
Nor grief that shuts thee from its heart,
  Nor suffering that can thee omit.
From these if thou be absent, I
To heaven in my need of thee must cry.

4. So, even from my final sleep
  When I awake, the single thing
Which I among thy gifts may keep
  Shall carry me upon its wing
Into thy presence, where thy word
At last shall fill my need of thee,
  O Lord.

(686)

570

RAVENSHAW. (6 6. 6 6.)

Moderately slow.

Melody abridged by W. H. Monk, 1823–89, from *Ave Hierarchia* (M. Weisse, 1480–1534).

ALTERNATIVE VERSION

Melody in Tenor or Alto.

Fa-burden by E. T. Cook.

Alternative for last verse, alto singing last note G.

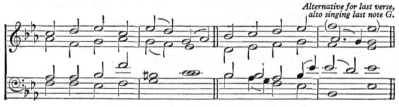

[*Copyright*, 1931, *by Oxford University Press.*]

Sir H. W. Baker,† 1821–77.

L ORD, thy word abideth,
And our footsteps guideth;
Who its truth believeth
Light and joy receiveth.

2 When our foes are near us,
Then thy word doth cheer us,
Word of consolation,
Message of salvation.

3 When the storms are o'er us
And dark clouds before us,
Then its light directeth
And our way protecteth.

4 Who can tell the pleasure,
Who recount the treasure,
By thy word imparted
To the simple-hearted?

5 Word of mercy, giving
Succour to the living;
Word of life, supplying
Comfort to the dying.

6. O that we, discerning
Its most holy learning,
Lord, may love and hear thee,
Evermore be near thee!

571

ST. VENANTIUS. (L.M.)
In moderate time. Unison.

Rouen Church Melody.

Sidney Godolphin, 1610–43. Cento. Percy Dearmer, 1867–1936.

LORD, when the wise men came from far,
 Led to thy cradle by a star,
Shepherds with humble fearfulness
Walked safely, though their light was less.

2 Wise men in tracing Nature's laws
Ascend unto the highest cause:
Though wise men better know the way,
It seems no honest heart can stray.

3 And since no creature comprehends
The Cause of causes, End of ends,
He who himself vouchsafes to know
Best pleases his Creator so.

4. There is no merit in the wise
But love, the shepherds' sacrifice:
Wise men, all ways of knowledge past,
To the shepherds' wonder came at last.

572

ST. MARTIN. (10 4. 10 4.)

In moderate time.

G. W. BRIGGS, 1875–1959.

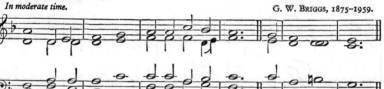

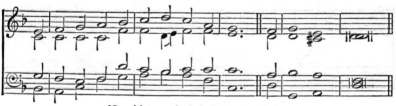

[*Copyright, 1931, by Oxford University Press.*]

G. W. Briggs, 1875–1959.

LORD, who thyself hast bidden us to pray
  For daily bread,
We ask thee but for grace and strength this day
  Our path to tread.

2 Not for to-morrow, its uncharted road,
  Shall be our prayer;
Sufficient for each day our daily load,
  Thy daily care.

3 Thine is the burden of the coming years;
  Their weal or woe,
Their joys and griefs, their laughter and their tears
  We would not know.

4 We could not bear to hear complete the tale,
  If it were told;
Enough to know thy mercies cannot fail,
  Nor love grow cold.

5. So day by day thy never-failing love
  Our soul shall stay;
So let us be content thy love to prove,
  Each passing day.

573

MORIAH. (8 7. 8 7. D.)
Moderately slow.

Welsh Hymn Melody.

C. Wesley, 1707–88.

LOVE divine, all loves excelling,
  Joy of heaven, to earth come down,
Fix in us thy humble dwelling,
  All thy faithful mercies crown.
Jesus, thou art all compassion,
  Pure unbounded love thou art;
Visit us with thy salvation,
  Enter every trembling heart.

2 Come, almighty to deliver,
  Let us all thy life receive;
Suddenly return, and never,
  Never more thy temples leave.
Thee we would be always blessing,
  Serve thee as thy hosts above,
Pray, and praise thee, without ceasing,
  Glory in thy perfect love.

SECOND TUNE

EXILE.　(8 7. 8 7. D.)
Moderately slow.

English Traditional Melody.

[*Copyright, 1931, by Martin Shaw.*]

3. Finish then thy new creation:
　　Pure and spotless let us be;
　Let us see thy great salvation,
　　Perfectly restored in thee,
　Changed from glory into glory,
　　Till in heaven we take our place,
　Till we cast our crowns before thee,
　　Lost in wonder, love, and praise.

574

SONG 22. (10 10. 10 10.)

In moderate time.

O. GIBBONS, 1583–1625.

The Holy Spirit. R. Bridges, 1844–1930. *Based on* Amor Patris et Filii, *12th cent.*

LOVE of the Father, Love of God the Son,
From whom all came, in whom was all begun;
Who formest heavenly beauty out of strife,
Creation's whole desire and breath of life:

2 Thou the all-holy, thou supreme in might,
Thou dost give peace, thy presence maketh right;
Thou with thy favour all things dost enfold,
With thine all-kindness free from harm wilt hold.

3*Hope of all comfort, splendour of all aid,
That dost not fail nor leave the heart afraid:
To all that cry thou dost all help accord,
The angels' armour, and the saints' reward.

4*Purest and highest, wisest and most just,
There is no truth save only in thy trust;
Thou dost the mind from earthly dreams recall,
And bring, through Christ, to him for whom are all.

5. Eternal glory, all men thee adore,
Who art and shalt be worshipped evermore:
Us whom thou madest, comfort with thy might,
And lead us to enjoy thy heavenly light.

575

BLACKBOURNE. (C.M.)

In moderate time.

Harrison's Sacred Harmony, 1784.

[This hymn may also be sung to RELIEF, 614.]

F. L. Hosmer, 1840–1929.

MADE lowly wise, we pray no more
 For miracle and sign:
Anoint our eyes to see within
 The common, the divine!

2 'Lo here, lo there,' no more we cry,
 Dividing with our call
The mantle of thy presence, Lord,
 That seamless covers all.

3 We turn from seeking thee afar
 And in unwonted ways,
To build from out our daily lives
 The temples of thy praise.

4 And if thy casual comings, Lord,
 To hearts of old were dear,
What joy should dwell within the faith
 That feels thee ever near!

5. And nobler yet shall duty grow,
 And more shall worship be,
When thou art found in all our life,
 And all our life in thee.

576

ZACHARY. (S.M.)

In moderate time.

English form of French (?) Melody.

[This hymn may also be sung to OLD 25TH, 195.]

George Matheson, 1842–1906.

MAKE me a captive, Lord,
 And then I shall be free;
Force me to render up my sword,
 And I shall conqueror be.

2 I sink in life's alarms
 When by myself I stand;
Imprison me within thine arms,
 And strong shall be my hand.

3 My heart is weak and poor
 Until it master find:
It has no spring of action sure,
 It varies with the wind:

4 It cannot freely move
 Till thou hast wrought its chain;
Enslave it with thy matchless love,
 And deathless it shall reign.

5 My will is not my own
 Till thou hast made it thine;
If it would reach a monarch's throne
 It must its crown resign;

6. It only stands unbent
 Amid the clashing strife,
When on thy bosom it has leant
 And found in thee its life.

(694)

577

NORWICH. (C.M.)

In moderate time.

Ravenscroft's Psalter, 1621.

[This hymn may also be sung to St. Flavian, 188.]

S. P.

MERCY thou art, Creator, Friend!
　O make me brave within,
Unselfish, wise, compassionate,
　Gentle when others sin.

2 Teach me who bear the name of Christ
　The truth to seek and hold;
From sect and party keep me free,
　From judgment overbold.

3 To all perversion close my ears;
　Keep me from love of gain;
The Pharisee within me curb,
　The Christ in me sustain.

4 Dark thoughts and cruel fade away
　Before thy beauty, Friend;
Unwise and bitter words and deeds,
　And baseness, come to end.

5 When I in others evil find,
　The evil 's here, not there;
And when myself I rightly judge,
　All other things seem fair.

6. My fault the bitterness within,
　The sweetness is of thee:
Thou art the perfect one, O God—
　Would I might perfect be!

(695)

578

BATTLE SONG. (Irregular.)

With life.

MARTIN SHAW, 1875–1958.

Voices in unison. 1. Mine

eyes have seen the glo - ry of the com - ing of the Lord; He is
seen him in the watch-fires of a hun - dred cir - cling camps; They have
read a fie - ry gos - pel, writ in bur-nished rows of steel: 'As ye
sound - ed forth the trum - pet that shall nev - er call re - treat; He is
beau - ty of the li - lies Christ was born a-cross the sea, With a
com - ing like the glo - ry of the morn - ing on the wave; He is

tramp - ling out the vin - tage where the grapes of wrath are stored; He hath
build - ed him an al - tar in the eve - ning dews and damps; I have
deal with my con - tem - ners, so with you my grace shall deal; Let the
sift - ing out the hearts of men be - fore his judg - ment - seat; O be
glo - ry in his bo - som that trans - fi - gures you and me; As he
wis - dom to the migh - ty, he is suc - cour to the brave; So the

loosed the fate - ful light-ning of his ter - ri - ble swift sword: His
read his right-eous sen - tence by the dim and flar - ing lamps: His
He - ro born of wo - man crush the ser - pent with his heel, Since
swift, my soul, to an - swer him; be ju - bi - lant, my feet! Our
died to make men ho - ly, let us die to make men free, While
world shall be his foot-stool, and the soul of time his slave: Our

Truth . . . . . . is march - ing on. . . . . . .
Day . . . . is march - ing on. . . . . . .
God . . . . is march - ing on. . . . . . .
God . . . . is march - ing on. . . . . . .
God . . . . is march - ing on. . . . . . .
God . . . . is march - ing on. . . . . . .

1st time. | *Last time.*

2.*I have
3.*I have
4. He has
5. In the
6. He is

[*By permission of J. Curwen & Sons, Ltd.*]

The Battle Song.   *Mrs. Julia Ward Howe, 1819–1910.*

(697)

579 FOUNTAINS ABBEY. (8 4. 8 4. 10 10.)

Quietly.

GORDON SLATER.

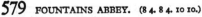

[Copyright, 1931, by Oxford University Press.]

Rest.

Eleanor Farjeon.

MORE lovely than the noonday rest
In summer heat,
When the warm earth gives every guest
A welcome sweet,
Is that content by which I am possessed
When I am laid at my Creator's feet.

2 More wonderful than rest at night,
When heaven charms
Slumber with spells whose starry light
Allays alarms,

Is that repose which covers sense and sight
When I am held in my Creator's arms.

3. More perfect than the ease can be
When old ones rest,
Or than the sleep of infancy
Before life's test,
Is that last breath of peace which falls
on me
When I am cast on my Creator's
breast.

580 DENBIGH. (6 6 4. 6 6 6. 4.)

In moderate time.

Welsh Hymn Melody.

Ray Palmer, 1808–87.

MY faith looks up to thee,
  Thou Lamb of Calvary,
  Saviour divine!
Now hear me while I pray,
Take all my guilt away,
O let me from this day
  Be wholly thine.

2 May thy rich grace impart
  Strength to my fainting heart,
  My zeal inspire;
As thou hast died for me,
O may my love to thee
Pure, warm, and changeless be,
  A living fire.

3 While life's dark maze I tread,
  And griefs around me spread,
  Be thou my guide;
Bid darkness turn to day,
Wipe sorrow's tears away,
Nor let me ever stray
  From thee aside.

4. When ends life's transient dream,
  When death's cold sullen stream
  Shall o'er me roll,
Blest Saviour, then in love
Fear and distrust remove;
O bear me safe above,
  A ransomed soul.

581 WESTMINSTER. (C.M.)
In moderate time.

J. TURLE, 1802–82.

F. W. Faber,‡ 1814–63.

MY God, how wonderful thou art,
  Thy majesty how bright,
How beautiful thy mercy-seat,
  In depths of burning light!

2 How dread are thine eternal years,
  O everlasting Lord,
By shining spirits day and night
  Incessantly adored!

3 Yet I may love thee too, O Lord,
  Almighty as thou art,

For thou hast stooped to ask of me
  The love of my poor heart.

4 No earthly father loves like thee,
  No mother, e'er so mild,
Bears and forbears as thou hast done
  With me thy wilful child.

5. How wonderful, how beautiful,
  The sight of thee must be,
Thine endless wisdom, boundless power,
  And aweful purity!

(699)

582

SEVERN. (8 4. 8 4. 8 4.)

Moderately fast. Unison.

HERBERT HOWELLS.

1. My God,   I thank thee who hast made The earth so bright; So full   of splen - dour and of joy, ; ; ; Beau - ty and light; So ma - ny glo - rious things   are here, ; ; ; No - ble and right.

2. I thank   thee, too, that thou hast made Joy to a - bound; So ma - - - ny gen - tle thoughts and deeds . . . Cir - cling us round, That on the dark - est spot on earth Some love ; ; is found.

3. I thank   thee, Lord, that here our souls, Though am - ply blest, Can ne - - - ver find, al - though they seek, . . A per - fect rest; Nor ev - er shall, un - til they reach The last ; ; and best.

A. A. Procter,‡ 1825–64.

(700)

583

MEYER (ES IST KEIN TAG). (8 8. 8 4.)

Moderately slow.   Melody in J. MEYER'S *Seelenfreud*, 1692.

Frederick Mann, 1846–1928.

MY God, my Father, make me strong,
When tasks of life seem hard and long,
To greet them with this triumph song:
    Thy will be done.

2 Draw from my timid eyes the veil,
To show, where earthly forces fail,
Thy power and love must still prevail,
    Thy will be done.

3 With confident and humble mind,
Freedom in service I would find,
Praying through every toil assigned,
    Thy will be done.

4 Things deemed impossible I dare,
Thine is the call and thine the care,
Thy wisdom shall the way prepare,
    Thy will be done.

5 All power is here and round me now,
Faithful I stand in rule and vow,
While 'tis not I, but ever thou:
    Thy will be done.

6. Heaven's music chimes the glad days in,
Hope soars beyond death, pain, and sin,
Faith shouts in triumph, Love must win,
    Thy will be done.

584

SONG 20.   (S.M.)
In moderate time.

O. GIBBONS, 1583-1625.

R. *Bridges*, 1844-1930, *based on* I. *Watts*, 1674-1748.

MY Lord, my Life, my Love,
    To thee, to thee I call;
I cannot live if thou remove:
    Thou art my joy, my all.

2 My only sun to cheer
    The darkness where I dwell;
The best and only true delight
    My song hath found to tell.

3 To thee in very heaven
    The angels owe their bliss;
To thee the saints, whom thou hast called
    Where perfect pleasure is.

4 And how shall man, thy child,
    Without thee happy be,
Who hath no comfort nor desire
    In all the world but thee?

5. Return, my Love, my Life,
    Thy grace hath won my heart;
If thou forgive, if thou return,
    I will no more depart.

585

CHRISTUS DER IST MEIN LEBEN. (7 6. 7 6.) Melody by MELCHIOR VULPIUS, c. 1560–1616.
Adapted and harmonized by J. S. BACH, 1685–1750.

v. 1. My soul, there is a coun - try : Far be - yond the stars,
v. 3. He is thy gra - cious friend, And— O my soul, a - wake!—

Where stands a wing - ed sen - try All
Did in pure love de - scend, . . . To

v. 2. There a - bove noise, and dan - ger, Sweet peace sits crown'd with smiles,

Henry Vaughan the Silurist, 1622–95.

MY soul, there is a country
Far beyond the stars,
Where stands a wingèd sentry
All skilful in the wars:

2 There above noise, and danger,
Sweet peace sits crowned with smiles,
And one born in a manger
Commands the beauteous files.

3 He is thy gracious friend,
And—O my soul, awake!—
Did in pure love descend,
To die here for thy sake.

4 If thou canst get but thither,
There grows the flower of peace,
The Rose that cannot wither,
Thy fortress and thy ease.

5. Leave then thy foolish ranges,
For none can thee secure
But one, who never changes,
Thy God, thy life, thy cure.

(703)

586

ROTHWELL. (6 4. 6 4. 6 6 4.)　　　FIRST TUNE

In moderate time.　　　　　　　　　GEOFFREY SHAW, 1879–1943.

[Copyright, 1915, by J. Curwen & Sons, Ltd.]

LIVERPOOL. (6 4. 6 4. 6 6 4.)　　SECOND TUNE

Moderately slow.　　　　　　　　IEUAN GWYLLT, 1822–77.

THIRD TUNE

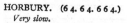

HORBURY. (6 4. 6 4. 6 6 4.)

Very slow.

J. B. DYKES, 1823–76.

Mrs. Sarah F. Adams, 1805–48.

NEARER, my God, to thee,
      Nearer to thee!
E'en though it be a cross
      That raiseth me,
Still all my song would be,
'Nearer, my God, to thee,
      Nearer to thee!'

2 Though, like the wanderer,
      The sun gone down,
Darkness be over me,
      My rest a stone;
Yet in my dreams I'd be
Nearer, my God, to thee,
      Nearer to thee.

3 There let the way appear
      Steps unto heaven;
All that thou send'st to me
      In mercy given,
Angels to beckon me
Nearer, my God, to thee,
      Nearer to thee.

4*Then, with my waking thoughts
      Bright with thy praise,
Out of my stony griefs
      Beth-el I'll raise;
So by my woes to be
Nearer, my God, to thee,
      Nearer to thee.

5.*Or if on joyful wing
      Cleaving the sky,
Sun, moon, and stars forgot,
      Upwards I fly,
Still all my song shall be,
'Nearer, my God, to thee,
      Nearer to thee!'

A a

587 WEATHER-BEATEN SAIL. (13. 13. 15. 13.)

T. CAMPIAN, 1567–1620.
(Harmony slightly adapted.)

In moderate time.

O come quick-ly,

O come quick-ly, O come quick-ly,

T. Campian, 1567–1620.

NEVER weather-beaten sail more willing bent to shore,
Never tired pilgrim's limbs affected slumber more,
Than my wearied sprite now longs to fly out of my troubled breast.
O come quickly, sweetest Lord, and take my soul to rest.

2. Ever blooming are the joys of heaven's high paradise,
Cold age deafs not there our ears, nor vapour dims our eyes;
Glory there the sun outshines, whose beams the blessèd only see;
O come quickly, glorious Lord, and raise my sprite to thee.

588 GLYNTHORPE. (6 10. 6 10.)

In moderate time. Unison.

GEOFFREY SHAW, 1879–1943.

Faith. *Emily Brontë, 1818–48.*

NO coward soul is mine,
No trembler in the world's storm-
        troubled sphere:
    I see heaven's glories shine,
And faith shines equal, arming me from
        fear.

2 O God within my breast,
Almighty, ever-present Deity!
    Life—that in me has rest,
As I, undying Life, have power in thee!

3* Vain are the thousand creeds
That move men's hearts—unutterably
        vain,
    Worthless as withered weeds,
Or idlest froth amid the boundless main,

4* To waken doubt in one
Holding so fast by thine infinity;

So surely anchored on
The steadfast rock of immortality.

5   With wide-embracing love
Thy spirit animates eternal years,
    Pervades and broods above,
Changes, sustains, dissolves, creates,
        and rears.

6   Though earth and man were gone,
And suns and universes ceased to be,
    And thou were left alone,
Every existence would exist in thee.

7.   There is not room for death,
Nor atom that his might could render
        void:
    Thou—thou art Being and Breath,
And what thou art may never be
        destroyed.

589 WHITEHALL. (L.M.)
In moderate time. Melody by H. LAWES, 1596–1662.

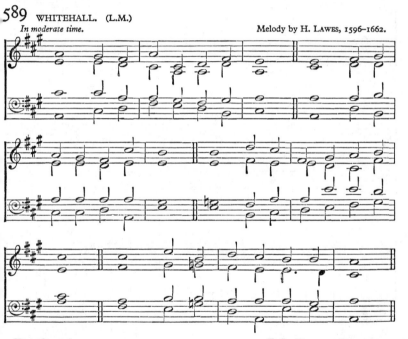

Transfiguration. *F. L. Hosmer, 1840–1929.*

NOT always on the mount may we
Rapt in the heavenly vision be;
The shores of thought and feeling know
The Spirit's tidal ebb and flow.

2 'Lord, it is good abiding here,'
We cry, the heavenly presence near:
The vision vanishes, our eyes
Are lifted into vacant skies.

3 Yet hath one such exalted hour
Upon the soul redeeming power,

And in its strength through after days
We travel our appointed ways;

4 Till all the lowly vale grows bright,
Transfigured in remembered light,
And in untiring souls we bear
The freshness of the upper air.

5. The mount for vision: but below
The paths of daily duty go,
And nobler life therein shall own
The pattern on the mountain shown.

590

BERRY DOWN. (11 6. 11 6. D.)

In moderate time.
Verses 1, 3, and 5 may be sung in unison.

ERNEST BULLOCK.

VOICES:

ORGAN.

Sir Edmund Gosse, 1849–1928.

NOT with a choir of angels without
  number,
  And noise of lutes and lyres,   [ber
But gently, with the woven veil of slum-
  Across thine aweful fires,
We yearn to watch thy face, serene and
  tender,
  Melt, smiling, calm and sweet,
Where round the print of thorns, in
  thornlike splendour,
  Transcendent glories meet.

2 We have no hopes if thou art close be-
  side us,
  And no profane despairs,
Since all we need is thy great hand to
  guide us,
  Thy heart to take our cares;
For us is no to-day, to-night, to-morrow,
  No past time nor to be,
We have no joy but thee, there is no
  sorrow,
  No life to live but thee.

PART II

3 The cross, like pilgrim warriors, we follow,
    Led by our eastern star;
  The wild crane greets us, and the wandering swallow
    Bound southward for Shinar;
  All night that single star shines bright above us;
    We go with weary feet,
  But in the end we know are they who love us,
    Whose pure embrace is sweet.

4 Most sweet of all, when dark the way and moonless,
    To feel a touch, a breath,
  And know our weary spirits are not tuneless,
    Our unseen goal not death;
  To know that thou, in all thy old sweet fashion,
    Art near us to sustain!
  We praise thee, Lord, by all thy tears and passion,
    By all thy cross and pain.

5. For when this night of toil and tears is over,
    Across the hills of spice,
  Thyself wilt meet us, glowing like a lover
    Before love's paradise;
  There are the saints, with palms and hymns and roses,
    And, better still than all,
  The long, long day of bliss that never closes,
    Thy marriage festival!

(709)

591

MAGDALENA. (7 6. 7 6.)

In moderate time.

German Traditional Melody. (*c.* 16th cent.)

Truth.

Ernest Myers, 1844–1921.

NOW in life's breezy morning,
Here on life's sunny shore,
To all the powers of falsehood
We vow eternal war:

2 Eternal hate to falsehood;
And then, as needs must be,
O Truth, O lady peerless,
Eternal love to thee.

3 All fair things that seem true things,
Our hearts shall ay receive,
Not over-quick to seize them,
Nor over-loath to leave;

4 Not over-loath or hasty
To leave them or to seize,
Not eager still to wander,
Nor clinging still to ease.

5. But one vow links us ever,
That whatso'er shall be,
Nor life nor death shall sever
Our souls, O Truth, from thee.

592

GLAN GEIRIONYDD. (6 6. 8 6. 8 6. 8 8 6.)

With vigour.

Welsh Hymn Melody.
Harmonized by DAVID EVANS, 1874–1948.

Fellowship.

P. *Dearmer*, 1867–1936.

NOW join, ye comrades true!
  Praise God with praises due,
    And take the grip of fellowship,
God's praises to renew.
  Let pipes advance, with strings and dance!
Hurrah! We raise our song
    For Christ, who came with heart aflame
    To tell God's name, his Realm proclaim,
And triumph over wrong!

2. Then set with deeds your song,
     Fit descant to belong
       To songs of praise, in these our days
   Which need the brave and strong.
     God give us worth to serve on earth,
   Till earth like heaven shall grow;
       God give us might to do the right,
       In him unite, all ills to smite,
   And serve him here below!

593 GONFALON ROYAL. (L.M.)

With movement. Unison.

P. C. BUCK, 1871–1947.

The Everlasting Mercy. *John Masefield.*

O CHRIST who holds the open gate,
  O Christ who drives the furrow straight,
O Christ, the plough, O Christ, the laughter
Of holy white birds flying after,

2 Lo, all my heart's field red and torn,
And thou wilt bring the young green corn,
The young green corn divinely springing,
The young green corn for ever singing;

3 And when the field is fresh and fair
Thy blessèd feet shall glitter there,
And we will walk the weeded field,
And tell the golden harvest's yield,

4. The corn that makes the holy bread
By which the soul of man is fed,
The holy bread, the food unpriced,
Thy everlasting mercy, Christ.

594 ROCHESTER. (C.M.)

In moderate time.

C. HYLTON STEWART.

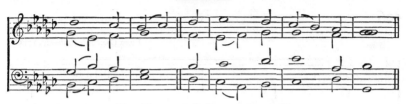

Trust.

W. H. Bathurst, 1796–1877.

O FOR a faith that will not shrink,
　Though pressed by many a foe,
That will not tremble on the brink
　Of poverty or woe,

2 That will not murmur nor complain
　Beneath the chastening rod,
But, in the hour of grief or pain,
　Can lean upon its God;

3 A faith that shines more bright and clear
　When tempests rage without,

That when in danger knows no fear,
　In darkness feels no doubt;

4 A faith that keeps the narrow way
　Till life's last spark is fled,
And with a pure and heavenly ray
　Lights up a dying bed!

5. Lord, give me such a faith as this,
　And then, whate'er may come,
I taste even now the hallowed bliss
　Of an eternal home.

595

O GOD OF LOVE. (C.M.)

Moderately slow.

'B. R.' in *The Divine Companion,* 1722.

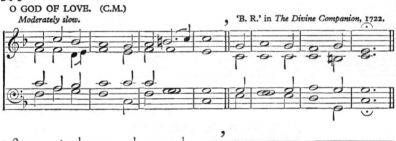

[This hymn may also be sung to RICHMOND, 468.]

C. Wesley, 1707–88.

O FOR a thousand tongues to sing
　My dear Redeemer's praise,
The glories of my God and King,
　The triumphs of his grace!

2 Jesus—the name that charms our fears,
　That bids our sorrows cease;
'Tis music in the sinner's ears,
　'Tis life, and health, and peace.

3 He speaks; and, listening to his voice,
　New life the dead receive,

The mournful broken hearts rejoice,
　The humble poor believe.

4 Hear him, ye deaf; his praise, ye dumb,
　Your loosened tongues employ;
Ye blind, behold your Saviour come;
　And leap, ye lame, for joy!

5. My gracious Master and my God,
　Assist me to proclaim
And spread through all the earth abroad
　The honours of thy name.

596

BURFORD. (C.M.)
Slow.

From *Chetham's Psalmody*, 1718.

P. Doddridge, 1702–51, and others.

O GOD of Bethel, by whose hand
  Thy people still are fed,
Who through this weary pilgrimage
  Hast all our fathers led:

2 Our vows, our prayers, we now present
  Before thy throne of grace;
God of our fathers, be the God
  Of their succeeding race.

3 Through each perplexing path of life
  Our wandering footsteps guide;
Give us each day our daily bread,
  And raiment fit provide.

4. O spread thy covering wings around,
  Till all our wanderings cease,
And at our Father's loved abode
  Our souls arrive in peace.

597

MARTYRS. (C.M.)

Slow and solemn. **Unison.** Scottish Psalter, 1635 (original form of the melody).

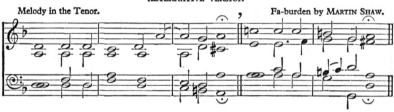

ALTERNATIVE VERSION

Melody in the Tenor. Fa-burden by MARTIN SHAW.

[*Copyright, 1915, by J. Curwen & Sons, Ltd.*]

Truth.   *Thomas Hughes, 1822–96.*

O GOD of truth, whose living word
   Upholds whate'er hath breath,
Look down on thy creation, Lord,
   Enslaved by sin and death.

2 Set up thy standard, Lord, that we,
   Who claim a heavenly birth
May march with thee to smite the lies
   That vex thy groaning earth.

3*Ah! would we join that blest array
   And follow in the might
Of him, the faithful and the true,
   In raiment clean and white!

4 We fight for truth? we fight for God?
   Poor slaves of lies and sin!
He who would fight for thee on earth
   Must first be true within.

5 Then, God of truth, for whom we long,
   Thou who wilt hear our prayer,
Do thine own battle in our hearts
   And slay the falsehood there.

6. Yea, come! Then, tried as in the fire,
   From every lie set free,
Thy perfect truth shall dwell in us,
   And we shall live in thee.

See also
673 Thou long disowned

(715)

598

ST. ANNE. (C.M.)
Slow and dignified.

Melody from the *Supplement to the New Version*, 1708.
Probably by W. CROFT, 1678–1727.

ALTERNATIVE VERSION

Melody in the Tenor.

Fa-burden by MARTIN SHAW.

Ps. 90.

I. *Watts,*‡ 1674–1748.

O GOD, our help in ages past,
  Our hope for years to come,
Our shelter from the stormy blast,
  And our eternal home;

2 Under the shadow of thy throne
  Thy saints have dwelt secure;
Sufficient is thine arm alone,
  And our defence is sure.

3 Before the hills in order stood,
  Or earth received her frame,
From everlasting thou art God,
  To endless years the same.

4 A thousand ages in thy sight
  Are like an evening gone,
Short as the watch that ends the night
  Before the rising sun.

5 Time, like an ever-rolling stream,
  Bears all its sons away;
They fly forgotten, as a dream
  Dies at the opening day.

6. O God, our help in ages past,
  Our hope for years to come,
Be thou our guard while troubles last,
  And our eternal home.

599

CHERRY TREE. (7 6. 7 6.)

In moderate time, not slow.

Traditional English Carol Melody.

J. M. Neale, 1818–66.

O HAPPY band of pilgrims
  If onward ye will tread
With Jesus as your fellow
  To Jesus as your Head!

2 O happy if ye labour
    As Jesus did for men;
  O happy if ye hunger
    As Jesus hungered then!

3*The faith by which ye see him,
    The hope in which ye yearn,
  The love that through all troubles
    To him alone will turn,

4*What are they but forerunners
    To lead you to his sight?
  What are they save the effluence
    Of uncreated Light?

5 The trials that beset you,
    The sorrows ye endure,
  The manifold temptations
    That death alone can cure,

6 What are they but his jewels
    Of right celestial worth?
  What are they but the ladder
    Set up to heaven on earth?

7. O happy band of pilgrims,
    Look upward to the skies,
  Where such a light affliction
    Shall win you such a prize!

(717)

600

O JESULEIN SÜSS. (8 8. 8 8 8.)

In moderate time.

Melody from S. SCHEIDT's *Tablaturbuch*, 1650.

[This hymn may also be sung to PACHELBEL, 403.]

E. Allison Peers, 1890–1952.

O HEAVENLY Beauty, lovelier far
 Than any beauty we can know,
On starriest night thou fairest star,
 Thou light most glorious from below,
 Thou hidden world with radiant glow!

2 O heavenly Truth, that here dost shine,
 A beacon-light our path to guide,
Set by a hand unseen, divine,
 To all revealed, to none denied,
 On high, yet ever at our side!

3 Beacon ahead and star above.
 To such as journey both are one—
One, too, with mystic fire of love,
 Consuming flame that stays for none—
 For all are kindled by a Sun.

4. Lord God of light, no strength have we
 To walk securely on our way,
But our desires are known to thee:
 By beacon, then, and star, we pray,
 Lead us through night to glorious day.

(718)

601

DRUMCONDRA. (S.M.)

In moderate time.

DAVID F. R. WILSON, 1871–1957.

The Eternal Spirit.

P. *Dearmer*, 1867–1936.

O HOLY Spirit, God,
  All loveliness is thine;
Great things and small are both in thee,
  The star-world is thy shrine.

2 The sunshine thou of God,
    The life of man and flower,
The wisdom and the energy
    That fills the world with power.

3 Thou art the stream of love,
    The unity divine;
Good men and true are one in thee,
    And in thy radiance shine.

4 The heroes and the saints
    Thy messengers became;
And all the lamps that guide the world
    Were kindled at thy flame.

5 The calls that come to us
    Upon thy winds are brought;
The light that gleams beyond our dreams
    Is something thou hast thought.

6. Give fellowship, we pray,
    In love and joy and peace,
That we in counsel, knowledge, might,
    And wisdom, may increase.

(For a Doxology see 417.)

602

HERONGATE. (L.M.)
In moderate time.

English Traditional Melody.

Assembly.

S. Longfellow, 1819–92.

O LIFE that makest all things new,
 The blooming earth, the thoughts of men:
Our pilgrim feet, wet with thy dew,
 In gladness hither turn again.

2 From hand to hand the greeting flows,
 From eye to eye the signals run,
From heart to heart the bright hope glows;
 The seekers of the light are one:

3 One in the freedom of the truth,
 One in the joy of paths untrod,
One in the soul's perennial youth,
 One in the larger thought of God:

4. The freer step, the fuller breath,
 The wide horizon's grander view,
The sense of life that knows no death—
 The life that maketh all things new!

(720)

603

WALSALL. (C.M.)
Slow.

From *A Choice Collection of Psalm Tunes*,
W. ANCHORS (*c.* 1721).

[This hymn may also be sung to KING'S NORTON, 547.]

J. G. Whittier, 1807–92.

O LORD and Master of us all,
    Whate'er our name or sign,
We own thy sway, we hear thy call,
    We test our lives by thine.

2 Thou judgest us; thy purity
    Doth all our lusts condemn;
The love that draws us nearer thee
    Is hot with wrath to them;

3 Our thoughts lie open to thy sight;
    And naked to thy glance
Our secret sins are in the light
    Of thy pure countenance.

4 Yet weak and blinded though we be
    Thou dost our service own;
We bring our varying gifts to thee,
    And thou rejectest none.

5 To thee our full humanity,
    Its joys and pains belong;
The wrong of man to man on thee
    Inflicts a deeper wrong.

6. Who hates, hates thee; who loves, becomes
    Therein to thee allied:
All sweet accords of hearts and homes
    In thee are multiplied.

(721)

604

SONG 18. (8 8 6. D.)
Slow.

O. GIBBONS, 1583–1625.

Peace.

J. Anstice,† 1808–36.

O LORD, how happy should we be
  If we could cast our care on thee,
    If we from self could rest;
And feel at heart that one above,
In perfect wisdom, perfect love,
    Is working for the best.

2 Could we but kneel, and cast our load,
  E'en while we pray, upon our God,
    Then rise with lightened cheer;
  Sure that the Father, who is nigh
  To still the famished raven's cry,
    Is greater than our fear.

3. Lord, make these faithless hearts of ours
    Such lessons learn from birds and flowers:
      Make them from self to cease;
  Leave all things to a Father's will,
  And taste, before him lying still,
    E'en in affliction, peace.

SECOND TUNE

ADVENT. (8 8 6. D.)
In moderate time.

'Western Melody' in *Plymouth Collection* (U.S.A.), 1855.

[This hymn may also be sung to MAGDALEN COLLEGE, 690.]

Peace.   J. Anstice,† 1808–36.

O LORD, how happy should we be
    If we could cast our care on thee,
        If we from self could rest;
And feel at heart that one above,
In perfect wisdom, perfect love,
        Is working for the best.

2 Could we but kneel, and cast our load,
    E'en while we pray, upon our God,
        Then rise with lightened cheer;
Sure that the Father, who is nigh
To still the famished raven's cry,
        Is greater than our fear.

3. Lord, make these faithless hearts of ours
    Such lessons learn from birds and flowers:
        Make them from self to cease;
Leave all things to a Father's will,
And taste, before him lying still,
        E'en in affliction, peace.

(723)

605

LEICESTER (OR BEDFORD).　(8 8. 4 4. 8. 8 8, or 8 8. 8 8. 8 8.)

Moderately slow.

JOHN BISHOP (*c.* 1665–1737), from
A Sett of New Psalm Tunes (1700).

Ps. 139.　　*Sir Philip Sidney, 1554–86, and Mary, Lady Pembroke, 1561–1621.*

O LORD, in me there lieth nought
　　But to thy search revealèd lies;
　　　　For when I sit
　　　　Thou markest it,
　　No less thou notest when I rise;
　　The closest closet of my thought
　　Hath open windows to thine eyes.

2 Thou walkest with me when I walk;
　　When to my bed for rest I go,
　　　　I find thee there,
　　　　And everywhere;

Not youngest thought in me doth
　　　　grow,
No, not one word I cast to talk,
　　But, yet unuttered, thou dost know.

3. Do thou thy best, O secret night,
　　In sable veil to cover me;
　　　　The sable pall
　　　　Shall vainly fall,
　　With day unmasked my night shall be:
For night is day and darkness light,
　　O Father of all lights, to thee.

606

NEUMARK.　(9 8. 9 8. 8 8.)
Moderately slow.

Original version of melody by G. NEUMARK, 1621–81.

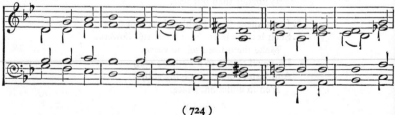

Knowledge.

E. H. Plumptre, 1821–91.

O LORD of hosts, all heaven possessing,
　Behold us from thy sapphire throne.
In doubt and darkness dimly guessing,
　We might thy glory half have known;
But thou in Christ hast made us thine,
And on us all thy beauties shine.

2 Illumine all, disciples, teachers,
　　Thy law's deep wonders to unfold;
With reverent hand let wisdom's preachers
　　Bring forth their treasures, new and old;
Let oldest, youngest, find in thee
Of truth and love the boundless sea.

3 Let faith still light the lamp of science,
　　And knowledge pass from truth to truth,
And wisdom, in its full reliance,
　　Renew the primal awe of youth;
So holier, wiser, may we grow,
As time's swift currents onward flow.

4.*Bind thou our life in fullest union
　　With all thy saints from sin set free;
Uphold us in that blest communion
　　Of all thy saints on earth with thee;
Keep thou our souls, or there, or here,
In mightiest love, that casts out fear.

See also
452 Before thy feet I fall　　　|　　　567 Lord of health

607

HYMNUS EUCHARISTICUS (*The Magdalen Tower Hymn*). (L.M.)

Very slow.

B. ROGERS, 1641–98.

SECOND TUNE

O AMOR QUAM EXSTATICUS. (L.M.)

In moderate time. Unison.

Old French Melody (?). Mode I.
Set by BASIL HARWOOD, 1859–1949.

H. Bonar,† 1808–89.

O LOVE of God, how strong and true,
Eternal, and yet ever new,
Uncomprehended and unbought,
Beyond all knowledge and all thought!

2*O heavenly love, how precious still,
In days of weariness and ill,
In nights of pain and helplessness,
To heal, to comfort, and to bless!

3 O wide-embracing, wondrous love,
We read thee in the sky above;
We read thee in the earth below,
In seas that swell and streams that flow.

4 We read thee in the flowers, the trees,
The freshness of the fragrant breeze,
The songs of birds upon the wing,
The joy of summer and of spring.

5 We read thee best in him who came
And bore for us the cross of shame,
Sent by the Father from on high,
Our life to live, our death to die.

6. O love of God, our shield and stay
Through all the perils of our way;
Eternal love, in thee we rest,
For ever safe, for ever blest.

608

LAMBETH. (8 8. 8 8. 8 8.)
Moderately slow.

S. AKEROYDE in the *Divine Companion*, 1701.

[This hymn may also be sung to VENI, CREATOR (ATTWOOD), 181.]

J. Scheffler, 1624–77. Tr. C. Winkworth.‡

Liebe die du mich zum Bilde.

O LOVE who formest me to wear
    The image of thy Godhead here;
Who seekest me with tender care
    Through all my wanderings wild and drear:

    O Love, I give myself to thee,
    Thine ever, only thine to be.

2 O Love, who once in time wast slain,
    Pierced through and through with bitter woe;
  O Love, who wrestling thus didst gain
    That we eternal joy might know:

3 O Love, of whom is truth and light,
    The Word and Spirit, life and power,
  Whose heart was bared to them that smite,
    To shield us in our trial hour:

4.*O Love, who lovest us for ay,
    Who for our souls dost ever plead;
  O Love, who showest us the way,
    Whose power sufficeth in our stead:

609

CRUGYBAR. (9 8. 9 8. D.)

Welsh Hymn Melody.
Harmonized by DAVID EVANS, 1874–1948.

In moderate time.

A. G.

O SING to the Lord now, his greatness
  Conceive, and with praises draw nigh;
His energy worketh in all things,
  His wisdom reigns watching on high;
The arms everlasting are round us,
  From sorrow and pain to release;
For God is our refuge eternal,
  Our haven and heaven of peace.

2. Thou infinite joy and resplendence,
  Thou centre of wisdom and might,
Unfathomed thou art and unbounded;
  We lift up our hearts to thy height.
Forgetting our fears we look upward:
  Thy love shall all phantoms dispel;
For lo, thou art love and love only,
  And in thy fulfilment we dwell.

610

ILLSLEY. (L.M.)

Slow.

J. BISHOP, 1665–1737.

[This hymn may also be sung to RICHARD, 25.]

ALTERNATIVE VERSION

The trebles sing the upper part, the other voices sing the melody or the harmonies.

Descant by HARVEY GRACE.

[*Copyright, 1931, by Oxford University Press.*]

J. G. Whittier, 1807–92.

O SOMETIMES gleams upon our sight,
Through present wrong, the eternal right;
And step by step since time began
We see the steady gain of man:

2 That all of good the past hath had
Remains to make our own time glad,
Our common daily life divine,
And every land a Palestine.

3 Through the harsh noises of our day
A low sweet prelude finds its way;
Through clouds of doubt and creeds of fear,
A light is breaking calm and clear.

4. Henceforth my heart shall sigh no more
For olden time and holier shore:
God's love and blessing, then and there,
Are now, and here, and everywhere.

(729)

611

LONDONDERRY. (11 10. 11 10. D.)

Irish Traditional Melody,
Harmonized by HENRY G. LEY, 1887–1962

Slow. Unison.

GENERAL

[*Copyright, 1931, by Oxford University Press.*]

Frank Fletcher, 1870–1954.

O SON of man, our hero strong and tender,
 Whose servants are the brave in all the earth,
Our living sacrifice to thee we render,
 Who sharest all our sorrow, all our mirth.

2 O feet so strong to climb the path of duty,
 O lips divine that taught the words of truth,
Kind eyes that marked the lilies in their beauty,
 And heart that kindled at the zeal of youth.

3 Lover of children, boyhood's inspiration,
 Of all mankind the servant and the king,
O Lord of joy and hope and consolation,
 To thee our fears and joys and hopes we bring.

4. Not in our failures only and our sadness,
 We seek thy presence, comforter and friend;
O rich man's guest, be with us in our gladness!
 O poor man's mate, our lowliest tasks attend!

(731)

612

MONTGOMERY. (L.M.)

Moderately slow.

Attributed to W. CHAMPNESS in
Chapman's *Musical Companion,* 1772.

John Sterling, 1806–44.

O SOURCE divine, and life of all,
　The fount of being's wondrous sea!
Thy depth would every heart appal
　That saw not love supreme in thee.

2 We shrink before thy vast abyss,
　Where worlds on worlds eternal brood;
We know thee truly but in this—
　That thou bestowest all our good.

3 And so, 'mid boundless time and space,
　O grant us still in thee to dwell,
And through the ceaseless web to trace
　Thy presence working all things well.

4 Nor let thou life's delightful play
　Thy truth's transcendent vision hide;
Nor strength and gladness lead astray
　From thee, our nature's only guide.

5. Bestow on every joyous thrill
　Thy deeper tones of reverent awe;
Make pure thy children's erring will,
　And teach their hearts to love thy law.

(732)

613

HARINGTON (RETIREMENT). (C.M.)

In moderate time.

H. HARINGTON, 1727–1816.

S. T. *Coleridge*, 1772–1834, *and another*

O SWEETER than the marriage-feast,
'Tis sweeter far to me,
To walk together to the kirk
With a goodly company;

2 To walk together to the kirk,
And all together pray:
Old men and babes and loving friends
And youths and maidens gay.

3 He prayeth well, who loveth well
Both man and bird and beast;
And he that loveth all God made
That man he prayeth best.

4. He prayeth best, who loveth best
All things both great and small;
For the dear God who loveth us
He made and loveth all.

614

RELIEF. (C.M.)

Moderately slow.

From *A New Set of Sacred Music*
by JOHN FAWCETT, 1830.

[This hymn may also be sung to WIGTOWN, 630.]

F. L. Hosmer, 1840–1929.

O THOU in all thy might so far,
 In all thy love so near,
Beyond the range of sun and star,
 And yet beside us here:

2 What heart can comprehend thy name,
 Or searching find thee out,
Who art within, a quickening flame,
 A presence round about?

3 Yet though I know thee but in part,
 I ask not, Lord, for more;
Enough for me to know thou art,
 To love thee, and adore.

4. And dearer than all things I know
 Is childlike faith to me,
That makes the darkest way I go
 An open path to thee.

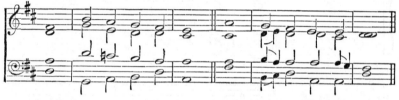

615

OLD 120TH. (6 6. 6 6. 6 6.)

Moderately slow.

Melody from *Este's Psalter*, 1592.
(Rhythm slightly adapted.)

God's City.

F. T. Palgrave, 1824–97.

O THOU not made with hands,
Not throned above the skies,
Nor walled with shining walls,
Nor framed with stones of price,
More bright than gold or gem,
God's own Jerusalem!

2 Where'er the gentle heart
Finds courage from above;
Where'er the heart forsook
Warms with the breath of love;
Where faith bids fear depart,
City of God, thou art.

3 Thou art where'er the proud
In humbleness melts down;
Where self itself yields up;
Where martyrs win their crown;
Where faithful souls possess
Themselves in perfect peace;

4 Where in life's common ways
With cheerful feet we go;
Where in his steps we tread,
Who trod the way of woe;
Where he is in the heart,
City of God, thou art.

5.*Not throned above the skies,
Nor golden-walled afar,
But where Christ's two or three
In his name gathered are,
Be in the midst of them,
God's own Jerusalem!

See also
468 City of God, how broad and far | 475 Come now, all people

616 HENHAM. (9 8. 9 8. D.)

In moderate time. Not too fast. Voices in unison.

MARTIN SHAW, 1875–1958.

1. O thou that mov-est all, O Pow - er That bring-est life where-'er thou

art, O breath of God in star and flow - er, . .

. . . Mys - ter - ious aim of soul and heart: With - in the thought that can-not

grasp thee In its un - fath - om-a-ble hold,

(736)

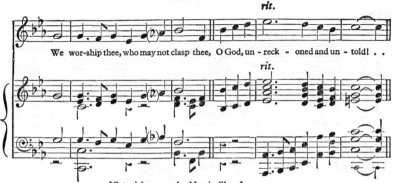

We wor-ship thee, who may not clasp thee, O God, un - reck - oned and un - told! . .

[*Copyright, 1931, by Martin Shaw.*]

2 O source and sea of love, O Spirit
    That makest every soul akin,
O Comforter whom we inherit,
    We turn and worship thee within!
To give beyond all dreams of giving,
    To lose ourselves as thou in us,
We long; for thou, O Fount of Living,
    Art lost in thy creation thus.

PART II

3 The mass of unborn matter knew thee,
    And lo! the splendid silent sun
Sprang out to be a witness to thee
    Who art the All, who art the One;
The airy plants unseen that flourish
    Their floating strands of filmy rose,
Too small for sight, are thine to nourish;
    For thou art all that breathes and grows.

4 Thou art the ripening of the fallows,
    The swelling of the buds in rain;
Thou art the joy of birth that hallows
    The rending of the flesh in twain;
O Life, O Love, how undivided
    Thou broodest o'er this world of thine,
Obscure and strange, yet surely guided
    To reach a distant end divine!

5 We knew thee in the doubt and terror
    That reels before the world we see;
We knew thee in the faiths of error;
    We know thee most who most are free.
This phantom of the world around thee
    Is vast, divine, but not the whole:
We worship thee, and we have found thee
    In all that satisfies the soul.

Conclusion, for either Part

6. How shall we serve, how shall we own thee,
    O breath of love and life and thought?
How shall we praise, who are not shown thee?
    How shall we serve, who are as nought?
Yet, though thy worlds maintain unbroken
    The silence of their aweful round,
A voice within our souls hath spoken,
    And we who seek have more than found.

The Eternal Spirit.   *A. Mary F. Robinson (Madame Duclaux), 1857–1944.*

617

PIMLICO ROAD. (9 8. 9 8; Irreg.)

In moderate time. Voices in unison.

MARTIN SHAW, 1875-1958.

1. O world in - vis - i - ble, we view thee, O world in -
2. Does the fish soar to find the o - cean, The ea - gle
3. Not where the wheel - ing sys - tems dark - en, And our be -
4. The an - gels keep their an - cient pla - ces: Turn but a

- tang - i - ble, we touch thee, O world un - know - a - ble, we
plunge to find the air— . . . . That we ask of the stars in
- numbed con - ceiv - ing soars! . . . The drift of pin - ions, would we
stone, and start a wing! . . . 'Tis ye, 'tis your es - tran - ged

know thee, In - ap - pre - hen - si - ble, we clutch thee!
mo - tion If they have ru - mour of thee there? . .
heark - en, Beats at our own clay - shut - - tered doors. . .
fa - ces, That miss the ma - ny - splen - doured thing. . .

5.* Yea, in the night, my soul, my daugh-ter, Cry—; . . . . cling-ing hea-ven by the hems; And lo, . . . Christ walk-ing on the wa - ter Not of Gen-nes-a-reth, but Thames!

(*If desired, the 5th verse may be sung to the same tune as the first four.*)

Francis Thompson, 1859–1907.

618

HANOVER. (5 5. 5 5. 6 5. 6 5.)

Moderately slow.

Probably by W. CROFT, 1678–1727.

(For alternative version with Fa-burden see following page.)

Ps. 104.   *Sir Robert Grant,*‡ 1779–1838.

O WORSHIP the King
  All glorious above;
O gratefully sing
  His power and his love:
Our shield and defender,
  The ancient of days,
Pavilioned in splendour,
  And girded with praise.

2 O tell of his might,
    O sing of his grace,
  Whose robe is the light,
    Whose canopy space.
  His chariots of wrath
    The deep thunder-clouds form,
  And dark is his path
    On the wings of the storm.

3 This earth, with its store
    Of wonders untold,
  Almighty, thy power
    Hath founded of old;
  Hath stablished it fast
    By a changeless decree,
  And round it hath cast,
    Like a mantle, the sea.

(740)

ALTERNATIVE VERSION

Melody in the Tenor.

Fa-burden by HARVEY GRACE.

4 Thy bountiful care
　　What tongue can recite?
It breathes in the air,
　　It shines in the light;
It streams from the hills,
　　It descends to the plain,
And sweetly distils
　　In the dew and the rain.

5*Frail children of dust,
　　And feeble as frail,
In thee do we trust,
　　Nor find thee to fail;
Thy mercies how tender,
　　How firm to the end!
Our maker, defender,
　　Redeemer, and friend!

6. O measureless Might,
　　Ineffable Love,
While angels delight
　　To hymn thee above,
Thy humbler creation,
　　Though feeble their lays,
With true adoration
　　Shall sing to thy praise.

619

UNIVERSITY COLLEGE. (7 7. 7 7.)

Moderately fast.

H. J. GAUNTLETT, 1805–76.

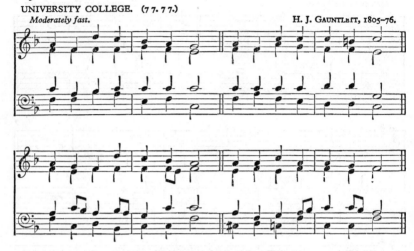

[This hymn may also be sung to MELLING, 463.]

H. Kirke White (1806), *and others* (1812–33).

OFT in danger, oft in woe,
  Onward, Christians, onward go;
Bear the toil, maintain the strife,
Strengthened with the Bread of Life.

2 Onward, Christians, onward go,
   Join the war, and face the foe;
   Will ye flee in danger's hour?
   Know ye not your Captain's power?

3 Let your drooping hearts be glad;
   March in heavenly armour clad;
   Fight, nor think the battle long:
   Victory soon shall tune your song.

4 Let not sorrow dim your eye,
   Soon shall every tear be dry;
   Let not fears your course impede,
   Great your strength, if great your need.

5. Onward then in battle move;
   More than conquerors ye shall prove;
   Though opposed by many a foe,
   Christian soldiers, onward go.

620

BALFOUR. (C.M.)
Moderately slow.   Scottish Hymn Melody.

The Star of Love.   *O. Wendell Holmes*, 1809–94.

OUR Father, while our hearts unlearn
  The creeds that wrong thy name,
Still let our hallowed altars burn
  With faith's undying flame.

2 Not by the lightning-gleams of wrath
  Our souls thy face shall see:
The star of love must light the path
  That leads to heaven and thee.

3 Help us to read our Master's will
  Through every darkening stain
That clouds his sacred image still,
  And see him once again,

4 The brother man, the pitying friend,
  Who weeps for human woes,
Whose pleading words of pardon blend
  With cries of raging foes.

5*If 'mid the gathering storms of doubt
  Our hearts grow faint and cold,
The strength we cannot live without
  Thy love will not withhold.

6. Our prayers accept, our sins forgive,
  Our youthful zeal renew;
Shape for us holier lives to live,
  And nobler work to do.

(743)

621

DARMSTADT (O GOTT, DU FROMMER GOTT). (6 7. 6 7. 6 6. 6 6.)

Melody by A. FRITSCH, 1679.
Adapted and harmonized by J. S. BACH, 1685-1750.

Slow.

The Eternal Order.   *Edward Grubb*, 1854–1939.

OUR God, to whom we turn
    When weary with illusion,
Whose stars serenely burn
    Above this earth's confusion,
Thine is the mighty plan,
    The steadfast order sure,
In which the world began,
    Endures, and shall endure.

2 Thou art thyself the Truth;
    Though we, who fain would find thee,
Have tried, with thoughts uncouth,
    In feeble words to bind thee,
It is because thou art
    We're driven to the quest;
Till truth from falsehood part
    Our souls can find no rest.

3 All Beauty speaks of thee—
    The mountains and the rivers,
The line of lifted sea,
    Where spreading moonlight quivers,
The deep-toned organ blast
    That rolls through arches dim—
Hints of the music vast
    Of thy eternal hymn.

4 Wherever Goodness lurks
    We catch thy tones appealing;
Where man for justice works
    Thou art thyself revealing;
The blood of man, for man
    On friendship's altar spilt,
Betrays the mystic plan
    On which thy house is built.

5.*Thou hidden fount of love,
    Of peace, and truth, and beauty,
Inspire us from above
    With joy and strength for duty
May thy fresh light arise
    Within each clouded heart,
And give us open eyes
    To see thee as thou art.

622

CONGLETON. (10 10. 10 10.)

Moderately slow.

The Standard Psalm Tune-book, 1852
(attributed there to M. WISE, *c.* 1648–87).

Begin v. 4 here.

Soul and Body.   *W.* Shakespeare, 1564–1616.

POOR Soul, the centre of my sinful earth,
  Fooled by these rebel powers that thee array,
Why dost thou pine within, and suffer dearth,
  Painting thy outward walls so costly gay?

2 Why so large cost, having so short a lease,
    Dost thou upon thy fading mansion spend?
  Shall worms, inheritors of this excess,
    Eat up thy charge? Is this thy body's end?

3 Then, Soul, live thou upon thy servant's loss,
    And let that pine to aggravate thy store;
  Buy terms divine in selling hours of dross;
    Within be fed, without be rich no more:

4. So shalt thou feed on death, that feeds on men,
  And death once dead, there 's no more dying then.

623

PRAISE, MY SOUL.* (8 7. 8 7. 8 7.)

In moderate time. Voices in unison.

J. GOSS, 1800-80.

1. Praise, my soul, the King of hea - ven; To his feet thy tri - bute bring.

Ransom'd, heal'd, re-stor'd, for - giv - en, Who like me his praise should sing?

Praise him! Praise him! Praise him! Praise him! Praise the ev - er - last - ing King.

[This hymn may also be sung to TANTUM ERGO, 199.]

* If desired, the music of verse 2 may be used for the hymn throughout.

623 (*continued*)

Harmony. (*Verses 2 & 3.*)

2. Praise him for his grace and fa - - vour To our fa - thers
   in dis - tress; Praise him still the same for ev - er,
   Slow to chide, and swift to bless. Praise him! Praise him!
   Praise him! Praise him! Glo - rious in his faith - ful - ness.

3. Fa - ther - like, he tends and spares us; Well our fee - ble
   frame he knows; In his hands he gen - tly bears us,
   Res - cues us from all our foes. Praise him! Praise him!
   Praise him! Praise him! Wide - ly as his mer - cy flows.

4. An-gels, help us to a - dore him; Ye be-hold him face to face;

Sun and moon, bow down be - fore him, Dwell-ers all in time and space.

Praise him! Praise him! Praise him! Praise him! Praise with us the God of grace.

Ps. 103.

H. F. Lyte, 1793–1847.

624

PRAISE. (8 7. 8 7. D.)

With spirit.

GEOFFREY SHAW, 1879–1943.

[This hymn may also be sung to AUSTRIAN HYMN, 500.]

Ps. 148.   *Foundling Hospital Coll.* (1796).

PRAISE the Lord! Ye heavens, adore him;
   Praise him, angels, in the height;
Sun and moon, rejoice before him;
   Praise him, all ye stars and light:
Praise the Lord, for he hath spoken;
   Worlds his mighty voice obeyed;
Laws, which never shall be broken,
   For their guidance hath he made.

2 Praise the Lord, for he is glorious!
   Never shall his promise fail;
God hath made his saints victorious;
   Sin and death shall not prevail.
Praise the God of our salvation;
   Hosts on high, his power proclaim;
Heaven and earth, and all creation,
   Laud and magnify his name!

PART II

                                   E. Osler, 1798–1863.

3. Worship, honour, glory, blessing,
   Lord, we offer to thy name;
Young and old, thy praise expressing,
   Join their Saviour to proclaim.
As the saints in heaven adore thee,
   We would bow before thy throne;
As thine angels serve before thee,
   So on earth thy will be done.

625 FIRST MODE MELODY. (D.C.M.)

In moderate time.   T. TALLIS, *c.* 1510–85. (Harmony slightly adapted.)

NOTE.—*Verse 7 must be sung to the 1st half of the tune.*
[This hymn may also be sung to the C.M. tune RICHMOND, 468.]

J. H. Newman, 1801–90.

PRAISE to the Holiest in the height,
     And in the depth be praise,
In all his words most wonderful,
     Most sure in all his ways.

2 O loving wisdom of our God!
     When all was sin and shame,
A second Adam to the fight
     And to the rescue came.

3*O wisest love! that flesh and blood,
     Which did in Adam fail,
Should strive afresh against their foe,
     Should strive and should prevail;

4*And that a higher gift than grace
     Should flesh and blood refine,
God's presence and his very self,
     And essence all-divine.

5 O generous love! that he who smote
     In Man for man the foe,
The double agony in Man
     For man should undergo;

6 And in the garden secretly,
     And on the cross on high,
Should teach his brethren, and inspire
     To suffer and to die.

7. Praise to the Holiest in the height,
     And in the depth be praise,
In all his words most wonderful,
     Most sure in all his ways.

(752)

626

LOBE DEN HERREN. (14 14. 4. 7. 8.)

Moderately slow.

Later form of melody in *Stralsund Gesangbuch*, 1665
(as given in *The Chorale Book for England*, 1863).

J. Neander, 1650–80. Tr. C. Winkworth, S.P.V.

Lobe den Herren.

PRAISE to the Lord, the Almighty,
the King of creation;
O my soul, praise him, for he is thy
health and salvation:
Come, ye who hear,
Brothers and sisters, draw near,
Praise him in glad adoration.

2 Praise to the Lord, who o'er all things
so wondrously reigneth,
Shelters thee under his wings, yea, so
gently sustaineth:
Hast thou not seen?
All that is needful hath been
Granted in what he ordaineth.

3 Praise to the Lord, who doth prosper
thy work and defend thee;
Surely his goodness and mercy here
daily attend thee:
Ponder anew
All the Almighty can do,
He who with love doth befriend thee.

4. Praise to the Lord! O let all that is in
me adore him!
All that hath life and breath come now
with praises before him!
Let the amen
Sound from his people again:
Gladly for ay we adore him!

627

FRAGRANCE. (9 8. 9 8. 9 8.)

In moderate time.

French Carol Melody.

Steuart Wilson.

PRAISE we the Lord, who made all beauty
    For all our senses to enjoy;
Give we our humble thanks and duty
    That simple pleasures never cloy;
Praise we the Lord, who made all beauty
    For all our senses to enjoy.

2 Praise him who makes our life a pleasure,
    Sending us things which glad our eyes;
Thank him who gives us welcome leisure,
    That in our heart sweet thoughts may rise;
Praise him who makes our life a pleasure,
    Sending us things which glad our eyes.

3*Praise him who loves to see young lovers,
    Fresh hearts that swell with youthful pride;
Thank him who sends the sun above us,
    As bridegroom fit to meet his bride;
Praise him who loves to see young lovers,
    Fresh hearts that swell with youthful pride.

4. Praise him who by a simple flower
    Lifts up our hearts to things above;
Thank him who gives to each one power
    To find a friend to know and love;
Praise him who by a simple flower
    Lifts up our hearts to things above.

(*Verse* 1 *may be repeated.*)

628

YORK. (C.M.)

Moderately slow.

Melody from *Scottish Psalter*, 1615.
Harmony from J. MILTON, d. 1647.

Pss. 122, 133, 116.

Scottish Psalter (1650).

PRAY that Jerusalem may have
  Peace and felicity :
Let them that love thee and thy peace
  Have still prosperity.

2 Behold how good a thing it is,
  And how becoming well,
Together such as brethren are
  In unity to dwell.

3 Therefore I wish that peace may still
  Within thy walls remain,
And ever may thy palaces
  Prosperity retain.

4 Now, for my friends' and brethren's sake,
  Peace be in thee, I'll say;
And for the house of God our Lord
  I'll seek thy good alway.

5.*Within the courts of God's own house,
  Within the midst of thee,
O City of Jerusalem,
  Praise to the Lord give ye.

ALTERNATIVE VERSION

Melody in the Tenor.
PEOPLE'S PART.

Fa-burden by S. STUBBS in *Ravenscroft's Psalter*, 1621.

CHOIR OR ORGAN.

Pss. 122, 133, 116.

Scottish Psalter (1650).

PRAY that Jerusalem may have
  Peace and felicity:
Let them that love thee and thy peace
  Have still prosperity.

2 Behold how good a thing it is,
    And how becoming well,
  Together such as brethren are
    In unity to dwell.

3 Therefore I wish that peace may still
    Within thy walls remain,
  And ever may thy palaces
    Prosperity retain.

4 Now, for my friends' and brethren's sake,
    Peace be in thee, I'll say;
  And for the house of God our Lord
    I'll seek thy good alway.

5.*Within the courts of God's own house,
    Within the midst of thee,
  O City of Jerusalem,
    Praise to the Lord give ye.

(757)

629

MEIRIONYDD. (7 6. 7 6. D.)

In moderate time.

Later form of melody by
W. LLOYD, 1785–1852.

Mrs. J. C. Simpson, 1811–86, and others.

PRAY when the morn is breaking,
　Pray when the noon is bright,
Pray with the eve's declining,
　Pray in the hush of night:
With mind made clear of tumult,
　All meaner thoughts away,
Make thou thy soul transparent,
　Seek thou with God to pray.

2 Remember all who love thee,
　All who are loved by thee,
And next for those that hate thee
　Pray thou, if such there be:
Last for thyself in meekness
　A blessing humbly claim,
And link with each petition
　Thy great Redeemer's name.

3. But if 'tis e'er denied thee
　In solitude to pray,
Should holy thoughts come o'er thee
　Upon life's crowded way,
E'en then the silent breathing
　That lifts thy soul above
Shall reach the thronèd Presence
　Of mercy, truth, and love.

See also 630 below

630

WIGTOWN. (C.M.)
Moderately slow.   *Scottish Psalter, 1635.*

Prayer.   *J. Montgomery, 1771–1854.*

PRAYER is the soul's sincere desire,
    Uttered or unexpressed;
The motion of a hidden fire
    That trembles in the breast.

2 Prayer is the burden of a sigh,
    The falling of a tear,
The upward glancing of an eye
    When none but God is near.

3 Prayer is the simplest form of speech
    That infant lips can try;
Prayer the sublimest strains that reach
    The Majesty on high.

4 Prayer is the contrite sinner's voice,
    Returning from his ways,
While angels in their songs rejoice,
    And cry, 'Behold, he prays!'

5 Prayer is the Christian's vital breath,
    The Christian's native air,
His watchword at the gates of death:
    He enters heaven with prayer.

6. O thou by whom we come to God,
    The Life, the Truth, the Way,
The path of prayer thyself hast trod:
    Lord, teach us how to pray.

See also
551 Jesus, where'er thy people meet | 629 Pray when the morn is breaking

631

WAREHAM. (L.M.)

Very slow and dignified. Later version of melody by W. KNAPP, 1698-1768.

R. Bridges, 1844-1930.

REJOICE, O land, in God thy might;
His will obey, him serve aright;
For thee the saints uplift their voice:
Fear not, O land, in God rejoice.

2 Glad shalt thou be, with blessing crowned,
With joy and peace thou shalt abound;
Yea, love with thee shall make his home
Until thou see God's Kingdom come

3. He shall forgive thy sins untold:
Remember thou his love of old;
Walk in his way, his word adore,
And keep his truth for evermore.

ALTERNATIVE VERSION

DESCANT (Trebles).

Descant by GEOFFREY SHAW.

MELODY (all other voices).

[By permission of Novello & Co., Ltd.]

632

GOPSAL. (6 6. 6 6. 8 8.)
In moderate time.

G. F. HANDEL, 1685-1759.

C. Wesley, 1707-88.

REJOICE! The Lord is King,
    Your Lord and King adore;
Mortals, give thanks and sing,
    And triumph evermore:

      Lift up your heart, lift up your voice;
      Rejoice, again I say, rejoice.

2 Jesus, the Saviour, reigns,
    The God of truth and love;
When he had purged our stains,
    He took his seat above:

3 His kingdom cannot fail;
    He rules o'er earth and heaven;
The keys of death and hell
    Are to our Jesus given:

4. He sits at God's right hand
    Till all his foes submit,
And bow to his command,
    And fall beneath his feet:

633

DEUS TUORUM MILITUM. (L.M.)

In moderate time. *Unison.*   Grenoble Church Melody.

[This hymn may also be sung to DEO GRACIAS, 684.]

Alfred Tennyson, 1809–92.

> *Ring out, wild bells, to the wild sky,*
> *The flying cloud, the frosty light:*
> *The year is dying in the night;*
> *Ring out, wild bells, and let him die.*

RING out the grief that saps the mind,
  For those that here we see no more;
  Ring out the feud of rich and poor,
Ring in redress to all mankind.

2 Ring out a slowly dying cause,
  And ancient forms of party strife;
  Ring in the nobler modes of life,
With sweeter manners, purer laws.

3 Ring out false pride in place and blood,
  The civic slander and the spite;
  Ring in the love of truth and right,
Ring in the common love of good.

4 Ring out old shapes of foul disease;
  Ring out the narrowing lust of gold;
  Ring out the thousand wars of old,
Ring in the thousand years of peace.

5. Ring in the valiant man and free,
  The larger heart, the kindlier hand;
  Ring out the darkness of the land,
Ring in the Christ that is to be.

(The first verse may be sung as a solo.)

634

RING OUT. (6 6 10. 6 6 10. 8 12. Slightly irregular.)

Moderately fast.

GEOFFREY SHAW, 1879–1943.

v. 3. wear - ing,

Mer - cy

Org.

Voices in unison.

Org.

v. 3. steer - ing

Org.

John Milton, 1608–74.

RING out, ye crystal spheres!
Once bless our human ears,
If ye have power to touch our senses so;
And let your silver chime
Move in melodious time;
And let the bass of heaven's deep organ blow;
And with your ninefold harmony
Make up full consort to the angelic symphony.

2 For if such holy song
Enwrap our fancy long,
Time will run back, and fetch the age of gold;
And speckled vanity
Will sicken soon and die,
And leprous sin will melt from earthly mould;
And hell itself will pass away,
And leave her dolorous mansions to the peering day.

3. Yea, truth and justice then
Will down return to men,
Orbed in a rainbow; and, like glories wearing,
Mercy will sit between
Throned in celestial sheen,
With radiant feet the tissued clouds down steering;
And heaven, as at some festival,
Will open wide the gates of her high palace hall.

635

FALCON STREET (SILVER STREET). (S.M.)

In moderate time.   Later form of melody by ISAAC SMITH, *c.* 1770.

[This hymn may also be sung to ST. MICHAEL, 702.]

W. P. Merrill, 1867–1954.

RISE up, O men of God!
Have done with lesser things;
Give heart and soul and mind and strength
To serve the King of Kings.

2 Rise up, O men of God!
His Kingdom tarries long;
Bring in the day of brotherhood
And end the night of wrong.

3 Rise up, O men of God!
The Church for you doth wait:
Her strength unequal to her task;
Rise up, and make her great!

4. Lift high the cross of Christ!
Tread where his feet have trod,
As brothers of the Son of Man
Rise up, O men of God!

636

FIRST TUNE

CHRISTOPHER (IHR GESTIRN'). (7 7. 7 7. 7 7.)

Later form of melody by CHRISTOPH PETER, 1626–69.
(Slightly adapted.)

Moderately slow.

REDHEAD No. 76. (7 7. 7 7. 7 7.)

SECOND TUNE

R. REDHEAD, 1820–1901.

Moderately slow.

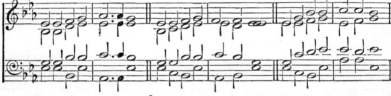

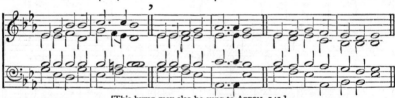

[This hymn may also be sung to ARFON, 141.]

A. M. Toplady,† 1740–78.

ROCK of ages, cleft for me,
  Let me hide myself in thee;
Let the water and the blood,
From thy riven side which flowed,
Be of sin the double cure:
Cleanse me from its guilt and power.

2*Not the labours of my hands
  Can fulfil thy law's demands;
Could my zeal no respite know,
Could my tears for ever flow,
All for sin could not atone:
Thou must save, and thou alone.

3 Nothing in my hand I bring;
  Simply to thy cross I cling;
  Naked, come to thee for dress;
  Helpless, look to thee for grace;
  Foul, I to the fountain fly;
  Wash me, Saviour, or I die.

4. While I draw this fleeting breath,
  When mine eyes are closed in death,
  When I soar through tracts unknown,
  See thee on thy judgment throne;
  Rock of ages, cleft for me,
  Let me hide myself in thee.

637

WEISSE (GOTTLOB, ES GEHT NUN MEHR ZUM ENDE). (9 8. 9 8.)

Source unknown. (Rhythm slightly adapted.)
Harmonized by J. S. BACH, 1685–1750.

In moderate time.

Arthur Hugh Clough, 1819–61.

SAY not, 'The struggle nought availeth,
  The labour and the wounds are vain,
The enemy faints not, nor faileth,
  And as things have been they remain.'

2 If hopes were dupes, fears may be liars;
    It may be, in yon smoke concealed,
  Your comrades chase e'en now the fliers,
    And, but for you, possess the field.

3 For while the tired waves, vainly breaking,
    Seem here no painful inch to gain,
  Far back, through creeks and inlets making,
    Comes silent, flooding in, the main.

4. And not by eastern windows only,
    When daylight comes, comes in the light;
  In front the sun climbs slow, how slowly,
    But westward, look, the land is bright!

637 (*continued*)

SECOND TUNE

ESSEX. (9 8. 9 8.)
In moderate time. Unison.

English Traditional Melody.

Arthur Hugh Clough, 1819–61.

SAY not, 'The struggle nought availeth,
    The labour and the wounds are vain,
The enemy faints not, nor faileth,
    And as things have been they remain.'

2 If hopes were dupes, fears may be liars;
    It may be, in yon smoke concealed,
Your comrades chase e'en now the fliers,
    And, but for you, possess the field.

3 For while the tired waves, vainly breaking,
    Seem here no painful inch to gain,
Far back, through creeks and inlets making,
    Comes silent, flooding in, the main.

4. And not by eastern windows only,
    When daylight comes, comes in the light;
In front the sun climbs slow, how slowly,
    But westward, look, the land is bright!

638

WIR CHRISTENLEUT. (4 4. 11. 4 4. 11.)

Dresden *Gesangbuch*, 1593.
Adapted and harmonized by J. S. BACH, 1685–1750.

In moderate time.

(The first line of each verse is sung twice.)

G. W. Briggs, 1875–1959.

SHALL God not share
His children's care,
If such a heart as mine their sorrows heedeth?
Can my poor love
Rise high above
The love of him from whom all love proceedeth?

2   How dull and blind
Our doubting mind!
Not higher than its source can rise the river;
Forgive, dear Lord,
Each foolish word,
Each faithless thought, of thee the only Giver.

3.   Boundless and free
Thy love must be,
If thou hast planted in our hearts such treasure:
Love infinite,
Its depth and height,
Its breadth, the Infinite alone can measure!

639 SONG OF JOY. (10. 14.)

Moderately fast.

Melody by THOMAS CAMPIAN, 1567-1620.

Thomas Campian, 1567-1620.

SING a song of joy, praise our God with mirth.
His flock who can destroy? Is he not Lord of heaven and earth?

2 Sing we then secure, tuning well our strings,
With voice as echo pure, let us renown the King of Kings.

3 First who taught the day from the east to rise?
Whom doth the sun obey when in the seas his glory dies?

4 He the stars directs that in order stand:
Who heaven and earth protects but he that framed them with his hand?

5 All that dread his name, and his hests observe,
His arm will shield from shame, their steps from truth shall never swerve.

6. Let us then rejoice, sounding loud his praise,
So will he hear our voice, and bless on earth our peaceful days.

640

NUN FREUT EUCH. (8 7. 8 7. 8 8 7.)

Slow and dignified.

Christliche Lieder (Wittenberg, 1524).
Adapted and harmonized by J. S. BACH, 1685-1750.

P. Dearmer, 1867–1936.

S ING praise to God, who spoke through man
  In differing times and manners,
For those great seers who've led the van,
  Truth writ upon their banners;
For those who once blazed out the way,
For those who still lead on to-day,
  To God be thanks and glory.

2 For Amos, of the prophets first
  The vast confusion rending
Of many gods that blest or curst,
  To find One, Good, Transcending;
For all who taught mankind to rise
Out of the old familiar lies,
  To God be thanks and glory.

3 For Socrates who, phrase by phrase,
  Talked men to truth, unshrinking,
And left for Plato's mighty grace
  To mould our ways of thinking;
For all who wrestled, sane and free,
To win the unseen reality,
  To God be thanks and glory.

4. For all the poets, who have wrought
  Through music, words, and vision
To tell the beauty of God's thought
  By art's sublime precision,
Who bring our highest dreams to shape
And help the soul in her escape,
  To God be thanks and glory.

641

FIRST TUNE

FROM STRENGTH TO STRENGTH. (D.S.M.)

With vigour. Unison.

E. W. NAYLOR, 1867-1934.

ST. ETHELWALD. (S.M.)

SECOND TUNE

In moderate time.

W. H. MONK, 1823-89.

[This hymn may also be sung to MILITES, 343.]

(772)

C. *Wesley*, 1707–88.

SOLDIERS of Christ, arise,
   And put your armour on;
Strong in the strength which God sup-
         plies,
   Through his eternal Son;

2 Strong in the Lord of Hosts,
   And in his mighty power;
Who in the strength of Jesus trusts
   Is more than conqueror.

3 Stand then in his great might,
   With all his strength endued;
And take, to arm you for the fight,
   The panoply of God.

4 To keep your armour bright
   Attend with constant care,
Still walking in your Captain's sight,
   And watching unto prayer.

5 From strength to strength go on;
   Wrestle, and fight, and pray;
Tread all the powers of darkness down,
   And win the well-fought day;

6. That having all things done,
   And all your conflicts past,
Ye may o'ercome, through Christ alone,
   And stand entire at last.

642

MÜLLER.   (7 7. 7 7. D.)

In moderate time.

Melody from *Koralbok for den Norske Kirke*, 1928.
Attributed there to J. M. MÜLLER, b. 1683.

[This hymn may also be sung to DENT DALE, 88, *or* GOTT SEI DANK, 645.]

Bp. W. W. How, 1823–97.

SOLDIERS of the cross, arise!
   Gird you with your armour bright;
Mighty are your enemies,
   Hard the battle ye must fight.

2 'Mid the homes of want and woe,
   Strangers to the living word,
Let the Saviour's herald go,
   Let the voice of hope be heard.

3 Where the shadows deepest lie,
   Carry truth's unsullied ray;
Where are crimes of blackest dye,
   There the saving sign display.

4 To the weary and the worn
   Tell of realms where sorrows cease;
To the outcast and forlorn
   Speak of mercy and of peace.

5 Guard the helpless; seek the strayed;
   Comfort troubles; banish grief;
In the might of God arrayed,
   Scatter sin and unbelief.

6. Be the banner still unfurled,
   Still unsheathed the Spirit's sword,
Till the kingdoms of the world
   Are the Kingdom of the Lord.

643

FIRST TUNE

LLANGLOFFAN. (7 6. 7 6. D.)
In moderate time.

Welsh Hymn Melody.

[This hymn may also be sung to MEIRIONYDD, 629.]

W. Cowper, 1731–1800.

SOMETIMES a light surprises
   The Christian while he sings:
It is the Lord who rises
   With healing in his wings;
When comforts are declining
   He grants the soul again
A season of clear shining
   To cheer it after rain.

2 In holy contemplation
   We sweetly then pursue
The theme of God's salvation,
   And find it ever new!

GENERAL

SECOND TUNE

RHYDDID. (7 6. 7 6. D.)

In moderate time.

Welsh Hymn Melody.

Set free from present sorrow,
  We cheerfully can say,
E'en let the unknown to-morrow
  Bring with it what it may.

3. Though vine nor fig-tree neither
  Their wonted fruit should bear,
Though all the fields should wither,
  Nor flocks nor herds be there;
Yet, God the same abiding,
  His praise shall tune my voice;
For, while in him confiding,
  I cannot but rejoice.

(775)

644

RILEY. (7 7. 7 7. D.)

Brightly.

MARTIN SHAW, 1875–1958.

[*Copyright, 1915, by J. Curwen & Sons, Ltd.*]

J. *Montgomery,*† 1771–1854.

SONGS of praise the angels sang,
Heaven with alleluyas rang,
When creation was begun,
When God spake and it was done.

2 Songs of praise awoke the morn
When the Prince of Peace was born:
Songs of praise arose when he
Captive led captivity.

3*Heaven and earth must pass away,
Songs of praise shall crown that day;
God will make new heavens and earth,
Songs of praise shall hail their birth.

4*And will man alone be dumb
Till that glorious kingdom come?
No, the Church delights to raise
Psalms and hymns and songs of praise.

5 Saints below, with heart and voice,
Still in songs of praise rejoice,
Learning here by faith and love
Songs of praise to sing above.

6. Hymns of glory, songs of praise,
Father, unto thee we raise;
Jesus, glory unto thee,
With the Spirit ever be.

645

GOTT SEI DANK. (7 7. 7 7.)

Moderately slow.

FREYLINGHAUSEN'S *Geistreiches Gesangbuch,* 1704.

The Message.　　　　　*J. F. Bahnmaier,* 1774–1841. *Pr. S. P.*

Walte fürder, nah und fern.

SPREAD, still spread, thou mighty word,
　Show the Kingdom of the Lord,
Spread to every soul on earth,
Tell them their immortal worth.

2 Tell them how the Father's will
　Made the world, and makes it still,
　How the Christ proclaimed his love,
　Taught the wisdom from above.

3 Mighty word of many hues,
　Heavenward pointing, tell the news,
　Word, by thy divine impact,
　Teach men how to will and act.

4 Word of life, so clean and strong,
　Word for which the nations long,
　Spread, till from its tangled night
　All the earth stirs up to light.

5*Lo, the world is ripe to win!
　Up, and bring the harvest in!
　Though the reapers still are few,
　Vast the work they have to do.

6. Father, great and good, we ask
　Nerve and courage for the task,
　Joyfully thy love to blaze
　O'er the earth's unlighted ways.

646

LITTLE BADDOW. (7 6. 7 6. D.)

In moderate time. Voices in unison.

C. ARMSTRONG GIBBS, 1889–1960.

1. Stand up, stand up for Je - sus, Ye sol - diers of the cross!
2. Stand up, stand up for Je - sus! The sol - emn watch-word hear:
3.*Stand up, stand up for Je - sus! The trum - pet call o - bey:
4.*Stand up, stand up for Je - sus! Stand in his strength a - lone;

Lift high his roy - al ban - ner; It must not suf - fer loss.
If while ye sleep he suf - fers, A - way with shame and fear;
Forth to the migh - ty con - flict In this his glo - rious day.
The arm of flesh will fail you, Ye dare not trust your own.

From vic - tory un - to vic - tory His ar - my he shall
Where - 'er ye meet with e - vil, With - in you or with -
Ye that are men now serve him A - gainst un - num-bered
Put on the Gos - pel ar - mour, Each piece put on with

lead, Till ev - 'ry foe is van - quished,
- out, Charge for the God of free - dom,
foes; Let cour - age rise with dan - ger,
prayer; Where du - ty calls or dan - ger,

And Christ is Lord in - deed.
And put the foe to rout.
And strength to strength op - pose.
Be ne - ver want - ing there!

Last verse.

5. Stand up, stand up for

Je - sus! The strife will not be long;

[Continued overleaf.

(779)

646 (*continued*)

This day the noise of bat - tle, The next the vic - tor's song. To him that o - ver - com - eth A crown of life shall be; He with the King of Glo - ry Shall reign e - ter - nal - ly.

G. Duffield,† 1818-88.

MORNING LIGHT. (7 6. 7 6. D.)
Brightly.

G. J. WEBB, 1803–87.

G. *Duffield*,† 1818–88.

STAND up, stand up for Jesus,
  Ye soldiers of the cross!
Lift high his royal banner;
  It must not suffer loss.
From victory unto victory
  His army he shall lead,
Till every foe is vanquished,
  And Christ is Lord indeed.

2 Stand up, stand up for Jesus!
  The solemn watchword hear:
If while ye sleep he suffers,
  Away with shame and fear;
Where'er ye meet with evil,
  Within you or without,
Charge for the God of freedom,
  And put the foe to rout.

3*Stand up, stand up for Jesus!
  The trumpet call obey:
Forth to the mighty conflict
  In this his glorious day.
Ye that are men now serve him
  Against unnumbered foes;
Let courage rise with danger,
  And strength to strength oppose.

4*Stand up, stand up for Jesus!
  Stand in his strength alone;
The arm of flesh will fail you,
  Ye dare not trust your own.
Put on the Gospel armour,
  Each piece put on with prayer;
Where duty calls or danger,
  Be never wanting there!

5. Stand up, stand up for Jesus!
  The strife will not be long;
This day the noise of battle,
  The next the victor's song.
To him that overcometh
  A crown of life shall be;
He with the King of Glory
  Shall reign eternally.

647 SANTWAT. (8 8. 8 8. 8 8. 8 12.)

In moderate time. Adapted by MARTIN SHAW, 1875–1958, from a Manx Melody.

Duty.

W. *Wordsworth*, 1770–1850.

STERN daughter of the Voice of God!
O Duty! if that name thou love,
Who art a light to guide, a rod
    To check the erring, and reprove;
Thou, who art victory and law
When empty terrors overawe,
From vain temptations dost set free,
And calm'st the weary strife of frail
    humanity.

2 Serene will be our days and bright,
    And happy will our nature be,
When love is an unerring light,
    And joy its own security;
And they a blissful course may hold
Even now, who, not unwisely bold,
Live in the spirit of this creed,
Yet seek thy firm support, according to
    their need.

3 Stern lawgiver! yet thou dost wear
    The Godhead's most benignant grace;
Nor know we anything so fair
    As is the smile upon thy face:
Flowers laugh before thee on their beds
And fragrance in thy footing treads;
Thou dost preserve the stars from wrong;
And the most ancient heavens, through
    thee, are fresh and strong.

4.*To humbler functions, aweful power,
    I call thee! I myself commend
Unto thy guidance from this hour;
    O let my weakness have an end!
Give unto me, made lowly wise,
The spirit of self-sacrifice;
The confidence of reason give,
And in the light of truth thy bondman
    let me live!

648

SONG 5. (L.M.)
Slow and dignified.

O. GIBBONS, 1583–1625.
(Rhythm slightly adapted.)

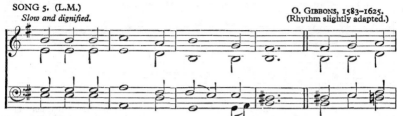

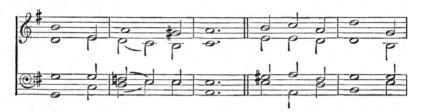

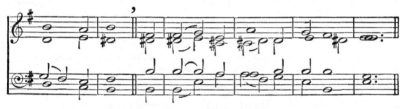

[This hymn may also be sung to WAREHAM, 631.]

Alfred Tennyson, 1809–92.

STRONG Son of God, immortal Love,
  Whom we, that have not seen thy face,
  By faith, and faith alone, embrace,
  Believing where we cannot prove:

2 Thou wilt not leave us in the dust;
  Thou madest man, he knows not why;
  He thinks he was not made to die:
  And thou hast made him: thou art just.

3 Thou seemest human and divine,
  The highest, holiest manhood thou:
  Our wills are ours, we know not how;
  Our wills are ours, to make them thine.

4. Our little systems have their day;
  They have their day and cease to be:
  They are but broken lights of thee,
  And thou, O Lord, art more than they.

649 GILLAM. (Irregular.)
Not too slow. Unison.

GEOFFREY SHAW, 1879–1943.

1. Sun - set and eve - ning star, ... And one clear call for me! And may there be no moan - ing of the bar, When I put out to sea, 2. But such a tide .... as mov - ing seems a - sleep, ... Too full for sound and foam, ... When that which drew from out ... ... the bound - less deep Turns .. a - gain home.

A little slower.

Tempo 1mo.

3. Twi - light and evening bell, .. And af - ter that the dark! And

(784)

may there be no sad - ness of fare - well, When I em -

- bark; 4. For though from out . . . . our bourne of time and place . .

. . . The flood may bear me far, . . . I hope to see my Pi -

poco rit.

- lot face to face When I . . . have crost the bar.

Crossing the Bar.   *Alfred Tennyson, 1809-92.*

650 GAZA. (8 8. 8 4.)

Slow.

Adapted from an Ancient Jewish Melody.

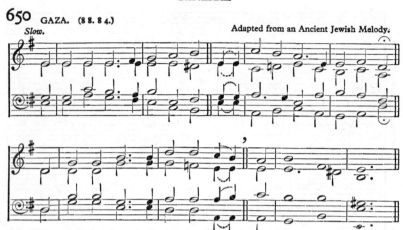

Virtue.

George Herbert, 1593-1633.

SWEET day, so cool, so calm, so bright,
   The bridal of the earth and sky,
The dew shall weep thy fall to-night;
   For thou must die.

2 Sweet rose, whose hue, angry and brave,
   Bids the rash gazer wipe his eye,
Thy root is ever in its grave,
   And thou must die.

3 Sweet spring, full of sweet days and roses,
   A box where sweets compacted lie,
My music shows you have your closes,
   And all must die.

4. Only a sweet and virtuous soul,
   Like seasoned timber, never gives;
But, though the whole world turn to coal,
   Then chiefly lives.

651 ESKDALE. (4. 8 4. 4 8.)

Slow. Unison.

J. M. JOSEPH, 1894-1929.

col 8va.

The Rapture.   Thomas Traherne, 1637–74.

SWEET Infancy!
    O heavenly fire! O sacred light!
How fair and bright!
    How great am I
Whom the whole world doth magnify!

2   O heavenly joy!
    O great and sacred blessedness
        Which I possess!
    So great a joy
Who did into my arms convey?

3   From God above
    Being sent, the gift doth me enflame
        To praise his name;
    The stars do move,
The sun doth shine, to show his love.

4.   O how divine
    Am I! To all this sacred wealth,
        This life and health,
    Who raised? Who mine
Did make the same? What hand divine!

652

SANDYS. (S.M.)

In moderate time.

English Traditional (?) Carol
(from *Sandys' Collection*, 1833).

The Elixir.   George Herbert, 1593–1633.

TEACH me, my God and King,
    In all things thee to see,
And what I do in anything
    To do it as for thee.

2   A man that looks on glass,
        On it may stay his eye;
    Or if he pleaseth, through it pass,
        And then the heaven espy.

3   All may of thee partake;
        Nothing can be so mean,
    Which with this tincture, 'for thy sake,'
        Will not grow bright and clean.

4   A servant with this clause
        Makes drudgery divine;
    Who sweeps a room, as for thy laws,
        Makes that and the action fine.

5. This is the famous stone
        That turneth all to gold;
    For that which God doth touch and own
        Cannot for less be told.

653 UNIVERSITY. (C.M.)

In moderate time.

Probably by J. RANDALL, 1715-99.

ALTERNATIVE VERSION

Melody in the Tenor.

Fa-burden by MARTIN SHAW.

Ps. 23.

George Herbert, 1593-1633.

THE God of love my shepherd is,
And he that doth me feed;
While he is mine and I am his,
What can I want or need?

2 He leads me to the tender grass,
Where I both feed and rest;
Then to the streams that gently pass:
In both I have the best.

3 Or if I stray, he doth convert,
And bring my mind in frame,
And all this not for my desert,
But for his holy name.

4 Yea, in death's shady black abode
Well may I walk, not fear;
For thou art with me, and thy rod
To guide, thy staff to bear.

5. Surely thy sweet and wondrous love
Shall measure all my days;
And, as it never shall remove,
So neither shall my praise.

(*See also* 654, 656.)

654

FIRST TUNE

ST. COLUMBA. (8 7. 8 7.)
In moderate time.

Ancient Irish Hymn Melody (Original form).

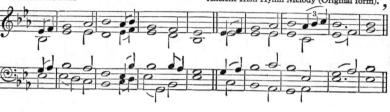

SECOND TUNE

DOMINUS REGIT ME. (8 7. 8 7.)
In moderate time.

J. B. DYKES, 1823–76.

Ps. 23.

Sir H. W. Baker, 1821–77.

THE King of love my shepherd is,
　Whose goodness faileth never;
I nothing lack if I am his
　And he is mine for ever.

2 Where streams of living water flow
　My ransomed soul he leadeth,
And where the verdant pastures grow
　With food celestial feedeth.

3 Perverse and foolish oft I strayed,
　But yet in love he sought me,
And on his shoulder gently laid,
　And home, rejoicing, brought me.

4 In death's dark vale I fear no ill
　With thee, dear Lord, beside me;
Thy rod and staff my comfort still,
　Thy cross before to guide me.

5 Thou spread'st a table in my sight;
　Thy unction grace bestoweth:
And O what transport of delight
　From thy pure chalice floweth!

6. And so through all the length of days
　Thy goodness faileth never;
Good Shepherd, may I sing thy praise
　Within thy house for ever.

655

OLD 44TH. (D.C.M.)

In moderate time.

Anglo-Genevan Psalter, 1556.
Melody as in *Este's Psalter*, 1592.

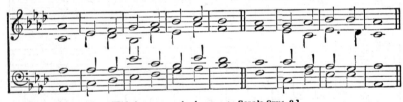

[This hymn may also be sung to SOLL'S SEIN, 8.]

W. C. Gannett, 1840–1923.

THE Lord is in his holy place
  In all things near and far:
Shekinah of the snowflake he,
  And glory of the star,
And secret of the April land
  That stirs the fields to flowers,
Whose little tabernacles rise
  To hold him through the hours.

2 He hides himself within the love
  Of those whom we love best;
The smiles and tones that make our
    homes
  Are shrines by him possessed;

He tents within the lonely heart
  And shepherds every thought;
We find him not by seeking long,
  We lose him not, unsought.

3. Our art may build its Holy Place,
  Our feet on Sinai stand,
But Holiest of Holy knows
  No tread, no touch of hand;
The listening soul makes Sinai still
  Wherever we may be,
And in the vow, 'Thy will be done',
  Lies all Gethsemane.

(Shekinah, *the visible glory of God. See e.g. Ex.* xl: 34.)

656

SURREY. (8 8. 8 8. 8 8.)

Moderately slow.

H. CAREY, 1692 ?–1743.

Ps. 23.

J. Addison, 1672–1719.

THE Lord my pasture shall prepare,
  And feed me with a shepherd's
    care;
His presence shall my wants supply,
And guard me with a watchful eye;
My noonday walks he shall attend,
And all my midnight hours defend.

2 When in the sultry glebe I faint,
  Or on the thirsty mountain pant,
  To fertile vales and dewy meads
  My weary wandering steps he leads,
  Where peaceful rivers, soft and slow,
  Amid the verdant landscape flow.

3 Though in a bare and rugged way
  Through devious lonely wilds I stray,
  Thy bounty shall my pains beguile;
  The barren wilderness shall smile
  With sudden greens and herbage
    crowned,
  And streams shall murmur all around.

4. Though in the paths of death I tread,
  With gloomy horrors overspread,
  My steadfast heart shall fear no ill,
  For thou, O Lord, art with me still:
  Thy friendly crook shall give me aid,
  And guide me through the dreadful
    shade.

657 CROFT'S 136TH. (6 6. 6 6. 8 8.)
In moderate time.

W. CROFT, 1678-1727:

[This hymn may also be sung to DARWALL'S 148TH, 701.]

Melody in Tenor or Bass.
ALTERNATIVE VERSION
Fa-burden by GEOFFREY SHAW.

(Small notes, if too high.)

Ps. 148. *George Wither*, 1588–1667.

THE Lord of Heaven confess;
On high his glory raise:
Him let all angels bless,
Him all his armies praise.
Him glorify
Sun, moon, and stars;
Ye higher spheres,
And cloudy sky.

2 Praise God from earth below,
Ye dragons, and ye deeps,
Fire, hail, clouds, wind, and snow,
Whom in command he keeps.
Praise ye his name,
Hills great and small,
Trees low and tall,
Beasts wild and tame.

3. O let God's name be praised
Above both earth and sky;
For he his saints hath raised,
And set their horn on high;
Yea, they that are
Of Israel's race,
Are in his grace
And ever dear.

658

COLESHILL. (C.M.)

Slow. *Barton's Psalms*, 1706 (later version of melody).

[This hymn may also be sung to ST. STEPHEN, 250.]

Pss. 82, 85–6. *J. Milton* (*cento*), 1608–74.

THE Lord will come and not be slow,
His footsteps cannot err;
Before him righteousness shall go,
His royal harbinger.

2 Truth from the earth, like to a flower,
Shall bud and blossom then;
And justice, from her heavenly bower,
Look down on mortal men.

3 Rise, God, judge thou the earth in might,
This wicked earth redress;
For thou art he who shalt by right
The nations all possess.

4 The nations all whom thou hast made
Shall come, and all shall frame
To bow them low before thee, Lord,
And glorify thy name.

5. For great thou art, and wonders great
By thy strong hand are done:
Thou in thy everlasting seat
Remainest God alone.

659

LONDON (or ADDISON'S). (D.L.M.)

In moderate time.

JOHN SHEELES, c. 1720.

J. *Addison*, 1672–1719.

THE spacious firmament on high,
  With all the blue ethereal sky,
And spangled heavens, a shining frame,
Their great Original proclaim.
The unwearied sun from day to day
Does his Creator's power display,
And publishes to every land
The works of an almighty hand.

2 Soon as the evening shades prevail
  The moon takes up the wondrous tale,
  And nightly to the listening earth
  Repeats the story of her birth;
  Whilst all the stars that round her burn
  And all the planets in their turn,
  Confirm the tidings, as they roll,
  And spread the truth from pole to pole.

3. What though in solemn silence all
  Move round the dark terrestrial ball;
  What though nor real voice nor sound
  Amid their radiant orbs be found;
  In reason's ear they all rejoice,
  And utter forth a glorious voice;
  For ever singing as they shine,
  'The hand that made us is divine.'

660

WOLDER (AUS MEINES HERZENS GRUNDE). (8 6. 8 6. 6 8. 8 6.)

Later form of melody from WOLDER'S
Catechismus-Gesangbüchlein, 1598.

In moderate time.

Scripture.

G. W. Briggs, 1875–1959.

THE Spirit of the Lord revealed
His will to saints of old,
Their heart and mind and lips unsealed
His glory to unfold:
In gloom of ancient night
They witnessed to the dawning word,
And in the coming of the light
Proclaimed the coming Lord.

2 The prophets passed: at length there came,
To sojourn and abide,
The Word incarnate, to whose name
The prophets testified:
The twilight overpast,
Himself the very Light of light,
As man with men, revealed at last
The Father to our sight.

3. Eternal Spirit, who dost speak
To mind and conscience still,
That we, in this our day, may seek
To do our Father's will:
Thy word of life impart,
That tells of Christ, the living Way;
Give us the quiet humble heart
To hear and to obey.

See also
457 Book of books | 212 Prophets, teachers

661

PSALM 138 (8 9. 8 9. D.)

In moderate time.

Melody from *Genevan Psalter.*
Harmony adapted from C. GOUDIMEL (d. 1572).

R. Bridges, 1844–1930.

THEE will I love, my God and King,
  Thee will I sing,
  My strength and tower:
For evermore thee will I trust,
    O God most just
Of truth and power;
    Who all things hast
    In order placed,
Yea, for thy pleasure hast created;
    And on thy throne
    Unseen, unknown,
    Reignest alone
In glory seated.

2 Set in my heart thy love I find;
  My wandering mind
  To thee thou leadest:
My trembling hope, my strong desire
    With heavenly fire
Thou kindly feedest.
    Lo, all things fair
    Thy path prepare,
Thy beauty to my spirit calleth,
    Thine to remain
    In joy or pain,
    And count it gain
Whate'er befalleth.

3. O more and more thy love extend,
  My life befriend
With heavenly pleasure;
That I may win thy paradise,
  Thy pearl of price,
Thy countless treasure;
  Since but in thee
  I can go free
From earthly care and vain oppression,
  This prayer I make
  For Jesus' sake
  That thou me take
In thy possession.

661 (*continued*)

SECOND TUNE

CROSSINGS. (8 9. 8 9. D.)
In moderate time. Unison.

C. ARMSTRONG GIBBS, 1889–1960.

[*Copyright, 1930, by Armstrong Gibbs.*]

R. Bridges, 1844–1930.

THEE will I love, my God and King,
   Thee will I sing,
  My strength and tower:
For evermore thee will I trust,
   O God most just
  Of truth and power;
   Who all things hast
   In order placed,
Yea, for thy pleasure hast created;
   And on thy throne
   Unseen, unknown,
   Reignest alone
  In glory seated.

2 Set in my heart thy love I find;
   My wandering mind
  To thee thou leadest:
My trembling hope, my strong desire
   With heavenly fire
  Thou kindly feedest.
   Lo, all things fair
   Thy path prepare,
Thy beauty to my spirit calleth,
   Thine to remain
   In joy or pain,
   And count it gain
  Whate'er befalleth.

3. O more and more thy love extend,
   My life befriend
  With heavenly pleasure;
That I may win thy paradise,
   Thy pearl of price,
  Thy countless treasure;
   Since but in thee
   I can go free
From earthly care and vain oppression,
   This prayer I make
   For Jesus' sake
   That thou me take
  In thy possession.

(799)

662

ST. GABRIEL. (6 6 10. 6 6 12.)

Moderately slow.

Adapted from a 17th-century German
Hymn Melody.

Robert Browning, 1812–89.

THEN welcome each **rebuff**
That turns earth's smoothness **rough,**
Each sting that bids nor sit nor stand but go!
Be our joys three parts pain!
Strive, and hold cheap the strain;
Learn, nor account the pang; dare, never grudge the throe!

2   Yet gifts should prove their use:
I own the Past profuse
Of power each side, perfection **every turn:**
Eyes, ears took in their dole,
Brain treasured up the whole;
Should not the heart beat once 'How good to live and learn!'

3   Not once beat 'Praise be thine!
I see the whole design,
I who saw power, see now love perfect too:
Perfect I call thy plan:
Thanks that I was a man!
Maker, remake, complete; I trust what thou shalt do.'

4.   So, take and use thy work!
Amend what flaws may lurk,
What strain o' the stuff, what warpings past the aim!
My times be in thy hand!
Perfect the cup as planned!
Let age approve of youth, and death complete **the same!**

(800)

663

O JESU. (8 6. 8 6. 8 8.)

Moderately slow.

J. B. REIMANN, 1702–49.

Geoffrey Dearmer.

THERE are a myriad means, O Lord,
By which we hear and see
The echo of thy living word,
The shadow thrown by thee;
Thy glory is beyond the powers
Of any instrument of ours.

2 The hueless wind is all thy breath,
And every stream a vein;
Time is the heart that beats beneath
The organ of thy brain,
Which is the unbounded vast of space,
And every open flower thy face.

3 The world's wide arches heavenward fly
From pillars of the air:
Behold now in the eastern sky
The great rose window flare,
As day reveals beneath the dome
The old familiar streets of home.

4 We have the power to make or mar
This heritage and home:
Lord, look not on us as we are
But as we shall become,
When we have made on earth complete
Thy Kingdom where all kingdoms meet.

5.*To thee, O young and princely Heart,
All living things return:
We love not them and thee apart,
For through that love we learn
In them to feel and hear and see
The radiant certainty of thee.

664

TALLIS' ORDINAL ('9th Tune'). (C.M.)

Moderately slow.

T. TALLIS, c. 1510–85.

ALTERNATIVE VERSION

Melody in the Tenor.

Fa-burden by GEOFFREY SHAW.

(This hymn may also be sung to ST. FLAVIAN, 188.)

J. Keble, 1792–1866.

THERE is a book who runs may read,
　Which heavenly truth imparts;
And all the lore its scholars need,
　Pure eyes and Christian hearts.

2 The works of God, above, below,
　Within us and around,
Are pages in that book, to show
　How God himself is found.

3 The glorious sky, embracing all,
　Is like the Maker's love,
Wherewith encompassed, great and small
　In peace and order move.

4*The moon above, the Church below,
　A wondrous race they run;
But all their radiance, all their glow,
　Each borrows of its sun.

(802)

5*The raging fire, the roaring wind,
    Thy boundless power display;
But in the gentler breeze we find
    Thy Spirit's viewless way.

6*Two worlds are ours: 'tis only sin
    Forbids us to descry
The mystic heaven and earth within,
    Plain as the sea and sky.

7. Thou, who hast given me eyes to see
    And love this sight so fair,
Give me a heart to find out thee,
    And read thee everywhere.

665

ELGIN. (C.M.)
Rather slow.

Scottish Psalter, 1625.

Mrs. Jane Crewdson, 1809–63.

THERE is no sorrow, Lord, too slight
    To bring in prayer to thee;
There is no burdening care too light
    To wake thy sympathy.

2 Thou who hast trod the thorny road
    Wilt share each small distress;
The love which bore the greater load
    Will not refuse the less.

3 There is no secret sigh we breathe
    But meets thine ear divine;
And every cross grows light beneath
    The shadow, Lord, of thine.

4. Life's ills without, sin's strife within,
    The heart would overflow,
But for that love which died for sin,
    That love which wept with woe.

666

LLANSANNAN. (8 7. 8 7. D.)

In moderate time, dignified.

Welsh Hymn Melody.

F. W. Faber, 1814–63.

THERE'S a wideness in God's mercy
Like the wideness of the sea;
There's a kindness in his justice
Which is more than liberty.

2 There is no place where earth's sorrows
Are more felt than up in heaven;
There is no place where earth's failings
Have such kindly judgment given.

3 There is grace enough for thousands
Of new worlds as great as this;
There is room for fresh creations
In that upper home of bliss.

4 For the love of God is broader
Than the measures of man's mind;
And the heart of the Eternal
Is most wonderfully kind:

5 But we make his love too narrow
By false limits of our own;
And we magnify his strictness
With a zeal he will not own.

6. If our love were but more simple,
We should take him at his word;
And our lives would be all sunshine
In the sweetness of our Lord.

667

ICH FAHR DAHIN. (8 8. 8 8 8.)

In moderate time.

German Traditional Melody, harmonized by J. BRAHMS, 1833–97.

v. 3, lines 4 & 5.

Ere stars were thun-der-girt, or piled The heavens, God thought on me his child.

Robert Browning, 1812–89.

THERE 'S heaven above, and night by night
    I look right through its gorgeous roof;
No suns and moons though e'er so bright
    Avail to stop me; splendour-proof,
    I keep the brood of stars aloof.

2 For I intend to get to God,
    For 'tis to God I speed so fast,
For in God's breast, my own abode,
    Those shoals of dazzling glory passed,
    I lay my spirit down at last.

3*I lie where I have always lain,
    God smiles as he has always smiled;
Ere suns and moons could wax and wane,
    Ere stars were thundergirt, or piled
    The heavens, God thought on me his child.

4. God, whom I praise: how could I praise,
    If such as I might understand,
Make out and reckon on his ways,
    And bargain for his love, and stand,
    Paying a price, at his right hand!

668

CHILDHOOD. (8 8. 8 6.)

In moderate time.

'University of Wales' (*Students' Hymnal*), 1923.

George MacDonald, 1824–1905.

THEY all were looking for a king
   To slay their foes, and lift them high:
Thou cam'st a little baby thing
   That made a woman cry.

2 O son of man, to right my lot
   Nought but thy presence can avail;
Yet on the road thy wheels are not,
   Nor on the sea thy sail!

3. My fancied ways why should'st thou heed?
   Thou com'st down thine own secret stair;
Com'st down to answer all my need,
   Yea, every bygone prayer!

669

ALTA TRINITA BEATA. (8 7. 8 7. D.)

In moderate time. Unison.

Adapted from a melody in
Laudi Spirituali, 14th century, Florence.

Agrapha.   G. D.

THOSE who love and those who labour follow in the way of Christ;
   Thus the first disciples found him, thus the gift of love sufficed.
Jesus says to those who seek him, I will never pass thee by;
Raise the stone and thou shalt find me; cleave the wood, and there am I.

2 Where the many work together, they with God himself abide,
  But the lonely worker also finds him ever at his side.
  Lo, the Prince of common welfare dwells within the market strife;
  Lo, the bread of heaven is broken in the sacrament of life.

3. Let the seeker never falter till he finds himself afar
  With the great men of the ages underneath a giant star,
  With the rich man and the poor man, of the sum of things possessed,
  Like a child at first to wonder, like a king at last to rest.

670 LÖWENSTERN (HEUT' IST O MENSCH). (10. 10. 10.)

Melody by M. von LÖWENSTERN, 1594–1648.
(Harmony by the same, slightly altered.)

Slow.

Francis Quarles, 1592–1644.

THOU art my life; if thou but turn away
My life's a thousand deaths: thou art my way;
Without thee, Lord, I travel not, but stray.

2 My light thou art; without thy glorious sight
My eyes are darkened with perpetual night:
My God, thou art my way, my life, my light.

3 Thou art my way; I wander, if thou fly:
Thou art my light; if hid, how blind am I!
Thou art my life; if thou withdraw, I die.

4. Disclose thy sunbeams; close thy wings and stay;
See, see how I am blind, and dead, and stray,
O thou that art my light, my life, my way!

671 NEW 113TH. (8 8. 8 8. 8 8.)
Moderately slow.

W. HAYES, 1706–77.

G. *Tersteegen,* 1697–1769. *Tr. J. Wesley,* 1703–91.

Verborgen Gottesliebe.

THOU hidden Love of God, whose height,
  Whose depth unfathomed, no man knows,
I see from far thy beauteous light,
  Inly I sigh for thy repose;
My heart is pained, nor can it be
At rest till it finds rest in thee.

2 'Tis mercy all, that thou hast brought
  My mind to seek her peace in thee;
Yet, while I seek but find thee not,
  No peace my wandering soul shall see.
O when shall all my wanderings end,
And all my steps to thee-ward tend?

3*Thy secret voice invites me still
  The sweetness of thy yoke to prove;
And fain I would; but, though my will
  Seem fixed, yet wide my passions rove;
Yet hindrances strew all the way;
I aim at thee, yet from thee stray.

4. O Love! Thy sovereign aid impart
  To save me from low-thoughted care;
Chase this self-will through all my heart,
  Through all its latent mazes there;
Make me thy duteous child, that I
Ceaseless may 'Abba, Father,' cry?

(809)

672 LUTHER'S HYMN (NUN FREUT EUCH). (8 7. 8 7. 8 8 7.)

Slow.   Present form of melody in *Geistliche Lieder* (Wittenberg, 1535).

Judgment.   P. Dearmer, 1867–1936.

THOU Judge by whom each Empire
  fell,
  When pride of power o'ercame it,
Convict us now, if we rebel;
  Our nation judge, and shame it:
In each sharp crisis, Lord, appear,
Forgive, and show our duty clear—
  To serve thee by repentance.

2 Search, Lord, our spirits in thy sight,
  In best and worst reveal us;
Shed on our souls a blaze of light,

And judge, that thou may'st heal us.
The present be our Judgment Day,
When all our lack thou dost survey:
  Show us ourselves and save us.

3. Lo, fearing nought we come to thee,
  Though by our fault confounded;
Though selfish, mean, and base we be,
  Thy justice is unbounded,
So large, it nought but love requires,
And, judging, pardons, frees, inspires.
  Deliver us from evil!

673 MANCHESTER. (C.M.)

Slow.   ROBERT WAINWRIGHT, 1748–82.

Truth.   *Eliza Scudder,* 1821–96.

THOU long disowned, reviled, op-
    pressed,
  Strange friend of human kind,
Seeking through weary years a rest
  Within our heart to find.

2 How late thy bright and aweful brow
    Breaks through these clouds of sin!
  Hail, Truth divine! we know thee now;
    Angel of God, come in!

3 Come, though with purifying fire
    And desolating sword;
  Thou of all nations the desire,
    Earth waits thy cleansing word.

4 Struck by the lightning of thy glance,
    Let old oppressions die:
  Before thy cloudless countenance
    Let fear and falsehood fly.

5 Anoint our eyes with healing grace,
    To see, as ne'er before,
  Our Father in our brother's face,
    Our Master in his poor.

6.*Flood our dark life with golden day:
    Convince, subdue, enthral;
  Then to a mightier yield thy sway,
    And Love be all in all.

(This hymn may be begun at verse 3.)

See also
597 O God of truth

674 ZUM FRIEDEN. (8 7. 8 7. D.)

Very slow and dignified.   Attributed to J. S. BACH, 1685–1750.

[This hymn may also be sung to PLEADING SAVIOUR, 516.]

The Vine.   *T. S. N.*

THOU true Vine, that heals the nations,
    Tree of life, thy branches we.
They who leave thee fade and wither,
    None bear fruit except in thee.
Cleanse us, make us sane and simple,
    Till we merge our lives in thine,
Gain ourselves in thee, the Vintage,
  Give ourselves through thee, the Vine.

2. Nothing can we do without thee;
    On thy life depends each one;
If we keep thy words and love thee,
    All we ask for shall be done.
May we, loving one another,
    Radiant in thy light abide;
So through us, made fruitful by thee,
    Shall our God be glorified.

(811)

675 THIRD MODE MELODY. (D.C.M.)

T. TALLIS, c. 1510–85 (rhythm slightly simplified).

Slow.

[This hymn may also be sung to OLD 44TH, 655.]

ALTERNATIVE VERSION

Melody in the Tenor.

Fa-burden by TALLIS.
(Original version, rhythm slightly simplified.)

Slightly slower.

John Mason, c. 1645–94.

THOU wast, O God, and thou wast blest,
Before the world began;
Of thine eternity possest
Before time's hour-glass ran.
Thou needest none thy praise to sing,
As if thy joy could fade;
Could'st thou have needed anything,
Thou could'st have nothing made.

2 Great and good God, it pleasèd thee
Thy Godhead to declare;
And what thy goodness did decree
Thy greatness did prepare;

Thou spak'st, and heaven and earth appeared,
And answered to thy call;
As if their maker's voice they heard,
Which is the creature's all.

3. To whom, Lord, should I sing, but thee,
The maker of my tongue?
Lo, other lords would seize on me,
But I to thee belong.
As waters haste into their sea,
And earth into its earth,
So let my soul return to thee,
From whom it had its birth.

676 ASCENDIT. (C.M.)
In moderate time.

Composed or adapted by F. D. MORICE, 19th cent.

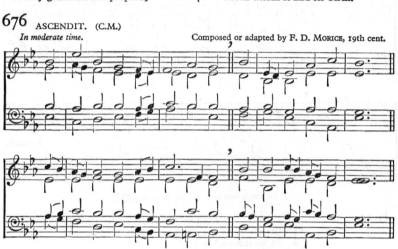

[This hymn may also be sung to ABRIDGE, 100.]

William Gaskell, 1805–84.

THOUGH lowly here our lot may be,
High work have we to do—
In faith and trust to follow him
Whose lot was lowly too.

2 Our days of darkness we may bear,
Strong in our Father's love;
We lean on his almighty arm,
And fix our hopes above.

3 Our lives enriched with gentle thoughts
And loving deeds may be,
As streams that still the nobler grow,
The nearer to the sea.

4 To duty firm, to conscience true,
However tried and pressed,
In God's clear sight high work we do,
If we but do our best.

5. Thus may we make the lowliest lot
With rays of glory bright;
Thus may we turn a crown of thorns
Into a crown of light.

677

WILTSHIRE. (C.M.)
In moderate time.

G. SMART, 1776–1867.

A - men.

[This hymn may also be sung to YORK, 628.]

Ps. 34.

N. Tate and N. Brady (New Version, 1696).

THROUGH all the changing scenes of life,
  In trouble and in joy,
The praises of my God shall still
  My heart and tongue employ.

2 O magnify the Lord with me,
  With me exalt his name;
When in distress to him I called,
  He to my rescue came.

3*The hosts of God encamped around
  The dwellings of the just;
Deliverance he affords to all
  Who on his succour trust.

4 O make but trial of his love;
  Experience will decide
How blest they are, and only they,
  Who in his truth confide.

5 Fear him, ye saints, and you will then
  Have nothing else to fear;
Make you his service your delight,
  Your wants shall be his care.

6. To Father, Son, and Holy Ghost,
  The God whom we adore,
Be glory, as it was, is now,
  And shall be evermore.

(814)

GENERAL

ALTERNATIVE VERSION

DESCANT (*Trebles*).

Descant by GEOFFREY SHAW.

MELODY (*all other voices*).

ORGAN.

678

MARCHING. (8 7. 8 7.)

With vigour.

MARTIN SHAW, 1875–1958.

[*Copyright, 1915, by J. Curwen & Sons, Ltd.*]

B. S. Ingemann, 1789–1862. *Tr. S. Baring-Gould.*

Igjennem Nat og Trængsel.

THROUGH the night of doubt and sorrow
    Onward goes the pilgrim band,
Singing songs of expectation,
    Marching to the Promised Land.

2 Clear before us through the darkness
    Gleams and burns the guiding light;
Brother clasps the hand of brother,
    Stepping fearless through the night.

3 One the light of God's own presence
    O'er his ransomed people shed,
Chasing far the gloom and terror,
    Brightening all the path we tread;

4 One the object of our journey,
    One the faith which never tires,
One the earnest looking forward,
    One the hope our God inspires:

5*One the strain that lips of thousands
    Lift as from the heart of one;
One the conflict, one the peril,
    One the march in God begun;

6.*One the gladness of rejoicing
    On the far eternal shore,
Where the one almighty Father
    Reigns in love for evermore.

(816)

679

DAS WALT' GOTT VATER. (L.M.)
Moderately slow.

Later form of melody by D. VETTER, d. *c.* **1730**.
Harmony from J. S. BACH, 1685-1750.

Thomas Moore, 1779–1852.

THY heaven, on which 'tis bliss to look,
Shall be my pure and shining book,
Where I shall read, in words of flame,
The glories of thy wondrous name.

2 There 's nothing bright, above, below,
From flowers that bloom to stars that glow,
But in its light my soul can see
Some feature of thy deity:

3. There 's nothing dark, below, above,
But in its gloom I trace thy love,
And meekly wait that moment, when
Thy touch shall turn all bright **again.**

680

IRISH. (C.M.)
Moderately slow.

Melody from *A Collection of Hymns and Sacred Poems*, Dublin, 1749.

F. L. Hosmer, 1840–1929.

THY Kingdom come! on bended knee
    The passing ages pray;
And faithful souls have yearned to see
    On earth that Kingdom's day:

2 But the slow watches of the night
    Not less to God belong;
And for the everlasting right
    The silent stars are strong.

3 And lo, already on the hills
    The flags of dawn appear;
Gird up your loins, ye prophet souls,
    Proclaim the day is near:

4 The day in whose clear-shining light
    All wrong shall stand revealed,
When justice shall be throned in might,
    And every hurt be healed;

5. When knowledge, hand in hand with peace,
    Shall walk the earth abroad:
The day of perfect righteousness,
    The promised day of God.

681

SONG 24. (10 10. 10 10.)

Moderately slow.

O. GIBBONS, 1583-1625.

The Supreme Values.

J. Addington Symonds, 1840-93.

TO God, the everlasting, who abides,
    One Life within things infinite that die;
To him whose unity no thought divides:
    Whose breath is breathèd through immensity!

2 Him neither eye hath seen, nor ear hath heard;
    Nor reason, seated in the souls of men,
Though pondering oft on the mysterious word,
    Hath e'er revealed his Being to mortal ken.

3 Only we feel him; and in aching dreams,
    Swift intuitions, pangs of keen delight,
The sudden vision of his glory seems
    To sear our souls, dividing the dull night:

4 And we yearn toward him: Beauty, Goodness, Truth,
    These three are one; one life, one thought, one being;
One source of still rejuvenescent youth;
    One light for endless and unclouded seeing.

5. O God, unknown, invisible, secure,
    Whose Being by dim resemblances we guess,
Who in man's fear and love abidest sure,
    Whose power we feel in darkness and confess!

682

EPSOM. (C.M.)

In moderate time.

Melody in ARNOLD'S *Complete Psalter*, 1756.
(Rhythm slightly adapted.)

William Blake, 1757–1827.

TO Mercy, Pity, Peace, and Love
　　All pray in their distress,
And to these virtues of delight
　　Return their thankfulness.

2 For Mercy, Pity, Peace, and Love
　　Is God our Father dear;
And Mercy, Pity, Peace, and Love
　　Is Man, his child and care.

3 For Mercy has a human heart,
　　Pity, a human face,
And Love, the human form divine,
　　And Peace, the human dress.

4. Then every man, of every clime,
　　That prays in his distress,
Prays to the human form divine,
　　Love, Mercy, Pity, Peace.

ALTERNATIVE VERSION

DESCANT (Trebles).

Descant by STANLEY MARCHANT.

MELODY (all other Voices).

ORGAN.

683

ORIEL. (8 7. 8 7. 8 7.)
Moderately slow.

C. ETT, *Cantica Sacra*, 1840.

God's Name.

P. Dearmer, 1867–1936.

TO the Name that is salvation
   Praise and homage let us pay;
Life of every generation,
   Law that all the stars obey,
Love and light by whose creation
   All that is stands fast to-day.

2 Fairest Name beyond all speaking,
   Fullest end of all desire;
Close, yet far beyond all seeking,
   Goodness, beauty, truth, entire;
Wisdom, never vengeance wreaking,
   Radiance never vexed with ire.

3 'Tis the Name of mercy, speeding
   Just and unjust with his ray;
Power that rules by patient leading,
   Not by force, the easier way,
So that man, in freedom heeding,
   May the law of love obey.

ALTERNATIVE VERSION

Trebles sing the top line, all other voices the melody ORIEL.

Descant by ALAN GRAY.

4 Name of awe and Name of pleasure,
   Glow divine of grace untold,
Sum of values, whose full treasure
   Striving art can ne'er unfold;
Sea of virtue passing measure,
   Life that doth all life uphold.

5. Hail, O Father, all creating
   Now, as when the world began;
Master Mind, amazed we hail thee,
   As the light-year depths we scan;
Spirit of transcendent union,
   True and just thy ways to man!

GENERAL

684 DEO GRACIAS. (L.M.)

In moderate time, dignified. Unison.   English Melody, 15th cent.

[This hymn may also be sung to ILLSLEY, 610.]

Magnificat.   *Thomas Hardy*, 1840–1928.

TO thee whose eye all nature owns,
 Who hurlest dynasts from their
   thrones
And liftest those of low estate,
We sing, with her men consecrate!

2 Yea, Great and Good, thee, thee, we
   hail,
Who shak'st the strong, who shield'st
   the frail,
Who hadst not shaped such souls as we
If tender mercy lacked in thee.

3 Though times be when the mortal moan
Seems unascending to thy throne;
Though seers do not as yet explain
Why suffering sobs to thee in vain;

4 We hold that thy unscanted scope
Affords a food for final hope,
That mild-eyed Prescience ponders nigh
Life's loom, to lull it by and by.

5 Therefore we quire to highest height
The Wellwiller, the kindly Might
That balances the Vast for weal,
That purges as by wounds to heal.

6*The systemed suns the skies enscroll
Obey thee in their rhythmic roll,
Ride radiantly at thy command,
Are darkened by thy master-hand.

7*And these pale panting multitudes
Seen surging here, their moils, their
   moods,
All shall fulfil their joy in thee,
In thee abide eternally.

8. Exultant adoration give
The Alone, through whom all living live,
The Alone, in whom all dying die,
Whose means the End shall justify!

685 EIA, EIA (ZU BETHLEHEM GEBOREN). (7 6. 7 6. 4 6.)

Moderately slow.   Melody from NORDSTERN's *Führer zur Seligkeit*, 1671.

Eia.

Cölner Psalter, 1638. Pr. O. B. C.

To us in Bethlem city
　Was born a little son;
In him all gentle graces
　Were gathered into one,
　　Eia, Eia,
　Were gathered into one.

2 And all our love and fortune
　Lie in his mighty hands;
Our sorrows, joys, and failures,
　He sees and understands,
　　Eia, Eia,
　He sees and understands.

3 O Shepherd ever near us,
　We'll go where thou dost lead;
No matter where the pasture,
　With thee at hand to feed,
　　Eia, Eia,
　With thee at hand to feed.

4. No grief shall part us from thee,
　However sharp the edge:
We'll serve, and do thy bidding—
　O take our hearts in pledge!
　　Eia, Eia,
　Take thou our hearts in pledge!

(Eia *is a Latin exclamation of joy, and is pronounced 'ïyah'.*)

686

MELROSE. (C.M.)
Moderately slow.
Scottish Psalter, 1635.

Ps. 121.

Henry Vaughan the Silurist, 1622–95.

UP to those bright and gladsome hills,
　Whence flows my weal and mirth,
I look, and sigh for him who fills,
　Unseen, both heaven and earth.

2 He is alone my help and hope,
　That I shall not be moved;
His watchful eye is ever ope,
　And guardeth his beloved.

3 The glorious God is my sole stay,
　He is my sun and shade:
The cold by night, the heat by day,
　Neither shall me invade.

4. Whether abroad, amidst the crowd,
　Or else within my door,
He is my pillar and my cloud,
　Now and for evermore.

687

WACHET AUF. (8 9 8. 8 9 8. 6 6 4. 4 4 8.)

Very slow and solemn.

Melody attributed to P. NICOLAI, 1556–1608.
Adapted and harmonized by J. S. BACH, 1685–1750.

P. Nicolai, 1556–1608. Tr. S. P.

Wachet auf.

WAKE, O wake, for night is flying!
　The watchmen from the heights are crying,
　　Come all ye people to the tryst.
Midnight's past, the saints are saying,
The hour is come—no more delaying!
　　　To arms, all ye that love the Christ!
　　　　Behold he comes in sight,
　　　　Raise high your cressets bright!
　　　　　　Alleluya!
　　　　Ring out the chime
　　　　In buoyant rhyme;
　　　　Rise up and meet him; it is time!

2 Now we hear the heralds singing,
And all our hearts with joy are springing;
　　We leap to arms with eager eyes;
Light shines clear, our star is blazing;
Comes forth our Friend with grace amazing,
　　　His beauty, strength, and truth are ours.
　　　　All hail, thou radiant Lord,
　　　　Our crown and our reward!
　　　　　　Hosianna!
　　　　Lo, great and small,
　　　　We answer all,
　　　　We follow where thy voice shall call!

3.*Honour, fame, to thee the Giver,
From men and angel-choirs, for ever!
　　We see thy coming, and give praise.
Gates are open, saints receive us;
Thy Kingdom never more shall leave us,
　　　'Twill lie about us all our days:
　　　　No pearl hath ever bought,
　　　　Nor eye nor ear hath caught
　　　　　　Such a rapture!
　　　　The advent song
　　　　Shout loud and strong;
　　　　Come all, and join the festal throng!

688

ANNUE CHRISTE. (6 6. 6 6. D.)

Unison. *In free rhythm.*

LA FEILLÉE, *Méthode du Plain-Chant*, 1808.

[This hymn may also be sung to MAINZ, 111.]

W. Bullock, 1798–1874, *and others.*

WE love the place, O God,
  Wherein thine honour dwells;
The joy of thine abode
  All earthly joys excels.

2 We love the house of prayer
  Wherein thy servants meet;
For thou, O Lord, art there,
  Thy folded flock to greet;

3 The font of blessing—there
  Our babes in Christ are named;
The pulpit whence we hear
  The truth in Christ proclaimed;

4 The altar of our faith,
  For at that board so dear
We show thy conquering death
  And find thy presence near.

5 We love the word of life,
  Told out in noble phrase,
Which nerves us for the strife
  And guides in all our ways.

6 We sing, and love the song
  That swells at morn and even,
And, loving thee, we long
  To see thy face in heaven.

7.*Then give us here the strength
  On earth to love thee well,
That all may come at length
  In heaven with thee to dwell.

(828)

689 FARMBOROUGH. (8 8. 8 8. 8 8.)

Moderately slow.

ARTHUR S. WARRELL, 1883–1939.

[This hymn may also be sung to DAVID'S HARP, 476.]
[*Copyright, 1931, by Oxford University Press.*]

A. F.

WE saw thee not when, far away,
    Among the hills of Galilee,
Thou and thy brothers used to stray,
    Nor Joseph's workshop did we see;
But we divine thy boyhood's grace,
Shaping to serve the human race.

2 Unseen by us thy steadfast youth
    Long spent in homely servitude,
Thy lips so full of fearless truth,
    Thy deeds of perfect brotherhood:

We did not see, but we believe
Thy way alone the world can save.

3 Not ours to see on mount and shore
    Thy smile, thine eyes alert and kind,
Thy hands that sick men could restore,
    Thy heralding God's Reign and mind;
But we do know thy Spirit's range
Men's souls and bodies still can change.

PART II

4 We saw not when thou cam'st to die,
    Forsaken, mocked, and piercèd
        through,
Nor heard the marvel of that cry—
    'Forgive! they know not what they do.'
But well we know that thou didst die
The hero of thine agony.

5 Nor ours to see thy form appear
    In risen power those forty days,
To find thy sudden presence near,
    Or, at thy parting, heavenward gaze;
But here to-day our spirit cries,
There is no death, since thou didst rise.

Conclusion, for either Part

6. We see thee now in all mankind,
    We serve thee in each little one,
We miss thee but when we are blind
    With careless webs ourselves have spun.
Lord, from our eyes the hindrance tear,
That **we may see** thee everywhere!

(829)

690 MAGDALEN COLLEGE. (8 8 6. D.)
In moderate time.
W. HAYES, 1706–77.

Christopher Smart,† 1722–71.

WE sing of God, the mighty source
Of all things, the stupendous force
On which all strength depends,
From whose right arm, beneath whose eyes,
All period, power, and enterprise
Commences, reigns, and ends.

2 Glorious the sun in mid career,
Glorious the assembled fires appear,
Glorious the comet's train,
Glorious the trumpet and alarm,
Glorious the almighty stretched-out arm,
Glorious the enraptured main.

3*The world, the clustering spheres he made,
The glorious light, the soothing shade,
Dale, champaigne, grove, and hill,
The multitudinous abyss,
Where secrecy remains in bliss,
And wisdom hides her skill.

4 Strong is the lion, like a coal
His eyeball, like a bastion's mole
His chest against the foes:
Strong the gier-eagle on his sail;
Strong against tide the enormous whale
Emerges as he goes;

5. But stronger still—in earth and air,
And in the sea—the man of prayer;
And far beneath the tide,
And in the seat to faith assigned,
Where ask is have, where seek is find,
Where knock is open wide.

691 NEW SABBATH. (L.M.)

In moderate time.   H. Phillips, *c.* 1806.

[This hymn may also be sung to Brockham, 228.]

Bishop G. E. L. Cotton, 1813–66.

WE thank thee, Lord, for this fair earth,
    The glittering sky, the silver sea;
For all their beauty, all their worth,
    Their light and glory, come from thee.

2 Thanks for the flowers that clothe the ground,
    The trees that wave their arms above,
The hills that gird our dwellings round,
    As thou dost gird thine own with love.

3 Yet teach us still how far more fair,
    More glorious, Father, in thy sight,
Is one pure deed, one holy prayer,
    One heart that owns thy Spirit's might.

4. So, while we gaze with thoughtful eye
    On all the gifts thy love has given,
Help us in thee to live and die,
    By thee to rise from earth to heaven.

(831)

692

ABENDLIED (DER TAG MIT SEINEM LICHTE). (7 7. 7 7 6. D.)

In moderate time.   J. G. EBELING, 1637–76.

Jan Struther, 1901–53.

WE thank you, Lord of Heaven,
 For all the joys that greet us,
For all that you have given
 To help us and delight us
  In earth and sky and seas;
The sunlight on the meadows,
 The rainbow's fleeting wonder,
The clouds with cooling shadows,
 The stars that shine in splendour—
  We thank you, Lord, for these.

2 For swift and gallant horses,
 For lambs in pastures springing,
For dogs with friendly faces,
 For birds with music thronging
  Their chantries in the trees;

For herbs to cool our fever,
 For flowers of field and garden,
For bees among the clover
 With stolen sweetness laden—
  We thank you, Lord, for these.

3. For homely dwelling-places
 Where childhood's visions linger,
For friends and kindly voices,
 For bread to stay our hunger
  And sleep to bring us ease;
For zeal and zest of living,
 For faith and understanding,
For words to tell our loving,
 For hope of peace unending—
  We thank you, Lord, for these.

693

OLD 30TH. (D.C.M.)
Slow.

Melody in *Este's Psalter,* 1592.
(Harmony adapted from that of J. FARMER in the same work.)

[This hymn may also be sung to WINDSOR, 547.]

Alexander Pope, 1688–1744.

WHAT conscience dictates to be done,
Or warns me not to do,
This, teach me ever, Lord, to shun,
That, ever to pursue.

2 If I am right, thy grace impart
Still in the right to stay;
If I am wrong, O teach my heart
To find that better way.

3 Save me alike from foolish pride,
Or impious discontent
At aught thy wisdom has denied,
Or aught thy goodness lent.

4. Teach me to feel another's woe,
To hide the fault I see;
The mercy I to others show,
That mercy show to me.

(833)

B e

694

BELGRAVE. (C.M.)

In moderate time.

W. HORSLEY, 1774–1858.

Joseph Addison, 1672–1719.

WHEN all thy mercies, O my God,
 My rising soul surveys,
Transported with the view, I'm lost
 In wonder, love, and praise.

2 Unnumbered comforts to my soul
 Thy tender care bestowed,
Before my infant heart conceived
 From whom those comforts flowed.

3 When in the slippery paths of youth
 With heedless steps I ran,
Thine arm, unseen, conveyed me safe,
 And led me up to man.

4*When worn with sickness oft hast thou
 With health renewed my face;
And when in sins and sorrows sunk,
 Revived my soul with grace.

5 Through every period of my life
 Thy goodness I'll pursue,
And after death in distant worlds
 The glorious theme renew.

6. Through all eternity to thee
 A joyful song I'll raise;
For O! eternity's too short
 To utter all thy praise.

695

ARDUDWY. (8 7. 8 7. 8 7.)
In moderate time.

IEUAN GWYLLT, 1822–77.

[This hymn may also be sung to CALVARY, 333.]

Confidence.

P. Dearmer, 1867–1936.

WHEN by fear my heart is daunted,
   Thou dost hold me in thy hand;
Prayerless, anxious, vainly haunted,
   Thou dost make my courage stand:
Foolish worries, fretting troubles
   Melt away at thy command.

2 God, thou art unfailing treasure,
   Refuge thou, and faithful friend;
Thy resources none can measure,
   Nought thy steadfastness can bend.
Life and light and love immortal,
   Firmly we on thee depend.

3. Held by love, to peace I win me,
   Confident whate'er betide;
Safe in hope, thy spirit in me,
   With the eternal power I hide;
Strength and health are mine, and valour—
   Bravely over care I ride.

(835)

696

O SEIGNEUR. (6 6 7. 6 6 7. D.)
With vigour.

Psalm 3 in *Genevan Psalter*, 1551.

19th cent. Tr. E. Caswall and others.

Beim frühen Morgenlicht.

WHEN morning gilds the skies,
  My heart awaking cries:
    May Jesus Christ be praisèd:
Alike at work and prayer
To him I would repair:
    May Jesus Christ be praisèd.

2 Whene'er the sweet church bell
  Peals over hill and dell:
  O hark to what it sings,
  As joyously it rings:

3*When sleep her balm denies,
  My silent spirit sighs:
  When evil thoughts molest,
  With this I shield my breast:

4*Does sadness fill my mind?
  A solace here I find:
  Or fades my earthly bliss?
  My comfort still is this:

5 Let earth's wide circle round
  In joyful notes resound:
  Let air, and sea, and sky
  From depth to height reply:

6.*Be this, while life is mine,
  My canticle divine:
  Be this the eternal song
  Through all the ages long:

697

STANSTEAD. (11 10. 11 6.)
In moderate time. Unison.

S. L. RUSSELL.

[*Copyright, 1931, by Oxford University Press.*]

J. G. Whittier, 1807-93.

WHEN on my day of life the night is falling,
And, in the winds from unsunned spaces blown,
I hear far voices out of darkness calling
My feet to paths unknown;

2 Be near me when all else is from me drifting—
Earth, sky, home's pictures, days of shade and shine,
And kindly faces, to my own uplifting
The love which answers mine.

3 I have but thee, my Father! Let thy Spirit
Be with me then to comfort and uphold;
No gate of pearl, no branch of palm I merit,
Nor street of shining gold.

4 Suffice it if—my good and ill unreckoned,
And both forgiven through thy abounding grace—
I find myself by hands familiar beckoned
Unto my fitting place.

5. There, from the music round about me stealing,
I fain would learn the new and holy song,
And find at last, beneath thy trees of healing,
The life for which I long.

(This hymn may be begun at verse 3.)

(838)

698

LOMBARD STREET. (11 10. 11 10.)

Slow. Unison.

F. G. RUSSELL, 1867–1929.

G. A. Studdert-Kennedy, 1883–1929.

WHEN through the whirl of wheels, and engines humming,
  Patiently powerful for the sons of men,
Peals like a trumpet promise of his coming
  Who in the clouds is pledged to come again;

2 When through the night the furnace fires a-flaring,
    Shooting out tongues of flame like leaping blood,
  Speak to the heart of Love, alive and daring,
    Sing of the boundless energy of God;

3 When in the depths the patient miner striving
    Feels in his arms the vigour of the Lord,
  Strikes for a kingdom and his King's arriving,
    Holding his pick more splendid than the sword;

4 When on the sweat of labour and its sorrow,
    Toiling in twilight flickering and dim,
  Flames out the sunshine of the great to-morrow,
    When all the world looks up because of him—

5. Then will he come with meekness for his glory,
    God in a workman's jacket as before,
  Living again the eternal gospel story,
    Sweeping the shavings from his workshop floor.

(839)

699

ST. BRIDE. (S.M.)
Moderately slow, dignified.

S. HOWARD, 1710–82.

T. T. *Lynch*, 1818–71.

WHERE is thy God, my soul?
    Is he within thy heart,
Or ruler of a distant realm
    In which thou hast no part?

2   Where is thy God, my soul?
        Only in stars and sun,
Or have the holy words of truth
        His light in every one?

3   Where is thy God, my soul?
        Confined to Scripture's page,
Or does his Spirit check and guide
        The spirit of each age?

4   O ruler of the sky,
        Rule thou within my heart:
O great adorner of the world,
        Thy light of life impart.

5   Giver of holy words,
        Bestow thy holy power,
And aid me, whether work or thought
        Engage the varying hour.

6.   In thee have I my help,
        As all my fathers had;
I'll trust thee when I'm sorrowful,
        And serve thee when I'm glad.

(This hymn may be begun at verse 4.)

(840)

GENERAL

ALTERNATIVE VERSION

Melody in the Tenor.   Fa-burden by GEOFFREY SHAW.

T. T. Lynch, 1818–71.

WHERE is thy God, my soul?
  Is he within thy heart,
Or ruler of a distant realm
  In which thou hast no part?

2   Where is thy God, my soul?
  Only in stars and sun,
Or have the holy words of truth
  His light in every one?

3   Where is thy God, my soul?
  Confined to Scripture's page,
Or does his Spirit check and guide
  The spirit of each age?

4   O ruler of the sky,
  Rule thou within my heart:
O great adorner of the world,
  Thy light of life impart.

5   Giver of holy words,
  Bestow thy holy power,
And aid me, whether work or thought
  Engage the varying hour.

6.   In thee have I my help,
  As all my fathers had;
I'll trust thee when I'm sorrowful,
  And serve thee when I'm glad.

(This hymn may be begun at verse 4.)

(841)

700

RESONET IN LAUDIBUS. (7 8. 7 11, and refrain 10 9. 7 4. 4. 10.)

Moderately fast. Unison.

German Carol Melody, 14th cent.

1. Who with-in that sta-ble cries, Gen-tle babe that in

man-ger lies? 'Tis the Lord, our heart re-plies. So

fol-low him, his bid-ding do for ev-er:

To-geth-er now tri-um-phant-ly cry, Tri-um-phant-ly cry, with

one ac-cord. We will praise and glo-ri-fy The

(842)

Christ, the Lord! Ev - er, ev - er; Je - sus, bea - con for our high en - dea - vour!

A F.

WHO within that stable cries,
  Gentle babe that in manger lies?
    'Tis the Lord, our heart replies.
  So follow him, his bidding do for ever:

Together now triumphantly cry,
  Triumphantly cry, with one accord.
We will praise and glorify
  The Christ, the Lord!
    Ever, ever,
      Jesus, beacon for our high endeavour!

2 Who is he, the man full-grown,
    Working on in the busy town?
      'Tis the Lord, obscure, unknown.
    So follow him, his bidding do for ever:

3 Healing lame and blind and dumb,
    Herald now that the Kingdom 's come?
      'Tis the friend of every home.
    So follow him, his bidding do for ever:

PART II

4 Who is he whom crowds acclaim
    As he enters Jerusalem?
      'Tis the Lord of happy fame.
    So follow him, his bidding do for ever:

5 Taken in Gethsemane,
    Martyred on the forlorn cross-tree?
      He who died for you and me.
    So follow him, his bidding do for ever:

6 From the tomb triumphant now,
    Deathless splendour upon his brow?
      He to whom all creatures bow.
    So follow him, his bidding do for ever:

Conclusion, for either Part

7. Passing still to every place,
    Radiant friend of the human race!
      'Tis the Lord, the fount of grace.
    So follow him, his bidding do for ever:

(*The verses may be sung as a solo, the refrain being sung by all.*)

(843)

701

DARWALL'S 148TH. (6 6. 6 6. 8 8.)
In moderate time.

J. DARWALL, 1731–89.

ALTERNATIVE VERSION

Melody in the Tenor.

Fa-burden by MARTIN SHAW.

(When this setting is sung in four-part harmony, omit the small notes.)

R. Baxter, 1615–91, *and others.*

YE holy angels bright,
    Who wait at God's right hand,
Or through the realms of light
    Stream at your Lord's command,
        Assist our song,
            For else the theme
            Too high doth seem
        For mortal tongue.

2 Ye blessèd souls at rest,
    Who ran this earthly race,
And now, from care released,
    Behold the Saviour's face,
        God's praises sound,
            As in his sight
            With sweet delight
        Ye do abound.

3 Ye saints, who toil below,
    Adore your heavenly King,
And onward as ye go
    Some joyful anthem sing;
        Take what he gives
            And praise him still,
            Through good or ill,
        Who ever lives.

4. My soul, bear thou thy part,
    Triumph in God above:
And with a well-tuned heart
    Sing thou the songs of love.
        Let all thy days
            Till life shall end,
            Whate'er he send,
        Be filled with praise.

(845)

702

ST. MICHAEL (OLD 134TH). (S.M.)

In moderate time.

Melody adapted from *Genevan Psalter*, 1551.

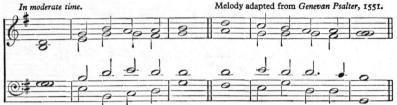

[This hymn may also be sung to ST. EDMUND, 120.]

P. Doddridge,† 1702–51.

YE servants of the Lord,
    Each in his office wait,
Observant of his heavenly word,
    And watchful at his gate.

2   Let all your lamps be bright,
    And trim the golden flame;
Gird up your loins as in his sight,
    For aweful is his name.

3   Watch! 'tis your Lord's command,
    And while we speak, he 's near;
Mark the first signal of his hand,
    And ready all appear.

4   O happy servant he,
    In such a posture found!
He shall his Lord with rapture see,
    And be with honour crowned.

5.   Christ shall the banquet spread
    With his own royal hand,
And raise that faithful servant's head
    Amidst the angelic band.

ALTERNATIVE VERSION

Melody in Tenor or Bass.

Fa-burden by MARTIN SHAW.

[*Copyright*, 1931, *by Martin Shaw.*]

P. Doddridge,† 1702–51.

YE servants of the Lord,
  Each in his office wait,
Observant of his heavenly word,
  And watchful at his gate.

2 Let all your lamps be bright,
    And trim the golden flame;
  Gird up your loins as in his sight,
    For aweful is his name.

3 Watch! 'tis your Lord's command,
    And while we speak, he 's near;
  Mark the first signal of his hand,
    And ready all appear.

4 O happy servant he,
    In such a posture found!
  He shall his Lord with rapture see,
    And be with honour crowned.

5. Christ shall the banquet spread
    With his own royal hand,
  And raise that faithful servant's head
    Amidst the angelic band.

703

DESSLER (WIE WOHL IST MIR). (9 8. 9 8. 9 9 8. 9 9 8.)

In moderate time.   Unison.   Melody and Bass by J. S. BACH, 1685–1750.

S. P.

ZEAL of the Lord, for ever burning,
   Thou wilt perform it by thy might.
That government for which in yearning
   Men strain from darkness to great light:
      His armour fails each proud transgressor,
      His yoke and rod each cruel oppressor;
   The world is turning for the right,
Its ancient blood-stained phantoms spurning,
And from the Prince of Peace is learning
   In God's deep wisdom to unite.

2. Wisdom of God, thou heavenly sower,
   On rocks, 'mid thorns, thy words alight;
Broadcast thy seed, thou truth bestower!
   Good men and honest use it right,
      And all shall know them by this token—
      Their mutual love, unforced, unbroken,
   Which friendly glows in all men's sight,
A flame of God that nought can lower.
Take then thy grain, eternal mower;
   For e'en to-day the fields are white!

APPENDIX

I

COBBOLD. (8 7. 8 7. 8 7. 8 7. 7 7.)
Moderately fast.

From a Melody by 'S. M. W. V. R.'
(rhythm of last line slightly adapted).

C. A. Alington, 1872–1955.

SING, brothers, sing and praise your King!
  Gone is the night of sorrow!
Have ye not heard his royal word,
  'God careth for the sparrow'?
Our watch we kept while others slept,
  We saw where Joseph laid him,
Saw women bring their offering,
  The last sad tribute paid him.
    But now from us they'll borrow
    Songs for a joyful morrow!

2. For we have heard a greater word,
  And seen a greater glory;
Sing, brothers, sing this fair morning,
  And tell the world the story!
We heard a voice that bade rejoice,
  Where late our Lord was lying,
No more, it saith, shall there be death,
  Sorrow, nor pain, nor crying:
    And men from birds may borrow
    Songs for a glad to-morrow!

(850)

ALTERNATIVE TUNE TO HYMN 554

GORRAN. (10 4. 10 4. 10 10.)

In moderate time. Voices in unison.

RONALD DUSSEK, 1891-1961.

ORGAN.

VOICES IN HARMONY AND ORGAN.

Org.

Ped.

J. H. Newman, 1801-90.

LEAD, kindly Light, amid the encircling gloom,
    Lead thou me on;
The night is dark, and I am far from home,
    Lead thou me on.
Keep thou my feet; I do not ask to see
The distant scene; one step enough for me.

2 I was not ever thus, nor prayed that thou
    Should'st lead me on;
I loved to choose and see my path; but now
    Lead thou me on.

I loved the garish day, and, spite of fears,
Pride ruled my will : remember not past years.

3. So long thy power hath blest me, sure it still
    Will lead me on
O'er moor and fen, o'er crag and torrent, till
    The night is gone,
And with the morn those angel faces smile,
Which I have loved long since, and lost awhile.

AMENS for use at the end of a Service.

3

HYMNS ARRANGED FOR SUNDAYS AND OTHER DAYS THROUGHOUT THE YEAR

THE Scheme below shows the principle upon which this Table is arranged, four different services being given for each day, with six or seven alternatives at the end. Four hymns are suggested for each service. In the Rally (R), or young people's service, two of these are from the other services for the day (being there printed in *italic*), and the last is a doxology. By this use of italic a certain prominence is given to the simpler hymns, which in many places will be more frequently used. The hymn set down for the Rally is suitable also for the other services; most of the hymns indeed need not be confined to the service for which they are here suggested.

When *Songs of Praise* is first introduced, not more than one new hymn (or tune) at the most should be sung each Sunday; and new hymns when introduced should be repeated till they are familiar. This List is therefore suggested for full use only after the lapse of some years.

SCHEME

M. MORNING SERVICE.
    1st Hymn. *Key-note of the Service.*
    2nd Hymn. (In the place of the Anthem.) *The least simple, but often an easy hymn.*
    Before Sermon. *On ordinary Sundays for one of the Lessons* (L).
    Last Hymn. *The longest.*

C. COMMUNION SERVICE.
    1st Hymn. *On ordinary Sundays for the Gospel* (G).
    Offertory. *The longest.*
    Communion. (*A second hymn from Part III, 259–81, or elsewhere may sometimes be needed.*)
    Last Hymn. *Short hymn of praise.*

R. RALLY. (*For Boys and Girls. Hymns for little children only (as in Part VI) are not included.*)
    1st Hymn.
    2nd Hymn. *One of those in italic above or below.*
    3rd Hymn. *Another of those in italic.*
    D., Doxology. *From Part VIII or elsewhere.* (The Doxology may also be useful in other services.)

E. EVENING SERVICE.
    1st Hymn. (Before the Psalms): *Key-note.*
    2nd Hymn. (In the place of the Anthem.)
    Before Sermon. *For one of the Lessons* (L).
    Last Hymn. *The longest, and the most popular in character.*

    On Festivals three Processions (P) *with a Doxology* (D) *are added.*

ADVENT SUNDAY

Preparation for the Kingdom

M.
63 High o'er the lonely hills
61 Hark! a herald voice
60 Christ is the world's (L)
684 To thee whose eye
C.
62 *Hark the glad sound* (G)
65 Lo! he comes
562 Lord Christ, when first

485 Eternal Ruler
680 Thy Kingdom come
R.
69 With Jesus for hero
68 The advent of ⎫ *On subsequent occa-*
62 Hark the glad ⎬ *sions these 2nd and*
            ⎭ *3rd hymns will not be repeated.*[1]
D. 408 From all that dwell
E.
68 *The advent of our God*

[1] In every case they are the hymns noted in italic for the day.

687 Wake, O wake
59 Ah! think not (L)
64 Hills of the North

ALTERNATIVES

410 I to the hills
602 O life that makest all things
310 The day of the Lord
658 The Lord will come
328 The night is ended

ADVENT II

The Old Testament and the New

M.
457 *Book of books*
559 Life of ages
212 Prophets, teachers (L)
214 *Virtue supreme*
C.
511 Hark what a sound (G)
570 Lord, thy word
275 O God, in whom we live
60 Christ is the world's true light
R.
658 The Lord will come
(*See note above*)
D. **65** (4) Yea, amen, let all adore
E.
660 The Spirit of the Lord
61 Hark! a herald voice
59 Ah! think not (L)
645 Spread, still spread

ALTERNATIVES

27 Come, thou bright (M)
309 Once to every man
680 Thy Kingdom come
698 When through the whirl
699 Where is thy God

ADVENT III

The Ministry of the Kingdom

M.
298 Pour out thy Spirit
304 All the past we leave
67 *On Jordan's bank* (L)
687 Wake, O wake
C.
545 Jesus shall reign (G)
645 Spread, still spread
66 O come, O come, Emmanuel
702 *Ye servants of the Lord*
R.
552 Judge eternal
D. **414** Praise the Lord of heaven
E.
297 Dismiss me not
561 Lo, in the wilderness
63 High o'er the lonely hills (L)
456 Blest be the day

ALTERNATIVES

450 Awake, awake to love
635 Rise up, O men of God
34 So here hath been dawning
680 Thy Kingdom come
69 With Jesus for hero

ADVENT IV

The Coming of the Kingdom

M.
68 *The advent of our God*
637 Say not, 'The struggle
327 Sound over all waters (L)
329 Turn back, O Man
C.
67 On Jordan's bank (G)
687 Wake, O wake
62 *Hark the glad sound*
680 Thy Kingdom come
R.
545 Jesus shall reign
D. **65** (4) Yea, amen, let all adore
E.
69 With Jesus for hero
50 O gladsome light
672 Thou Judge by whom (L)
312 These things shall be

ALTERNATIVES

410 I to the hills
575 Made lowly wise
578 Mine eyes have seen
633 Ring out the grief
634 Ring out, ye crystal spheres
311 The world's great age

CHRISTMAS DAY

M.
73 Christians, awake
79 O little town
74 *Hark! the herald angels*
82 *While shepherds watched*
P. **78** O come. D. **81** (1–2) Thou whose
C.
70 A great and mighty
74 Hark! the herald angels
71 Angels from, **387** Of the Father's
634 Ring out, ye crystal spheres
R.
76 It came upon the midnight
P. **78** O come. D. **82** (6) All glory be
E.
74 Hark! the herald angels
(**77** It was the calm and silent)
(**75** In the bleak mid-winter)
P. **387** Of the Father's, *or* **78** O come.
D. **78** (6) Sing, choirs, *or* **82** (6) All
glory

AND CAROLS [1]

[1] There are many Carols also for Spring, Easter,
and other seasons in the *Oxford Book of Carols.*

SUNDAY AFTER CHRISTMAS

God with us

M.
78 O come, all ye faithful
81 Thou whose birth
74 *Hark! the herald angels*
76 It came upon the midnight
P. 387 Of the Father's. D. 79 (5) O holy Child

C.
70 A great and mighty
82 While shepherds watched
72 Behold the great Creator
74 Hark! the herald angels

R.
379 When the herds
P. 78 O come. D. 79 (5) O holy Child

E.
75 *In the bleak mid-winter*
71 Angels from the realms
79 O little town
633 Ring out the grief
P. 76 It came (*or as above*). D. 82 (6) All glory

AND CAROLS

cf. *New Year*, 1 For thy mercy, *and cross-references*, e.g. 677 Through all the changing scenes.

EPIPHANY AND EPIPHANY I

The Manifestation of Christ to the Peoples:

Manifestation in the Life of the Church

M.
84 Bethlehem of noblest cities
90 How brightly beams
91 *In Asia born*
85 Brightest and best
P. 388 From the eastern. D. 78 (4) Lo, star-led

C.
571 Lord, when the wise men
87 *Hail to the Lord's anointed*
93 O worship the Lord
94 The greatness of God

R.
64 Hills of the North
P. 388 From the eastern. D. 78 (4) Lo, star-led

E.
84 Bethlehem of noblest cities
93 O worship the Lord
85 Brightest and best
83 As with gladness
P. 87 Hail to the Lord's. D. 78 (4) Lo, star-led

ALTERNATIVES

468 City of God
88 Hark, how all the welkin
89 Hearts at Christmas time
545 Jesus shall reign
96 The race that long

EPIPHANY II

Manifestation in Missionary Work

M.
300 God is working his purpose
611 O Son of man
302 I, Servants of the great (L)
87 Hail to the Lord's anointed

C.
340 Father, who on man (G)
76 *It came upon the midnight*
95 The Lord is come
96 *The race that long*

R.
369 Remember all the people
D. 243 (5) Evermore their life abides

E.
91 In Asia born
497 Gather us in
94 The greatness of God (L)
64 Hills of the North

ALTERNATIVES

60 Christ is the world's
495 For the might of thine arm
537 In Christ there is
642 Soldiers of the cross
303 Thou whose almighty
16 'Tis winter now

EPIPHANY III

Manifestation in Individuals

M.
60 Christ is the world's true light
89 Hearts at Christmas time
603 O Lord and Master (L)
88 Hark, how all the welkin

C.
95 The Lord is come (G)
480 *Crown him*
90 How brightly beams
92 Love came down

R.
87 Hail to the Lord's anointed
D. 84 (5) Holy Jesus in thy brightness

E.
94 *The greatness of God*
634 Ring out, ye crystal spheres
575 Made lowly wise (L)
615 O thou not made

OTHER DAYS THROUGHOUT THE YEAR

SEXAGESIMA

Christ the Interpreter of Human Life

M.
611 O Son of man, our hero
692 We thank you, Lord
541 Jesus, Lord, we look (L)
480 Crown him upon the throne
C.
703 Zeal of the Lord (G)
438 All as God wills
689 We saw thee not
537 *In Christ there is*
R.
499 Glad that I live
D. 407 Be, Lord, the happy guide
E.
652 Teach me, my God and King
469 Close by the heedless
672 Thou Judge by whom (L)
466 Christian, do you see him

ALTERNATIVES
509 Happy are they
531 I learned it in the meadow
640 Sing praise to God
648 Strong Son of God
662 Then welcome each rebuff

QUINQUAGESIMA

Christ the Revelation of God in Love

M.
607 O love of God, how strong
682 *To Mercy, Pity, Peace*
523 How blest (L)
574 Love of the Father
C.
507 Gracious Spirit, Holy Ghost (E)
577 Mercy thou art
573 Love divine

92 Love came down at Christmas
R.
502 God is love: his the care
D. 396 (31-2) O God in whose working
E.
609 O sing to the Lord
653 The God of love
669 *Those who love* (L)
620 Our Father, while our hearts

ALTERNATIVES
480 Crown him upon the throne
307 O brother man
608 O love who formest
638 Shall God not share
665 There is no sorrow

LENT

Ash Wednesday and other week-days

M.
121 To my humble supplication
120 Thou say'st, 'Take up
117 O thou from whom all goodness
103 Lighten the darkness

658 The Lord will come
105 Lord, it belongs not
104 Long did I toil
C.
123 Wilt thou forgive
99 Ah, holy Jesus
476 Come, O thou Traveller unknown
107 *Lord, thou hast told us*
R.
646 Stand up, stand up for Jesus
D. 119 (6) To thee, great Lord
E.
116 O Lord, turn not away
586 Nearer, my God, to thee
109 *Lord, who hast made me*
98 Now quit your care

The following groups of hymns from Part X are suggested when special week-day services are held in Lent and Holy Week:

I.—465 Christ of all, 491 Fight the good, 449 As pants the hart, 691 We thank thee, 612 O source divine.

II.—650 Sweet day, 463 Children of, 647 Stern daughter, 574 Love of the Father, 437 Abide with me.

III.—686 Up to those bright, 455 Blest are the pure, 529 I heard the voice, 472 Come, let us join, 698 When through the whirl.

IV.—542 Jesus, lover, 585 My soul, there is, 527 How sweet the name, 670 Thou art my life, 659 The spacious firmament.

V.—525 How lovely are, 474 Come, my way, 676 Though lowly here, 503 God moves, 576 Make me a captive.

VI.—501 God be in my head, 473 Come, my soul, 553 King of glory, 587 Never weather-beaten.

VII.—636 Rock of ages, 699 Where is thy God, 564 Lord of all being, 584 My Lord, my Life, 595 O for a thousand tongues.

(857)

LENT I

God First: The Choice

M.
661 Thee will I love, my God
681 To God the everlasting
231 Let thine example (L)
98 Now quit your care
C.
97 *Forty days* (G)
526 How shall I sing that majesty
671 Thou hidden Love of God
639 Sing a song of joy
R.
630 Prayer is the soul's
D. 526 (4) How great a being, Lord
E.
675 Thou wast, O God
621 Our God, to whom we turn
595 *O for a thousand tongues* (L)
309 Once to every man

ALTERNATIVES

535 Immortal, invisible
110 My God, I love thee
113 O for a heart
605 O Lord, in me there lieth
650 Sweet day, so cool
667 There's heaven above
120 Thou say'st, 'Take up

LENT II

God First: In Conduct and Worship

M.
597 O God of truth
99 Ah, holy Jesus
481 Dear Lord and Father (L)
683 To the Name
C.
550 Jesus, these eyes (G)
298 Pour out thy Spirit
590 Not with a choir of angels
553 King of glory
R.
97 Forty days
D. 418 Worship, honour, glory
E.
583 *My God, my Father, make me strong*
512 Hast thou not known
232 Look up (L)
678 *Through the night of doubt*

ALTERNATIVES

124 A voice upon (E, L)
453 Believe not those
520 Holy Spirit, truth divine
113 O for a heart
618 O worship the King
619 Oft in danger
119 Take up thy cross

LENT III

God First: In Service and Work

M.
642 Soldiers of the cross
329 Turn back, O Man
676 Though lowly here (L)
669 Those who love
C.
483 Enter thy courts (G)
109 Lord, who hast made
102 Lead us, O Father
278 Strengthen for service
R.
702 Ye servants of the Lord
D. 375 (2) North and south
E.
641 *Soldiers of Christ*
97 Forty days
610 O sometimes gleams (L)
98 Now quit your care

ALTERNATIVES

469 Close by the heedless
496 From glory to glory
606 O Lord of hosts
652 *Teach me, my God and King*
328 The night is ended
698 When through the whirl

MOTHERING SUNDAY
(MID-LENT OR REFRESHMENT SUNDAY)

God First: In the Home

M.
492 Fill thou my life
565 Lord of all hopefulness
94 The greatness of God (L)
656 The Lord my pasture
C.
653 *The God of love* (G)
98 Now quit your care
274 Lord, enthroned
509 Happy are they
R.
502 God is love
D. 626 (3) Praise to the Lord, who
E.
516 *Heavenly Father, may thy blessing*
655 The Lord is in his holy place
546 Jesus so lowly (L)
53 Saviour, again

ALTERNATIVES

539 It fell upon a summer
541 Jesus, Lord, we look
607 O love of God, how strong
6 The year's at the spring
686 Up to those bright
692 We thank you, Lord

PASSION SUNDAY

M.
129 Sing, my tongue

126 Into the woods
132 *We sing the praise* (L)
603 O Lord and Master
C.
562 Lord Christ, when first (G)
128 O sacred head
110 My God, I love thee
101 Jesus, name all names above
R.
119 Take up thy cross
D. 129 (5) Unto God be praise
E.
130 The royal banners
546 Jesus, so lowly
133 *When I survey* (L)
127 My song is love unknown

ALTERNATIVES

447 And didst thou love
568 Lord of the strong
234 Lord, who shall sit (M, L)
117 O thou from whom
134 When my love to God

PALM SUNDAY
M.
129 Sing, my tongue
124 A voice upon the midnight
133 When I survey
137 *Ride on*
P. 136 Come, faithful, 135 All glory.
   D. 130 (6) Father of all
C.
125 Drop, drop, slow tears
127 *My song is love unknown*
99 Ah, holy Jesus
689 II, We saw not
R.
132 We sing the praise
P. 136 Come, faithful, 135 All glory.
   D. 130 (6) Father of all
E.
130 The royal banners
128 O sacred head
137 Ride on
562 Lord Christ, when first

ALTERNATIVES

126 Into the woods
101 Jesus, name all names above
110 My God, I love thee
131 There is a green hill
134 When my love to God

HOLY WEEK

*Passiontide hymns, as above; and also,
   among others:*
580 My faith looks up
620 Our Father, while our hearts
636 Rock of ages

MAUNDY THURSDAY
259 According to thy gracious
265 Bread of heaven
279 Thee we adore
   GOOD FRIDAY, *as above, especially:*
140 O come and mourn
128 O sacred head
543 Jesus, meek and gentle

133 When I survey
101 Jesus, name all names above
138 In the place of sorrow
141 Throned upon
546 Jesus, so lowly
139 It is finished
480 Crown him (*After any service*)

125 Drop, drop, slow tears
142 At eve, when now

EASTER DAY
M.
143 I, Ye sons, *or* 148 A messenger
153 Christ the Lord is risen
144 Come, ye faithful
145 *Jesus Christ is risen*
P. 389 Hail thee, *or* 159 Lo, when, *or* 143
   Ye sons. D. 147 (1–4) The strife
C.
155 Jesus lives
157 *Let us rejoice*
150 Alleluya . . . Hearts to heaven, 266
   Come, risen Lord, 159 Lo, when the
   day, 145 Jesus Christ is risen
154 Good Christian men
R.
160 Love's redeeming work
P. 143 Ye sons, *or* 477 Come, ye people.
   D. 157 (3) Thou boundless
E.
145 Jesus Christ is risen
163 Sing, all ye Christian people
146 The day of resurrection
157 Let us rejoice (*with dox.* 415)
P. 143 Ye sons, *or* 390 Welcome, Day.
   D. 147 (1) The strife

ALTERNATIVES, *among others:*

151 Awake, arise
158 Life is good
162 Round the earth
  5 Spring bursts to-day
166 Take heart

LITTLE EASTER DAY
(LOW SUNDAY)
Newness of Life
M.
149 All the toil
146 The day of resurrection

159 Lo, when the day (L)
157 Let us rejoice (*with dox.* 415)
P. 389 Hail thee, *or* 390 Welcome, Day of
the Lord. D. 147 (1) The strife
C.
151 Awake, arise (G)
145 *Jesus Christ is risen*
147 *The strife is o'er*
155 Jesus lives
R.
163 Sing, all ye Christian people
P. 477 Come, ye people. D. 157 (3) Thou
boundless
E.
162 Round the earth
160 Love's redeeming work
143 II, When Thomas afterward (L)
145 Jesus Christ is risen
P. 159 Lo, when, *or* 157 Let us rejoice:
with 415. D. 147 (1) The strife

ALTERNATIVES

152 Christ is risen, Christ is risen
144 Come, ye faithful
158 Life is good
165 Sing, men and angels
167 The whole bright world
168 Thou hallowed chosen

SHEPHERD SUNDAY

The Good Shepherd

M.
656 The Lord my pasture
167 The whole bright world
158 Life is good (L)
162 Round the earth
C.
435 *A brighter dawn* (G)
654 The King of love
153 Christ the Lord
443 All people that on earth
R.
502 God is love
D. 626 (1) Praise to the Lord
E.
653 *The God of love*
164 Sing, brothers, sing
610 O sometimes gleams (L)
152 Christ is risen

ALTERNATIVES

527 How sweet the name
3 Lift your hidden faces
623 Praise, my soul, the King
166 Take heart, friends
168 Thou hallowed chosen
685 To us in Bethlem city

EASTER III

The Bread of Life

M.
265 Bread of the world
148 A messenger within
165 Sing, men and angels (L)
157 Let us rejoice
C.
161 Rejoice and be glad (G)
90 How brightly beams
267 II, Sun, who all my life
154 *Good Christian men, rejoice*
R.
540 Jesus, good
D. 148 (6) To thee who, dead
E.
508 Guide me, O thou great
166 *Take heart, friends*
152 Christ is risen (L)
4 *Spring has now unwrapped*

ALTERNATIVES

264 Bread of heaven
169 How great the harvest
272 I hunger and I thirst
549 Jesus, thou joy
156 Let all the multitudes
593 O Christ who holds
163 Sing, all ye Christian
164 Sing, brothers, sing

EASTER IV

The True Vine

M.
674 Thou true Vine
160 *Love's redeeming work*
435 A brighter dawn (L)
150 Alleluya ... Hearts to heaven
C.
149 All the toil (G)
168 Thou hallowed chosen
270 Here, O my Lord
163 Sing, all ye Christian people
R.
700 II, Who is he
D. 161 (4) To God be the glory
E.
674 Thou true Vine
156 Let all the multitudes
165 Sing, men and angels (L)
477 *Come, ye people*

ALTERNATIVES

272 I hunger and I thirst
595 O for a thousand tongues (E, L)
644 Songs of praise
167 The whole bright world
673 Thou long disowned (M, L)
689 II, We saw not
21 When spring unlocks

ROGATION SUNDAY
Prayer and Unity

M.
170 God of mercy
149 All the toil
158 Life is good (L)
  4 Spring has now unwrapped
C.
171 Lord, in thy name (G)
630 *Prayer is the soul's*
439 All creatures
  2 Kindly spring
R.
613 O sweeter than the marriage-feast
D. 160 (5) Hail the Lord
E.
628 Pray that Jerusalem
629 *Pray when the morn*
 69 With Jesus for hero (L)
 20 Thou art, O God

Alternatives
 19 Hark, my soul, how
618 O worship the King
631 Rejoice, O land
162 Round the earth
678 Through the night
690 We sing of God
P. 421 O all ye works, 396 O Father
  above us, 169 How great the harvest.
  D. 598 O God, our help

ASCENSION DAY
AND THE SUNDAY AFTER

M.
174 The eternal gates
161 *Rejoice and be glad*
440 All hail the power
172 *Hail the day*
P. 389 Hail thee, *or* 169 How great. D.
  407 Be, Lord
C.
156 Let all the multitudes
173 See the Conquerer
274 Lord, enthroned
585 My soul, there is a country
R.
477 Come, ye people
P. 392 At the name of Jesus. D. 173 (4)
  Glory be to God the Father
E.
175 The head that once
162 Round the earth, *or* 480 Crown him
176 To God with heart
169 How great the harvest
P. 172 Hail the day, *or* 162 Round the
  earth. D. 553 King of glory
Alternatives
149 All the toil
 90 How brightly beams

632 Rejoice! The Lord is King
165 Sing, men and angels
159 (6–8) Then once again
 69 With Jesus for hero

WHITSUNDAY
M.
179 Come, O creator Spirit
601 *O Holy Spirit, God*
574 Love of the Father
181 Creator Spirit
P. 389 Hail thee, *or* 616 O thou that
  movest. D. 178 (4) Teach us
C.
180 Come, thou holy Paraclete
616 O thou that movest all
177 Come down, O Love, 271 Holy God
520 Holy Spirit, truth divine
R.
184 Spirit of mercy
P. 391 Holy Spirit, make us. D. 417 To
  thee, who makest all
E.
178 Come, Holy Ghost, our souls
183 Our Lord, his Passion
506 Gracious Spirit, dwell
185 *When Christ had shown*
P. 391 Holy Spirit, make us, *or* 169 How
  great. D. 184 Spirit of mercy

Alternatives
454 Beyond, beyond
482 Enduring Soul
559 Life of ages
182 Our blest Redeemer
660 The Spirit of the Lord

TRINITY SUNDAY
M.
186 Father most holy
675 Thou wast, O God
188 Most ancient of all mysteries
566 Lord of all majesty
P. 683 To the name, *or* 485 Eternal
  Ruler. D. 413 Praise God, *or* 556
  Let all the world
C.
441 All hail to the Power
614 O thou in all thy might
526 *How shall I sing*
460 Bright the vision
R.
535 Immortal, invisible
P. 396 O Father above, *with the Conclusion,*
  vv. 31–3
E.
609 O sing to the Lord now, his greatness
485 Eternal Ruler
626 Praise to the Lord
618 *O worship the King*
P. 169 How great. D. 528 (5) I bind, *or*
  396 (*as above*) with D. 396 (31–3).

ALTERNATIVES

187 Holy, holy, holy
412 In God rejoice
398 The God of Abraham praise

659 The spacious firmament
663 There are a myriad means
690 We sing of God

A sequence of special subjects is here suggested for the Sundays in the second half of the year. Hymns suitable to these subjects are therefore given, as well as hymns suggested by the Scriptures. The subjects are: (1) The Kingdom of God and its Instruments (Trinity I to X); The Duty of the Individual (Trinity XI to XV); (3) God and Man (Trinity XVI to XVIII); (4) The Christian's Strength (Trinity XIX–XXV).

TRINITY I

1.—*The Kingdom of God and its Instruments*

God's Purpose

(For Hospital Sunday see Trinity VI)
M.
680 *Thy Kingdom come*
598 *O God, our help*
536 Immortal love (L)
304 All the past we leave
C.
307 O brother man (G)
615 O thou not made with hands
271 Holy God, we show forth
703 Zeal of the Lord
R.
613 O sweeter than the marriage-feast
D. 415 Through north and south
E.
468 City of God
545 Jesus shall reign
668 They all were looking (L)
578 Mine eyes have seen

ALTERNATIVES

446 And did those feet
475 Come now, all people
503 God moves in a mysterious way
639 Sing a song of joy
673 Thou long disowned (G)

TRINITY II

The Church

M.
245 Christ hath a garden
246 O faith of England
550 Jesus, these eyes (L)
678 Through the night
C.
497 Gather us in (G)
615 O thou not made with hands
281 Wherefore, O Father
468 *City of God*
R.
369 Remember all the people
D. 485 (3) We would be one
E.
628 *Pray that Jerusalem*
475 Come now, all people

385 Unto us a boy is born (L)
495 For the might of thine arm

ALTERNATIVES

443 All people
500 Glorious things
557 Let saints on earth
248 The Church of God
222 To Damascus (E, L)
244 Unknown and unrewarded

TRINITY III

The Nation

M.
320 Lord, while for all mankind
308 O God of earth and altar
703 Zeal of the Lord (L)
488 *Father in heaven who lovest*
C.
623 Praise, my soul, the King (G)
633 Ring out the grief
324 II, In thee our fathers
446 And did those feet
R.
631 Rejoice, O land
D. 318 (2) One realm of races four
E.
552 Judge eternal
322 *O beautiful, my country*
466 Christian, do you see him (L)
317 God of our fathers, known of old

ALTERNATIVES

316 England, arise
495 For the might of thine arm
523 How blest are they (E, L)
319 I vow to thee, my country
564 Lord of all being
321 Men of England

TRINITY IV

International Relations

M.
328 The night is ended
312 These things shall be
689 I, We saw thee not (L)
633 Ring out the grief
C.
682 To Mercy, Pity, Peace (G)
300 God is working his purpose out

485 Eternal Ruler
537 *In Christ there is*
R.
443 All people
D. 642 (6) Be the banner still
E.
329 *Turn back, O Man*
327 Sound over all waters
659 The spacious firmament (L)
326 Father eternal, ruler

ALTERNATIVES

466 Christian, do you (E, L)
577 Mercy thou art (E, L)
578 Mine eyes have seen
607 O brother man
658 The Lord will come
683 To the Name (E, L)
634 Ring out, ye crystal spheres

623 Praise, my soul, the King
535 Immortal, invisible
435 A brighter dawn
R.
499 Glad that I live
D. 413 Praise God, from whom
E.
285 *From thee all skill*
461 Can I see another's woe
577 Mercy thou art (L)
536 Immortal love

ALTERNATIVES

466 Christian, do you see him
505 Good cheer
537 In Christ there is (E, L)
567 Lord of health
633 Ring out the grief
640 Sing praise to God (E, L)

TRINITY V
Local Government
M.
340 *Father, who on man*
637 Say not, 'The struggle
568 Lord of the strong (L)
615 O thou not made with hands
C.
481 Dear Lord and Father (G)
262 As the disciples
552 *Judge eternal*
484 Eternal Father, who didst all
R.
488 Land of our birth
D. 414 Praise the Lord of heaven
E.
592 Now join, ye comrades
446 And did those feet
611 O Son of man (L)
633 Ring out the grief

ALTERNATIVES

461 Can I see another's woe
532 I look to thee (E, L)
604 O Lord, how happy (E, L)
341 Quick sympathy (M, L)
230 True Son of Man (E, L)
314 When wilt thou save
315 With wonderful deathless

TRINITY VI
(Or Hospital Sunday)
Health and Healing
M.
286 Life and health
341 Quick sympathy
287 *Thine arm, O Lord* (L)
567 Lord of health
C.
541 Jesus, Lord, we look (G)

TRINITY VII
Education
M.
346 Lord, from whose hand
640 Sing praise to God
589 Not always on the mount (L)
600 O heavenly beauty
C.
596 O God of Bethel (G)
560 'Lift up your hearts!'
606 O Lord of hosts
598 O God, our help
R.
538 In our work
D. 407 Be, Lord, the happy guide
E.
516 *Heavenly Father, may thy blessing*
601 *O Holy Spirit, God*
212 Prophets, teachers (L)
440 All hail the power

ALTERNATIVES

564 Lord of all being
567 Lord of health
571 Lord, when the wise men
597 O God of truth
621 Our God, to whom we turn
312 These things shall be

TRINITY VIII
Art and Letters
M.
601 O Holy Spirit, God
482 Enduring Soul
539 It fell upon a summer (L)
681 To God, the everlasting
C.
640 Sing praise to God (G)
621 Our God, to whom we turn
494 For the beauty

498 Gird on thy sword
R.
559 Life of ages
D. 417 To thee, who makest all
E.
214 Virtue supreme
692 *We thank you, Lord*
695 When by fear (L)
444 *All things bright*

ALTERNATIVES

513 He that is down (M, L)
534 I sought thee round (E, L)
558 Let the whole creation
600 O heavenly beauty
311 The world's great age
315 With wonderful deathless

TRINITY IX
Industry and Business

M.
469 Close by the heedless
450 Awake, awake, to love
590 Not with a choir of angels (L)
583 My God, my Father, make me strong
C.
339 *Son of God, eternal Saviour* (G)
647 Stern daughter of the Voice
442 All my hope on God
598 O God, our help
R.
538 In our work
D. 399 Day by day
E.
669 Those who love
652 *Teach me, my God and King*
561 Lo, in the wilderness (L)
698 When through the whirl

ALTERNATIVES

564 Lord of all being
567 Lord of health
592 Now join, ye comrades
610 O sometimes gleams
673 Thou long disowned

TRINITY X
Recreation

M.
692 We thank you, Lord
504 God, who created me
226 A message came (L)
18 By the breadth of the blue
C.
525 How lovely are thy dwellings (G)
340 *Father, who on man*
612 O source divine
516 Heavenly Father, may thy blessing
R.
377 When a knight

D. 404 Thank you for the world
E.
567 Lord of health
565 *Lord of all hopefulness*
69 With Jesus for hero (L)
444 All things bright

ALTERNATIVES

493 For mercy, courage, kindness
518 Here in the country's heart
531 I learned it in the meadow
337 Lord, in the hollow (E, L)
627 Praise we the Lord, who made
8 The summer days

TRINITY XI
2.—*The Duty of the Individual*
As a Member of the Church

M.
702 *Ye servants of the Lord*
619 Oft in danger
67 On Jordan's bank (L)
615 *O thou not made with hands*
C.
107 Lord, thou hast told us (G)
620 Our Father, while our hearts
661 Thee will I love
628 Pray that Jerusalem
R.
591 Now in life's breezy morning
D. 418 Worship, honour
E.
642 Soldiers of the cross
56 The day thou gavest
120 Thou say'st, 'Take up (L)
701 Ye holy angels bright

ALTERNATIVES

450 Awake, awake to love
491 Fight the good fight
540 Jesus, good above all other
577 Mercy thou art (M, L)
693 What conscience dictates
699 Where is thy God

TRINITY XII
As a Worker in the World

M
669 Those who love
25 I, Awake, my soul
97 Forty days (L)
309 Once to every man
C.
286 Life and health (G)
662 Then welcome each rebuff
626 Praise to the Lord, the Almighty
652 Teach me, my God and King
R.
700 Who within that stable

D. 556 (1) Let all the world
E.
583 *My God, my Father, make me*
491 *Fight the good fight*
275 O God, in whom we live (L)
55 Sun of my soul

ALTERNATIVES

232 Look up, by failure daunted (E, L)
592 Now join, ye comrades
613 O sweeter than the marriage-feast
641 Soldiers of Christ, arise
676 Though lowly here
686 Up to those bright

TRINITY XIII
Earning and Spending

M.
450 Awake, awake to love
622 Poor Soul, the centre
595 O for a thousand tongues (L)
237 He sat to watch
C.
633 Ring out the grief (G)
39 Behold us, Lord
520 Holy Spirit, truth divine
217 Jesus calls us
R.
538 In our work
D. 403 Our Father
E.
331 *Thine are all the gifts*
515 *He who would valiant be*
234 Lord, who shall sit (L)
57 The duteous day

ALTERNATIVES

455 Blest are the pure
481 Dear Lord and Father (M, L)
29 Forth in thy name (M)
572 Lord, who thyself hast bidden
31 New every morning (M)
693 What conscience dictates

TRINITY XIV
Home and Friendship

M.
31 New every morning
565 Lord of all hopefulness
577 Mercy thou art (L)
494 For the beauty of the earth
C.
492 Fill thou my life (G)
694 When all thy mercies
655 The Lord is in his holy place
516 *Heavenly Father, may thy blessing*
R.
611 O Son of man, our hero
D. 405 We thank thee
E.
692 *We thank you, Lord*

509 Happy are they
561 Lo, in the wilderness (L)
48 Now God be with us

ALTERNATIVES

485 Eternal Ruler (E, L)
514 He wants not friends
524 How happy is he born
22 Most glorious Lord (M)
627 Praise we the Lord, who made
52 Round me falls (E)

TRINITY XV
Responsibility for Others

M.
470 Come, kindred
338 Father of men, in whom
344 Lord, who didst send (L)
689 *We saw thee not*
C.
438 All as God wills (G)
634 Ring out, ye crystal spheres
323 O Lord almighty, thou whose
517 Help us to help
R.
488 Father in heaven who lovest
D. 642 (6) Be the banner
E.
635 Rise up, O men of God
642 Soldiers of the cross
435 *A brighter dawn* (L)
339 Son of God, eternal Saviour

ALTERNATIVES

461 Can I see another's woe
479 Commit thou all thy griefs (G)
306 Men, whose boast
55 Sun of my soul (E)
310 The day of the Lord
15 The year is swiftly waning

TRINITY XVI
3.—God and Man
God's Fatherly Care

M.
466 *Christian, do you see him*
588 No coward soul
690 We sing of God (L)
444 *All things bright*
C.
575 Made lowly wise (G)
623 Praise, my soul, the King
581 My God, how wonderful
522 How are thy servants blest
R.
462 Can you count the stars
D. 558 (1) Let the whole creation cry
E.
638 Shall God not share

F f

52 Round me falls the night
568 Lord of the strong (L)
521 Hosanna! Music is divine

ALTERNATIVES

503 God moves in a mysterious way
 12 Let us, with a gladsome mind
569 Lord, thou who gav'st me
109 Lord, who hast made me free
572 Lord, who thyself hast bidden
656 The Lord my pasture

TRINITY XVII
God's Forgiving Love
M.
573 *Love divine*
474 Come, my way, my truth
603 O Lord and Master (L)
478 Cometh sunshine
C.
513 *He that is down* (G)
534 I sought thee
584 My Lord, my Life
579 More lovely than the noonday
R.
502 God is love
D. 280 (2) Glory let us give
E.
666 There's a wideness
483 Enter thy courts
641 Soldiers of Christ (L)
 45 Glory to thee, my God

ALTERNATIVES

519 Hold thou my hands
558 Let the whole creation
623 Praise, my soul, the King
121 To my humble
694 When all thy mercies
123 Wilt thou forgive

TRINITY XVIII
God's Renewing Grace
M.
451 Awake, our souls
643 Sometimes a light surprises
638 Shall God not share (L)
391 Holy Spirit, make us strong
C.
620 Our Father, while our hearts (G)
506 Gracious Spirit, dwell
177 Come down, O Love divine
496 From glory to glory
R.
500 Glorious things
D. 416 To Father, Son
E.
601 O Holy Spirit, God
486 *Everything changes*
541 *Jesus, Lord, we look* (L)
181 Creator Spirit

ALTERNATIVES

454 Beyond, beyond
458 Breathe on me, Breath of God
 26 Christ, whose glory (M)
520 Holy Spirit, truth
542 Jesu, lover of my soul
564 Lord of all being
616 O thou that movest all

TRINITY XIX
4.—The Christian's Strength
Prayer, Communion
M.
553 King of glory
613 O sweeter than the marriage-feast
511 Hark what a sound (L)
630 *Prayer is the soul's sincere*
C.
689 I, We saw thee not (G)
262 As the disciples
270 Here, O my Lord, I see thee
551 Jesus, where'er thy people
R.
522 How are thy servants blest
D. 412 In God rejoice (*or* 418)
E.
629 *Pray when the morn*
467 Christian, seek not yet repose
559 Life of ages (L)
437 Abide with me

ALTERNATIVES

438 All as God wills
456 Blest be the day (M, L)
473 Come, my soul, thy suit
474 Come, my way (M, L)
515 He who would valiant be (M, L)
183 Our Lord, his Passion (E, L)
690 We sing of God

See also Trinity XXV, XXVI.

TRINITY XX
Wisdom, Knowledge, and Understanding
M.
452 Before thy feet
588 No coward soul is mine
602 O life that makest (L)
640 *Sing praise to God*
C.
670 Thou art my life (G)
566 Lord of all majesty
600 O heavenly Beauty
212 Prophets, teachers
R.
601 O Holy Spirit, God
D. 89 (4) Art and science
E.
563 Lord, my weak thought
571 Lord, when the wise men

674 Thou true Vine (L)
214 *Virtue supreme*
ALTERNATIVES
507 Gracious Spirit, Holy (E, L)
597 O God of truth
659 The spacious firmament
663 There are a myriad means
673 Thou long disowned
681 To God, the everlasting

TRINITY XXI
Confidence and Peace
M.
604 O Lord, how happy should we be
512 Hast thou not known
513 He that is down (L)
697 When on my day of life
C.
611 *O Son of man, our hero* (G)
479 Commit thou all thy griefs
522 *How are thy servants blest*
530 I know not what the future
R.
358 God who made the earth
D. 409 Honour and glory
E.
695 When by fear
442 All my hope
480 Crown him upon the throne (L)
438 All as God wills

ALTERNATIVES
502 God is love (E, L)
529 I heard the voice
104 Long did I toil
585 My soul, there is a country
182 Our blest Redeemer (E, L)
52 Round me falls the night (E)
661 Thee will I love
662 Then welcome each rebuff

TRINITY XXII
Joy and Gratitude
M.
38 You that have spent
544 Jesus, priceless treasure
288 Christ who knows (L)
157 Let us rejoice
C.
577 Mercy thou art (G)
558 Let the whole creation cry
247 Sing alleluya forth
582 My God, I thank thee
R.
657 The Lord of heaven confess
D. 626 (1) Praise to the Lord
E.
499 *Glad that I live am I*
443 *All people*

557 Let saints on earth (L)
623 Praise, my soul, the King
ALTERNATIVES
509 Happy are they
553 King of glory
609 O sing to the Lord
627 Praise we the Lord who made
632 Rejoice! The Lord is King
639 Sing a song of joy
643 Sometimes a light

TRINITY XXIII
The Divine Guidance
M.
508 *Guide me, O thou great*
670 Thou art my life
310 The day of the Lord (L)
566 Lord of all majesty
C.
575 Made lowly wise (G)
528 I bind unto myself
269 Father, we greet thee
614 *O thou in all thy might*
R.
487 Father, hear the prayer
D. 408 From all that dwell
E.
554 Lead, kindly Light
572 Lord, who thyself
700 Who within (L)
456 Blest be the day

ALTERNATIVES
441 All hail to the Power
507 Gracious Spirit (E, L)
515 He who would valiant be
555 Lead us, heavenly Father
596 O God of Bethel
605 O Lord, in me (M, L)
684 To thee whose eye
699 Where is thy God

TRINITY XXIV
The Divine Protection
M.
572 Lord, who thyself hast bidden
579 More lovely than the noonday
480 Crown him upon the throne (L)
532 I look to thee in every need
C.
536 *Immortal love* (G)
478 Cometh sunshine
576 Make me a captive
530 I know not what the future
R.
376 To God who makes
D. 526 (4) How great a being
E.
564 *Lord of all being*

641 Soldiers of Christ
685 To us in Bethlem city (L)
436 A safe stronghold
ALTERNATIVES
453 Believe not those who say
563 Lord, my weak thought
603 O Lord and Master (M, L)
648 Strong Son of God
659 The spacious firmament
686 Up to those bright

TRINITY XXV
The Divine Inspiration
M.
520 *Holy Spirit, truth divine*
588 No coward soul is mine
673 Thou long disowned (L)
454 Beyond, beyond that boundless sea
C.
509 Happy are they (*Ep. V, G*)
699 Where is thy God, my soul
482 Enduring Soul
691 We thank thee, Lord, for this
R.
591 Now in life's breezy morning
D. 534 (2) But now, my God, *or* 417 To thee, who makest all
E.
606 O Lord of hosts, all heaven
498 Gird on thy sword
620 Our Father, while our hearts (L)
486 *Everything changes*
ALTERNATIVES
442 All my hope
391 Holy Spirit, make us strong
602 O life that makest all things
256 O thou who camest from above
651 Sweet Infancy

See also Whitsunday, and Celebrations.

TRINITY XXVI
The Divine Grace
M.
27 Come, thou bright
23 This is the day
608 O love who formest me (L)
500 *Glorious things*
C.
26 Christ, whose glory (*Ep. VI, G*)
273 Let all mortal flesh
266 Come, risen Lord
263 Author of life divine
R.
618 O worship the King
D. 501 God be in my head
E.
449 *As pants the hart*
638 Shall God not share

139 It is finished (L)
57 The duteous day
ALTERNATIVES
451 Awake, our souls
524 How happy is he
584 My Lord, my Life
612 O source divine
643 Sometimes a light surprises
654 The King of love

LAST SUNDAY AFTER TRINITY
Hope and Praise
M.
443 *All people*
556 Let all the world
689 II, We saw not (L)
626 Praise to the Lord, the Almighty
D. 634 Ring out, ye crystal spheres
C.
331 Thine are all the gifts (G)
448 Angels holy
623 Praise, my soul, the King
624 Praise the Lord, ye heavens
R.
439 All creatures of our God
D. 415 Through north and south
E.
558 Let the whole creation cry
677 Through all the changing scenes
526 How shall I sing
157 Let us rejoice (L)
598 *O God, our help*
D. 350 Now thank we all
ALTERNATIVES
459 Brief life
351 O praise ye the Lord
637 Say not, 'The struggle
644 Songs of praise
657 The Lord of heaven
697 When on my day of life

SAINTS' DAYS AND OTHER OCCASIONS
A Saint's Day
M.
217–44 (*Of the Saint*)
207 How bright ⎫
205 Hail, glorious ⎬ *Or Apostles, &c.,*
206 Hark the sound ⎭ 211–16.
P. 202 For all the saints, *or* 210 Who are these. D. 418 Worship, honour
C.
204 Give me the wings
209 What are these that glow
291 Joy and triumph everlasting
208 Rejoice, ye dead
R.
203 For thy dear saint

P. 393 City of Peace, *or* 210 Who are
  these. D. 206 (5) God of God
E.
217–44 (*Of the Saint*)
247 Sing alleluya
216 I, III, *The Son of God* } *Or Apostles,*
210 *Who are these*   } *&c.*, 211–16.
P. *As above*, *or* 198 Jerusalem the golden.
  D. 413 Praise God

ALTERNATIVES

197 Jerusalem on high
200 O what their joy
213 Servants of God
  4 Spring has now unwrapped
201 There is a land
      See also All Saints.

The Transfiguration

235 *O Master, it is good*
679 Thy heaven, on which 'tis bliss
589 *Not always on the mount* (L)
514 He wants not friends
P. 440 All hail the power, *or* 459 Brief
  life. D. 415 Through north

ALTERNATIVES

510 Hark, my soul! it is the Lord
527 How sweet the name
529 I heard the voice
609 O sing to the Lord now

Michaelmas

238 *Angels and ministers*
617 O world invisible
240 Service and strength (L)
273 Let all mortal flesh
P. 209 What are these, *or* 701 Ye holy
  angels bright. D. 460 (4–6) Heaven
  is still

ALTERNATIVES

448 Angels holy
239 *Around the throne*
472 Come, let us join
205 (1, 4) Hail, glorious spirits
198 Jerusalem the golden
291 (1–3) Joy and triumph
199 Light's abode
585 My soul, there is a country
623 Praise, my soul, the King
624 (I, II) Praise the Lord! Ye heavens
644 Songs of praise
201 There is a land
395 (16–21) Thy vineyards

All Saints

244 *Unknown and unrewarded*
208 Rejoice, ye dead
216 The Son of God (I, II) (L)
243 *For the brave*
P. 202 For all the saints. D. 418 Worship,
  honour (*See also A Saint's Day*).

ALTERNATIVES FOR ALL SAINTS, &c.

211 Disposer supreme
203 (2–5) For all thy saints, O Lord
289 For those we love
204 Give me the wings
205 Hail, glorious spirits
206 Hark the sound
207 How bright
514 He wants not friends
196 I would choose to be
197 Jerusalem on high
198 Jerusalem the golden
557 Let saints on earth
199 Light's abode
200 O what their joy
247 Sing alleluya
201 There is a land
294 They are all gone
295 They whose course
209 What are these
210 Who are these (L)

DEDICATION FESTIVAL OR ANNIVERSARY

M.
602 O life that makest
189 All things are thine
194 Our Father, by whose servants
190 Blessèd city
P. 389 Hail thee, *or* 190 Blessèd city.
  D. 191 Lo, God is here
C.
295 They whose course
688 We love the place
275 O God, in whom
613 *O sweeter than the marriage-feast*
R.
525 How lovely are thy dwellings
P. 393 City of Peace. D. 624 (1) Praise
  the Lord
E.
464 Christ is our corner-stone
192 O Light, from age to age
468 *City of God*
193 Sing, all good people gathered
P. 246 O faith of England, *or* 395 Jerusalem. D. 626 Praise to the Lord

ALTERNATIVES

245 Christ hath a garden
243 For the brave
495 For the might of thine arm
551 Jesus, where'er thy people
248 The Church of God a kingdom
244 Unknown and unrewarded

Sunday School Anniversary

516 Heavenly Father, may thy blessing
462 Can you count the stars
538 In our work
700 Who within that stable
P. 396 O Father above us. D. 624 Praise
  the Lord

ALTERNATIVES

445 All things which live
499 Glad that I live
502 God is love
567 Lord of health
685 To us in Bethlem

And the hymns for Children, 352–85.

Flower Service

 17 All the scenes of nature
439 All creatures of our God
 21 When spring unlocks
 12 Let us, with a gladsome mind
444 All things bright
P. 396 O Father above us. D. 396 (31–3)
O God in whose working

ALTERNATIVES

448 Angels holy
354 Daisies are our silver
531 I learned it in the meadow
361 I love God's tiny creatures
535 Immortal, invisible
376 To God who makes

HARVEST FESTIVAL

M.
 9 Come, ye thankful people
 11 Fields of corn
618 O worship the King
 12 *Let us, with a gladsome mind*
P. 14 *We plough the fields.* D. 624 Praise the Lord
C.
631 Rejoice, O land
439 All creatures of our God
 10 Fair waved, *or* 518 Here in the
626 Praise to the Lord
R.
376 To God who makes
P. (*As M. or E.*)
E.
 13 To thee, O Lord, our hearts
 12 Let us, with a gladsome mind
331 Thine are all the gifts
 14 We plough the fields
P. 396 O Father above us. D. 350 Now thank we all

See also cross-references after 14.

MISSIONARY FESTIVAL

M.
301 Lift up your heads
497 Gather us in
537 In Christ there is
300 God is working his purpose out
P. 302 Servants of the great adventure. D. 415 Through north and south
C.
 60 Christ is the world's
 64 *Hills of the North*
556 Let all the world, 645 Spread, still

475 Come now, all people
R.
369 Remember all the people
440 All hail the power. D. 415 Through north and south
E.
443 All people
303 Thou whose almighty Word
299 *Far round the world*
645 Spread, still spread
P. 302 Servants. D. 408 From all that dwell

ALTERNATIVES

304 All the past
 87 Hail to the Lord's anointed
 63 High o'er the lonely hills
 91 In Asia born
545 Jesus shall reign
635 Rise up, O men of God
162 Round the earth
328 The night is ended
680 Thy Kingdom come
703 Zeal of the Lord

CELEBRATIONS
General

208 Rejoice, ye dead
214 Virtue supreme
328 The night is ended
304 All the past
P. 202 For all the saints. D. 408 From all that dwell, *or* 412 In God rejoice

ALTERNATIVES

475 Come now, all people
486 Everything changes
600 O heavenly Beauty
683 To the Name
See also All Saints Alternatives

Poets and other Artists

315 With wonderful deathless
311 The world's great age
494 For the beauty of the earth
558 Let the whole creation cry
P. 312 These things shall be. D. 441 All hail to the Power

ALTERNATIVES

245 Christ hath a garden
482 Enduring Soul
498 Gird on thy sword
412 In God rejoice
627 Praise we the Lord

Pioneers of Science and Thought

212 Prophets, teachers
610 O sometimes gleams
601 O Holy Spirit, God
640 Sing praise to God
P. 440 All hail the power. D. 89 (4) Art and science

OTHER DAYS THROUGHOUT THE YEAR

ALTERNATIVES

452 Before thy feet
495 For the might
285 From thee all skill
 91 In Asia born
571 Lord, when the wise

Adventure and Discovery

470 Come, kindred
300 God is working his purpose out
293 O valiant hearts
633 Ring out the grief
P. 578 Mine eyes. D. 408 From all that

ALTERNATIVES

 63 High o'er the lonely hills
207 How bright these glorious spirits
328 The night is ended

Civic Celebration

592 Now join, ye comrades
468 City of God
446 And did those feet
306 Men, whose boast it is
P. 338 Father of men. D. 339 (5) Son of God

ALTERNATIVES

475 Come now, all people
552 Judge eternal
310 The day of the Lord
673 Thou long disowned
313 Through all the long dark night
314 When wilt thou save

NATIONAL FESTIVAL

M.
320 *Lord, while for all*
325 What heroes thou hast bred
319 I vow to thee
327 Sound over all waters
P. 324 The King, O God. 318 God save
C.
631 Rejoice, O land
495 For the might
323 O Lord almighty, thou whose
552 Judge eternal
R.
488 Land of our birth
P. 396 IV, O Father of wisdom. D. 396 (31-3) O God in whose working
E.
322 *O beautiful, my country*
321 Men of England
329 Turn back, O Man
316 England, arise
P 317 God of our fathers. 446 And did those feet

ALTERNATIVES

436 A safe stronghold
243 For the brave
227 Lord God of Hosts
328 The night is ended
312 These things shall be
672 Thou Judge by whom
703 Zeal of the Lord

'Songs of Praise' is divided into Parts and sections in order that hymns may be easily found; but, as is shown by the above Table of suggestions, hymns may be taken from any special section and put to more general use when they are appropriate to the subject of a Lesson or Sermon.

OCCASIONAL VERSES.—The field of choice is very large for the selection of verses or small groups of verses, such as are used in some places as an introduction to a special service or part of a service. The following selection might be indefinitely expanded, and in many cases another verse might be added to the verse or verses here suggested.

Morning and Evening: 22 (2-3), 25 (9-10), 27 (1), 28 (1), 32 (1), 33 (1-2), 44 (4), 48 (4-5), 50 (1, 3), 51 (1-2), 57 (1); Advent: 60 (1), 407, 410; Christmas, &c.: 78 (1), 88 (5-7), 90 (2), 93 (1); Lent: 108 (3-4), 109 (4), 130 (6), 483 (1); Easter: 148 (4-5), 154 (3-4), 162 (4), 165 (1); Whitsun: 179 (1), 184 (1-2); Trinity: 186 (3-4); Dedication: 190 (7), 191 (1); Saints' Days: 194 (4), 243 (5), 247 (1-3); General: 399, 407, 410, 411, 441, 479 (4), 481 (1), 483 (3), 505 (1), 517 (2-3), 525 (1-2), 534 (3), 573 (1), 621 (5), 639 (1-2), 661 (1), 671 (4).

A very large number of short hymns is also provided by the system of starring verses with this special end in view, in the body of the book.

ANTHEMS.—Many of the hymns in 'Songs of Praise' may be sung as anthems. Among these are 5, 71, 75, 86, 90, 99, 107, 123, 128, 139, 150, 163, 169, 196, 226, 240, 265, 267, 270, 271, 280², 288, 294, 322, 381, 391, 432, 434, 498, 499, 501¹, 617, 638. Many carols, suitable for use as simple anthems, at all seasons of the year, will be found in the 'Oxford Book of Carols'.

(871)

METRICAL INDEX OF TUNES

* *Denotes the provision of a Fa-burden, Descant, or alternative harmonization of the tune.*

The Tunes marked φ are set to sonnets and their use involves the repetition of the last 2 strains of the tune for the final couplet of the sonnet.

The metres are IAMBIC *unless otherwise stated.*

S. M.
Short Measure.
6 6. 8 6.

*Carlisle, 458.
Drumcondra, 601.
Falcon Street (Silver Street), 635.
Franconia, 455.
Mount Ephraim, 203.
Old134th (*see* St. Michael).
*St. Bride, 699.
St. Edmund, 120 ii.
St. Ethelwald, 641 ii.
*St. Michael (Old 134th), 702.
St. Thomas, 68.
Sandys, 652.
Selma, 10.
Silver Street (*see* Falcon Street).
Song 20, 584.
*Southwell, 106.
Windermere, 332.
Wirksworth, 120 i.
Zachary, 576.

D. S. M.
Double Short Measure.
6 6. 8 6. D.

Dinbych, 479.
From Strength to Strength, 641 i.
Ich halte treulich still, 480.
Llanllyfni, 453.
Milites, 343.
Old 25th, 195.

C. M.
Common Measure.
8 6. 8 6.

Abbey, 492.
Aberdeen, 320.
*Abridge, 100.
Ascendit, 676.
Attercliffe, 118.
Balfour, 620.
Ballerma, 257.
Bangor, 209.
*Bedford (Weale), 114.
Belgrave, 694.

Binchester, 509.
Bishopthorpe (St. Paul's), 536.
Blackbourne, 575.
*Bristol, 62.
Bromsgrove, 23.
Burford, 596.
Butler, 378.
Caithness, 112.
Capel, 248.
Cheerful, 472.
*Cheshire, 105.
Coleshill, 658.
Cornhill, 41.
Crediton, 35.
Crowle, 482.
Culross, 530.
Dibdin, 254.
Dorking, 205.
*Dundee (French), 557.
*Dunfermline, 517.
Dunstan, 393 ii.
Durham, 525.
Eardisley, 393 iii.
Eatington, 192.
Elgin, 665.
*Epsom, 682.
Epworth, 224.
Farnham, 285.
*Farrant, 275.
Ferry, 39.
French (*see* Dundee).
Für dein empfangen Speis und Trank (*see* Praetorius).
Glenluce, 523.
Gräfenberg (Nun danket all), 38.
Harington (Retirement), 613.
*Horsley, 131.
Hunnys, 108.
Irish, 680.
Jackson, 445.
Kilmarnock, 522.
King's Langley (Irreg.), 229.
King's Norton, 547 i.
*Lincoln, 171.
*London New, 503.
Manchester, 673.

*Martyrdom, 449.
*Martyrs, 597.
Melrose, 686.
Mendip, 201.
*Miles Lane, 440.
Newbury, 395, Part III.
Ninth Tune (*see* Tallis' Ordinal).
Northrop, 82 ii.
Norwich, 577.
Nottingham (*see* St. Magnus).
Nun danket all (*see* Gräfenberg).
O God of Love, 595.
Oliver, 117.
Osborne, 550.
Praetorius (Für dein empfangen Speis und Trank), 174.
Relief, 614.
Retirement (*see* Harington).
*Richmond, 468.
Rochester, 594.
Rodmell, 221.
*St. Anne, 598.
St. Austin, 395, Part I.
St. Bernard, 537.
St. Botolph, 527 i.
*St. David, 301.
*St. Flavian, 188.
*St. Fulbert, 151.
St. Hugh, 371.
*St. James, 96.
*St. Magnus (Nottingham), 175.
*St. Mary, 116.
St. Nicholas, 395, Part IV.
St. Paul's (*see* Bishopthorpe).
*St. Peter, 527 ii.
*St. Stephen, 250.
Solomon, 110.
Song 67, 204.
Southill, 395, Part II.
Stalham, 393 i.
Stockton, 113.
Stracathro, 438.
Strassburg, 400.
Stroudwater, 185.

(872)

METRICAL INDEX OF TUNES

*Tallis' Ordinal ('9th Tune'), 664.
This endris Nyght, 72.
Tiverton, 456.
*University, 653.
Walsall, 603.
Warwick, 513.
Westminster, 581.
Wigtown, 630.
*Wiltshire, 677.
*Winchester Old, 82 i.
*Windsor, 547 ii.
*Worcester, 323.
*York, 628.

D. C. M.
Double Common Measure.
8 6 8 6. D.
Bilsdale (Irreg.), 361.
Christmas Carol (Irreg.), 79 ii.
First Mode Melody, 625.
Forest Green (Irreg.), 79 i.
Kingsfold, 529.
Noel, 76.
Nun seht (see Stettin).
Old 18th, 43.
Old 22nd, 176.
Old 30th, 693.
Old 44th, 655.
Old 77th (see Old 81st).
*Old 81st (Old 77th), 216.
Old 107th, 512.
Old 137th, 526.
St. Matthew, 287.
Soll's sein, 8.
Stettin (Nun seht), 225.
*Third Mode Melody, 675.
Wellington Square, 219.

L. M.
Long Measure.
8 8. 8 8.
Ach bleib bei uns (see Calvisius).
Adesto sancta Trinitas, 51 ii.
Aeterna Christi munera, 37 i.
Affection, 284.
Alfreton, 189 ii, 237.
Andernach, 130 ii.
*Angel's Song (Song 34), 29.
Angelus (Du meiner Seelen), 42 ii.
Auctoritate saeculi, 67.
Babylon's Streams, 124.
Beata nobis gaudia, 44 ii.
Birling, 55.
*Breslau, 132.
Brockham, 228.

Calvisius (Ach bleib bei uns), 42 i.
Cameronian Midnight Hymn, 514.
Cannons, 337 i.
Cromer, 531.
Danby, 16.
Daniel, 376.
Das Leiden des Herrn, 119.
Das neugeborne Kindelein (see Jena).
Das walt' Gott Vater, 679.
Deo gracias, 684.
Der Tag bricht an, 563.
Deus tuorum militum, 633.
Die ganze Welt (see Hilariter).
Duke Street, 298, 491* i.
Du meiner Seelen (see Angelus).
Dulcis Jesu Memoria, 549 ii.
Ein Kind gebor'n, 91.
Erhalt' uns, Herr, 277 ii.
Gonfalon Royal, 593.
Herongate, 602.
Herr Jesu Christ, 40.
Hilariter (Die ganze Welt), 167.
Hymnus Eucharisticus (The Magdalen Tower Hymn), 607 i.
*Illsley, 610.
Jena (Das neugeborne Kindelein), 80 ii.
Kent, 524.
Leighton, 245.
Llangollen (Lledrod), 488.
Lledrod (see Llangollen).
Lucis Creator, 37 ii.
Magdalen Tower Hymn, The (see Hymnus Eucharisticus).
*Melcombe, 31.
Montesano, 491 ii.
Mont Richard, 148 ii.
Montgomery, 612.
*Morning Hymn, 25, Part I.
New Sabbath, 691.
O amor quam exstaticus, 607 ii.
O Jesu mi dulcissime, 184.
**Old 100th, 443.
Philippine, 251.
Plainsong, 33 Part I i, 33 Part II i, 44 i, 51 i, 130 i, 148 i, 549 i.
Plaistow, 122.
Puer nobis nascitur (see Splendour).

Richard, 25, Part II.
*Rockingham, 133.
St. Bartholomew, 256.
St. Cross, 140.
St. Venantius, 571.
Samson, 451.
Simeon, 551.
Solemnis haec festivitas, 33, Part I ii.
Solothurn, 239.
Song 5, 648.
Song 34 (see Angel's Song).
Splendour (Puer nobis nascitur), 33, Part II ii.
*Tallis' Canon, 45.
The Rosy Sequence, 548.
Truro, 337 ii, 545*.
Uffingham, 564.
Veni Creator (Mechlin), 179.
Veni Creator (Tallis), 178.
Verbum supernum, 277 i.
Vom Himmel hoch, 80 i.
Wainwright, 355.
*Wareham, 631.
Warrington, 25, Part III.
Whitehall, 589.
*Winchester New, 137.

D. L. M.
Double Long Measure.
8 8 8 8. D.
Addison's (see London).
Bucklebury, 189 i.
Cantate Domino, 95.
Dies irae (see Merthyr Tydvil).
Jerusalem, 446.
London (or Addison's), 659.
Merthyr Tydvil (Dies irae), 312.
St. Patrick, 528, Part I.
Tallis' Lamentation, 235.

2. 8 8 8. 8 8.
(SPONDAIC-IAMBIC)
Braint, 505 i.
Glan'rafon, 505 ii.

3 8. 6 5 6. 3.
Stonethwaite, 399.

4 4. 11. 4 4. 11.
Wir Christenleut, 638.

4 7. 4 6. 4 7. 6 4 8.
Quittez, pasteurs, 98.

4. 8 4. 4 8.
Eskdale, 651.

(873)

6 6. 7 7. 7 7.
Regnart (Auf meinen
lieben Gott), 109.

6 6. 8 4. D.
Leoni, 398.

6 6. 8 6. 8 6. 8 8 6.
Glan Geirionydd, 592.

6 6 10. 6 6 10. 8 12.
Ring out (Irreg.), 634.

6 6 10. 6 6 12.
St. Gabriel, 662.

6 6. 11. D.
Down Ampney, 177.

6 7. 6 7.
(TROCHAIC)
Hermitage, 92.

6 7. 6 7. 6 6. 6 6.
Darmstadt (O Gott, du
frommer Gott), 621.
Kommt Seelen (see Rin-
kart).
*Nun danket, 350.
O Gott, du frommer
Gott (see Darmstadt).
Rinkart (Kommt Seelen),
60.

6 7. 6 7. D. and refrain.
Vruechten, 169.

6 10. 6 10.
Glynthorpe, 588.

7 4. 7 4.
(ANAPAESTIC)
Stowey (Irreg.), 377.

7 4. 7 4. D.
(TROCHAIC)
Easter Hymn, 145.
Easter Hymn Original
Version (see Lyra).
Gwalchmai, 553.
Llanfair, 149.
Lyra (Easter Hymn Origi-
nal Version), 172.

7 5. 7 5.
(TROCHAIC)
St. Aidan, 331.

7 6. 7 6.
Bulstrode, 367.
Cherry Tree, 599.

Christus der ist mein
Leben, 585.
Devonshire, 459 i.
Hambridge, 15.
Magdalena, 591.
Paderborn, 234.
St. Alphege, 459 ii.

7 6. 7 6, and refrain.
Royal Oak, 444.

7 6. 7 6. D.
Ach Gott vom Himmel-
reiche (see Görlitz).
Au fort de ma détresse,
244.
Aurelia, 249 ii.
Bremen, 255 ii.
Caerlleon, 193 i.
*Crüger, 87.
Dank sei Gott in der
Höhe, 194 i.
Ellacombe, 193 ii.
Ewing, 198 i.
Freedom, 322 i.
Görlitz (Ach Gott vom
Himmelreiche), 146.
Helder (Wohlauf thut
nicht verzagen), 322 ii.
Herzlich thut mich er-
freuen, 249 i.
In der Wiegen, 369.
In Memoriam, 373.
King's Lynn, 308.
Komm, Seele, 255 i.
Little Baddow, 646 i.
Llangloffan, 643 i.
Loughborough, 194 ii.
Meirionydd, 629.
Morning Light, 646 ii.
*Passion Chorale, 128.
Pearsall, 198 ii.
Rhyddid, 643 ii.
St. Theodulph (Valet will
ich dir geben), 135.
Thornbury, 255 iii.
Valet will ich dir geben
(see St. Theodulph).
Wohlauf thut nicht ver-
zagen (see Helder).
(TROCHAIC)
Ave Virgo virginum, 144.
Tempus adest floridum, 4.
Weimar, 215.

7 6. 7 6. 4 6.
Eia, Eia (Zu Bethlehem
geboren), 685.

7 6. 7 6. 6 7 3.
Ave Maria klare, 223.

Es ist ein' Ros' ent-
sprungen, 70.

7 6. 7 6. 7 6.
Berwick Street (Irreg.),
372.

7 6. 7 6. 7 6. 7 6. 6 6. 8 4.
Wir pflügen, 14.

7 6. 7 6. 7 7 6. 7 7 6.
(TROCHAIC)
Cornfields, 11.

7 6. 7 6. 7 8. 7 6.
(TROCHAIC AND IAMBIC)
Amsterdam, 286.

7 6. 7 6. 8 6. 8 6.
Oslo, 232.

7 6. 7 6. 8 8. 7 7.
(TROCHAIC)
Werde munter, 101.

7 6. 7 6. 8 8 8. 5.
Kendal, 314.

7 6. 7 7.
(TROCHAIC)
Omega and Alpha (Puer
nobis nascitur), 385.

7 6. 8 6, and refrain.
Good-bye, 386, Part VI.

7 7 6. 7 7 8.
Innsbruck, 57.

7 7. 7 3.
(TROCHAIC)
Brookend, 348.
Robyn, 467.

7 7. 7 4. 4 4.
(TROCHAIC)
Heiliger Geist, 391.

7 7 7. 5.
(TROCHAIC)
*Capetown, 507.
Ton-mân, 47.

7 7. 7 7.
Nun lasst uns Gott dem
Herren (see Selnecker).
Selnecker (Nun lasst uns
Gott dem Herren), 435.
(TROCHAIC)
Aus der Tiefe (see Hein-
lein).

METRICAL INDEX OF TUNES

8 6. 8 6. 8 8 8. 7.
(IAMBIC AND ANAPAESTIC)
Mantegna (Irreg.), 126.

8 6. 8 8 6.
Lobt Gott (*see* Nicolaus).
Nicolaus (Lobt Gott), 481 ii.
Repton, 481 i.

8 7. 8 7.
Ach Gott und Herr, 278.
Brynhyfryd, 241.
Dominus regit me, 654 ii.
St. Columba, 654 i.
(TROCHAIC)
Goldschmidt (O, der Alles), 217 ii.
Gott will's machen, 487.
*Laus Deo (Redhead No. 46), 460.
Marching, 678.
Merton, 61.
Northumbria, 382.
O, der Alles (*see* Goldschmidt).
Omni die, 217 i.
Redhead No. 46 (*see* Laus Deo).
Shanghai, 17.
Shipston, 364.
*Stuttgart, 84.
Sussex, 321.

8 7. 8 7, and refrain.
(TROCHAIC)
Iris, 71.

8 7. 8 7. D.
Ach! wan doch Jesu, liebster mein (*see* Nachtigall).
Nachtigall (Ach! wan doch Jesu, liebster mein), 313.
St. Gall, 13.
(TROCHAIC)
Alta Trinità beata, 669.
*Austrian Hymn, 500.
Ebenezer (Ton-y-botel), 309.
Engadine, 516 ii.
Exile, 573 ii.
Gwalia, 54.
Hyfrydol, 260.
In Babilone, 173 i.
Llansannan, 666.
Marathon, 302.
Moriah, 573 i.
Pisgah, 233.
Pleading Saviour, 516 i.
Praise, 624.

Rex gloriae, 173 ii.
Ton-y-botel (*see* Ebenezer).
Vision, 206.
Würzburg, 150 ii.
Yn y Glyn, 339.
Zum Frieden, 674.

8 7. 8 7. 3 3 7.
(TROCHAIC)
Meine Hoffnung, 442.

8 7. 8 7. 4 7.
(TROCHAIC)
Bryn Calfaria, 274 i.
Caersalem, 508 ii.
*Helmsley, 65.
Llanilar, 508 i.
(*See also* 8 7. 8 7. 8 7.)

8 7. 8 7. 6 6. 6 6 7.
Ein' feste Burg, 436.

8 7. 8 7 7.
(TROCHAIC)
Il buon Pastor, 567.

8 7. 8 7. 7 5. 7 5. 8 7. 8 7.
(TROCHAIC)
Midhurst, 152.

8 7. 8 7. 7 7.
(TROCHAIC)
*All Saints, 210 i.
Gott des Himmels, 32 i.
Irby, 368.
Psalm 146, 210 ii.
St. Leonard, 32 ii.

8 7. 8 7. 7 7. 8 8.
(TROCHAIC)
Psalm 42, 291.

8 7. 8 7. 8 7.
(TROCHAIC)
Ad perennis vitae fontem, 274 ii.
Ardudwy, 695.
Blaencefn, 222.
Calvary, 333, Part I.
Dismissal, 333, Part II.
Grafton, 129 ii.
Lewes, 555 i.
Mannheim, 555 ii.
*Neander, 477.
Oriel, 190 ii, 683*.
Pange lingua, 280 i.
Picardy, 273.
Plainsong, 129 i, 190 i.
Praise, my Soul, 623.
Rhuddlan, 552.

St. Thomas (Webbe), 342.
*Tantum ergo (Webbe), 199.
Tantum ergo (No. 2), 280 ii.
(*See also* 8 7. 8 7. 4 7.)

8 7. 8 7. 8 7 7.
(TROCHAIC)
Divinum mysterium, 387.

8 7. 8 7. 8 7. 7 7.
(TROCHAIC)
Flanders, 448.

8 7. 8 7. 8 7. 8 7. 7 7.
Chelsea, 164.
Cobbold, Appendix 1.

8 7. 8 7. 8 8.
Dies ist der Tag, 168 ii.
Mach's mit mir Gott (*see* Schein).
Schein (Mach's mit mir Gott), 168 i.

8 7. 8 7. 8 8 7.
Allein Gott in der Höh' sei Ehr', 561.
Es ist das Heil (*see* Wittenberg).
Lobt Gott (*see* Melchior).
Luther's Hymn (Nun freut euch), 672.
Melchior (Lobt Gott), 475.
Mit Freuden zart, 214.
Nun freut euch, 640.
Nun freut euch (*see* Luther's Hymn).
Wächterlied, 562.
Wittenberg (Es ist das Heil), 156.

8 7. 8 7. 8 8. 8 7.
(TROCHAIC)
Trefaenan, 158, 462.

8 7. 8 7. 12 12. 11 11.
(TROCHAIC, refrain ANAPAESTIC)
Cöthen (Eins ist Not), 150 i.

8 8. 4 4. 8 8 and Alleluyas.
Easter Alleluya (Lasst uns erfreuen), 157.
Lasst uns erfreuen (*see* Easter Alleluya).
St. Francis, 439.

8 8. 4 4. 8 8 8.
Leicester (or Bedford), 605.
(*See also* 8 8. 8 8. 8 8.)

(877)

886. D.
Advent, 604 ii.
Allgütiger, mein Lebelang (see Erfurt).
Erfurt (Allgütiger, mein Lebelang), 521.
Magdalen College, 690.
Song 18, 604 i.

887. D.
(TROCHAIC)
Alles ist an Gottes Segen (see Auctor omnium bonorum).
Auctor omnium bonorum (Alles ist an Gottes Segen), 212.
Christi Mutter stund vor Schmerzen (see Corner).
Corner (Christi Mutter stund vor Schmerzen), 138 ii.
St. Olaf's Sequence, 59.
Stabat Mater, 138 i.

88.75.
Wonder, 107.

88.77. D.
(TROCHAIC)
Mon Dieu, prête-moi l'oreille, 121.

887.887. D.
Psalm 68, 246.

887.887.84.48.
(IAMBIC AND TROCHAIC)
*Wie schön leuchtet der Morgenstern, 90.

888.
Bohemia (O Mensch sieh), 142.
O Mensch sieh (see Bohemia).
Wulfrun, 401.

888 and Alleluyas.
O filii et filiae, 143 i and ii.

888. D.
Exeter, 338.
Llangoedmor, 242.

88.83.
White Gates, 489.

88.84.
Es ist kein Tag (see Meyer).
Gaza, 650.
Gelobt sei Gott (see Vulpius).
Meyer (Es ist kein Tag), 289, 583.
Victory, 147.
Vulpius (Gelobt sei Gott), 154.

88.86.
Childhood, 668.
Children All, 386, Part IV.
Fitzwilliam, 539.
Isleworth, 253.

888.7.
Come, faithful people, 136.
(TROCHAIC)
Charing, 340.
Quem pastores laudavere, 540.

88.88. D.
(TROCHAIC)
Morley, 528, Part II.
Schmücke dich, 267.

88.88.4.
Hermann (Erschienen ist der herrlich Tag), 159.

88.88.77.77.
(IAMBIC AND TROCHAIC)
Oakley, 58.

88.888.
Ich fahr dahin, 667.
O Jesulein süss, 600.
Pachelbel (Was Gott thut), 403.
Was Gott thut (see Pachelbel).

88.88.86.
Risby, 568.

88.88.88.
Bedford (Bishop) (see Leicester), 605.
David's Harp, 476.
Falkland, 227.
Farmborough, 689.
Folkingham, 317.
Gesius(Heut'triumphiret), 533.
Heut' triumphiret (see Gesius).

Lambeth, 346, 608.
Leicester(or Bedford),605.
Lodsworth, 336.
New 113th, 20, 671.
Old 117th, 191.
Surrey, 656.
*Vater unser, 566.
Veni Creator (Attwood), 181.
Veni Emmanuel, 66.

8888.8888.65.
Freylinghausen (Macht hoch die Thür), 77.

88.88.88.8.12.
Santwat, 647.

88.88.810.
Need, 569.

89.88. D.
(ANAPAESTIC)
Sion, 341.

898.898.664.448.
(TROCHAIC-IAMBIC)
Wachet auf, 687.

89.89. D.
Crossings, 661 ii.
Psalm 138, 661 i.

97.97.77.446.
De Boodschap, 226.

98.89.
(TROCHAIC)
Randolph, 334.

98.98.
Essex, 637 ii.
Gottlob, es geht nun mehr zum Ende (see Weisse).
Joldwynds, 56 ii.
Les commandemens de Dieu, 56 i.
Pimlico Road (Irreg.), 617.
Weisse (Gottlob, es geht nun mehr zum Ende), 637 i.

98.98. D.
Henham, 616.
Rendez à Dieu, 265.
(ANAPAESTIC)
Crugybar, 609.

98.98.88.
Neumark, 606.

ALPHABETICAL INDEX OF TUNES

Denotes the provision of a Fa-burden, Descant, or alternative harmonization of the tune.

(881)

ALPHABETICAL INDEX OF TUNES

Solomon, 110.
Solothurn, 239.
Song 1, 296, 485.
Song 4, 261.
Song 5, 648.
Song 13, 134.
Song 18, 604 i.
Song 20, 584.
Song 22, 574.
Song 24, 103, 681.
(Song 34), see Angel's Song, 29.
Song 46, 125.
Song 67, 204.
Song of Joy, 639.
Southill, 395, Part II.
*Southwell, 106.
Splendour (Puer nobis nascitur), 33, Part II, ii.
Spring, 5.
Springtime, 360.
Stabat Mater, 138 i.
Stalham, 393 i.
Stanstead, 697.
Stepney, 325.
Stettin (Nun seht), 225.
(Stockport), see Yorkshire, 73.
Stockton, 113.
Stonethwaite, 399.
Stowey, 377.
Stracathro, 438.
Strassburg, 400.
Stroudwater, 185.
*Stuttgart, 84.
Suo-gân, 380.
Surrey, 656.
Sussex, 321.
Sutton Valence, 115 i.
Swanwick, 546.

*Tallis' Canon, 45.
Tallis' Lamentation, 235.
*Tallis' Ordinal, 664.
*Tantum ergo (Webbe), 199.
Tantum ergo (No. 2), 280 ii.
Tempus adest floridum, 4.
Tenbury, 328 ii.
Thaxted, 319 i.
The Birds, 381.
The First Nowell, 384.
The Golden Sequence, 180 i.
The Rosy Sequence, 548.

Theodoric, 502.
*Third Mode Melody, 675.
This endris Nyght, 72.
Thornbury, 255 iii.
Tiverton, 456.
Ton-mân, 47.
(Ton-y-botel), see Ebenezer, 309.
Trefaenan (Harmonized arrangement), 158.
Trefaenan (Unison arrangement), 462.
Tres Magi de gentibus, 305.
Truro, 337 ii, *545.
Tunbridge, 474.

Uffingham, 564.
*University, 653.
University College, 619.
Ut queant laxis, 28 ii.

(Valet will ich dir geben), see St. Theodulph, 135.
*Valiant Hearts, 293 i.
Valor, 293 ii.
*Vater unser, 566.
Veni Creator (Attwood), 181.
Veni Creator (Mechlin), 179.
Veni Creator (Tallis), 178.
Veni Emmanuel, 66.
Veni Sancte Spiritus, 180 ii.
Verbum supernum, 277 i.
Victor King (Christus ist erstanden), 162.
Victory, 147.
Vienna, 357.
Vision, 206.
Voller Wunder, 374.
Vom Himmel hoch, 80 i.
Vruechten, 169.
Vulpius (Gelobt sei Gott), 154.

Wachet auf, 687.
Wächterlied, 562.
Wainwright, 355.
Walsall, 603.
*Wareham, 631.
Warrington, 25, Part III.
Warsaw, 252.
Warwick, 513.

(Warum sollt ich), see Bonn, 89.
(Was Gott thut), see Pachelbel, 403.
Was lebet, was schwebet, 470.
Watchman, 63.
Water-End, 499.
Weather-beaten Sail, 587.
Weimar, 215.
Weisse (Gottlob, es geht nun mehr zum Ende), 637 i.
Wellington Square, 219.
Werde munter, 101.
Westminster, 581.
Westridge, 363.
Whitehall, 589.
White Gates, 489.
White Ladies Aston, 370.
Wicklow, 182.
*Wie schön leuchtet der Morgenstern, 90.
(Wie wohl ist mir), see Dessler, 703.
Wigtown, 630.
*Wiltshire, 677.
*Winchester New, 137.
*Winchester Old, 82 i.
Windermere, 332.
*Windsor, 547 ii.
Wir Christenleut, 638.
Wirksworth, 120 i.
Wir pflügen, 14.
Wittenberg (Es ist das Heil), 156.
(Wohlauf thut nicht verzagen), see Helder, 322 ii.
Wolder (Aus meines Herzens Grunde), 660.
Wonder, 107.
Woodlands, 299.
*Worcester, 323.
Working, 345.
Wulfrun, 401.
Würzburg, 150 ii.

*York, 628.
*Yorkshire (Stockport), 73.
Yn y Glyn, 339.

Zachary, 576.
(Zu Bethlehem geboren), see Eia, Eia, 685.
Zum Frieden, 674.

(886)

INDEX OF COMPOSERS, ARRANGERS, AND
SOURCES OF MELODIES

* Denotes Fa-burden, Descant, arrangement, or alternative harmonization.

A Collection of Hymns and Sacred Poems (Dublin), 680.
A New Set of Sacred Music, 463, 614.
A Sett of New Psalm Tunes, 605.
Ahle, J. R., 547.
Air sur les hymnes sacrez, 143 i.
Akeroyde, S., 346, 608.
Albert, H., 32 i.
Anchors' *Choice Collection of Psalm Tunes*, 603.
Andächtige und auserlesene Gesänger, 150 ii.
Andernach *Gesangbuch*, 130 ii, 305, 478.
Angers Church Melody, 231.
Anglo-Genevan Psalter, 655.
Anon., *see* Unknown source.
Antiphonarium Romanum, 277 i.
Armstrong, T., 469.
Arnold's *Complete Psalter*, 682.
As Hymnodus Sacer, 132.
Atkins, Ivor, 323*, 370.
Attwood, T., 181.

B.R., 595.
Bach, J. C., 32 ii.
Bach, J. S., 42 i, 57, 60, 90*, 93 i, 99*, 123*, 128, 128*, 135*, 139*, 150 i, 156*, 159*, 194 i*, 264, 277 ii*, 278*, 480, 481 ii*, 533*, 544*, 558*, 566*, 585*, 621*, 637 i*, 638*, 640*, 674, 679*, 687*, 703.
Bairstow, E. C., 114*.
Baring-Gould, S., 49.
Barnby, J., 95.
Barthélémon, F. H., 25, 207
Barton's *Psalms*, 658.
Battishill, Jonathan, 538.
Bax, Arnold, 107.
Bayeux Antiphoner, 262 ii.
Bayeux Church Melody, 330
Bible Class Magazine, 14.
Bicknell, C., 136.
Bishop, John, 605, 610.

Bohemian Brethren's *Gesangbuch*, 11, 142, 214, 225.
Bourgeois, L., 50, 56 i, 121, 265, 291, 347.
Boyce, W., 375, 452.
Boyle, Ina, 240.
Brahms, J., 667*.
Bremner's *Collection*, 320.
Briggs, G. W., 194 ii, 243, 360, 401, 439, 501 ii, 572, Appendix 3 i.
Buck, P. C., 148 ii, 247, 593.
Bullock, Ernest, 46*, 216*, 590.
Burke, C., 528, Part II.
Byrd, William, Appendix 3 ii and vi.

Calvisius, S., 42 i.
Campian, Thomas, 124, 587, 639.
Cantica Sacra, 190 ii, 683.
Cantica Spiritualia, 42 ii.
Canzuns Spirituaelas, 516 ii, 567.
Carey, Henry, 550, 656.
Catechismus-Gesangbuchlein, 660.
Champness, W., 612.
Chants Ordinaires de l'Office Divin, 129 ii.
Chapman's *Musical Companion*, 612.
Charterhouse Founder's Day Service Book, 212.
Chartres Antiphoner, 51, ii.
Chetham's *Psalmody*, 596.
Chinese Melody, 17.
Choralbuch (MS.), Herrnhut, 160.
Chorale Book for England, The, 109, 217 ii, 626.
Christian Vespers, 438.
Christliche Lieder, 156, 640.
Clark, Jeremiah, 175, 228, 474, 536, 547 i, 564.
Clark, Thomas, 35, 252.
Clausener Gesangbuch, 184.
Cobbold, W., 43.

Cologne (Cöln) *Gesangbuch* (Brachel), 157, 163, 167, 478, 549 ii.
Cook, E. T., 570*.
Corner's *Geistliche Nachtigall*, 8, 369, 391.
Corner's *Gesangbuch*, 138 ii, 217 i.
Cornysshe, W., 467.
Courtville, R., 96.
Croft, W., 192, 287, 509, 598, 618, 657.
Crüger, J., 24, 87, 99, 186 ii, 267, 350, 544*.
Cunningham's *Selection of Psalm Tunes*, 266.
Custard, H. Goss, 507*.
Czech Traditional Carol, 381.

Damon's *Psalter*, 106, 547 ii.
Darke, Harold E., 41, 200*, 547 ii*.
Darmstadt *Gesangbuch*, 210 i, 217 ii.
Darwall, J., 701.
Davies, David, 505 ii.
Davies, H. Walford, 79 ii.
Day's *Psalter*, 43, 176, 188, 195, 216, 235, 329, 526.
Divine Companion, The, 346, 476, 595, 608.
Dix, L. L., 268*.
Doles, J. F., 2.
Dougall, Neil, 522.
Dowland, J., 443**, 461.
Dresden *Gesangbuch*, 638.
Dresden *Kirchen und Hausbuch*, 123.
Drese, A., 52.
Duncalf, Henry, 256.
Dussek, Ronald, Appendix 2.
Dutch Melody (17th cent.), 169.
Dutch Traditional Melody, 173 i, 226.
Dykes, J. B., 140, 187 i, 554 ii, 586 iii, 654 ii.

Early 19th cent. MS., 55.
Easter Gloria, 561.

ALPHABETICAL INDEX OF AUTHORS

The numbers in brackets refer to translations.

GENERAL INDEX

The Hymns most suitable for Young People are marked °. ★ *Denotes the provision of a Fa-burden, Descant, or alternative harmonization of the tune.*

NO.	FIRST LINE	METRE	NAME OF TUNE
435	°A brighter dawn is breaking	7 7.7 7.	Selnecker (Nun lasst uns Gott dem Herren).
70	A great and mighty wonder	7 6.7 6.6 7 6.	Es ist ein' Ros' entsprungen.
352	°A little child on the earth has been born	Irregular	A Little Child.
226	°A message came to a maiden young	9 7.9 7.7 7.4 4 6.	De Boodschap.
148	A messenger within the grave	L.M.	1. Plainsong. 2. Mont Richard.
436	A safe stronghold our God is still	8 7.8 7.6 6.6 6 7.	Ein' feste Burg.
124	A voice upon the midnight air	L.M.	Babylon's Streams.
437	Abide with me; fast falls the eventide	10 10.10 10.	Eventide.★
259	According to thy gracious word	C.M.	Bangor.
99	Ah, holy Jesus, how hast thou offended	11 11.11 5.	Herzliebster Jesu.★
59	Ah! think not, 'The Lord delayeth'	8 8 7. D.	St. Olaf's Sequence.
438	All as God wills, who wisely heeds	C.M.	Stracathro.
439	°All creatures of our God and King	8 8.4 4.8 8, and Alleluyas	St. Francis.
135	°*All glory, laud, and honour*	7 6.7 6. D.	St. Theodulph (Valet will ich dir geben).
440	°All hail the power of Jesus' name	C.M.	Miles Lane.★
441	°All hail to the Power who giveth men might	10 10.10 10.	St. Joseph.
442	All my hope on God is founded	8 7.8 7.3 3 7.	Meine Hoffnung.
443	°All people that on earth do dwell	L.M.	Old Hundredth.★★
406	°All praise and thanks to God	6 7.6 7.6 6.6.	*See* Nun danket, 350.
304	All the past we leave behind	7.8 8.8 8.7.	Pioneers.
17	°All the scenes of nature quicken	8 7.8 7.	Shanghai.
149	°All the toil and sorrow done, *Alleluya*	7 4.7 4. D.	Llanfair.
189	All things are thine; no gift have we	D.L.M. L.M.	1. Bucklebury. 2. Alfreton.
444	°*All things bright and beautiful*	7 6.7 6, and refrain	Royal Oak.
445	°All things which live below the sky	C.M.	Jackson.
150	Alleluya, alleluya! Hearts to heaven	8 7.8 7.12 12. 11 11. 8 7.8 7. D.	1. Cöthen (Eins ist Not). 2. Würzburg.
143	°Alleluya, alleluya, alleluya! Ye sons	8 8 8, and Alleluyas	1. O filii et filiae. 2. O filii et filiae (modern version).
260	Alleluya, sing to Jesus	8 7.8 7. D.	Hyfrydol.
Apr 3	Amen	. . .	. . .
446	And did those feet in ancient time	D.L.M.	Jerusalem.

(895)

NO.	FIRST LINE	METRE	NAME OF TUNE
447	*And didst thou love the race that loved not thee*	10 10.10 6.	Mundays.
261	And now, O Father, mindful of the love	10 10.10 10. 10 10	Song 4.
41	And now the wants are told that brought	C.M.	Cornhill.
238	°Angels and ministers, spirits of grace	10 10.10 10.	Quedlinburg.
71	Angels, from the realms of glory	8 7.8 7, and refrain	Iris.
448	°Angels holy, high and lowly	8 7.8 7.8 7.7 7.	Flanders.
239	°Around the throne of God a band	L.M.	Solothurn.
449	°As pants the hart for cooling streams	C.M.	Martyrdom.★
262	As the disciples, when thy Son had left them	11 11.11 5.	1. Coelites plaudant. 2. Diva servatrix.
83	°As with gladness men of old	7 7.7 7.7 7.	Dix.
142	At eve, when now he breathed no more	8 8 8.	Bohemia (O Mensch sieh).
42	At even when the sun was set	L.M.	1. Calvisius (Ach bleib bei uns). 2. Angelus (Du meiner Seelen).
392	°At the name of Jesus	6 5.6 5. D.	King's Weston.
24	At thy feet, O Christ, we lay	7 7.7 7.7 7.	Ratisbon (Jesu, meine Zuversicht).
263	Author of life divine	6 6.6 6.8 8.	Dolgelly.
151	°Awake, arise! lift up thy voice	C.M.	St. Fulbert.★
450	°Awake, awake to love and work	8 6.8 6.8 6.	Brunswick.
25	Awake, my soul, and with the sun	L.M.	*Part I,* Morning Hymn.★ *Part II,* Richard. *Part III,* Warrington.
451	Awake, our souls! away, our fears	L.M.	Samson.
353	°Away in a manger, no crib for a bed	11 11.11 11.	Cradle Song.
407	°Be, Lord, the happy guide	6 6 7.6 6 7. D.	*See* O Seigneur, 696, *or* Nunc Dimittis, 50.
100	Be thou my guardian and my guide	C.M.	Abridge.★
452	Before thy feet I fall	6 6.6 6.	Kingsland.
72	Behold the great Creator makes	C.M.	This endris Nyght.
43	Behold the sun, that seemed but now	D.C.M.	Old 18th.
39	Behold us, Lord, a little space	C.M.	Ferry.
453	Believe not those who say	D.S.M.	Llanllyfni.
84	°Bethlehem, of noblest cities	8 7.8 7.	Stuttgart.★
454	Beyond, beyond that boundless sea	8 6.8 6.8 6.	Arabia.
422	Blessed be the Lord God of Israel	(*Canticle.*)	. . .
190	°Blessèd city, heavenly Salem,	8 7.8 7.8 7.	1. Plainsong. 2. Oriel.
40	Blest are the moments, doubly blest	L.M.	Herr Jesu Christ.
455	°Blest are the pure in heart	S.M.	Franconia.
456	°Blest be the day when moved I was	C.M.	Tiverton.
457	Book of books, our people's strength	7 8.7 8.8 8.	Dessau (Liebster Jesu).

NO.	FIRST LINE	METRE	NAME OF TUNE
264	Bread of heaven, on thee we feed	7 7.7 7.7 7.	Nicht so traurig.
265	Bread of the world in mercy broken	9 8.9 8. D.	Rendez à Dieu.
458	Breathe on me, Breath of God	S.M.	Carlisle.*
459	Brief life is here our portion	7 6.7 6.	1. Devonshire. 2. St. Alphege.
460	°Bright the vision that delighted	8 7.8 7.	Laus Deo (Redhead No. 46).*
85	Brightest and best of the sons of the morning	11 10.11 10.	1. Liebster Immanuel. 2. Lime Street.
18	°By the breadth of the blue that shines in silence o'er me	Irregular	Hickling Broad.
86	By weary stages	5 5.5 4. D.	Hill Crest.
461	°Can I see another's woe	7 7.7 7.	Galliard.
462	°Can you count the stars that brightly	8 7.8 7.8 8.8 7.	Trefaenan.
463	°Children of the heavenly King	7 7.7 7.	Melling.
245	°Christ hath a garden walled around	L.M.	Leighton.
190 II	Christ is made the sure foundation	8 7.8 7.8 7.	1. Plainsong. 2. Oriel.
464	°Christ is our corner-stone	6 6.6 6.8 8.	1. Ramoth. 2. Harewood.
152	°Christ is risen! Christ is risen	8 7.8 7.7 5.7 5. 8 7.8 7.	Midhurst.
242	Christ is the King! O friends rejoice	8 8 8. D.	Llangoedmor.
60	°Christ is the world's true Light	6 7.6 7.6 6.6 6.	Rinkart (Kommt Seelen).
465	Christ, of all my hopes the ground	7 7.7 7.	Long Mynd.
153	Christ the Lord is risen again	7 7.7 7.4.	Orientis partibus.
288	Christ who knows all his sheep	6 6.6 5.6 5.	Cambridge.
26	Christ, whose glory fills the skies	7 7.7 7.7 7.	Ministres de l'Éternel.
466	°Christian, do you see him	6 5.6 5. D.	Gute Bäume bringen.
467	Christian, seek not yet repose	7 7.7 3.	Robyn.
73	Christians, awake, salute the happy morn	10 10.10 10. 10 10.	Yorkshire (or Stockport).*
468	°City of God, how broad and far	C.M.	Richmond.*
393	°City of Peace, our mother dear	C.M.	1. Stalham. 2. Dunstan. 3. Eardisley.
469	Close by the heedless worker's side	8 4.8 4.8 4.	Exon.
177	Come down, O Love divine	6 6.11. D.	Down Ampney.
136	°Come, faithful people, come away	8 8 8.7.	Come, faithful people.
178	Come, Holy Ghost, our souls inspire	L.M.	Veni Creator (Tallis).
470	Come, kindred, upstand in the valour of Jesus	12 11.12 11.	Was lebet, was schwebet.
471	Come, labour on	4 10.10 10 4.	Salonica.
472	°Come, let us join our cheerful songs	C.M.	Cheerful.
473	Come, my soul, thy suit prepare	7 7.7 7.	Louez Dieu.
474	Come, my way, my truth, my life	7 7.7 7.	Tunbridge.
475	°Come now, all people, keep high mirth	8 7.8 7.8 8 7.	Melchior (Lobt Gott).
179	Come, O creator Spirit, come	L.M.	Veni Creator (Mechlin).
476	Come, O thou Traveller unknown	8 8.8 8.8 8.	David's Harp.

NO.	FIRST LINE	METRE	NAME OF TUNE
338	°Father of men, in whom are one	8 8 8. D.	Exeter.
347	Father, to thee we look in all our sorrow	11 10.11 10.	L'Omnipotent.
269	Father, we greet thee, God of Love, whose glory	11 10.11 10.	Psalm 80.
28	Father, we praise thee, now the night is over	11 11.11 5.	1. Plainsong. 2. Ut queant laxis.
355	°Father, we thank thee for the night	L.M.	Wainwright.
340	°Father, who on man dost shower	8 8.8 7.	Charing.
11	°Fields of corn, give up your ears	7 6.7 6.7 7 6. 7 7 6.	Cornfields.
489	Fierce raged the tempest o'er the deep	8 8.8 3.	White Gates.
490	Fierce was the wild billow	6 4.6 4. D.	St. Issey.
491	°Fight the good fight with all thy might	L.M.	1. Duke Street.* 2. Montesano.
492	°Fill thou my life, O Lord my God	C.M.	Abbey.
202	°For all the saints who from their labours rest	10 10.10 4.	Sine Nomine.
195	'For ever with the Lord!'	D.S.M.	Old 25th.
493	For mercy, courage, kindness, mirth	7 7.7 7. Irregular	Lew Trenchard.
494	°For the beauty of the earth	7 7.7 7.7 7.	England's Lane.
243	°For the brave of every race	7 7.7 7. D.	Loughborough College.
495	For the might of thine arm we bless thee	14.14.14.14. Irregular	Cormac.
289	For those we love within the veil	8 8.8 4.	Meyer (Es ist kein Tag).
203	°For thy dear saint, O Lord	S.M.	Mount Ephraim.
1	For thy mercy and thy grace	7 7.7 7.	Culbach.
29	Forth in thy name, O Lord, I go	L.M.	Angel's Song (Song 34).*
97	°Forty days and forty nights	7 7.7 7.	Heinlein (Aus der Tiefe).*
394	°Forward! be our watchword	6 5.6 5. Ter.	Blencathra.
408	°From all that dwell below the skies	L.M.	See Illsley, 610, or Wareham, 631.
496	From glory to glory advancing	14 14.14 15.	Sheen.
381	°From out of a wood did a cuckoo fly	10 2.10 2.8 8 6.	The Birds.
388	°From the eastern mountains	6 5.6 5. D.	Laus tibi Christe.
285	°From thee all skill and science flow	C.M.	Farnham.
497	Gather us in, thou love that fillest all	10 10.10 10.4.	Billesley.
356	°Gentle Jesus, meek and mild	7 7.7 7.	Gentle Jesus.
498	Gird on thy sword, O man, thy strength endue	10 10.10 10.	Chilswell.
204	Give me the wings of faith to rise	C.M.	Song 67.
499	°Glad that I live am I	6 5.6 5. Irregular	Water-End.
500	°Glorious things of thee are spoken	8 7.8 7. D.	Austrian Hymn.*
431	Glory be to God on high	(Canticle.)	. . .
45	°Glory to thee, my God, this night	L.M.	Tallis' Canon.*
501	°God be in my head	Irregular	1. Constantia. 2. David.
427	God be merciful unto us, and bless us	(Canticle.)	. . .

NO.	FIRST LINE	METRE	NAME OF TUNE
574	Love of the Father, Love of God the Son	10 10.10 10.	Song 22.
160	°Love's redeeming work is done	7 7.7 7.	Savannah (or Herrnhut).
366	°Loving Shepherd of thy sheep	7 7.7 7.	Innocents.
575	Made lowly wise, we pray no more	C.M.	Blackbourne.
576	Make me a captive, Lord	S.M.	Zachary.
321	Men of England, who inherit	8 7.8 7.	Sussex.
306	°Men, whose boast it is that ye	7 7.7 7. D.	Ives.
577	°Mercy thou art, Creator, Friend	C.M.	Norwich.
578	°Mine eyes have seen the glory of the coming	Irregular.	Battle Song.
579	More lovely than the noonday rest	8 4.8 4.10 10.	Fountains Abbey.
30	°Morning has broken	5 5.5 4. D.	Bunessan.
188	Most ancient of all mysteries	C.M.	St. Flavian.★
22	°Most glorious Lord of life, that on this day	10 10.10 10.	Farley Castle.
580	My faith looks up to thee	6 6 4.6 6 6 4.	Denbigh.
254	My God, accept my heart this day	C.M.	Dibdin.
581	My God, how wonderful thou art	C.M.	Westminster.
110	My God, I love thee; not because	C.M.	Solomon.
582	My God, I thank thee who hast made	8 4.8 4.8 4.	Severn.
583	°My God, my Father, make me strong	8 8 8 4.	Meyer (Es ist kein Tag).
584	My Lord, my Life, my Love	S.M.	Song 20.
127	°My song is love unknown	6 6.6 6.4 4.4 4.	1. Love unknown. 2. Rhosymedre.
424	My soul doth magnify the Lord	(*Canticle.*)	. . .
585	°My soul, there is a country	7 6.7 6.	Christus der ist mein Leben.
111	My spirit longs for thee	6 6.6 6.	Mainz (Maria jung und zart).
586	Nearer, my God, to thee	6 4.6 4.6 6 4.	1. Rothwell. 2. Liverpool. 3. Horbury.
587	Never weather-beaten sail more willing bent	13.13.15.13.	Weather-beaten Sail.
31	°New every morning is the love	L.M.	Melcombe.★
588	No coward soul is mine	6 10.6 10.	Glynthorpe.
589	Not always on the mount may we	L.M.	Whitehall.
590	Not with a choir of angels without number	11 6.11 6. D.	Berry Down.
48	Now God be with us, for the night is falling	11 11.11 5.	1. Die Nacht ist kommen. 2. Christe sanctorum.
591	°Now in life's breezy morning	7 6.7 6.	Magdalena.
592	Now join, ye comrades true	6 6.8 6.8 6.8 8 6.	Glan Geirionydd.
98	Now quit your care	4 7.4 6.4 7.6 4 8.	Quittez, pasteurs.
350	°Now thank we all our God	6 7.6 7.6 6.6 6.	Nun danket.★
49	°Now the day is over	6 5.6 5.	Eudoxia.
32	Now the morn new light is pouring	8 7.8 7.7 7.	1. Gott des Himmels. 2. St. Leonard.
292	Now thy earthly work is done	7 7.7 7.7 7.	Pressburg (Nicht so traurig).
421	O all ye works of the Lord	(*Canticle.*)	. . .

NO.	FIRST LINE	METRE	NAME OF TUNE
423	O be joyful in the Lord, all ye lands	(*Canticle.*)	. . .
322	°O beautiful, my country	7 6.7 6. D.	1. Freedom. 2. Helder (Wohlauf thut nicht verzagen).
307	O brother man, fold to thy heart thy brother	11 10.11 10.	Intercessor.
593	O Christ who holds the open gate	L.M.	Gonfalon Royal.
78	°O come, all ye faithful	Irregular.	Adeste Fideles.*
140	O come and mourn with me awhile	L.M.	St. Cross.
419	O come, let us sing unto the Lord	(*Canticle.*)	. . .
66	O come, O come, Emmanuel	8 8.8 8.8 8.	Veni Emmanuel.
367	°O dear and lovely Brother	7 6.7 6.	Bulstrode.
246	°O faith of England, taught of old	8 7.7.8 8 7. D.	Psalm 68.
396	°O Father above us, our father in might	11 11.11 and refrain	1. Maddermarket. 2. Aldeby.
112	O for a closer walk with God	C.M.	Caithness.
594	O for a faith that will not shrink	C.M.	Rochester.
113	O for a heart to praise my God	C.M.	Stockton.
595	°O for a thousand tongues to sing	C.M.	O God of Love.
50	°O gladsome light, O grace	6 6 7.6 6 7.	Nunc Dimittis.
275	O God, in whom we live and move	C.M.	Farrant.*
596	°O God of Bethel, by whose hand	C.M.	Burford.
308	°O God of earth and altar	7 6.7 6. D.	King's Lynn.
597	°O God of truth, whose living word	C.M.	Martyrs.*
598	°O God, our help in ages past	C.M.	St. Anne.*
599	°O happy band of pilgrims	7 6.7 6.	Cherry Tree.
600	O heavenly Beauty, lovelier far	8 8.8 8 8.	O Jesulein süss.
114	O help us, Lord! Each hour of need	C.M.	Bedford.*
601	°O Holy Spirit, God	S.M.	Drumcondra.
255	°O Jesus, I have promised	7 6.7 6. D.	1. Komm, Seele. 2. Bremen. 3. Thornbury.
115	O let him whose sorrow	6 5.6 5. D.	1. Sutton Valence. 2. Dun Aluinn.
602	O life that makest all things new	L.M.	Herongate.
192	O Light, from age to age the same	C.M.	Eatington.
79	°O little town of Bethlehem	D.C.M. Irregular	1. Forest Green. 2. Christmas Carol.
323	O Lord almighty, thou whose hands	C.M.	Worcester.*
603	O Lord and Master of us all	C.M.	Walsall.
604	O Lord, how happy should we be	8 8 6. D.	1. Song 18. 2. Advent.
605	O Lord, in me there lieth nought	8 8.4 4.8.8 8, *or* 8 8.8 8.8 8.	Leicester (or Bedford).
606	O Lord of hosts, all heaven possessing	9 8.9 8.8 8.	Neumark.
251	°O Lord, thy people gathered here	L.M.	Philippine.
116	O Lord, turn not away thy face	C.M.	St. Mary.*
607	°O love of God, how strong and true	L.M.	1. Hymnus Eucharisticus. 2. O Amor quam extaticus.
608	O love who formest me to wear	8 8.8 8.8 8.	Lambeth.
235	O Master, it is good to be	D.L.M.	Tallis' Lamentation.
434	O most high, almighty, good Lord God	(*Canticle.*)	All Creatures.

NO.	FIRST LINE	METRE	NAME OF TUNE
276	O most merciful	10 7. 10 7.	Schönster Herr Jesu.
283	O perfect Love, all human thought transcending	11 10.11 10.	Charterhouse.
351	°O praise ye the Lord	5 5.5 5.6 5.6 5.	Laudate Dominum.
128	O sacred head, sore wounded	7 6.7 6. D.	Passion Chorale.*
236	O saint of summer, what can we sing for you	11 11.9 10.	Alcaic Ode.
277	°O Saviour victim, opening wide	L.M.	1. Verbum supernum.
			2. Erhalt' uns, Herr.
609	°O sing to the Lord now, his greatness	9 8.9 8. D.	Crugybar.
425	O sing unto the Lord a new song	(Canticle.)	. . .
610	O sometimes gleams upon our sight	L.M.	Illsley.*
611	°O Son of man, our hero strong and tender	11 10.11 10. D.	Londonderry.
612	O source divine, and life of all	L.M.	Montgomery.
33	O splendour of God's glory bright	L.M.	Part I, 1. Plainsong.
			Part I, 2. Solemnis haec festivitas.
			Part II, 1. Plainsong.
			Part II, 2. Splendour (Puer nobis nascitur).
613	O sweeter than the marriage-feast	C.M.	Harington (Retirement).
117	O thou from whom all goodness flows	C.M.	Oliver.
614	°O thou in all thy might so far	C.M.	Relief.
615	°O thou not made with hands	6 6.6 6.6 6.	Old 120th.
616	O thou that movest all, O Power	9 8.9 8. D.	Henham.
256	°O thou who camest from above	L.M.	St. Bartholomew.
284	O thou who gavest power to love	L.M.	Affection.
51	°O Trinity of blessèd light	L.M.	1. Plainsong.
			2. Adesto sancta Trinitas.
293	°O valiant hearts, who to your glory came	10 10.10 10.	1. Valiant Hearts.*
			2. Valor.
335	°O welcome in our midst	6 6.4 4 6, and refrain	Royden.
200	O what their joy and their glory must be	10 10.10 10.	Regnator orbis.*
617	O world invisible, we view thee	9 8.9 8. Irregular	Pimlico Road.
618	°O worship the King	5 5.5 5.6 5.6 5.	Hanover.*
93	O worship the Lord in the beauty of holiness	13.10.13.10. Irregular	1. Crasselius.
			2. Dymchurch.
387	Of the Father's heart begotten	8 7.8 7.8 7 7.	Divinum mysterium.
619	°Oft in danger, oft in woe	7 7.7 7.	University College.
67	°On Jordan's bank the Baptist's cry	L.M.	Auctoritate saeculi.
220	On the moorland of life God's Shepherd is seen	11.12.11.12.	Mason ('Old German').
368	°Once in royal David's city	8 7.8 7.7 7.	Irby.
309	°Once to every man and nation	8 7.8 7. D.	Ebenezer (Ton-y-botel).
397	°Onward, Christian soldiers	6 5.6 5. Ter.	Prince Rupert.
386 IV	°Our babies' names are on the roll	8 8.8 6.	Children All.
182	°Our blest Redeemer, ere he breathed	8 6.8 4.	Wicklow.
194	°Our Father, by whose servants	7 6.7 6. D.	1. Dank sei Gott in der Höhe.
			2. Loughborough.
403	°Our Father, for our daily bread	8 8.8 8 8.	Pachelbel (Was Gott thut).

NO.	FIRST LINE	METRE	NAME OF TUNE
686	Up to those bright and gladsome hills	C.M.	Melrose.
214	°Virtue supreme, thy mighty stream	8 7.8 7.8 8 7.	Mit Freuden zart.
687	Wake, O wake, for night is flying	8 9 8.8 9 8.6 6 4. 4 4 8.	Wachet auf.
332	°We give thee but thine own	S.M.	Windermere.
688	°We love the place, O God	6 6.6 6. D.	Annue Christe.
14	°We plough the fields, and scatter	7 6.7 6.7 6.7 6. 6 6.8 4.	Wir pflügen.
420	We praise thee, O God: we acknowledge thee	(Canticle.)	. . .
225	We praise thy name, all-holy Lord	D.C.M.	Stettin (Nun seht).
689	°We saw thee not when, far away	8 8.8 8.8 8.	Farmborough.
690	We sing of God, the mighty source	8 8 6. D.	Magdalen College.
132	We sing the praise of him who died	L.M.	Breslau.★
691	°We thank thee, Lord, for this fair earth	L.M.	New Sabbath.
405	°We thank thee, loving Father	7 6.7 6.	See Magdalena, 591.
692	°We thank you, Lord of Heaven	7 7.7 7 6. D.	Abendlied (Der Tag mit seinem Lichte).
386 III	°We wish you many happy returns of the day	12 12.8 10.	Birthday.
390	Welcome, Day of the Lord	Irregular	Salve Festa Dies.
209	°What are these that glow from afar	Irregular	Monk's March.
693	°What conscience dictates to be done	D.C.M.	Old 30th.
325	°What heroes thou hast bred	6 6 6 3.6 6 6 4.	Stepney.
377	°When a knight won his spurs, in the stories of old	7 4.7 4. Irregular	Stowey.
694	When all thy mercies, O my God	C.M.	Belgrave.
695	When by fear my heart is daunted	8 7.8 7.8 7.	Ardudwy.
185	°When Christ had shown God's dawning Reign	C.M.	Stroudwater.
221	°When Christ was born in Bethlehem	C.M.	Rodmell.
133	When I survey the wondrous cross	L.M.	Rockingham.★
224	When Judas did his Lord reject	C.M.	Epworth.
378	°When lamps are lighted in the town	C.M.	Butler.
223	°When Mary brought her treasure	7 6.7 6.6 7 6.	Ave Maria klare.
696	When morning gilds the skies	6 6 7.6 6 7. D.	O Seigneur.
134	When my love to God grows weak	7 7.7 7.	Song 13.
697	When on my day of life the night is falling	11 10.11 6.	Stanstead.
21	°When spring unlocks the flowers	13 13.14 14.	Gosterwood.
219	°When Stephen, full of power and grace	D.C.M.	Wellington Square.
379	°When the herds were watching	6 5.6 5. D.	Gamble.
122	When the unquiet hours depart	L.M.	Plaistow.
698	°When through the whirl of wheels	11 10.11 10.	Lombard Street.

GENERAL INDEX

PRINTED IN GREAT BRITAIN
AT THE UNIVERSITY PRESS, OXFORD
BY VIVIAN RIDLER
PRINTER TO THE UNIVERSITY

29/12/80.